METHODS IN VIROLOGY

VOLUME III

METHODS IN VIROLOGY
Advisory Board

METHODS IN VIROLOGY

EDITED BY

KARL MARAMOROSCH

BOYCE THOMPSON INSTITUTE FOR PLANT RESEARCH
YONKERS, NEW YORK

AND

HILARY KOPROWSKI

THE WISTAR INSTITUTE OF ANATOMY AND BIOLOGY
PHILADELPHIA, PENNSYLVANIA

Volume III

ACADEMIC PRESS   New York and London   1967

QR360
.M45
V.3

ACADEMIC PRESS, INC.
111 Fifth Avenue, New York, New York 10003

United Kingdom Edition published by
ACADEMIC PRESS, INC. (LONDON) LTD.
Berkeley Square House, London W.1

LIBRARY OF CONGRESS CATALOG CARD NUMBER: 66–30091

Second Printing, 1968

PRINTED IN THE UNITED STATES OF AMERICA

List of Contributors

Numbers in parentheses indicate the pages on which the authors' contributions begin.

AUGUST, J. THOMAS, Department of Molecular Biology, Albert Einstein College of Medicine, Bronx, New York (99, 337).

CASALS, JORDI, Department of Epidemiology and Public Health, Yale University School of Medicine, New Haven, Connecticut, and The Rockefeller Foundation, New York, New York (113).

COOPER, PETER D., Department of Microbiology, John Curtin School of Medical Research, Australian National University, Canberra, Australia (243).

EOYANG, LILLIAN, Department of Molecular Biology, Albert Einstein College of Medicine, Bronx, New York (99).

FINCH, J. T., Medical Research Council, Laboratory of Molecular Biology, Cambridge, England (351).

FRAENKEL-CONRAT, H., Department of Molecular Biology and Virus Laboratory, University of California, Berkeley, California (1).

GRANBOULAN, NICOLE, Laboratoire de Microscopie Electronique, Institut de Recherches sur le Cancer, Villejuif (Val de Marne), France (617).

HOLMES, K. C., Medical Research Council, Laboratory of Molecular Biology, Cambridge, England (351).

HORNE, ROBERT W., Agricultural Research Council, Institute of Animal Physiology, Babraham, Cambridge (521).

KRITCHEVSKY, DAVID, The Wistar Institute of Anatomy and Biology, and School of Veterinary Medicine, Philadelphia, Pennsylvania (77).

MACPHERSON, I. A., Medical Research Council, Experimental Virus Research Unit, University of Glasgow, Glasgow, W.1., United Kingdom (313).

MATTHEWS, R. E. F., Department of Cell Biology, University of Auckland, Auckland, New Zealand (199).

MORGAN, C., Department of Microbiology, College of Physicians and Surgeons, Columbia University, New York, New York (575).

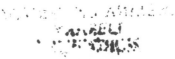

ROSE, H. M., Department of Microbiology, College of Physicians and Surgeons, Columbia University, New York, New York (575).

RUECKERT, R. R., Department of Biochemistry, and Biophysics Laboratory, University of Wisconsin, Madison, Wisconsin (1).

SHAPIRO, IRWIN L., The Wistar Institute of Anatomy and Biology, and Division of Animal Biology, School of Veterinary Medicine, University of Pennsylvania, Philadelphia, Pennsylvania (77).

*SPENDLOVE, REX S., Viral and Rickettsial Disease Laboratory, California State Department of Public Health, Berkeley, California (475).

STOKER, M. G. P., Medical Research Council, Experimental Virus Research Unit, University of Glasgow, Glasgow, W.1., Scotland, United Kingdom (313).

WATANABE, MAMORU, Department of Molecular Biology, Albert Einstein College of Medicine, Bronx, New York (337).

*Present address: Department of Bacteriology and Public Health, Utah State University, Logan, Utah.

Preface

Tanto sa Ciascuno Quanto Opera*
St. Francis

Virology is a scientific discipline which operates far beyond the narrow confinement of its goals. Hence, descriptions of methods used to study viruses are scattered throughout articles dealing with all imaginable branches of the life sciences. The search for a particular technique may occupy as much of the scientist's time as the completion of experiments based on that technique.

It was to correct this unfortunate situation that the idea of "Methods in Virology" was first conceived. The editors felt that, in view of the steadily increasing interest in the field of virology, publication of a comprehensive and authoritative treatise on methods used in the study of human, animal, plant, insect, and bacterial viruses would be welcomed by their colleagues. This work will enable virologists, graduate students, and prospective students of virology to appreciate the diversity and scope of the methods currently being used to study viruses, and, most important, to evaluate the advantages, limitations, and pitfalls of these methods.

The contributors were chosen on the basis of their outstanding knowledge of a given method, either as creators of new techniques, or as recognized authorities in their specialized fields. Other than clarity of expression and limitations on the length of presentations, no restrictions were imposed on the contributors. For example, the form of presentation of each chapter was the prerogative of its author. Some chapters follow the time-proven outline of recipes found in cookbooks, others are written in a highly original—even controversial—and sophisticated style.

It was the editors' intent to provide readers interested in one particular technique with a self-contained chapter describing this technique. As a result of this decision, it was sometimes impossible to avoid overlap of information in some chapters. The editors felt that completeness of description warranted this occasional duplication.

The first four volumes of "Methods in Virology" will be published in rapid succession. As new methods of study of viruses develop, their descriptions will be included in future volumes.

* Everybody knows as much as he works.

The editors wish to take this opportunity to thank their Board of Advisors—F. C. Bawden, Sven Gard, George K. Hirst, S. E. Luria, André Lwoff, Roy Markham, K. F. Meyer, George E. Palade, C. Vago, and Robley C. Williams—for invaluable assistance provided in the preparation of this work. They are confident that these efforts were not made in vain, since they will provide virologists everywhere with new and valuable tools to facilitate their quests for new discoveries.

October, 1967   KARL MARAMOROSCH
                                                                          HILARY KOPROWSKI

Table of Contents

Chapter 1—Analysis of Protein Constituents of Viruses

H. FRAENKEL-CONRAT AND R. R. RUECKERT

Chapter 2—Analysis of Lipid Components of Viruses

DAVID KRITCHEVSKY AND IRWIN L. SHAPIRO

Chapter 3—RNA Virus RNA Polymerase: Detection, Purification, and Properties

J. T. AUGUST AND LILLIAN EOYANG

Chapter 12—The Application of Thin Sectioning

C. MORGAN AND H. M. ROSE

Chapter 13—Autoradiographic Methods for Electron Microscopy

NICOLE GRANBOULAN

Contents of Other Volumes

* Deceased.

METHODS IN VIROLOGY

VOLUME III

1 Analysis of Protein Constituents of Viruses

H. Fraenkel-Conrat and R. R. Rueckert

I. Introduction

Methods for the study of virus proteins obviously do not differ in principle from those of general protein chemistry. The term "virus protein" usually refers to the coat protein, although other virus-specific protein products are also becoming of greater interest to researchers. One feature characteristic of virus proteins, yet not only of them, is that they are frequently available only in small amounts. Another feature peculiar to and characteristic of the coat proteins is their great tendency to aggregate to oligomers, polymers, and finally the typical virus particles. Thus protein methodology will here be discussed with particular attention to micromethods on the one hand and to proteins that tend to associate to high molecular weight complexes on the other. The fact that this chapter is addressed not only to virologists, and

1

that it resembles other chapters dealing with the methods of protein characterization, is not without a purpose. This field moves so rapidly that many of the methods here described will not yet have been critically evaluated, nor included in preceding volumes concerned with protein methodology.

The isolation of virus proteins usually requires steps that break secondary bonds and thus dissociate the virus particles and allow the separation of protein and nucleic acid. As a consequence, virus proteins are generally denatured and tend to be insoluble, although this process may be more or less completely reversible in individual cases. The method of isolation thus affects the suitability of virus proteins for specific tests or reactions. It will therefore frequently be referred to in subsequent discussions.

II. Chemical Methods for Characterization of Virus Proteins

A. Amino Acid Analysis

1. Automatic Analysis

With the advent of methods for automated amino acid analysis, this technique has become a primary tool in the course of purification, as well as in the structural analysis, of peptides and proteins. A complete analysis can now be obtained in 6.5 hours or less (Hamilton, 1963; Benson and Patterson, 1965). By use of either a larger flow cell giving a longer light path or by electronic amplification of the detector signal, as little as 0.01–0.04 μM amino acid can be analyzed with 2–5% accuracy.

Samples are prepared for analysis as follows. Amounts of 0.05–0.5 μmole of peptide or protein (0.2–5 mg) (for many purposes the amount need only be approximately known) are placed into Pyrex test tubes (125 $\times$ 15 mm), and water is removed by freeze-drying in a desiccator containing NaOH flakes and concentrated H_2SO_4. One milliliter of glass-redistilled constant-boiling HCl is then added, and the tubes are constricted, the contents frozen in Dry Ice, and the tubes connected to a high-vacuum pump, evacuated, and then sealed at the constriction. The tubes are then immersed in an oil bath of 108°C in a constant-temperature oven. It is generally advisable to hydrolyze two samples for two time periods, e.g., 24 and 72 hours. The tubes are then opened and quickly evaporated to dryness, preferably by attaching them to a rotatory evaporator in a water bath of about 40°–60°C. The residue is taken up in the acid citrate buffer used for the analyzer and applied *in toto* or as a suitable aliquot to contain the number of micromoles optimal for the particular analyzer setup used. The content in serine and to a lesser extent threonine and occasionally of other amino acids decreases with progressive hydrolysis time, and the actual amount can be ascertained by extrapolating back to zero time of hydrolysis. On the other hand, the isoleucine, and to a lesser extent the leucine and valine contents, usually increase from 24 to 72 hours of hydrolysis, and the highest value observed approaches the correct one, since peptide bonds between these residues are often quite resistant to hydrolysis. The basic amino acids are usually analyzed on a separate aliquot applied to a short column that is eluted with a higher pH gradient, but elution schedules that permit analysis of all amino acids on one sample have been proposed (Piez and Morris, 1960).

To obtain reliable data for proteins containing 100 or more amino acid residues requires that the analyzer be in the best possible working order and standardized with known protein hydrolysates or amino acid mixtures. The average of two or three analyses of each hydrolysate then permits calculation of the composition of such a protein in terms of residues per mole with reasonable assurance. This is usually done in terms of molar ratios, by means of an integer value for a stable amino acid that is not very abundant (e.g., six glycine residues in TMV protein).

2. Ninhydrin Reaction for Amino Groups (Moore and Stein, 1954)

Occasionally amino groups of amino acids or proteins are to be determined manually in individual tubes. This is conveniently done as follows: Reagents: 4 N sodium acetate at pH 5.5. To 544 gm of NaOAc· $3H_2O$ dissolved in 400 ml of hot H_2O are added after cooling 100 ml of glacial acetic acid and water to 1000 ml. Ninhydrin reagent: 20 gm of ninhydrin and 3 gm of hydrindantin are dissolved in 750 ml of methyl cellosolve. Then 250 ml of 4 N pH 5.5 acetate is added, and the mixture is transferred to a dark bottle and held under nitrogen. Procedure: To a 1-ml sample, 1 ml of ninhydrin reagent is added. The capped tubes are briefly shaken and then heated for 15 minutes at 100°C. They are then diluted to 10 ml with 50 : 50 ethanol–water, cooled, shaken for 30 seconds, and the blue color read on a spectrophotometer at 570 mμ (440 mμ for proline and hydroxyproline). For more details the reader is referred to the original papers.

3. Specific Analyses

Tryptophan largely decomposes during acid hydrolysis and must be separately determined. This is usually done by colorimetric or spectrophotometric methods. The simplest method is to determine the absorbance of the protein or peptide dissolved in 0.1 N NaOH at 294.4 mμ and 280.0 mμ. The molar ratio of tyrosine and tryptophan can be derived from these data as follows:

$$\text{m}M(\text{Tyr}) = 0.592 \times A_{294.4} - 0.263 \times A_{280.0}$$
$$\text{m}M(\text{Try}) = 0.263 \times A_{280.0} - 0.170 \times A_{294.4}$$

With the tryosine content of the protein established by the analyzer, tryptophan is thus also defined.

Cysteine, together with cystine, can be determined on the analyzer as cysteic acid if the protein is subjected to oxidation by performic acid prior to hydrolysis (Moore, 1963) (Section II,C,2,a). Alternatively, cysteine can be titrated in 4 M guanidine halide, 5% sodium carbonate, and 0.35% EDTA, with 0.001 M N-ethylmaleimide and nitroprusside as indicator (Fraenkel-Conrat, 1957); and cystine can be determined as such on the analyzer.

4. Other General Methods

If an amino acid analyzer is not available, amino acid analysis can conveniently be performed by dinitrophenylating the residue after evaporating the acid off the protein hydrolyzate in the usual manner. The mixture of amino acids (0.2–0.5 μmole of a small protein) is treated with fluorodinitrobenzene (FDNB) and sodium bicarbonate, and the dinitrophenyl (DNP) amino acids are determined after chromatographic separation, as described below, when the use of FDNB as an end-group reagent is discussed.

The use of 1-dimethylaminonaphthalene-5-sulfonyl chloride (dansyl chloride) has been advocated in similar manner (Boulton and Bush, 1964). This is an extremely sensitive micromethod, since dansyl amino acids can be visually detected by their fluorescence at the level of 10^{-3} to 10^{-4} μmoles, well below the amounts required for the standard analyzer or DNP methods. However, it must be noted that there is a distinct difference in this case, as with all ultrasensitive micromethods, between the theoretical and practical limits of such methods. When working with extremely small amounts of material, contaminants in the chromatographic paper, solvents, etc., introduce proportionately greater errors. Also the light sensitivity and other causes for instability or adsorbability of the reaction products create proportionately greater analytical problems. It appears advisable to operate whenever possible at the level of 0.1–1 μmole rather than to rely by choice on ultrasensitive methods. This, in the long run, saves time and effort.

5. Applications of Amino Acid Analysis

The determination of the complete amino acid composition of the protein is a useful parameter for the characterization of viruses and their strains. Thus four groups of TMV strains are known that are characterized by their content of 3, 2, 1, and 0 methionine and 7, 6, 5, and 4 tyrosine residues, the first also containing one histidine residue (Tsugita, 1962). Furthermore, in the course of studies of the fine structure of viral proteins, amino acid analysis is frequently resorted to for the purpose of determining the composition of peptides or analyzing for the presence of free amino acids. These objectives are achieved in exactly the same manner as the analysis of whole proteins, except that lesser accuracy is sufficient for these purposes. Obviously no hydrolysis is required if free amino acids are being determined, as is the case after exopeptidase action or hydrazinolysis.

B. END-GROUP ANALYSIS

1. N-Terminal Groups

The N-terminal groups of the peptide chains of most virus proteins have been found to be acylated and thus not to be able to react with the reagents for free terminal α-amino groups. Nevertheless, a search for such groups is the logical first step, since this is comparatively easy and economical of material. Only if this search is unsuccessful is it advisable to analyze the protein for the presence of acylated end groups (Section II,B,2).

a. *Dinitrophenylation.* To the aqueous protein solution are added NaHCO₃ to 10% and 2 volumes of a 2.5% (v/v) solution of FDNB in ethanol, and the mixture is shaken at room temperature for 2 hours (Sanger, 1945, 1949). Insoluble proteins may be solubilized by addition of 8 M urea or 4–5 M guanidine hydrochloride. This also tends to abolish conformational masking of terminal and other groups. The proteins usually precipitate in the course of the reaction. They can in this case be centrifuged off, washed twice each with alcohol and ether, air-dried, and hydrolyzed with 6 N HCl, all in the same tube. It is advisable, however, to monitor the quantitative aspects of the precipitation either by weighing the dry DNP protein (which should be at least 100% and usually about 120% of the original weight) or by thoroughly dialyzing the supernatant and verifying its intrinsic freedom from protein by the absence of a precipitate, or material giving the Folin-Lowry test (see Section IV,B,1), or showing an ultraviolet absorption peak at 270–280 mμ.

Acid hydrolysis is performed as described in Section II,A, but for shorter time periods (e.g., 4 and 12 hours). The bulk of the acid is then distilled off by flash evaporation, and the still acidic residue is taken up in water. It is then twice extracted with ether and the ether back-washed with a little water. The DNP derivatives of all free N-terminal amino acids are found in the ether extract except for two groups: α-DNP arginine, mono-DNP cystine, and α-DNP histidine, as well as di-DNP histidine, are not ether soluble, but can be detected in the aqueous phase; DNP tryptophan, DNP glycine, and DNP proline are to a varying extent unstable during acid hydrolysis. If the presence of one of the latter is suspected, then quite short hydrolysis times or the use of 12 N acid at 37°C may prove advantageous, and other methods of N-terminal analysis may be selected (e.g., the phenyl isothiocyanate reaction or the enzyme leucine aminopeptidase).

Procedure of DNP-amino acid analysis. The identification and quantitation of the DNP amino acids is usually performed by two-dimensional paper chromatography (Levy, 1954; Fraenkel-Conrat *et al.,* 1955). The separation of the ether-soluble amino acids is done on 17×22.5 inch Whatman 1 papers folded into cylinders which stand in the first solvent (30 ml of toluene, 9 ml of pyridine, 18 ml of 2-chloroethanol gently mixed with 18 ml of 0.8 N ammonia, upper phase, with a beaker containing 0.8 N ammonia in the center; alternatively, *n*-butanol saturated with ammonia). For the second dimension, 1.5 N pH 6 phosphate (138 gm of $NaH_2PO_4 \cdot H_2O$ + 71 gm of Na_2HPO_4 per liter) is used in descending fashion. The chromatography is performed in the dark.

The water-soluble DNP compounds in the aqueous phase are usually resolved one-dimensionally. Whatman 4 paper is sprayed with pH 6 phthalate (50 ml of 0.1 M KH phthalate + 45.5 ml of 0.1 N NaOH and 4.5 ml of water) and allowed to dry. The chromatogram is developed with tertiary amyl alcohol, saturated with buffer (Blackburn and Lowther, 1951). A two-dimensional system which is very useful for the detection and resolution of unsubstituted amino acids also permits separation of these more polar DNP amino acids (Levy and Chung, 1953).

The location of a yellow spot in relation to dinitrophenol, which is generally present, allows a preliminary identification or at least a limited choice. All yellow spots are then cut out, eluted with 1.5 ml of 2% $NaHCO_3$ at 50°C for 30 minutes, and their spectrum plotted. The absorbance maximum for most DNP amino acids is at 360 mμ, for DNP proline at 390 mμ, and for di-DNP lysine at 365 mμ. The solutions are subsequently acidified. Dinitrophenol is decolorized by acid. The yellow color of the other spots is again extracted into ether and the residue of the ether chromatographed one-dimensionally with markers of all suspected DNP amino acids in the same or other solvents. It should in this manner be possible to identify the terminal amino acid definitively.

Thin-layer chromatography has also proved a powerful tool for the separation and identification of DNP amino acids. The techniques of thin-layer chromatography are described in Section IV,B,4. For the purpose of separation of ether-soluble DNP amino acids, silica gel G plates are developed with the toluene–pyridine–chloroethanol solvent (above) in the first dimension (upper phase after pretreatment of layer by lower phase) and by either chloroform–benzyl alcohol–acetic acid or chloroform–*tert*-amyl alcohol–acetic acid (both 70 : 30 : 3) in the second dimension (Randerath, 1963). The aqueous phase containing DNP amino acids is developed with n-propanol, 34% NH_3 (7 : 3, v/v), after removing any excess acid by heating the plate for 10 minutes at 60°C in a strong air draft. It would seem that the thin-layer techniques would yield quantitative data at least as accurate as those obtained by paper chromatography with less material.

b. Dansylation. The use of 1-dimethylaminonaphthalene-5-sulfonyl (dansyl) chloride for amino acid analysis was mentioned earlier. Besides greater sensitivity, this reagent has an additional advantage over dinitrophenylation, in that the dansyl amino acids are more stable to acid hydrolysis. Thus this method should be suitable for end-group analysis, as well as, in conjunction with the phenyl isothiocyanate method, for sequence analysis of peptides or proteins (Gray and Hartley, 1963).

For end-group analysis, 10^{-3} μmoles of peptide is treated in 15 μl of 0.1 M $NaHCO_3$ with 15 μl of a 0.1% solution of dansyl chloride in acetone (Gray and Hartley, 1963). After 3 hours at room temperature the sample is dried *in vacuo*, treated with 20 μl of redistilled 6 N HCl at 105°C for 6–12 hours, again dried *in vacuo*, and the residue subjected to electrophoresis on Whatman 3 MM paper in 0.8% acetic acid–0.4% pyridine (pH 4.4) at 80 volts per centimeter for 3 hours with dansylamino acid markers. Only serine, proline, and alanine are not resolved, but these can be separated by electrophoresis at pH 12.7 (0.1 M Na_3PO_4, 0.1 M NaOH) for 2 hours at 30 volts per centimeter.

Alternatively, a series of chromatographic solvents can be used. The aliphatic amino acids and phenylalanine are separated on Whatman 4 paper by a mixture of hexane, acetic acid, and water (1 : 0.9 : 0.1, v/v), the hydrophilic amino acids in benzene, diisopropyl ether, acetic acid, and water (1 : 1 : 1 : 1, v/v), and the basic amino acids in diisopropyl ether, ethyl methyl ketone, acetic acid, and water (8 : 2 : 5 : 5, v/v) or hexane, toluene, acetic acid, and water (5 : 5 : 8 : 5 : 1.5, v/v).

2. *Acylated N-Terminal Groups*

Degradation of a terminally acylated protein by chymotrypsin, which splits with some preference next to aromatic residues and leucine, may yield an acylated peptide lacking any basic group if the first chymotrypsin-susceptible site precedes the first basic amino acid. Alternatively, an enzyme of broad specificity, e.g., pepsin or subtilisin, may be employed. Any terminal oligopeptide of the type acetyl-ABC in which A, B, and C are not arginine, lysine, or histidine differs from all other fragments in the digest by its lack of a basic function. This property is made use of in the isolation and identification of acylated termini (Narita, 1958).

Digestion with chymotrypsin or subtilisin can be carried out in a pH stat (pH 8) at room temperature for about 16 hours. Alternatively, fresh 0.05 M ammonium bicarbonate is used as buffer and removed by lyophilization. Digestion by pepsin is done at pH 1.5 (adjusted with HCl) for 3 hours at 37°C. The substrate–enzyme ratio is usually 10 or 20. The digest is then applied to a Dowex 50 × 2 column (hydrogen form, i.e., 1 N HCl-washed, then water-washed, 50–100 mesh, 2 × 20 cm). The column is eluted with 200 ml of water, and 5-ml fractions are collected. These are tested for acylpeptides by analyzing 0.3-ml aliquots of alternate tubes by means of the ninhydrin reaction with and without prior alkaline hydrolysis (Hirs et al., 1956). To this end 1 ml of 2.5 N NaOH is added, and the 18 × 150 mm tubes are heated unstoppered for 2.5 hours in an open water bath at 90°C. To the residue (0.1–0.2 ml) is added 1 ml of 30% acetic acid, and these tubes are then analyzed with ninhydrin (see Section II,A,2).

Acidic peptides are present in those tubes which give a ninhydrin test only after hydrolysis, and these are pooled. If the component amino acids (A, B, and C) contain tyrosine or tryptophan, their ultraviolet absorbance can be utilized as a means of detection in lieu of the hydrolyzed ninhydrin value. If acidic peptides are present, an aliquot of the pool may be subjected to amino acid analysis to ascertain whether a simple and stoichiometric amino acid composition suggests the presence of a single acyl peptide. However, in view of the nonspecificity of the enzymes used, this is an unlikely event. Usually one is faced with a mixture of several acyl peptides (such as acyl-A, acyl-AB, and acyl-ABC). Further, peptides with N-terminal glutamine tend to cyclize to a pyrrolidone carboxyl group and thus yield a peptide lacking a terminal NH_2 group, thus appearing in the fraction containing acyl peptides.

The nature of the acyl residue is best established at this stage by subjecting the mixture to hydrazinolysis (see Section II,B,3). The acyl hydrazide can be identified by paper chromatography of the hydrazides in pyridine–aniline–water, 9 : 1 : 4, or collidine–picoline–water, using a spray of 0.1 N $AgNO_3$–5 N NH_4OH–ethanol (1 : 1 : 2) for detection of the hydrazides (Narita, 1958; Narita and Ishii, 1962; Yaoi et al., 1964).

The best method for the separation of various acyl peptides is by means of a Dowex 1-X2 column (chloride form, 2.3 $\times$ 30 cm) washed with water and then eluted with increasing concentrations of HCl (up to 0.03 N). Paper chromatography (butanol–acetic acid–water, 4 : 1 : 1) can also be used. The acylated peptides are detected by ninhydrin only after alkaline hydrolysis and may not give a strong Folin-Lowry test (see Section IV,B,1) unless they contain aromatic residues, in which case direct ultraviolet spectrophotometry suffices to reveal their presence. On paper they are detected by the chlorine (or butyl hypochlorite) iodide–starch reaction (Rydon and Smith, 1952; Mazur et al., 1962).

3. Carboxy-Terminal Groups

Hydrazinolysis is the most reliable chemical method to ascertain the C-terminal amino acid. When peptides or proteins are heated for several hours in hydrazine, all internal amino acid residues form hydrazides, and the C-terminal is the only free amino acid present (Akabori et al., 1952, 1956) in the reaction mixture and can be identified and determined most conveniently by means of the amino acid analyzer.

Procedure: About 10 mg (0.1–1 μmole) of protein is dried in a test tube. To this is added 0.2 ml of hydrazine (95%+) and the tube is sealed *in vacuo*. It is then heated for 24 hours at 80°C. The hydrazine is subsequently removed by holding the opened tube *in vacuo* (at first water-pump and after a few hours oil-pump vacuum). The residue may be taken up directly in pH 2.2 citrate buffer and applied to the analyzer, although the great quantity of hydrazides that must be applied to determine the end group of a protein chain ($>$100 : 1) is difficult to wash off the column, and preliminary separation of the free amino acids on a short Amberlite IRC-50 (H^+ form) column may be advisable. Water elutes the neutral and acidic amino acids and 0.1 M ammonium acetate the basic ones.

Most amino acids can be detected and determined by the standard procedure. Special problems are presented by C-terminal arginine, asparagine, glutamine, and cyst(e)ine, which undergo decomposition. Cystine is recovered, though in poor yield, and usually it is accompanied by an appreciable amount of a ninhydrin-positive decomposition product. Arginine is to over 50% transformed to ornithine. The separation of the ornithine from lysine on the amino acid analyzer is done on the 29×0.9 cm column with 0.38 N citrate (pH 4.26, 185 minutes) at 33°C, followed by pH 5.28 citrate at 55°C.

C-terminal asparagine and glutamine yield the β- and γ-hydrazides, and these cannot be readily separated by chromatographic methods from the corresponding α-hydrazides derived from internal aspartic and glutamic acid residues. The only satisfactory method for their separation and determination appears to be after dinitrophenylation (Kawanishi et al., 1964). The β- and γ-hydrazides of C-terminal aspartic and glutamic residues, as well as the α-hydrazides of internal aspartic and glutamic residues, form acidic di-DNP derivatives, which can be separated from the nonpolar di-DNP derivatives of all other amino acid hydrazides by a solvent extraction procedure. The two classes of acidic di-DNP amino acid hydrazides can then be separated by the standard two-dimensional chromatographic systems devised for DNP compounds (see above, Levy, 1955).

4. Terminal Amino Acid Sequences

a. By Standard End-Group Methods. Each of the previously mentioned end-group methods may under fortunate circumstances supply some information about one or two neighboring amino acid residues. Shorter periods of acid hydrolysis after dinitrophenylation may yield DNP-A, DNP-AB, and even DNP-ABC if the peptide bonds between A, B, and C happen to be more stable than average. Such DNP peptides tend to be less ether soluble, but are extracted into ethyl acetate from acidified aqueous solution. Their presence is revealed by unidentified yellow spots upon two-dimensional chromatography, the amount of which decreases as a function of hydrolysis time in favor of the bona fide end group, DNP-A.

The standard method of detection of acylated end groups, as previously described, leads usually to a series of acylated peptides. Thus N-terminal sequences may be a by-product of the identification of the acylated end group.

Carboxy-terminal sequences may be revealed under favorable conditions by incomplete hydrazinolysis, which may yield not only the terminal amino acid in free dipolar form but also a di- and possibly a tripeptide (Z, YZ, XYZ). In this as in preceding instances, amino acid analysis of the complete acid hydrolyzate of the materials suspected of being peptides verifies this fact and usually reveals the terminal sequence.

b. *By Phenyl Isothiocyanate.* This reagent is used frequently to split one amino acid at a time from the N-terminal end of a protein or peptide (Edman, 1951, 1953). The released phenylthiohydantoin (PTH) can be identified as such (I), but the methodology for the separation of

$$
\begin{array}{c}
\overset{R'}{\underset{|}{}} \quad \overset{R-CH-NH_2}{\underset{|}{}} \quad + \quad \overset{C=S}{\underset{|}{}} \\
-CO-CH-NH-CO \qquad\qquad N-C_6H_5
\end{array}
$$

(Stage 1)

$$
\begin{array}{c}
\overset{R'}{\underset{|}{}} \quad \overset{R-CH-NH}{\underset{|}{}} \\
-CO-CH-NH-CO \quad C=S \\
\qquad\qquad HN-C_6H_5
\end{array}
$$

$+ H^+$ (Stage 2)

$$
\begin{array}{c}
\overset{R'}{\underset{|}{}} \qquad\qquad R-CH-NH \\
-CO-CH-NH_2 \quad + \quad CO \quad C=S \\
\qquad\qquad\qquad N-C_6H_5
\end{array}
$$

(I)

the PTH's on a microscale is somewhat problematical. Two procedures have been advocated that avoid the need for identification of the released PTH. The residual peptide lacking the N-terminal amino acid is purified by paper electrophoresis or column chromatography, and a suitable aliquot is then analyzed either for total amino acid composition after acid hydrolysis (Koenigsberg and Hill, 1962) or for its N-terminal amino acid by the sensitive dansyl method (see above, Gray and Hartley, 1963). The rest of the peptide is again subjected to the phenyl isothiocyanate treatment, and the new N-terminal amino acid is split off as the PTH. This series of steps can be repeated for several cycles.

To these writers direct determination of the released PTH continues to be the method of first choice, mainly because of its straightforward character. The purification of the remaining peptide between steps appears a valuable improvement of the method, since the conditions of acid catalysis required for release of the PTH cause some spurious internal peptide bond breakage. If, on the other hand, one decides to rely on analysis of the residual peptide, then the substractive method may be advisable with smaller peptides, provided an analyzer is readily available, while the positive identification by the dansyl method would be the method of choice for bigger peptides, or for lack of a readily available analyzer.

(a) *Peptide or protein in solution.* If the phenyl isothiocyanate procedure is to be performed in solution, the following procedure is recommended (Koenigsberg and Hill, 1962; Smyth *et al.*, 1962). The peptide is dissolved in 2 ml of a buffer solvent composed of 60 ml *N*-ethylmorpholine, 1.5 ml of glacial acetic acid, and 500 ml of 95% ethanol per liter. Phenyl isothiocyanate (0.1 ml) is added, and the reaction mixture is held at 37°C for at least 3 hours. The solvents are then evaporated *in vacuo*, and the residue is washed twice with benzene and finally dried at 60°C *in vacuo*. Anhydrous trifluoroacetic acid (2 ml) is then added, and the reaction mixture is held at about 25°C for 1 hour to achieve release of the phenylthiohydantoin. After evaporation of the solvent, the residue is taken up in 0.01 N HCl, and the PTH is extracted with benzene, or, if necessary, with ethyl acetate, for the purposes of its identification. The aqueous phase containing the remaining peptide is passed through a column (6 × 0.3 cm) of Dowex 50-X2 (up to 80 mesh), equilibrated in the hydrogen form. The resin is washed with 4 ml of 0.2 *M* acetic acid and then three times with 4 ml of 0.17 *M* pyridine acetate buffer of pH 4.8 and 4 ml of 1.07 *M* pyridine acetate of the same pH, and finally twice with 4 ml of an 8.5 *M* solution of the same buffer. Aliquots (25 λ) are spotted on paper and treated with ninhydrin to detect the peptide, which is usually eluted by 0.17 *M* buffer, unless it is basic or rich in aromatic residues. After evaporation of the buffer, an aliquot of the peptide is subjected to amino acid analysis or to end-group analysis by the dansyl method (as was the original peptide if identification of the phenylthiohydantoin is to be supplemented or supplanted by this procedure), and the rest is ready to be again treated with phenyl isothiocyanate.

(b) *Peptides or proteins on paper strips* (Fraenkel-Conrat, 1954; Schroeder *et al.*, 1963). An aqueous solution of a peptide or protein is distributed over several 1 × 7 cm strips of Whatman 1 filter paper (0.2 μmole per strip). The strips are suspended by a small hole near the end of glass hooks along glass rods, and dried. The strips are then wetted with 0.2 ml of 20% phenyl isothiocyanate in redistilled dioxane (redistilled within 2 weeks and stored frozen). The strips in pairs are then placed into 8-ounce screw-capped jars containing 25 ml each of pyridine, dioxane, and water. The jars, covered with aluminum foil and capped, are held at 40°C for 3 hours. The strips are dried in an airstream only to the point of losing their transparency, and then placed into 13×100 mm test tubes and covered with benzene. The benzene is replaced twice after about 1.5 hours, and a third washing is performed for many hours (e.g., overnight). After about 1 hour of aeration, the tubes are suspended in a desiccator containing 15 ml of glacial acetic acid and 6 N HCl in separate beakers. The desiccator is evacuated to 100 mm Hg and held at room temperature for 7 hours. The strips are then aerated overnight, or, alternatively, particularly if there is smog in the atmosphere, placed in a desiccator over Drierite. The strips are then extracted twice with redistilled acetone (1 hour). The redried strips are ready for the next cycle of phenyl isothiocyanate treatment, washing, acid treatment, and extraction. The acetone extracts are evaporated under reduced pressure, redissolved in a little acetone, and the aliquots ($\sim$0.1 μM) applied to paper (Whatman 1) for descending chromatography, the paper having previously been impregnated with a 0.5% solution (boiled) of soluble starch (Sjøquist, 1953).

To obtain reproducible chromatography of the phenylthiohydantoins, the paper should be equilibrated at 45–50% relative humidity, i.e., in a chamber containing a saturated K_2CO_3 solution. Three solvents have been proposed; solvent A is the most useful [A: heptane and pyridine (7 : 3); B and C: the upper phase of heptane, n-butanol, and formic acid (4 : 2 : 4 and 4 : 4 : 2, respectively)]. The papers are equilibrated with the solvents for several hours in the chromatographic chambers before the chromatograms are developed (about 4–6 hours). After the papers are well dried, they are sprayed with iodine–azide (0.01 M iodine in 0.5 M KI, mixed freshly with 0.5 M NaN$_3$). The PTH's give bleached spots on a purple to brown background, some, e.g., glycine, showing a pink and others a yellow tint.

For the separation of PTH leucine and PTH isoleucine, the starched sheet is dipped into a 20% solution of formamide in acetone. The acetone is allowed to evaporate, the sample applied, and the chromatogram developed with benzene–heptane (3 : 2, v/v) by descending chromatography for at least 40 cm (R_f, 0.71 and 0.66, respectively).

The PTH's of histidine, arginine, and cysteic acid are not soluble in acetone. If 5% water in acetone is used, they are eluted from the paper strip, but smaller peptides are also lost by such extraction. This difficulty can be overcome by sacrificing half a paper strip that is eluted with 5% water (in acetone), the residue of the eluate then being chromatographed by Sjøquist's solvent or electrophoresed according to Light *et al.* (1960).

c. By Exopeptidases. Two types of exopeptidases have proved valuable tools in the elucidation of virus proteins or their fragments. Leucine aminopeptidase, derived from swine kidney or intestinal mucosa, attacks peptides or proteins at pH 8–8.5 from the amino terminal end, splitting off one amino acid at a time, though the different classes of amino acids are released at quite different rates. Proline is released only very slowly. Mn^{2+} or Mg^{2+} is required.

Two carboxypeptidases occur in the pancreas, one of which releases the big aromatic and aliphatic amino acids with preference and other neutral and acidic amino acids more slowly (carboxypeptidase A), while the other enzyme is specific for the basic amino acids (carboxypeptidase B). Ammonium bicarbonate (0.1 M, pH 7.8 when freshly prepared) represents a suitable buffer for all of these enzymes, and digestion is usually performed at 25° or 30°C. The carboxypeptidases require no activating metal. Carboxypeptidase A is active in 4–6 M urea. The commercial carboxypeptidase usually contains both A and B activity. Carboxypeptidase may be contaminated with other pancreatic protease, and it is usually advisable to inhibit the endopeptidases by means of diisopropylphosphofluoridate (DFP). To this end 1 mg of carboxypeptidase dissolved in 0.45 ml of ammonium bicarbonate is treated with 0.05 ml of a 0.1 M solution of DFP in isopropanol, and this mixture is then added directly to about 20 mg of protein in the same buffer.

The first definitive structural information concerning TMV or its protein was the fact that carboxypeptidase released one threonine per peptide chain, and its action stopped there (Harris and Knight, 1952, 1955). We now know that this occurs because proline and prolyl bonds are very resistant to this enzyme and that from the terminal Pro-Ala-Thr sequence of TMV protein only the threonine was therefore released. In general, proteins vary greatly in their susceptibility to the exopeptidases when several amino acids are split off proteins or peptides under the influence of exopeptidases. The comparative kinetics of the release of each is used to deduce their order in the chain. However, various factors or sequences can lead to data that are difficult or impossible to interpret. Thus the results obtained with these enzymes should always be used in conjunction with other methods and cannot be relied upon as directly supplying definitive sequence information.

The amino acids released from proteins by these enzymes are determined by one of the methods previously discussed, preferably after separating them from the residual protein. This can be achieved by ultracentrifugation in the case of viruses, or by salt or isoelectric precipitation in the case of nonparticulate proteins. Dialysis or Sephadex chromatography can also be employed.

C. Modification of Functional Groups

1. *Use of Denaturants*

Native proteins consist of one or more peptide chains that are characteristically folded and often rather densely packed in a more or less precise conformation known as the tertiary structure. In addition, many virus proteins tend to aggregate in solution and form complexes or oligomers, usually associated through noncovalent forces that are generally considered to be of two types, ionic and nonpolar. One consequence of this complex structure is that many ordinarily reactive groups are relatively inaccessible to the outside environment and react only very slowly or not at all. These are said to be "masked," "buried," or "sluggish." Physical studies on constituent peptide chains often require dissociation of such complexes, particularly if more than one type of peptide chain is involved. As will be seen, it is generally desirable or necessary to dissociate and unfold these chains in order to carry out a desired chemical modification or physical study. Such disruption of tertiary folding is often referred to as "denaturation." Though there are many methods for denaturing proteins, the best choice is usually dictated by the objective of the experiment. High or low pH, urea, guanidinium halides, detergents, organic solvents, heat, and surface forces produced by agitating protein solutions with air or with immiscible solvents constitute the chief methods for bringing about denaturation. The last-mentioned methods are often unsatisfactory because they tend to produce insoluble products. Extremes of pH must be used cautiously, since they entail (particularly when one is working with proteins of unknown nature) the risk of undesirable chemical modifications. Six to 10 M urea has proved to be a particularly valuable denaturant, not only because of its great solving and denaturing power but also because it is an uncharged molecule, chemically rather inert, and of low absorption in the ultraviolet region above 240 mμ. In spite of these desirable properties, precautions are necessary in the use of urea, because it exists in solution in reversible equilibrium with cyanate, which reacts with amino groups to form carbamates and with sulfhydryl groups to form S-carbamyl cysteine (Stark *et al.*, 1960). However, freshly prepared or acidic solutions of urea do not contain cyanate. Guanidine salts (4–7 M) are even better solvents and denaturants than urea, but their ionic character represents a drawback for some applications, and they tend to be contaminated with metal ions and other products that generally have to be removed prior to use.

2. Cleavage of Disulfide Bonds

Disulfide bonds in proteins frequently play the role of architectural anchor points that tie together different peptide chains or lock folded peptide chains into particular configurations. When cystine-containing proteins and peptides are exposed to acid, alkaline, or denaturing conditions, they may undergo undesirable rearrangements to form incorrectly paired and crosslinked chains. Cleavage of the disulfide linkages is therefore often a necessary prerequisite for unfolding or uncoupling disulfide-linked peptide chains or for preventing random rearrangements. Three methods for cleaving disulfide bonds will be discussed: oxidation, thiosulfonation, and reduction.

a. Performic Acid Oxidation. Under controlled conditions, performic acid oxidizes the cystine residues of proteins to cysteic acid (Schram *et al.*, 1954; Hirs, 1956).

$$PSSP' \xrightarrow{(O)} PSO_3H + P'SO_3H$$

The reaction is controlled by avoiding a large excess of oxidant and by working at reduced temperatures. The following procedure has proved very useful for carrying out this oxidation (Moore, 1963).

Performic acid (prepared by mixing 0.1 ml of 30% hydrogen peroxide and 1.9 ml of 98% formic acid and allowing the solution to stand at room temperature for 2 hours before use) is cooled to 0°C, and an estimated 20-fold excess of the amount needed to oxidize all the cystine and methionine residues to cysteic acid and methionine sulfone residues, respectively, is added to the dry protein (for 20 mg of pancreatic ribonuclease, 0.2 ml of 99% HCOOH containing 5 μl of 30% H_2O_2). Oxidation is carried out for 1–2 hours at 0°C if the protein dissolves (or overnight if it does not dissolve). The reaction is terminated by adding 10–20 volumes of water and lyophilizing or dialyzing.

The yield of cysteic acid is often about 90%, while that of methionine sulfone is quantitative, but tryptophan is destroyed by this procedure. Tyrosine is also endangered, particularly if chloride is not carefully excluded during the oxidation.

Oxidized proteins are often more soluble than are their reduced denatured forms and do not undergo the troublesome disulfide interchange reactions commonly encountered with disulfide-containing proteins. The above method is therefore useful for chemical studies on disulfide-containing peptides. For reasons mentioned above, performic acid oxidation is generally not well suited for structural studies on tryptophan-containing proteins nor for studies in which regeneration of biological activity is contemplated.

b. Thiosulfonation. Another method that has proved useful for cleavage of disulfide bonds in proteins is treatment with sulfite to form thiosulfonates (Swan, 1957; Bailey and Cole, 1959).

$$PSSP' + HSO_3^- \rightarrow PSSO_3^- + P'SH$$

This is conveniently brought about by conducting the reaction in the presence of cuprammonium ion, which catalyzes the air oxidation of the resultant sulfhydryl to disulfide groups, and thus enables the sulfite to drive the reaction to completion.

$$PSSP' + 2SO_3^{2-} + 2Cu^{2+} \rightarrow PSSO_3^- + P'SSO_3^- + 2Cu^+$$

The following method (Weil and Seibles, 1959) illustrates an application of these principles.

Ten milligrams per milliliter of lactoglobulin is dissolved in a solution containing 0.01 M CuSO$_4$ and 0.066 M sodium sulfite and adjusted to pH 9.0 with ammonium hydroxide. After 2 hours the solution is dialyzed against 0.1 M sodium citrate, then water, and lyophilized.

The ease of this reaction varies considerably with different proteins, but the use of 8 M urea and an active oxidizing agent permits reasonably complete S-sulfonation with many proteins.

The following alternative procedure has been applied to a number of proteins (Bailey and Cole, 1959). To 1 ml of protein (20 mg per milliliter) in 8 M urea containing 0.2 M Tris at pH 7.4 is added 0.25 ml of 0.5 M Na$_2$SO$_3$ in 8 M urea. After allowing 10 minutes at 38°C for S-sulfonation, 0.25 ml of 0.5 M potassium iodosobenzoate in 8 M urea is added in order to oxidize the sulfhydryl groups that have formed. After 10 minutes the sodium sulfite treatment followed by oxidation is repeated twice more to complete further S-sulfonation, and the solution is then dialyzed against water and lyophilized to recover the protein.

The latter procedure permitted S-sulfonation of all the proteins investigated and appeared to be quite specific, as judged from quantitative amino acid analyses on the S-sulfonate derivative of chymotrypsinogen.

The S-sulfonate derivatives, unlike performic acid-oxidized sulfonates, are relatively labile, evidently being degraded to cysteine, which in turn is partially destroyed during complete acid hydrolysis. S-sulfoproteins may be reduced to their thiol forms by treatment with a 50- to 100-fold excess of mercaptoethanol for 2 hours at room temperature in 8 M urea at pH 8.6 (Raftery and Cole, 1963). Harris and Hindley (1961, 1965) have applied both performic acid oxidation and sulfitolysis procedures to disaggregate and solubilize the protein subunits of turnip yellow mosaic virus.

c. Reduction. Reduction is another effective method for cleaving disulfide bonds.

$$PSSP' + H_2 \rightarrow PSH + HSP'$$

Treatment of proteins with excess thiols in denaturing solvents of pH 7–9 appears to represent the gentlest and most satisfactory method for cleaving disulfide bonds.

$$PSSP' \underset{-RSH}{\overset{RSH}{\rightleftarrows}} PSSR + P'SH \underset{-RSH}{\overset{RSH}{\rightleftarrows}} PSH + P'SH + RSSR$$

In practice, the reaction is driven to the far right by employing a large molar excess (50- to 1000-fold) of thiol. Though many thiols have been employed for this purpose, mercaptoethanol, because of its ready availability, ease of use, and freedom from troublesome contaminants, is most widely used. Thioglycolate, which was often used in the past, has been reported to contain thioglycolide contaminants capable of "thiolating" amino groups (White, 1960) and should therefore be used with caution. A promising new reagent for reducing disulfides is dithiothreitol (Cleland, 1963). This substance has little tendency to be oxidized by air, little odor, and a high redox potential, enabling use of smaller excesses of thiol than have usually been employed with mercaptoethanol.

The following conditions (Crestfield *et al.*, 1963) have proved useful for thiol-mediated reduction of protein disulfide bonds. The method is suitable for either a simple reduction step or for reduction followed by an alkylation step.

d. Mixed Disulfides. Disulfide bonds can also be cleaved by treating the protein with an excess of a reagent disulfide, such as cystine, in the presence of trace amounts of thiol (Smithies, 1965). The thiol catalyzes disulfide interchange reactions under neutral and alkaline conditions (Ryle and Sanger, 1955). The reaction may be represented by the equation

$$PSSP' + RSSR \overset{RS^-}{\rightleftharpoons} PSSR + RSSP'$$

The reaction is analagous in principle to reduction by thiols and should be very gentle; it has the important additional advantage that the resulting mixed disulfide derivative is stable against air oxidation and may, therefore, be isolated and characterized with comparative ease.

According to Smithies (1965), the mixed disulfide derivatives of two Bence-Jones proteins and a defatted lipoprotein were readily obtained by treating with 0.1 M diethanol disulfide and 0.005 M mercapto-ethanol in 8 M urea and 0.004 M EDTA buffered with 0.1 M borate at pH 8.7 for 1 hour at 37°C. The regeneration of active enzyme from the mixed disulfide of lysozyme in the presence of traces of thiol has been described by Kanarek et al. (1965).

Using appropriate reagent disulfides, the reaction makes it possible to introduce at the disulfide groups of proteins specific side chains bearing positive or negative charges. Though not yet applied to studies on virus proteins, the gentleness of the reaction conditions and the stability and reversibility of the mixed disulfide derivative suggest many possible uses for the reaction.

Technique for reducing disulfide bonds in a protein (Crestfield et al., 1963). To the protein (5–100 mg) in a 12-ml screw-capped vial are added 3.6 gm of urea, 0.3 ml of 5% disodium EDTA, 3 ml of pH 8.6 Tris buffer [5.23 gm of Tris (2-amino-2-(hydroxymethyl)-1,3-propanediol hydrochloride), 9 ml of 1 N HCl, H_2O to 30 ml], and 0.1 ml of mercapto-ethanol. The vial is filled to a 7.5-ml mark with H_2O, and to the top with 8 M urea containing 0.2% EDTA. This reaction is generally carried out under a nitrogen atmosphere to exclude oxygen, and the reduction is usually complete after 4 hours at room temperature.

This procedure illustrates several principles: (1) the use of a denaturing solvent, (2) the use of excess thiol to drive the reaction to completion, and (3) the use of EDTA and nitrogen atmosphere to suppress metal-catalyzed air oxidation of protein sulfhydryl groups.

The type of denaturing solvent, concentration of thiol, and the time and temperature allowed for reduction will be dictated by the nature of the protein. For example, reduction may be incomplete if a protein fails to unfold completely in 8 M urea; in such an event, 7 M guanidine hydrochloride or some other denaturant may prove more effective.

The presence of excess thiol when using multimolar concentrations of urea has an additional advantage, since the reagent thiol presumably reacts rapidly with cyanate formed in urea solutions and serves to protect the protein from carbamylation, which might otherwise occur.

The high concentration of buffer outlined in the reduction procedure above is unnecessary if the operation is limited to a reduction step, but is conveniently included at this point if a subsequent alkylation step is intended (see below).

After reduction, the protein may be recovered free from the denaturing solvent and reaction components by any of a number of alternative procedures, including precipitation with organic solvents (5–6 volumes of ethanol or acetone), gel filtration, or dialysis. However, the tendency of proteins rich in sulfhydryl groups to become reoxidized, as well as to aggregate to insoluble complexes, may make the complete removal of excess reductants and/or denaturants a problematic and disadvantageous step. Whatever the procedure, reoxidation of the protein sulfhydryl groups during isolation is greatly suppressed by working at low pH values, i.e., in the range of pH 2–3 (Anfinsen and Haber, 1961).

The belief that the mercaptoethanol-mediated reduction of proteins is very gentle and cleaves no covalent linkages other than disulfide bonds is supported by the observation that ribonuclease (Anfinsen and Haber, 1961) and lysozyme (Kanarek et al., 1965) reduced by this procedure could be regenerated by air oxidation to full initial enzymatic activity.

3. Alkylation of Sulfhydryl Groups

Alkylation of sulfhydryl groups in proteins is of particular interest for a number of reasons. Because the thioether bond thus formed is very stable, the reaction may be employed for the quantitative determination of cysteine as its S-carboxymethyl or S-β-aminoethyl derivatives. These derivatives, unlike cysteine, are stable to the acid hydrolysis conditions usually employed in degrading proteins to their constituent amino acids, and, furthermore, they afford high color yields in the ninhydrin reaction. In addition, aminoethylation may be used when desired to produce a new trypsin-sensitive peptide bond. Proteins substituted with $-CH_2CH_2NH_2$ and $-CH_2CONH_2$ are generally more soluble than the parent protein or its $-CH_2COOH$ derivatives.

Another important application of the alkylation reaction is in preventing secondary reactions of sulfhydryl groups that may undergo oxidation or participate in disulfide exchange reactions under relatively mild conditions. This property when disregarded often leads to experimental difficulties. Of particular concern in both chemical and physical studies is the resulting formation of new disulfide bonds leading to new and usually undesirable molecular entities and large and often very insoluble aggregates of crosslinked proteins. Such reactions probably occur very frequently, particularly in the case of viral proteins, which are ordinarily prepared under denaturing conditions. The formation of spurious disulfide bonds can often be minimized by preparing the protein in the presence of a sulfhydryl-protecting reagent such as mercaptoethanol, but alkylation of the sulfhydryl groups represents the only certain way of achieving this end.

The reagents most commonly used for alkylating protein thiol groups include iodoacetamide, iodoacetate, N-ethylmaleimide (NEM), and more recently ethylenimine. Though none of these reagents is completely specific, each reacts (if conditions are suitably selected) by far more rapidly with exposed thiol groups than with other functional groups commonly present in proteins.

a. *Iodoacetate and Iodoacetamide.* These reagents react rapidly and quite specifically with protein thiol groups at pH 8.6, as follows (Fraenkel-Conrat *et al.*, 1951).

$$PSH + ICH_2COO^- \rightarrow PSCH_2COO^- + I^- + H^+$$

Since protons are released in this reaction, addition of alkali or the use of an adequate buffer is required in order to maintain the proper pH. The reaction should be carried out in subdued light in order to minimize the danger of possible photocatalytic oxidation of iodide to iodine, which may react with tyrosine, tryptophan, and histidine residues. In this regard, iodoacetic acid undergoes slow decomposition with the formation of iodine to give it a yellow color. This may be removed by passing an aqueous solution saturated at 45°C through a small column of acid-washed Norite A and crystallizing it at 0°C. The crystals should be snow white after drying in a vacuum desiccator at room temperature. Iodoacetate is also known to react with histidine, lysine, and methionine to form the products indicated in (II,a,b, and c), but the

(II)

rate of these reactions is much slower at pH 8.6 than is that of its reaction with thiol groups (Gundlach *et al.*, 1959). Since each of these adducts is stable to acid hydrolysis, the extent of the reaction may be monitored by analysis on the automatic amino acid analyzer.

Technique for carboxymethylating thiol groups in proteins (Fraenkel-Conrat *et al.*, 1951; Crestfield *et al.*, 1963). To a solution of protein

(1–10 mg/ml) in 8 M urea containing 0.5 M Tris HCl at pH 8.6 is added sodium iodoacetate (neutralized and recrystallized to remove contaminating free iodine) to a final concentration of 0.1 M (1 M sodium iodoacetate in 8 M urea is a convenient reagent for this purpose). The reaction is allowed to proceed for 15 minutes at room temperature and is then terminated by adding a 5- to 10-fold molar excess of mercaptoethanol compared to the iodoacetate.

It should be pointed out that though these conditions have been shown in some cases to give essentially quantitative carboxymethylation of reduced cysteinyl residues, it cannot be assumed that this will always be the case, since not all proteins are completely unfolded in 8 M urea, and the sulfhydryl may still be partially buried and unreactive under these conditions. More vigorous conditions (more effective denaturant, higher temperature, or longer reaction times) may be necessary to achieve quantitative reaction. As an example, the thiol groups of β-galactosidase have been reported to be only 80% alkylated by iodoacetate in 8 M urea compared to 10 M urea or 7 M guanidine hydrochloride (Craven et al., 1965).

The above procedure is applicable to proteins directly (with no preliminary reduction step) in order to alkylate free sulfhydryl groups. Alternatively, the protein may be reduced with excess thiol under the conditions described above in order to convert all disulfide bonds into sulfhydryl groups prior to alkylation. In the latter case, the excess thiol used in the reduction step may be removed prior to alkylating by precipitating or dialyzing the protein. However, to forestall autoxidation of the sulfhydryl groups, it may frequently be advisable to alkylate in the presence of some residual small-molecule mercaptan, adding sufficient alkylating agent to destroy the thiol, and then enough to bring the alkylating reagent to the desired concentration. The conditions usually employed are 0.05–0.20 M of any of the above-mentioned alkylating agents for 5–20 minutes.

b. Ethylenimine. This reagent reacts rapidly with thiol groups at slightly alkaline pH values to form S-β-aminoethyl adducts. The prod-

$$\text{PSH} + \overset{\displaystyle \text{NH}}{\overset{\displaystyle \diagup\diagdown}{\text{CH}_2\!-\!\text{CH}_2}} \rightarrow \text{PSCH}_2\text{CH}_2\text{NH}_2$$

uct is basic, and it is necessary to control the pH either by adding acid or by using adequate buffer. According to Raftery and Cole (1963), treatment with a 100-fold molar excess of ethylenimine for 2 hours at room temperature and pH 9 produced no modification of any amino acids other than cysteine, and the reagent afforded near quantitative recoveries of cysteine as its S-β-aminoethyl cysteine derivative after acid hydrolysis of the reduced β-chain of insulin, which had been treated with a 300 $\times$ molar excess of ethylenimine for 30 minutes at pH 8.6 at room temperature. The resultant S-β-ethyl cysteinyl site was said to be completely cleaved by trypsin. The sulfhydryl group of the TMV protein reacted completely only in the presence of 8 M urea and a small amount of mercaptoethanol (Tsung and Fraenkel-Conrat, 1966).

4. Reversible Masking of Amino Groups

Lysyl bonds may be rendered resistant to tryptic attack by acylation of the free amino groups in a protein. One reagent that appears particularly promising is ethylthiotrifluoroacetate, which acylates amino groups, rendering the lysyl bonds in the protein molecule resistant to hydrolysis by trypsin while the arginyl bonds are left susceptible. The trifluoroacetyl groups can be removed from the acylated protein by exposure to 1.0 M piperidine at 0°C (Goldberger and Anfinsen, 1962).

$$\text{PNH}_2 + \text{CF}_3\text{COSC}_2\text{H}_5 \xrightarrow{\text{pH 10}} \text{PNHCOCF}_3 \ (+\text{C}_2\text{H}_5\text{SH}) \xrightarrow{\text{Piperidine}} \text{PNH}_2 + \text{CF}_3\text{COOH}$$

a. *Preparation of Trifluoroacetylated Ribonuclease.* Five-hundred milligrams of ribonuclease is dissolved in 50 ml of water and 1 N KOH to pH 10. Ethylthiotrifluoroacetate is added (2.5 ml), and the solution is stirred vigorously with a magnetic stirrer to disperse the immiscible reagent. The pH is maintained between 9.95 and 10.0 by addition of KOH from a syringe. Alkali uptake is complete after about 1 hour. The protein is recovered by precipitation at pH 5 in 0.1 M sodium acetate by addition of 4 volumes of cold ethanol; it is then washed, dialyzed against distilled water, and the insoluble protein lyophilized.

b. *Removal of Trifluoroacetyl Groups.* Ten milligrams of trifluoroacetylated protein is dissolved in 0.5 ml of 1.0 M piperidine at room temperature and chilled for 2 hours at 0°C. The reaction mixture is transferred with good mixing to 1.5 ml of 0.5 N acetic acid cooled to 3°C and subjected to gel filtration on a column of Sephadex G-25 equilibrated against 0.1 N acetic acid. The deacylated produced can be regenerated after reduction with mercaptoethanol in 8 M urea by slow air oxidation to give a fully active enzyme.

The use of CS_2, which forms dithiocarbamyl derivatives with free amino groups, has been employed for the same purpose on lysozyme (Merigan et al., 1962) Dithiocarbamyl derivatives, like trifluoroacetyl esters, may be reconverted to the free amino form under relatively mild conditions.

5. Other Modification Reactions

The amino groups of virus proteins can be modified for various purposes by a variety of other reactions that are not readily reversible. Thus guanidination renders them more basic, and acetylation, carbobenzoxylation, or dinitrophenylation makes them nonpolar and more or less hydrophobic. Finally, succinylation, which transforms the amino groups into anionic groups, has been found to be an effective means of degrading virus particles and obtaining soluble nonaggregating subunits (Frist et al., 1965).

Among the protein groups, of particular structural significance are the phenolic groups of tyrosine. These can be transformed to mono- or diiodo-derivatives if the conformation of the protein permits. Thus in intact TMV, only one of the four tyrosines reacts at neutrality with iodine dissolved in KI, while all become gradually reactive when the isolated protein is iodinated in the same manner. The use of ^{131}I is advocated for such studies (Fraenkel-Conrat and Sherwood, 1967).

The disadvantage of iodine is its lack of specificity. Thus, it tends to oxidize other protein groups, particularly the sulfhydryl groups. In the case of TMV, the sulfhydryl group becomes substituted by the iodine, and the resulting sulfenyl iodide group decomposes upon degrading the virus (Fraenkel-Conrat, 1955).

Acetyl imidazole has been advocated as a gentle reagent for the selective acetylation of tyrosine groups in several proteins, although in other proteins it also acetylates amino groups (Riordan et al., 1965; Perlman, 1966). Acetic anhydride, long believed to acetylate selectively amino groups, was found to acetylate both amino and phenolic groups in the case of TMV protein (Colloms, 1966). The effect of these and many other reactions, including formaldehyde treatment, alkylation, and light in presence of dyes on the various protein groups, have been studied in terms of such properties as virus infectivity, antigenic specificity, and electrophoretic mobility (e.g., Anderer and Handschuh, 1963).

III. Physical Methods for Characterization of Virus Proteins

A. ELECTROPHORESIS

A large body of literature on the electrophoretic study of proteins, both analytical and preparative, has appeared since the pioneering work of Tiselius (1937). Among these methods are moving boundary electrophoresis, electrophoresis on membrane supports and slabs, and zone electrophoresis on columns stabilized against convection by density gradients, beads, or gels. The strong aggregating tendency of viral proteins has, however, imposed severe restrictions on these procedures, which have generally been designed for studying water-soluble proteins. As a result, studies on viral proteins have generally utilized the methods employing membrane supports or gels such as starch and polyacrylamide, which can be formed in the presence of strong denaturants. Urea, because it lacks charge, is the reagent of preference as a denaturant, though sodium dodecyl sulfate has been used successfully. Nonionic detergents seem so far to have been little used, though they should prove quite suitable for this purpose.

1. *Cellulose Acetate*

Because of its general availability, simplicity of use, and adaptability to small amounts of material, paper should be an excellent electrophoretic substrate. Its use has been limited, however, because of the unfortunate tendency of proteins even in the presence of denaturants to bind to paper. This property is evidently due to the existence of charged groups in the paper and may often be overcome by using acetylated cellulose. Though not all commercially available products are equivalent, possibly because of variations in the degree of acetylation, Oxoid (Colab Laboratories, North Chicago, Illinois), available in strips (36 × 5 cm), is suitable. The strips are wetted from the underside by floating or dipping them carefully, shiny side up, from one end of the strip to the other onto the buffer–urea surface to displace air from the interstitial spaces of the membrane. They are then removed, briefly drained, and applied to a cooled electrophoresis chamber. The strips are connected with the buffer reservoir via filter paper wicks and gently blotted with filter paper to remove excess buffer, but taking care not to remove too much buffer from the cellulose acetate matrix. The strips are equilibrated for 20–30 minutes with current applied to smooth out unevenly distributed buffer zones produced during the blotting operation. Heating is controlled by a cooling chamber, but one should take care that the temperature does not fall so low as to permit crystallization of the urea. Because of the tendency of urea to crystallize, it is difficult to use it in concentrations exceeding about 7 M.

About 1–5 μl of 1–5% solution of protein in the electrophoresis buffer is applied with a capillary pipet (fine polyethylene tubing is excellent for this purpose) to the center of the strip in a narrow line about 2 cm long. Delivery should be smooth and not too fast, since even volumes as small as 1 μl require about a minute to be absorbed, and application is an important factor in getting the smooth bands required for optimal resolution.

At the end of the run, the strip is fixed between two sheets of filter paper held together with paper clips (to control curling during the drying operation) and dried in an oven at 80°–90°C. The dried strips are then stained for 5–10 minutes in 2% amido black in 7% acetic acid, washed free of dye by repeated leaching in 7% acetic acid, and finally dried between sheets of filter paper at room temperature. Procedures for quantitative estimation of proteins by dye binding have been described (Fazekas de St. Groth *et al.*, 1963).

In general, urea-containing buffers containing 0.05–0.10 M electrolyte and affording current densities of the order of 5–50 mW/cm² of cellulose acetate are suitable. However, Laver (1964) described the use of a buffer with considerably higher conductivity for preparative resolution of several protein components from influenza virus. This buffer, a modification of that of Aronsson and Grönwall (1957), consists of 0.4% sodium dodecyl sulfate in a Tris–EDTA–borate buffer at pH 8.9 (80 gm of Tris, 8.0 gm of boric acid, 6.0 gm of EDTA per liter). This system was reported capable of separating the protein from 0.5 mg of virus on a single strip (10 × 5 cm) of cellulose acetate, and the separated components were readily recovered by soaking the protein-bearing strips in distilled water. In spite of the powerful denaturing action of sodium dodecyl sulfate, active hemagglutinating and sialidase components were recovered in some instances.

2. *Polyacrylamide Gels*

The chief advantage of using gels in electrophoresis is to suppress convective mixing due to density and thermal gradients that arise during the electrophoretic process. A gel of sufficient rigidity also functions as a mechanical support that enables the experimentalist to carry out staining and sampling operations after the respective components of the mixture have been separated. Polyacrylamide has a number of properties that make it very useful for the study of proteins. It is easily prepared, reproducible, forms gels even in the presence of high concentrations of many denaturants (of which urea has been particularly important), and has a glasslike transparency, which greatly facilitates detection of stained zones. Starch gel, which possesses many of these properties, has been widely used, particularly for electrophoretic studies on proteins in 8 M urea, and a comprehensive review on its use and applications is available (Smithies, 1959). Polyacrylamide, however, has some advantages over starch. For example, acrylamide is readily freed of ionic contaminants, which lead, under certain conditions, to binding of protein and to endosmotic flow. In addition, it need not be heated during preparation of the gel. The latter point may be of some importance in dealing with high concentrations of urea because of its tendency to form the carbamylating agent, ammonium cyanate, on heating. Finally, polyacrylamide can be gelled over a wide concentration range, permitting its use for "sieving" molecular weights of several hundred to several million.

   a. *Principles of Zone Electrophoresis and Zone Sharpening.* Electrophoresis on polyacrylamide gels is usually conducted in a vertical column or slab of gel connected via upper and lower buffer compartments to two electrodes (Fig. 1). The sample is applied at the top of

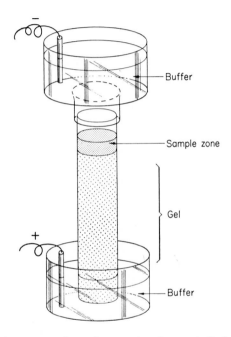

Fig. 1. Schematic presentation of apparatus for analytical gel electrophoresis. For details of procedure see text.

the gel and the polarity of the electrodes is arranged so that the sample will migrate through the gel, where, under the proper conditions, its components separate according to their respective mobilities.

   Two basic types of systems, designated (1) continuous and (2) discontinuous have been employed in work with acrylamide gels. In continuous electrophoresis, the same buffer is employed throughout the system, i.e., in both gel and electrode vessels. In discontinuous electrophoresis, the column is constructed in several layers containing several buffers of different pH and/or ionic composition. Thus in the simplest form of discontinuous electrophoresis a buffer of one composition is employed for the gel column, while a buffer of another composition is employed in the upper electrode vessel (see below).

As in classical moving boundary or zone electrophoresis in liquid media, the mobility of any component in a gel is a function of its net electrical charge. In addition, a "sieving" or filtration effect may be imposed upon the migrating molecules by making the gel network sufficiently dense to impede its progress. This latter effect may be made important or negligible by suitably arranging the gel density or "pore" size, as discussed below. The gel also serves as an anticonvection medium, thus permitting the use of higher current densities than can be used with free electrophoresis without appreciable convective mixing of migrating bands or zones. The latter property introduces the additional and very important possibility of producing and maintaining narrow starting zones, the width of which determines resolution obtainable between two zones differing only slightly in migration velocity.

Concentration or "sharpening" of the starting zone may be effected in several different ways. (1) The sample may be introduced above the gel in a liquid layer (see Fig. 1). Large molecules as they enter a gel surface move more slowly and are overtaken by the following molecules, which still find themselves in the liquid layer. It should be clear that larger molecules will form relatively sharper starting zones by this mechanism than small molecules, the migration of which is relatively less diminished by the gel network. (2) The sample may be introduced in a zone of lower conductivity (higher resistance) (for example, by dilution with water) than that of the underlying gel buffer (Hjertén et al., 1965b). In this case, the sample layer becomes a zone of relatively high potential, in which the charged molecules will have relatively high mobilities. As the front enters the gel, a region of lower potential, it is slowed down in comparison to molecules in the rear, which are still in a high potential zone. This leads to a net sharpening of the starting zone. (3) By suitable modification of pH in the sample zone, the electric charge of the sample molecules may be increased by addition of a little acetic acid or ammonium hydroxide, which endows upon proteins a more positive or negative net charge, respectively. The sample upon reaching the gel of more neutral pH then loses a portion of its charge, slows down, and is overtaken by the more highly charged molecules following in the sample zone. (4) Discontinuous buffer systems are used that are arranged so that the "leading ion" in the gel buffer has a mobility exceeding that of the "following" ion in the upper electrode buffer. This is done by constructing a column of several layers arranged in various combinations of pH and ionic composition such that the protein during the early stages of electrophoresis is collected between a boundary of ions of widely differing mobility. The mechanism of this process has been described in some detail (Ornstein, 1964) and need not be repeated here.

b. *Preparation of Polyacrylamide Gel.* Polyacrylamide gels are formed by polymerization of aqueous solutions of acrylamide monomer with an appropriate free-radical generating system. Ammonium persulfate or light-irradiated riboflavin are most commonly used for this purpose. The rate of polymerization is markedly increased by the presence of tertiary amines (called "accelerators"). Of the amines used for this purpose, tetramethylethylenenediamine (TEMED) is most efficient. The gel may be represented as a network of linear polyethylene chains bearing amide groups on alternating methylene carbon atoms. These chains may be chemically crosslinked to almost any desired degree by including in the acrylamide monomer appropriate ratios of methylenebisacrylamide. The degree of crosslinking markedly affects the mechanical properties of the gel. Thus a 10% solution of monomer consisting of acrylamide : bisacrylamide ratios of 100 : 0, 98 : 2, and 85 : 15 polymerizes to form a free-flowing solution, a firm elastic transparent gel, and a brittle, friable opalescent gel, respectively. Gels can be formed from monomers in concentrations ranging from less than 2% to greater than 60%, affording a very wide range of pore sizes. Thus a 4%—(1✕) gel permits passage of ribosomes with particle weights of several million (Hjertén *et al.*, 1965a,b). Gels of 5%—(5✕) to 15%—(1✕) are often used for proteins with molecular weights in the range of 10,000–100,000, and higher concentrations may prove suitable for work with peptides.

Preparation of a typical gel useful for electrophoresis of virus proteins in 8 *M* urea (Rueckert, 1965) is summarized in Table I. The monomers and urea are dissolved in distilled water to a final volume of 85 ml and may, if desired, be passed through a 10-ml column of dry mixed-bed ion-exchange resin to remove undesirable ionic contaminants, the presence of which are readily detectable by a conductivity appreciably higher than that of distilled water. This step also assures the absence of cyanate from the urea and minimizes the possibility of incorporating adventitious charged groups from acrylamide into the gel, thus enabling the experimentalist to take full advantage of the nonionic character of polyacrylamide. It should be clear that the urea could be omitted or used in any other desired concentration or replaced with a number of other denaturants, such as nonionic detergents. Any ionic denaturants must, of course, be added only after deionizing the monomer solutions.

Polymerization of the gel is initiated by addition of ammonium persulfate or of riboflavin in the presence of TEMED. Gelation should occur in 10–20 minutes for most applications and may be accelerated by warming the initiated solution or increasing the amount of catalyst or accelerator. Conversely, gelation rate is decelerated by taking the opposite steps. Ammonium persulfate, though particularly convenient to use, is an effective oxidant and introduces into the experiment uncertainties regarding its influence on the materials being investigated.

TABLE I

PREPARATION OF A TYPICAL POLYACRYLAMIDE GEL

[5%—(5×);[a] pH 4.8; 8 M urea]

	Per 100 ml of gel
Acrylamide	4.75 gm
Bisacrylamide[b]	0.25 gm
Urea	48 gm
Distilled water to	85 ml
Gel buffer, pH 4.8 (10×)[c]	10 ml
Riboflavin, 0.01%[d]	5 ml

[a] The description of a gel specifies both gel concentration and degree of crosslinking. Thus 5%—(5×) indicates that the gel was formed from a solution of 5% (w/v) monomer, and that the monomer contained 5% by weight of crosslinker (bisacrylamide).

[b] Methylenebisacrylamide.

[c] Gel buffer pH 4.8 is a stock concentrate for the support gel in the pH 4.8 "disc" electrophoresis system (see Tables IIA and B, which also list a number of alternative buffers for other pH systems).

[d] Gelation is initiated by photopolymerization, e.g., by illumination with a 15-W daylight fluorescent lamp; alternatively, riboflavin may be replaced by ammonium persulfate (final concentration 250–500 μg/ml), which requires no illumination and is preferred at alkaline pH.

Polymerization of gels with riboflavin as catalyst is carried out by irradiation with a fluorescent (daylight) lamp. Irradiation must be quite uniform to assure formation of homogeneous gels. Riboflavin is conveniently stored frozen at a concentration of 0.5% in 8 M urea or 0.005% in water. One percent ammonium persulfate solutions may be stored several weeks in the refrigerator, though freshly prepared solutions will probably yield the most reproducible results.

The amounts of TEMED, riboflavin, and ammonium persulfate required for polymerization is a function of monomer concentration and pH. For example, the 5%—(5×) gel described in Table I uses final concentrations of 0.25% TEMED and 5 μg/ml riboflavin (or 500 μg/ml ammonium persulfate). At pH 7–9, the concentrations of TEMED and riboflavin (or persulfate) may be reduced to about a quarter of these levels. Gelation is also influenced by oxygen concentration and may be accelerated by deaerating the solutions with the aid of a water pump just before adding the free-radical initiator. With the aid of these simple manipulations, the investigator can quickly establish the optimum concentrations for adjusting gelation rates to his particular requirements with a few exploratory experiments.

Both catalysts and accelerators remain in the gel unless removed. For many purposes their presence seems to be of no consequence other than increasing the conductivity of the gel. Nevertheless, their presence is always a potential problem. The amounts necessary for inducing gelation can be minimized by thorough deaeration, as mentioned above. In the case of continuous electrophoresis systems, the initiating catalysts may be removed by electrophoresis against the gel buffer prior to initiating the experiment. Completion of the process is conveniently monitored by the progress of a dye (e.g., 1 μl of 1% methylene blue) applied at the appropriate end of the gel. Such electrophoretic "sweeping" is, however, impractical for disc columns employing spacer gels (unless conducted prior to applying the spacer gel) because of the necessity of maintaining two different buffer systems in the column. An alternative way of minimizing the danger of persulfate is to include an appropriate charge-bearing mercaptan, such as mercaptoethylamine or thioglycolate, either mixed with or laid over or under the sample. When using these reagents, however, consideration must be given to their possible influence (as salts) on the conductivity of the sample zone, particularly if one is using the low-conductivity principle as a means of zone sharpening.

It is generally desirable to check the effect of various additives to the gel in any given application, either by removing them electrophoretically or by comparing the patterns obtained in their presence with those obtained upon their replacement or removal.

c. *Buffers for Gel Electrophoresis.* A list of buffers suitable for electrophoresis at selected pH values in the discontinuous systems is summarized in Table IIA. Some buffers for use in continuous electrophoresis systems are indicated in Table IIB.

d. *Small-Scale or Analytical Electrophoresis. Apparatus and Procedure.* Disc electrophoresis (Davis, 1964) has proved a useful tool for small-scale electrophoresis of proteins. The method, while reasonably simple to perform, is capable of excellent resolution and permits separation within a few hours of mixtures of proteins and peptides and detection under favorable circumstances of as little as 5 μg or less of protein. The procedures described below for construction and operation

TABLE IIA

STOCK BUFFER CONCENTRATES FOR DISCONTINUOUS BUFFER SYSTEMS[a,b]

Gel buffer	Electrode buffer	Elution buffer
(pH 4.3)	(pH 3.7)	(pH 4.3)
30 gm potassium acetate	80 ml acetic acid	120 gm ammonium acetate
420 ml acetic acid	140 gm glycine	880 ml acetic acid
25 ml TEMED		
(pH 4.8)[c]	(pH 4.5)[c]	(pH 4.9)
30 gm potassium acetate	80 ml acetic acid	140 gm ammonium acetate
120 ml acetic acid	312 gm β-alanine	190 ml acetic acid
25 ml TEMED		
(pH 9.4)[d]	(pH 8.7)[d]	(pH 8.7)
200 gm Tris	200 gm glycine	29 ml acetic acid
30 ml 10 N HCl	60 gm Tris	120 gm Tris
5 ml TEMED		

[a] Duesberg and Rueckert (1965). Principles for the design of new disc electrophoresis buffer systems are discussed by Williams and Reisfeld (1964).

[b] The specified quantities are for 1 liter of buffer concentrated 10-fold with respect to that required for electrophoresis. The indicated pH values of the gel and elution buffers are those of the stock after 10-fold dilution in a final concentration of 8 M urea, while those listed for electrode buffers (used in both upper and lower compartments) are the pH's after 10-fold dilution in water. The use of urea in the electrode buffers has up to now been found unnecessary. Buffers diluted in 8 M urea are generally 0.4–0.6 pH units more alkaline than those diluted in water. Elution buffers are used with the end-elution preparative electrophoresis apparatus described in the text.

[c] Reisfeld et al. (1962).

[d] Adapted from a brochure from Canal Industrial Corp., Bethesda, Maryland.

of analytical polyacrylamide gels are essentially those of Davis (1964), modified for use with urea. The apparatus is constructed from materials readily available in most research laboratories (see Fig. 1).

(a) *Buffer reservoirs.* Buffer reservoirs consist of an upper and lower vessel and may be constructed from a variety of inert, nonconductive materials. The upper reservoir serves two purposes (1) to contain the upper electrode buffer and (2) to support and align the gel tubes during the electrophoresis operation. A suitable reservoir may be improvised from a glass, methacrylate, or polyethylene tube 3–4 inches in diameter fitted at one end with a rubber stopper containing 10 or 12 regularly spaced 6-mm holes equidistant from a similar hole at the center of the stopper. Into the latter hole is inserted a solid glass or plastic rod 7 mm in diameter and 15–20 cm long. This rod, which should fit loosely enough to be movable but tight enough to provide a watertight seal, serves to center the electrode wires used for the upper and lower buffer compartments. The peripheral holes provide the sockets

TABLE IIB

STOCK BUFFER CONCENTRATES FOR CONTINUOUS BUFFER SYSTEMS

pH	Components[a]	TEMED	Catalyst
2.1[b]	750 ml propionic acid	—	APS (60 μg/ml) plus SHS (90 μg/ml)
6.5[b]	7.9 gm NaOH 47 gm cacodylic acid	0.03%	APS (350 μg/ml)
7.2[c]	102 gm Na_2HPO_4 38.6 gm $NaH_2PO_4 \cdot H_2O$	0.05%	APS (750 μg/ml) or Rib (10 μg/ml)
9.4[d]	100 gm Tris 10 gm disodium versenate $\cdot 2H_2O$ 3.8 gm boric acid	0.05%	APS (250 μg/ml)

[a] For 1 liter of buffer concentrate. pH is that of the buffer after 10-fold dilution in water. Abbreviations: TEMED, tetramethylethylenediamine; APS, ammonium persulfate; Rib, riboflavin; SDS, sodium dodecyl sulfate; SHS, sodium hydrosulfite. Each of these solutions may be added to the gel solution as a 100-fold concentrate to reach the final desired concentration. SHS is rapidly oxidized by air and should be dissolved just before use.

[b] Choules and Zimm (1965).

[c] Maizel (1966). This buffer system is used in combination with 0.1% SDS if desired.

[d] E. C. Apparatus Corp., Philadelphia, Pennsylvania, Tech. Bull. No. 134.

for insertion of the gel tubes and should be carefully drilled to assure good vertical alignment of the tubes during electrophoresis. The upper reservoir is supported over the lower buffer reservoir with a support ring or a clamp attached to a stand. A suitably sized beaker provides a convenient lower buffer reservoir. Electrodes for the upper and lower reservoirs are fashioned from platinum wire wrapped around the respective ends of a central supporting rod secured in the upper reservoir, as described above. The wire is fastened to the rod with a short sleeve of rubber or tygon tubing. The investigator will not find it difficult to improvise alternative arrangements to suit his purpose.

(b) *Gel tubes.* Containers for the gel columns are prepared from 7-mm (outside diameter) Pyrex tubing cut into lengths of 8 cm (longer or shorter if desired). The tubes should be as nearly uniform as possible to minimize differences in electrical resistance from tube to tube. The ends of the tubes should be square-cut to facilitate removal of the gel at the end of the electrophoretic run. Sharp edges are preferably removed by polishing with carborundum cloth or by cautious fire polishing, taking care to avoid any constriction at the end of the tube. Some workers find it useful to seal the tubes at one end to female ground-glass joints, which may be conveniently affixed to matching male joints secured in the base of the upper buffer compartment. Though initially more costly, such an arrangement markedly facilitates the attachment and detachment of gel tubes from the reservoir and has the additional advantage that the tubes are rigidly aligned in vertical position. The tubes should be cleaned with detergent or cleaning acid, thoroughly rinsed, and dried before each use.

(c) *Electrical destainer.* This unit, used for removing dye from stained gels, is employed with the same apparatus as described above except that the stopper is fitted with detachable tubes 10 mm in diameter and 8 cm long. These tubes are closed at the bottom end either with 10% polyacrylamide gel plugs or with a section of dialysis membrane held in place with a Tygon sleeve. When not in use the tubes are stored in 7% acetic acid to prevent the plugs from drying out.

(d) *Preparation of gel column.* The clean and dry gel tubes are closed at one end with a square of Parafilm tightly pressed around the outside edges. An alternative closure is made with a used stopper from a B-D Vacutainer blood-collection tube available from clinical hospital laboratories. The latter is particularly convenient, since it also provides an excellent stand that holds the tube in good vertical alignment. The gel solution is then introduced into the tube through a long-tipped Pasteur pipet (disposable variety) beginning with the tip near the base of the tube to avoid trapping air bubbles in the viscous liquid and filling it to a level previously marked 6 cm from the bottom. The solution is then carefully overlaid with 0.1 ml of gel buffer through a 23–25-gage needle affixed to a 1-ml tuberculin syringe and bent near the tip at right angles. This buffer overlay counteracts surface tension at the gel boundary and leads to formation of a flat meniscus necessary for achieving flat protein bands. Mixing between buffer and gel solution must be avoided as much as possible. A small portion of the gel solution adjacent to the water overlay does not gel because atmospheric oxygen inhibits gelation. The resultant "buffer" zone of ungelled solution reduces dilution of urea at the gel boundary, so it is generally unnecessary to include urea in the buffer overlay. Gelation is accompanied by the formation of an easily visible sharp zone and should be complete in 5–20 minutes, depending on the composition of the gel.

(e) *Application of sample.* The most direct and most nearly quantitative method is to layer the sample under the buffer and on top of the gel column. With this procedure the operator must exercise care to avoid mixing and dispersing the sample in the overlying buffer due to accidental shaking or convective circulation arising from ohmic heating of the sample when current is applied. The latter can be minimized by holding the current strength low until the sample has migrated into the gel.

For the reasons just mentioned, the sample is often incorporated in a gel such as starch, Sephadex, or polyacrylamide. This maneuver considerably simplifies the mechanics of manipulating the columns and apparatus when starting the electrophoresis run. Gelling the sample in polyacrylamide works well, but usually leads to trapping some of the protein (usually only a rather small portion) in the matrix. Furthermore, the sample often contains substances that inhibit polymerization of acrylamide, such as dyes and thiols. Starch (partially hydrolyzed, according to Smithies, 1959) is generally suitable below pH 5, but should be used cautiously at more alkaline pH values and particularly at low ionic strengths, when considerable binding of protein to the starch may occur (evidently due to the presence of cationic components).

(*f*) *Electrophoresis.* The columns are attached to the base of the upper buffer reservoir, which is then filled with electrode buffer. A drop of buffer is applied to the outer edge of the base of each electrophoresis tube and allowed to flow into the bottom cavity of the gel, thereby displacing any air that would otherwise be trapped in the base of the gel column in the subsequent immersion step. The entire assembly is then lowered into the bottom buffer reservoir. It is frequently preferred to immerse the tubes to the level of the samples in the buffer, so that the gel columns are adequately cooled during electrophoresis. Electrophoresis is performed at about 5 mA for the desired time. It is desirable if the sample has been layered over the gel, rather than incorporated into a sample gel, to begin with a lower current (2–3 mA) until the sample has migrated into the gel. (The Heathkit Model TPW-32, capacity 400 mA, 400 V, Heath Company, Benton Harbor, Michigan, is suitable for analytical electrophoresis. It may also be used for preparative electrophoresis on a small scale, but it is often useful to have a power supply of at least twice this capacity for preparative electrophoresis.) The purpose of this step is to minimize convective mixing due to excessive ohmic heating in the sample zone.

At the end of the run the columns are detached from the reservoir and the gels removed. This is most readily done by gently turning the column between the fingers after carefully inserting a 22-gage needle attached to a small syringe full of water into the gel column at the outer periphery of the gel. Water, injected as the column is turned, frees the gel from the glass wall. This operation is repeated, if necessary, from the other end of the gel column. A rubber bulb full of water attached to one end of the "rimmed" column is often useful in sliding the gel out of its container.

(*g*) *Staining and destaining.* The protein bands, generally invisible

at the end of the run, are stained by immersing the gels in about 5 ml
1% amido black in 7% acetic acid for an hour. Many proteins form
an insoluble, virtually irreversible, complex with the dye under these
conditions and are said to be "fixed." To remove unbound dye, the
gels are first soaked in 7% acetic acid for 30 minutes (or overnight
if desired) and then destained completely, either by repeated washing
in 7% acetic acid or more conveniently by "electrophoretic" destaining,
a process that removes the unbound but not the protein-bound dye.

To destain, the gels are transferred to the "destainer" tubes (described above). Each tube, half filled with 7% acetic acid containing
about 25% glycerol, is attached to the upper buffer reservoir. The
reservoir is then filled with 7% acetic acid, which also fills the gel-
containing tube and partially mixes with the heavier glycerol solution.
The resulting crude density gradient suppresses the tendency of the
upward-migrating dye to recirculate back downward by convective mixing during the destaining operation. The gels are destained with a
current flow of about 10 mA per tube (150–200 V), with the anode in
the upper buffer reservoir.

The staining–destaining procedure calls for several precautions. If
destaining is initiated before "fixation" of the protein is complete, the
partially stained protein may migrate during electric destaining. This
is recognized as a thickened, blurred, and upward curving band,
especially pronounced in the central portion of the gel, since fixation
occurs from the periphery to the center of the gel. Difficulty in complete removal of the dye from the upper end of the gel is usually due
to the presence of excess dye and may be avoided by staining with a
lower dye concentration or soaking the gel overnight in 7% acetic acid
prior to destaining. Finally, it should be remembered that the staining
procedure described is almost certainly not universally applicable, and
the possibility that some substances are not "fixed" and therefore not
detected should always be considered. The possible use of the above
dye in combination with alcohol, trichloroacetic acid, heavy metals, or
other effective precipitating agents may prove desirable, especially
when dealing with peptide mixtures.

The destained gels are conveniently stored in 7% acetic acid in
labeled screw-cap vials or test tubes, where they may be kept for years
without deterioration. Photographs prepared with the Polaroid camera provide convenient permanent records (Burns and Pollak, 1963).
The gels are conveniently photographed by transmitted light. Densitometer tracings may be obtained with the type of unit employed for
reading ultracentrifuge photographs (for example, the Joyce-Loebe Mi-
crodensitomer or the Spinco Analytrol). Such tracings are often useful

in making quantitative approximations of the relative amounts of material in several bands.

While results are generally quite reproducible from run to run, migrations are not always identical. It is possible, however, to compare two proteins of very similar mobility in the same gel column (referred to as a "split gel") by including a liquid-tight insert in the gel tube to form two compartments in which the respective samples can be introduced. Different protein samples are placed on either side of the insert and the run is carried out in the usual fashion.

e. Preparative Gel Electrophoresis. The impressive success of small-scale disc electrophoresis has provided powerful impetus for development of corresponding preparative procedures. The chief problems in preparative electrophoresis are heat dissipation and the recovery of samples from the supporting medium, particularly from gels. The former problem, which essentially determines the limits to which the technique can be scaled up, is generally solved by preparing thin (0.8 cm or less) slabs of gel (either flat or cylindrical) bounded on both sides by a cooled surface. The capacity of the method depends upon the cross-sectional area of the gel and upon the relative mobilities of the substances to be separated, and it ranges roughly from 0.5 to 10 mg/cm^2 cross section of gel, depending on whether the components are closely spaced or widely separated.

Several methods have been applied to recover material from the gel. (1) The most direct method for preparative work is to cut the gel and isolate the material from suitable sections. Several procedures are applicable: (a) The gel is broken into pieces by cutting it, forcing it through a screen, or smashing it in a piston in a steel cylinder after freezing it in liquid nitrogen. The macerated gel is then extracted with a suitable solvent such as 8 M urea, dilute or concentrated acetic acid, or ammonia. The solvent may subsequently be removed by dialysis or evaporation. Recoveries are generally rather variable and incomplete, and the samples are recovered in dilute form. (b) The sample may be recovered by electrophoresis out of the gel. A porous gel (such as described in Table I) is formed in a Pyrex tube closed at one end with a rubber stopper penetrating 3–5 mm. After the gel has formed, the rubber stopper is carefully removed and the end of the tube filled with buffer and covered with a section of dialysis membrane to form a small buffer compartment. This operation is conveniently carried out with the tube held below the surface of the buffer to prevent trapping of bubbles in the compartment. The membrane is affixed to the tube with the aid of a rubber band or a sleeve of rubber tubing. The macerated gel sample (which has either been incorporated into the gel of the tube or simply layered over the gel) is then electrophoresed out of the gel and into the bottom buffer compartment between the gel and dialysis membrane. The sample is collected by inverting the tube and removing the membrane at the end of the experiment. This method has the advantage of concentrating the sample, but is applicable only to nondialyzable components, and recoveries are not generally quantitative. (c) Radioactive ^{35}S is reported to be recovered quantitatively by digesting gel sections with hydrogen peroxide (Young and Fulhorst, 1965). Carbon-14 is also recovered in yields of 85% or greater of the counts found in the absence of gel by such a procedure. One- or 2-mm segments sliced from a frozen gel are digested 2 hours at 65°C in 0.2 ml of 30% hydrogen peroxide in a tightly capped 20-ml glass scintillation vial. To the digest is added 0.3 ml of water and 9.5 ml of dioxane-based scintillation fluid. Alternatively, polyacrylamide gels may be prepared with an alkali-labile crosslinker by substituting ethylene diacrylate for methylenebisacrylamide in the preparation of the gel (Choules and Zimm, 1965). Such a modified gel appears to have mechanical properties similar to conventional gels, but can be dissolved with 1 M piperidine to give a clear homogeneous solution in a dioxane-based scintillation fluid. A counting efficiency of 10% for tritium was reported. A mechanical fractionator for sequential extrusion and recovery of ^{14}C-labeled proteins from polyacrylamide columns has been described by Maizel (1966).

(2) Preparative methods that do not require sectioning the gel are of interest, since they considerably reduce the labor required for sampling and recovering components from complex electrophoretic patterns such as might be encountered in mixtures of proteins or in enzymatic digests of a protein. Two basically different approaches have been described, which might be classified as end elution and side elution. In the end-elution technique the sample is collected in a flowing stream of buffer as it migrates from the end of the column.

(a) *Apparatus.* A convenient and relatively economical all-glass apparatus that has proved useful for preparative resolution of milligram quantities of viral proteins (Duesberg and Rueckert, 1965) is shown in Fig. 2. This arrangement is readily automated.

The basic features of the apparatus are a cylindrical upper chamber containing the gel and a lower collection chamber bounded by an upper and lower sintered glass disc. The respective bands migrate through the gel block, passing through the sintered glass disc and into the chamber, from which they are immediately swept out by continuous flow of buffer emerging upward from the lower disc. The course of the experiment is conveniently monitored through a suitable

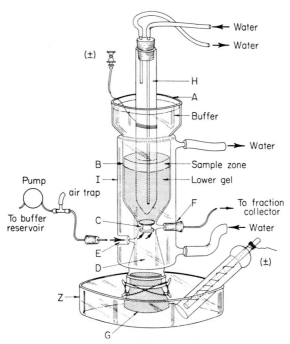

Fig. 2. Apparatus for preparative acrylamide electrophoresis. The sample migrates in an electric field from the top through the body (B) of a prepolymerized acrylamide gel into the collection chamber (C). As the bands leave the gel and enter the collection chamber, they are flushed out to a fraction collector by a continuous upward flow of buffer entering (C) through a porous bottom disc.

spectrophotometer cell linked to a recorder, and the effluent is then passed into a fraction collector.

(b) *Preparation of the column.* Before use the apparatus should be thoroughly freed of any residual polyacrylamide (particularly that trapped in the upper sintered glass disc) by washing it with warm chromic acid followed by dilute alkali and distilled water. The polyacrylamide plug is then inserted into the inverted buffer-filled glass column. To fill the plug with polyacrylamide it is dipped first in distilled water to displace any air from the glass interstices, then inserted, sintered disc end down, into a beaker nearly filled with a freshly initiated gel solution [10%—(1×) acrylamide with 0.25% TEMED in electrode buffer and 0.05% ammonium persulfate is suitable]. The gel solution should be allowed to flow freely through the disc before the plug is completely immersed. After gelation the entire block is removed from the beaker and the excess polyacrylamide trimmed away from the outside surface.

The lower chambers bounded by the glass discs are freed of air by appropriate tilting or flushing with "elution" buffer introduced with a syringe attached to the 1.2-mm outside diameter Teflon tubing secured with a rubber stopper to openings E and F (Fig. 2), respectively. Finally, the column is turned right side up and fixed vertically in operating position, with the plug immersed in electrode buffer and taking care to avoid trapping any air bubbles under the flat glass disc. The cooling rod (H) is centered in the column section (B), so the tapered end is about 0.5 cm above the upper disc (C). Final alignment of the cooling rod fixed in a clamp on a ring stand should be carried out by prefilling the chamber (B), cooling rod (H), and jacket (I) with water to reduce optical distortion. The column is then ready for introduction of the gel block.

It is important in this operation that the gel bond firmly with the walls and upper glass disc but that no gel be permitted to form in the collection chamber. This is accomplished by introducing with the aid of a syringe attached to outlet F a colored high-density liquid (20% sucrose in 8 M urea containing 0.01% dye) into the collection chamber (C) and then through the upper glass disc. Any excess sucrose–urea–dye solution that passes through the upper glass disc during this operation is removed from the gel chamber (B), and the gel column is prepared by introducing the desired gel solution into the chamber (B). The gel solution is then carefully overlaid with a 0.5-cm layer of water to form a flat upper meniscus and then permitted to sink about halfway into the upper disc (C) by carefully removing the colored high-density solution from the collection chamber through outlet (F). The dye greatly facilitates visual control of this process and makes it easy to be sure that gel has penetrated the disc but not the collection chamber. Bromphenol blue is used as the dye in the colored sucrose–urea solution with a lower anode and crystal violet or methylene blue with a lower cathode.

When gelation is complete (evident as a very sharp gel–water boundary at the top of the gel column) the overlying aqueous phase is removed and the upper compartment filled with electrode buffer. Urea, if used as a denaturant in the gel block, need not be incorporated in the electrode buffers with this apparatus.

(c) *Application of the sample and electrophoretic fractionation.* The sample (made denser than the buffer solution by addition of 5–10% sucrose or a suitable concentration of urea) is then introduced with a long-tipped pipet or cannula held on the chamber wall just over the upper gel surface and carefully layered at the top of the column. The sample zone is susceptible to convective mixing at this stage, and a low density current (0.2–0.4 W/cm²) is initially employed. The current may then be increased to 0.5–1 W/cm² after the sample has entered the gel. The beginner will find it highly rewarding to conduct a few preliminary experiments with a dye or colored protein (cytochrome c, which, unlike hemoglobin, has a covalently bound heme moiety, is especially suitable for experiments employing denaturing solvents such as 8 M urea), since their behavior is readily observed and technical difficulties are quickly detected. Typical runs take many hours.

(d) *Elution of fractions.* As the respective bands migrate out of the bottom of the gel they enter the collection chamber, from which they are swept by a continuous slow counterflow of the "elution" buffer entering through the lower disc and leaving the chamber through a side arm. The eluate is then passed through an absorption cell and into a fraction collector. Some proteins can be recovered with high efficiency even from solutions of 8 M urea and at concentrations as low as 0.1 mg/ml by precipitation overnight in the cold with 5 volumes of ethanol or acetone. Alternatively, dialysis, lyophilization, adsorption on ion-exchange resin, or some other method of recovery may be necessary.

In principle, the electrode or gel buffer may be employed for elution. It is often desirable, however, to make some modifications in the elution buffer. For example, the mobility of proteins is generally decreased by an increase in ionic strength. Therefore, an elution buffer with an ionic strength exceeding that of the gel buffer minimizes loss of samples due to migration through the lower disc at the base of the collection chamber and permits use of slower elution flows (hence higher protein concentrations) than would otherwise be possible.

Another reason for modifying an elution buffer hinges upon the method used for recovery of the sample after collection. Thus if one wishes to lyophilize, a volatile buffer is desirable. Alternatively, organic solvents, though often excellent protein precipitants, also precipitate many salts, necessitating further time-consuming desalting steps. This difficulty may often be avoided by replacing one salt with another. For example, replacing the β-alanine cation in the pH 4.9 buffer (Table IIA, column 2) with ammonium ion at the same pH (Table IIA, column 3) yields a buffer from which no salt precipitates after adding 5 volumes of acetone or ethanol. The essential principle in formulating the elution buffer is that the upward-moving ion (acetate in the pH 4.8 system with an upper anode) would be the same species as that in the gel and should have an ionic strength equal to or exceeding that of the upper electrode buffer.

Several other end-elution preparative columns have recently been described, notably by Jovin *et al.* (1964), Maizel (1964), and Hjertén *et al.* (1965a). End-elution methods all suffer two major disadvantages. (1) Slowly migrating samples require a long time for elution, and (2) the eluted protein is recovered in relatively dilute solution. While the latter problem can often be solved through the use of suitable concentration or precipitation techniques, the former problem presents difficulties, particularly when one is dealing with a complex mixture of components with a wide range of fast and slow mobility. In principle, elution of segments of the gel column would be the preferable procedure for this purpose. This can conveniently be achieved by the side elution technique. In this procedure the electrophoresis is conducted in a vertically oriented gel slab formed in a specially constructed chamber (Raymond, 1962), and migration is terminated before the desired components are eluted from the opposite end of the gel. To recover the separated materials, the gel slab is sandwiched together with a separating grid containing vertical furrows between two sheets of dialysis membrane and subjected in a special device (Raymond, 1964) to an electric field of appropriate polarity across the face of the slab, so that each zone is eluted in a direction normal to the face of the gel slab. Because each component must migrate no further than the thickness of the gel slab, elution is quite rapid. The eluted protein collects and concentrates at the surface of a bounding dialysis membrane, and by virtue of its density increment and the lower temperature at the externally cooled membrane surface effects a downward convection flow that carries the protein into collection chambers at the base of the grid. The protein is thus simultaneously eluted and concentrated. Though quantitative studies on recovery of proteins eluted by this method are lacking, it might be anticipated that yields will be good for quantities exceeding about 10–20 mg, but will be progressively poorer with smaller amounts of protein because of adhesion to the dialysis membrane and diffusion during circulation. Loss of dialyzable materials by passage through the dialysis membrane limits use of this procedure to recovery of nondialyzable components. This side-elution procedure is especially suitable for mixtures of nondialyzable components with a wide range of electrophoretic mobilities, since in contrast to end-elution techniques, slowly migrating materials are recovered almost as readily as rapidly migrating substances. In addition, it is technically somewhat simpler than the end-elution techniques presently available.

f. Applications. Zonal electrophoresis on polyacrylamide gel has been used for separation of peptides, proteins, and particles as large as ribosomes. A good example of the application of this method to the separation of peptide mixtures is given by Steers *et al.* (1965), who investigated the fragments resulting from β-galactosidase treated with cyanogen bromide, which cleaves protein chains at the site of methionine residues (see Section IV,A,2). Because methionine is present in relatively small amounts in most virus proteins, the fragments will tend to be large and consequently difficult to separate on paper or by ion-exchange chromatography. Gel electrophoresis, used in conjunction with urea or detergents when necessary, promises to fill the gap and represents a very sensitive tool for this purpose.

Gel electrophoresis has also proved useful for the resolution and detection of virus proteins, particularly scarce proteins such as those from animal viruses. For example, it has been used to demonstrate that several different picornaviruses, including poliovirus (Maizel, 1963) and ME, EMC, and Mengo viruses (Rueckert, 1965), each contain a characteristic set of different polypeptide chains. The method has also been applied to an analysis of sialidase from influenza virus (Seto and Hokama, 1964). Where insufficient material is available for systematic exploration of more conventional separation procedures, it is possible to scale up analytical columns to isolate milligram quantities of each polypeptide component free of the other (Duesberg and Rueckert, 1965; Maizel, 1964). Another modified gel-electrophoresis procedure has been applied to studying the biosynthesis of structural and other virus-induced proteins in the poliovirus-infected cell (Summers *et al.*, 1965).

Gel electrophoresis is also suited to the study of reactions that lead 'to changes in the charge of proteins, since it is possible to detect the effect of removing a single charge (Duesberg and Rueckert, 1965). The procedure should, therefore, be useful in monitoring such reactions as acetylation of lysine and alkylation of thiols with iodoacetate, which introduces a negative charge, or ethylenimine, which introduces a positive charge (Section II,C,3,4).

The procedure has also been adapted to separation of the particulate elements of the ribosomal particle (Hjertén *et al.*, 1965a), and should with suitable modification be applicable to electrophoretic studies on small virus particles.

3. *Electrophoresis without Supporting Matrix*

An instrument that appears very promising as a tool for preparative electrophoresis of proteins or peptides is the continuous-flow electrophoretic separator (Hannig, 1961), a type of curtain electrophoresis apparatus that employs no carrier other than a flowing buffer stream (available from Brinkman Instruments, Westburg, New York). The substance to be resolved is pumped at a slow rate into a separating chamber consisting of a thin sheet of buffer flowing at a uniform rate between two parallel glass plates (50 × 50 cm). The sample is separated according to the electrophoretic mobilities of its respective components by an electric field exerted normal to the direction of buffer flow. The sample separates as it flows in a continuous stream to the other end of the sheet, where the respective separated fractions are collected in 48 fractions.

Another technique that appears promising as a tool for the separation of proteins as well as of protein aggregates and particles, including viruses, is sucrose-gradient electrophoresis. Here the sucrose gradient fulfills the stabilizing role, which permits the separation of components while minimizing diffusion and abolishing adsorption problems. Sucrose gradients containing 4–6 M urea can be used to prevent aggregation of viral proteins (Cramer and Svensson, 1961).

At the end of the run, the sucrose is drained in dropwise manner, collected in fractions, and the contents are analyzed.

B. Gel Filtration

Gel filtration is a procedure in which separation is based to a large extent upon differences in molecular size. Three major classes of materials currently in use are agarose, polyacrylamide, and dextran gels. Of these, the first is primarily applicable to separation of very large macromolecules and particles in the size range of viruses (Steere and Akers, 1962) and subcellular particles (Hjertén, 1962, 1964) and need not concern us here.

The other two gels, polyacrylamide (available from Bio-Rad Laboratories, Richmond, California) and Sephadex (available from Pharmacia Fine Chemicals, Piscataway, New Jersey) are capable of resolving substances in the molecular weight range of 100–200,000. These materials are available in a range of different degrees of crosslinking, which is the principal determinant of the fractionation range. Polyacrylamide has only recently become available, and as yet there is relatively little information on which to compare it critically with Sephadex, the gel form most widely used.

1. Sephadex

a. Available Gels. The use of Sephadex in gel filtration was first described by Porath and Flodin (1959), who pointed out its applications to resolution of molecules of different size. Sephadex consists of small grains or beads of an insoluble dextran polymer crosslinked into a three-dimensional network of polysaccharide chains. It is neutral except for the presence of 10–20 microequivalents of anionic carboxyl groups per gram, these evidently originating by oxidation of residual aldehydic groups in the dextran. The gel is relatively stable to alkali and has been used with 0.1 N NaOH. It can also be used with weak acids such as acetic acid, withstanding concentrations as high as 50% for short periods. It is hydrolyzed by strong acids. Seven grades of standardized Sephadex are presently available, the physical properties and fractionation ranges of which are summarized in Table III. The indicated exclusion limits are determined from soluble dextran fractions and may vary somewhat for proteins.

TABLE III
PHYSICAL DATA ON SEPHADEX GELS

Type	Swelling time[a] (hours)	W_r[b]	d[c]	V_t[d]	V_o	V_i	Exclusion limit[e]	Fractionation range[f]
G-10	2	1.0	—	2	—	—	1,000	To 700
G-15	—	1.5	—	—	—	—	—	To 1,500
G-25	6	2.5	1.13	5	2	2.5	5,000	100–5,000
G-50	6	5.0	1.07	10	4	5	10,000	500–10,000
G-75	24	7.5	1.05	12–15	5	7	50,000	3,000–70,000
G-100	48	10	1.04	15–20	6	10	100,000	4,000–150,000
G-200	72	20	1.02	30–40	9	20	200,000	5,000–800,000

[a] Recommended time for Sephadex to swell in a given buffer.

[b] Water regain; i.e., grams of water taken up in inner phase per gram of dry gel.

[c] Density of gel column.

[d] Volume of 1 gm of gel when fully swollen with water; V_o represents the void volume and V_i the inner volume.

[e] Average molecular weight of dextran calibration fraction excluded from gel.

[f] Average molecular weight range that can be fractionated, determined with globular proteins.

b. *Preparation of the Gel.* The dry powder is added slowly to a salt solution with stirring. Solutions containing 0.01 M salt or higher should be used, since the aggregated gel is otherwise difficult to disperse. The gel grains are allowed to swell for the indicated times (Table III), since a column packed before the gel has fully swollen may have an excessively slow flow. It has been reported that the swelling time of Sephadex can be reduced to a few hours by suspending the gel in 6 M urea or 5 M guanidine hydrochloride (Wieland et al., 1963) or by boiling in distilled water for a few hours.

After the gel beads have swollen the fine particles are removed by repeated decantation. The gel is suspended in 10–20 volumes of buffer and allowed to settle for 30–60 minutes in a graduated cylinder for this operation. After the last decantation, the gel is suspended in 2–3 volumes of buffer and is ready for preparing the column. The gel suspensions can be kept indefinitely, provided precautions are taken to prevent microbial growth.

c. Column Design. Desirable features for a gel-filtration column include (1) uniform bore up to the bed support, (2) a suitable bed support, and (3) a small but well-drained chamber beneath the bed to prevent dilution and remixing of eluted zones after they emerge from the bed support. Large-scale columns with nylon-netting bed supports especially designed for the purpose are commercially available (Pharmacia Fine Chemicals, Inc.).

A suitable column can be constructed from glass or plastic tubing of the desired size fitted at one end with a rubber stopper equipped with a 2–4-cm length of 4-mm glass tubing. A short section of latex rubber tubing fitted with a stopcock or screw clamp is forced over the 4-mm glass tubing outlet to provide a flow-control device. For small-scale columns a length of surgical polyethylene tubing (e.g., size PE 160) inserted through a fine hole in the stopper is very practical. The tubing is cut sufficiently long that flow may be regulated by raising or lowering its distal end. The rubber stopper is anchored more securely in the base of the glass column, if necessary by wrapping it with a few turns of adhesive tape.

A bed support may be fashioned from a thin disc of porous polyethylene (Porex Materials Inc., Fairburn, Georgia) cut with a sharp cork borer to a size that fits snugly inside the tube. The disc is positioned with the aid of a suitable rod inside the column on top of the rubber stopper, leaving a very thin space between the stopper and the disc to provide good drainage for the buffer emerging from the porous support disc. A few small glass beads correctly positioned between disc and stopper ensure a proper space. Sintered glass discs, often used for this purpose, are not recommended, since they tend to become clogged by fine particles produced from abrasion of the swollen Sephadex grains by the glass.

Alternatively, a column satisfactory for many purposes can be constructed from a glass tube with a small plug of glass wool inserted in a constriction at the bottom.

d. Preparation of the Gel Bed. Since in gel filtration the separation volume is small compared to the bed volume, a carefully packed column is of special importance in achieving optimum performance. The column is mounted in a vertical position and half filled with buffer. Any air trapped in the porous disc at the bottom of the column may be removed at this step by connecting the upper end of the column to a water-aspirator pump until bubbles no longer emerge from the disc. Deaeration of buffers before use prevents subsequent formation of troublesome air bubbles during the packing and chromatography steps described below.

To prepare the bed, a homogeneous suspension of deaerated gel slurry is introduced into the column tube, which was previously half filled with buffer. The outflow tube should be closed at this step. The gel particles are permitted to settle through the buffer until a layer several centimeters deep forms at the bottom; thereafter, a slow flow of buffer is released through the bottom outlet. Fresh gel is added at intervals until the desired bed height is reached. In a properly packed column the rising bed surface remains level throughout the operation. Columns with a height-to-diameter ratio of 10 : 1 or 20 : 1 are customarily employed. Columns of G-100 and G-200 are very easily compressed and exhibit reduced flow rates with excessive pressures. They should not be packed with pressure heads exceeding 10–20 cm of water. It has been reported, however, that addition of cellulose powder (15–20%, w/w) to G-200 markedly increases the flow rate of the column without affecting the general characteristics of the filtration pattern (Craven et al., 1965).

To equilibrate the column, two or three bed volumes of the desired buffer are now passed through. If the surface is not completely level at this point, this can often be corrected by tapping the column or by carefully stirring the surface of the gel with a glass rod. The suspended gel will then settle to form a level surface.

Because the upper surface of the gel is very easily disturbed, especially during sample applications, many workers prefer to stabilize the surface by covering it with a disc of filter paper. When working with small amounts of protein, nylon netting or Teflon-coated glass cloth filters (Bel Art Products, Pequannock, New Jersey) are preferable because many proteins are strongly adsorbed to cellulose paper.

e. *Application of the Sample.* This is also a critical step in obtaining good results. Two procedures are commonly used.

(1) In the first procedure, excess buffer is carefully removed and the remaining eluent is allowed to drain into the surface of the bed without allowing the surface to dry. The sample is now applied, taking care not to disturb the gel particles, which should have a level surface. After letting the sample sink into the bed, a small amount of eluent is applied to the column in the same way to wash the sample into the

gel. The column is then overlaid with buffer and developed. This procedure is most suitable for the small pore gels (G-10 to G-75). For the large pore gels (G-100 and G-200), which are easily compressed, the following procedure is recommended.

(2) In the second procedure, the sample is applied as a layer underneath the buffer with the aid of a bent-tip pipet held on the wall of the tube just above the surface of the gel. For effective layering the sample must be denser than the overlying buffer. The density is commonly increased when necessary by adding a few percent by weight of sucrose or urea.

f. Determination of the Void Volume. With the data for the total bed volume (V_t), water regain (W_r), wet density (d), and dry weight of Sephadex used (a), the void volume, V_o, can be calculated from Eq. (1).

$$V_o = V_t - a(1 + W_r)/d \qquad (1)$$

The inner volume, V_i, can be calculated from the water regain by using the expression $V_i = aW_r$. V_i can also be calculated without knowing the dry weight of the gel from Eq. (2).

$$V_i = (V_t - V_o) \ W_r d/1 + W_r \qquad (2)$$

However, void volumes change somewhat from column to column due to various packing densities, and it is often desirable to determine this value experimentally. The void volume is the volume of buffer required to elute a high molecular weight substance that is completely excluded from the inner solvent of the gel. Hemoglobin, because of its visibility and availability, is commonly used for determining the void volume of G-25 and G-50, but is unsatisfactory for the larger pore gels (G-75 to G-200) because it is not completely excluded. A colored polymer (Blue Dextran 2000) (Pharmacia Fine Chemicals Inc., Piscataway, New Jersey), with an average molecular weight of about 2×10^6, has been developed for this purpose. It is also useful for checking flow behavior of a column to make sure that it has been properly packed. This material is readily soluble in water and salt solutions and is used at a concentration of 0.1–0.2%.

g. Applications of Gel Diffusion. The primary use of Sephadex is to separate macromolecules from small molecules or ions. Gel filtration is also applicable to a variety of situations in which one desires to transfer a protein into a new solvent. The method is a rapid alternative to dialysis and may be carried out without excessive dilution. Sephadex G-25 is generally used for this purpose because it excludes essentially all proteins that are eluted in the void volume, while small-molecular weight components follow. A bed volume of 6–10 times the sample volume is generally adequate for this purpose. For example, to transfer 5 ml protein in 8 M urea to a solvent such as 0.1 M acetic acid, one passes several bed volumes of the latter solvent through a 50-ml column in order to equilibrate it with the desired solvent. The sample is applied as described above and the column developed with 0.1 M acetic acid. According to Table III, the protein will emerge from the column after about 20 ml (the void volume of a column of G-25 with a total volume of 50 ml) and will be diluted by diffusion to a volume of 8 or 9 ml.

A convenient procedure to concentrate dilute protein solutions, as they frequently result from column fractionation and similar procedures, also utilizes Sephadex. The procedure consists in precipitating the protein by means of adding ammonium sulfate to the solution to the concentration necessary to precipitate the protein, and then desalting the precipitate, redissolved in a little water, by passage through a short Sephadex G-25 column, equilibrated with a 0.02 N volatile buffer such as ammonium acetate.

It is also possible to separate proteins of different sizes on Sephadex and polyacrylamide gels. The larger-pore-size gels (G-75 to G-200) with higher fractionation limits are used for this purpose. For example, Crestfield et al. (1963) resolved the reduced carboxymethylated A and B chains of insulin on the basis of their differences in size by chromatography on Sephadex G-75 equilibrated with 50% acetic acid. This procedure, using acetic acid and/or other disaggregating solvents, should be suitable for resolution of viral proteins of different sizes, but so far it does not appear to have been applied for this purpose. Difficult separations on gel columns can sometimes be achieved by recycling chromatography. A special apparatus for this purpose is commercially available (LKB Instruments, Washington, D.C.).

The estimation of molecular weight by gel chromatography has also been described. The method rests upon comparison of the elution volume of an unknown protein with standard proteins of known molecular weight. Good linear correlations have been reported between the molecular weight or molecular radius of a number of proteins with the ratio $V : V_o$ of elution volume to void volume (Whitaker, 1963; Andrews, 1964; Akers, 1964). Again the method appears not to have been applied to estimating the molecular weight of virus proteins, where the aggregation problem poses itself. Differences in the state of aggregation of TMV protein in various buffers at pH 7 have been evaluated by Sephadex chromatography (Colloms, 1966). The application of dissociating solvents in conjunction with considerations similar to those discussed under ultracentrifugation may prove fruitful in applying gel filtration to virus protein.

Certain precautions are necessary in using Sephadex. In the absence of salts, small quantities of proteins such as RNase, lysozyme, trypsin, and bovine serum albumin have been reported to adsorb to Sephadex. These proteins were readily eluted with dilute sodium chloride but not with distilled water (Glazer and Wellner, 1962). This behavior is attributed to the small amounts of carboxyl groups in the gel. Some proteins behave anomalously on Sephadex. For example, lysozyme has been reported to elute from G-75 and G-100 much later than expected on the basis of its molecular weight (Whitaker, 1963). This behavior was not affected by ionic strength and is, therefore, evidently not attributable to the ion-exchange effect mentioned above. Similar cases are known for certain other proteins. It is possible that such effects might be corrected by the use of aromatic solvents that have been shown to correct the adsorption of phenylalanine, tyrosine, and tryptophan to dextran gels (Porath, 1960; Synge and Youngson, 1961).

h. Thin-Layer Chromatography with Sephadex. Another technique that looks promising for microscale work with peptides and proteins is thin-layer chromatography with superfine Sephadex gels that have been especially developed for this purpose. These powders require no binder and adhere readily, provided the glass plates are scrupulously clean. The slurry is applied to the plate in a layer 0.5 mm deep with a conventional spreader. Proper consistency of the gel during spreading is a prerequisite to preparing good layers, particularly for the larger gels G-100 and G-200. Morris (1964) recommends 6% and 4% (w/v) suspensions of G-100 and G-200, respectively, and employs the following procedure. The slurries are spread on 10×20 cm plates, and after equilibrating 18 hours in a closed solvent-saturated chamber (which is said to improve reproducibility), 1–20 μg of protein in 0.5–1 μl of buffer is applied as a series of spots 1.5 cm apart in a line about 3 cm from the short edge of the plate. The plate is then developed by descending chromatography. Solvent is introduced to the upper end of the tilted plate through a strip of Whatman 3 MM filter paper, and the solvent flow is regulated by tilting the plate to the proper angle (10–20 degrees). A corresponding wick of filter paper is placed at the other end to prevent accumulation of excess fluid at the bottom of the plate. The progress of the experiment is followed with a colored marker protein such as cytochrome c or hemoglobin, which should migrate about 70 mm in 4–8 hours for good results. At the end of the migration the plate is carefully covered with a sheet of 10×20 cm filter paper (Schleicher and Schuell No. 2042 b was recommended) and dried 30 minutes at 80°–90°C. Protein spots are detected by staining with 0.2% Ponceau red in 10% aqueous acetic acid or with 1% naphthalene black 12B or 0.01% nigrosine in methanol–water–acetic acid (50 : 40 : 10). The dye is removed by repeated rinsing in water, at which time the filter paper again comes free from the surface, exposing the stained protein spots.

Thin-layer gel-filtration procedures for the small-pored Sephadex gels have also been described (Determan, 1962; Johansson and Rymo, 1962, 1964; Andrews, 1964).

C. ULTRACENTRIFUGATION

The ultracentrifuge is particularly suited to quantitative studies on the size and homogeneity of macromolecules in solution, and it was the introduction of ultracentrifugation that led to general acceptance of the concept of proteins as macromolecules of defined size. It is today one of the most useful and versatile tools for determination of particle size, homogeneity, and interactions. The method is nondestructive and under favorable circumstances yields molecular weight data on a few milligrams or less of protein. Today most analytical studies on the ultracentrifuge are carried out in the electrically driven Model E analytical ultracentrifuge (Beckman-Spinco), the general availability of which has done much to popularize ultracentrifugal measurements. Increased sensitivity and accuracy in ultracentrifuge methods has been achieved by the use of interference optics (Richards and Schachman, 1959; LaBar and Baldwin, 1962). The recent introduction of a photoelectric absorption scanning system offers still greater sensitivity (Schachman, 1963). This latter system should prove particularly valuable for studies on scarce materials and aggregating proteins, such as virus subunits, which tend to dissociate more readily at high dilution. Refractive index optics require concentration of the order of several milligrams per milliliter, while ultraviolet absorption optics are about 3–10 times as sensitive.

The two basic methods employed for molecular weight determinations with the ultracentrifuge are the sedimentation velocity method and the sedimentation equilibrium method.

1. Sedimentation Velocity

The sedimentation velocity method is commonly employed (1) as a means of evaluating sedimentation homogeneity or heterogeneity and (2) as a means of determining sedimentation coefficients, which serve as characteristic properties of any particular protein and which may be used in molecular weight determinations. The protein solution is centrifuged at high speeds, typically near 60,000 rpm, because of the relatively low sedimentation velocity of proteins. An approximate idea of the size and homogeneity of a preparation is quickly obtained in this way. Heterogeneous protein solutions containing two or more species differing appreciably in size are revealed as multiple sedimenting boundaries. Different proteins with relatively similar sedimentation coefficients may or may not be revealed by the sedimentation velocity method, and it is important to remember that a single boundary indicates size homogeneity but is not a sufficient, nor even an especially good, criterion of purity.

The sedimentation coefficient of a preparation is a useful characteristic of a protein preparation and may be used as a reference constant. Methods for calculating and correcting sedimentation coefficients to water at 20°C and zero protein concentration are described by Schachman (1957).

The molecular weight of a protein may be estimated from determinations of its sedimentation coefficient, s, its diffusion coefficient, D, and from a knowledge of its partial specific volume, $\bar{v}$, using Eq. (3) (Svedberg and Pedersen, 1940).

$$ M = \frac{RT}{1 - \bar{v}\rho} \frac{s}{D} \tag{3} $$

where M is the molecular weight, R the gas constant, T the absolute temperature, and ρ, the density of the solution.

The partial specific volume of most proteins is in the range 0.70–0.75. A reasonably accurate value may be calculated from the amino acid composition of the protein on the assumption that the volume of the protein in solution is equal to the sum of the volumes of its constituent amino acid residues (Cohn and Edsall, 1943). This method assumes that the protein is free of lipid and carbohydrate, the presence of which could lead to significant errors. The most reliable procedure for determining partial specific volumes is based on density measurements. An example of the experimental determination of a partial specific volume with a pycnometer is given by McMeekin et al. (1949).

2. Sedimentation Equilibrium Method

In the sedimentation equilibrium method, the solution is centrifuged at relatively low speeds, so that gravitational forces are insufficient (because of counteracting diffusional forces) to completely sediment the protein to the bottom of the cell. When equilibrium has been reached, one can calculate the molecular weight from semilogarithmic plots of the relative protein concentration at various distances from the center of rotation by means of Eq. (4) (Svedberg and Pedersen, 1940).

$$M = \frac{2RT}{(1 - \bar{v}\rho)\omega^2} \, d \ln \frac{c}{dr^2} \tag{4}$$

where ω is the angular velocity in radians per second, c the relative concentration of protein, and r the distance from the center of rotation in centimeters. According to this equation, a plot of log c against r^2 should give a line of constant slope for a homogeneous protein.

A number of useful variations that considerably reduce the time requirement for sedimentation equilibrium experiments have been developed. A low-speed sedimentation equilibrium method is described by Klainer and Kegeles (1955). The use of very short sedimentation columns (van Holde and Baldwin, 1958; Yphantis, 1964) reduces the time periods involved to a few hours.

3. *Applications*

Ultracentrifugal studies on proteins in aqueous solutions are generally carried out in 0.1–0.2 M salt such as NaCl or KCl in order to swamp out coulombic effects produced by sedimentation of the charged molecules away from their smaller counter ions. Unfortunately, while molecular weight determinations in the ultracentrifuge require a homogeneous population of molecules, virus proteins are generally strongly aggregated or even insoluble in neutral salt solutions, and appropriate steps must generally be taken to define the proper conditions for preparing monodisperse solutions. These include preventing formation of disulfide crosslinkage between polypeptide chains and the use of appropriate solvents that will not only dissolve the protein but also dissociate its smallest polypeptide subunits into their monomer forms.

Disulfide crosslinking may be prevented by blocking all sulfhydryl groups in a form that precludes formation of disulfide crosslinks. This is generally done either by oxidation of sulfhydryl and disulfide bonds to the sulfonate form with performic acid or by reduction and subsequent alkylation of all disulfide groups (methods for carrying out these procedures are described in Section II,C,2,3). The relatively gentle reduction and alkylation procedures seem preferable to the considerably more drastic performic acid oxidation procedure. It must be noted that the neutral, negatively, or positively charged groups that can be introduced by alkylation of the cysteine residues give enough variety so that the insolubility problems sometimes encountered with certain alkylated polypeptide derivatives are usually successfully surmounted by another.

The next step is to find an appropriate solvent for the protein, which, as mentioned above, is generally associated into polydisperse aggregates. Many denaturants, including 0.01–0.1 N NaOH, 0.1 M acetic acid, 67% acetic acid, 70% formic acid, 8 M urea, 5 M guanidine hydrochloride, 30% pyridine, and 0.1–1% sodium dodecyl sulfate, have been used to disaggregate virus proteins for molecular weight determinations. Though polypeptides appear to be sufficiently stable to tolerate (at least for a limited time) the extreme pH ranges represented above, the use of strongly acid and basic solvents is generally regarded as unwise, particularly in investigating proteins of unknown nature, and exploration of the neutral solvents, including detergents, guanidine, and urea, is much preferred. Of the latter, sodium dodecyl sulfate has been most widely used because it is effective, even in relatively low concentration, for disrupting aggregates into their respective monomers. Having found a suitable solvent, the appropriate sedimentation diffusion or sedimentation equilibrium experiments are carried out and a molecular weight calculated by the usual procedures.

Up to this point the possible preferential binding of solute components to the protein has been ignored. For example, detergent molecules bound to the sedimenting protein increase both the particle weight and partial specific volume of the sedimenting unit, and this effect can be considerable. Procedures for calculating the molecular weight of the unbound protein from the particle weight of the protein–detergent complex are given by Hersh and Schachman (1958). The results of Kielley and Harrington (1960) and of Trautman and Crampton (1959) in model studies on RNase indicate that valid molecular weight determinations may also be obtained with 5 M guanidine hydrochloride and 6 M urea as solvents. Finally, it should be noted that three component systems such as those referred to above are still being actively investigated, and, though it appears that their use is valid, it is desirable to check the results by as many independent techniques as possible. Their chief value in the characterization of polypeptide chains is in setting limits on the maximum molecular weight of any particular protein. Such information is particularly valuable when used in conjunction with amino acid compositions that give minimum molecular weight data.

D. ZONAL CENTRIFUGATION ON DENSITY GRADIENTS

Another exceedingly valuable and versatile technique applicable to both analytical and preparative studies on viral proteins is that of zonal centrifugation on density gradients (Brakke, 1955). This procedure is generally carried out in the swinging bucket rotors of the Spinco Model L preparative ultracentrifuge and has the considerable advantage of requiring much less technical proficiency and interpretive skill than that demanded by analytical ultracentrifugation. Two types of rotors are in general use: a small SW-39 (or SW-50) rotor that holds three tubes of 5-ml capacity and a larger SW-25 rotor holding three tubes of 34-ml capacity. The smaller rotor, capable of higher speeds, is generally used for analytical or small-scale preparative work and the larger rotor mainly for preparative work.

1. *Preparation of Gradients*

Though a variety of substances have been employed for the production of gradients, sucrose is by far the most widely used. A very useful table summarizing the densities and viscosities of sucrose solutions over a wide range of concentrations has been compiled by de Duve *et al.* (1959).

Crude sucrose gradients that are quite suitable for many applications may be prepared without special equipment by carefully layering into the 5-ml Lusteroid tube 1.1 ml each of four solutions of decreasing density, e.g., of 20, 15, 10, and 5% sucrose dissolved in a suitable buffer. If stored 24–48 hours at constant temperature (sucrose gradients are preferably stored at low temperature to avoid the growth of microorganisms; alternatively, an inhibitor such as 0.05% sodium azide may be used), a very smooth and reproducible gradient is produced by diffusion.

A more rapid and very convenient device for generating sucrose gradients is that described by Britten and Roberts (1960). The unit consists of a Lucite block containing two parallel chambers connected at the bottom by a fine channel which may be closed off with a screw pin or stopcock. A polyethylene outflow tube about 8–10 cm in length extending from one of the chambers completes the device. It is convenient to have two units, one designed to fill the small tubes of the SW-39 rotor (holding about 2.5 ml in each chamber), and the other designed to fill the larger SW-25 tubes (capacity of about 15 ml in each chamber).

To prepare a linear 5–20% sucrose gradient in the 5-ml Lusteroid centrifuge tube, the connecting channel between the two chambers is filled with 5% sucrose to displace any air bubbles, then closed by turning the screw pin or stopcock. With the outflow tube elevated, the chambers are loaded with 2.3 ml of the respective 5 and 20% sucrose solutions, filling the mixing (outflow) chamber with the denser solution. A small metal mixing paddle or platinum bacteriological inoculating loop mounted on a stirring motor is then inserted into the outflow chamber so that the stirrer just clears the floor of the mixing chamber. Magnetic stirring is also possible. The stirring speed is adjusted to give good mixing with minimum disturbance of the meniscus. The connecting channel between the chambers is now opened and the tip of the polyethylene outflow tube is placed at the top of the centrifuge tube to initiate the preparation of the gradient. For maximum linearity of the gradient the outflow should be sufficiently slow that the fluid levels in the two chambers are the same during emptying. The finished gradients are stable for at least 48 hours if stored at constant temperature.

2. Layering the Sample

To start a run the sample (0.1–0.5 ml, depending upon the purpose of the experiment) is carefully layered on the gradient. In order to achieve maximum performance from the density-gradient columns, it is important that the operator be cognizant of the "droplet-sedimentation" phenomenon that may occur upon layering a sample over a density-gradient column (Brakke, 1955). After application of the sample to the column, the sucrose molecules diffuse into the protein band faster than the protein diffuses out. Because of the density increment due to the protein, the density of the solution at the edge of the sample boundary exceeds that of the underlying sucrose solution and droplets begin to settle. These form fine streamers, which are often visible because of the difference in refractive index of the two solutions. This effect is not serious if the sample contains less than about 2% protein and is layered on at least 5% sucrose and does not seem to occur after centrifugation has been initiated. It is important, however, to be aware of the phenomenon and not to delay too long between layering the sample and beginning centrifugation.

3. Centrifugation

It is desirable, especially with the small SW-39 rotor, to initiate acceleration slowly for the first 10–20 seconds in order to avoid the starting lash imparted to the rotor by the drive shaft when the two are not fully engaged. Full acceleration may be applied as soon as the rotor reaches slow speed. For most reproducible results, the rotor should be brought to operating temperature prior to beginning centrifugation and temperature settings set at the desired point. Some warming of the contents occurs during prolonged high-speed runs, and in cases where this is of importance, control settings should be adjusted to that required for the proper sample temperature. At the end of the run the small rotor should be decelerated without braking. This precaution is unnecessary in the case of the large rotor.

4. Sampling

The gradient column is customarily sampled by collecting drops through a hole pierced in the bottom of the centrifuge tube. Several special devices for more accurate collection of drops have been described (Szybalski, 1960; Martin and Ames, 1961). The latter authors showed that the volume of the drop sizes from a linear 5–20% sucrose gradient were essentially constant throughout the gradient, delivering about 15 μl per drop through a 21-gage syringe needle.

5. Applications

Zonal density-gradient centrifugation using the swinging-bucket rotor has been used in the determination of sedimentation coefficients and preparative resolution of viruses, ribosomes, nucleic acids, and proteins. The present discussion will be confined to the latter. The method is valuable as a preliminary means of determining particle size, particularly for very scarce materials where insufficient material is available for conventional optical methods in the analytical ultracentrifuge. Martin and Ames (1961) developed the method for determination of sedimentation coefficients down to about 2S. In their procedure, a 0.1-ml aliquot of the material to be investigated is layered over 4.55 ml of a linear 5–20% sucrose gradient in an appropriate buffer. Sedimentation is carried out at 3°C and 39,000 rpm for periods up to 18 hours. A useful feature of such gradients is that the increasing density and viscosity of the sucrose gradient is almost exactly counterbalanced by the increasing gravitational force encountered by the sedimenting particle as it moves outward. As a result, most proteins exhibit a linear migration with time, so that the ratio of the distances traveled by any two solutes from the meniscus is constant and independent of time. For solutes with similar partial specific volumes, the sedimentation coefficient of an unknown can be determined by comparison of its rate of sedimentation with that of a reference protein with a known sedimentation constant. The method is capable of surprising accuracy with appropriate care. A major advantage of this procedure is that any suitable property such as radioactivity, infectivity, hemagglutination, enzyme activity, or absorbancy can be used in locating the material of interest. For globular, or almost globular, proteins with similar partial specific volumes, a crude estimate of the molecular weight, M, may be determined from the sedimentation constant alone (Schachman, 1959) according to the relation in Eq. (5).

$$s_1/s_2 = (M_1/M_2)^{2/3} \tag{5}$$

The zonal sedimentation method has been used to estimate the particle size of an isolated hemagglutinin from influenza virus using the hemagglutinating activity as an assay and 7S and 19S γ-globulin as reference proteins (Laver, 1964). In another case, the molecular size of radioactive protein from guanidine-degraded poliovirus was determined (Scharff et al., 1964). In this case, 4 M guanidine hydrochloride was included in the gradient to prevent aggregation of the virus protein. RNase, determined enzymatically, and bovine serum albumen, determined by its absorbancy at 280 mμ, were used as reference proteins. In still another case, the split products of detergent-treated myeloblastosis virus were separated and characterized by the ATPase activity and antigenicity (complement fixation) of the respective components (Eckert et al., 1964).

E. Other Physical Methods

Low-angle x-ray scattering in solutions, though not often mentioned, is a means of determining molecular weight and shape of proteins. In a recent study using this method (Anderer et al., 1964), evidence was presented that TMV protein exists in 60% acetic acid as a fully dissociated monomer in which the tertiary structure is disrupted but the secondary coiling (α-helix) is unaffected. Tobacco mosaic virus protein in 0.01 N NaOH was shown, however, to be incompletely dissociated. A review on the use of low-angle x-ray scattering is given by Beeman et al. (1957).

A good introduction to the application of light scattering to molecular weight determinations is given by Tanford (1961).

A recent review on the application of osmotic-pressure techniques to the determination of molecular weights in the presence of high concentrations of urea or guanidinium hydrochloride is given by Kupke (1960).

A very direct method for examining macromolecular assemblies is that of electron microscopy. It has been employed widely to studies on the substructure of viruses.

IV. Amino Acid-Sequence Analysis of Virus Proteins

A. Specific Cleavage of Peptide Chains

The structural analysis of a protein usually requires two principal steps: The dissociation of multichain proteins into their single-chain components, and the determination of the sequence of amino acids in the latter. The first objective is achieved by methods discussed in Section II,C,2,3. If the peptide chains are held together only by secondary linkages, then detergents, urea, or guanidine salts serve to dissociate them. If disulfide bonds are involved, and this has not as yet been observed to be the case for virus proteins, then these must be split, a process that can be achieved by oxidation or reduction. Oxidation usually destroys tryptophan and other residues, and reduction is therefore generally the method of choice. To prevent reoxidation and reformation of disulfide bonds by atmospheric oxygen, the reduced proteins are usually stabilized by alkylating agents, as discussed above.

If the virus protein was composed of more than one type of peptide chain, then these have to be separated. DEAE-cellulose chromatography may be useful for this purpose, but electrophoretic methods on paper or polyacrylamide gel have proved more generally successful (see Section III,A).

The determination of the sequence of amino acids in a single-chain protein should in principle be possible by the repeated application of the stepwise degradation by phenyl isothiocyanate (see Section II,B,4). However, in practice, this has rarely been possible for sequences of more than eight residues.* The customary procedure is, therefore, to degrade the protein by various means of specific cleavage to fragments that are more amenable to phenyl isothiocyanate and the other methods of sequence analysis given above. Methods for specific cleavage are either enzymatic or chemical, and are discussed below.

1. Specific Enzymatic Cleavage

The most important tool of protein structural analysis is the enzyme trypsin, which splits proteins only at the carboxyl end of arginine and lysine. Theoretically, this would degrade every protein to $X + 1$ peptides if X is the number of arginine and lysine residues per mole. In actuality, some of these bonds may be quite resistant to trypsin, as for instance Lys–Pro and Arg–Arg. On the other hand, traces of chymotrypsin present in most trypsin preparations lead to varying extents of splitting of the peptides at sites particularly susceptible to that contaminant enzyme, so that minor components may be present in the digests amounting to more than $X + 1$. Of the various suggestions as to how to suppress the chymotrypsin activity in trypsin preparations, the most effective appears to be the use of TPCK-treated trypsin. TPCK, 1-(1-tosylamido-2-phenyl)ethylchloromethyl ketone, is a specific inhibitor of chymotrypsin (Schoellmann and Shaw, 1963; Kostka and Carpenter, 1964). The specificity of trypsin can be sharpened to

* See, however, Edman's Sequenator [Edman and Begg (1967)].

attack only at arginines by blocking the lysine groups by various reagents (see Section II,C,4). On the other hand, trypsin can be made to split the peptide chain at cysteine residues by transforming these to ethylamino groups (see Section II,C,3,b).

Other proteolytic enzymes have less clearly defined specificities. Chymotrypsin attacks the carboxyl end of the aromatic and large aliphatic amino acids with some preference and can be used as an alternate primary agent for the degradation of proteins. More frequently, however, chymotrypsin, as well as the bacterial protease, subtilisin or nagarse, are employed for secondary degradation of protein fragments, e.g., big peptides obtained by trypsin or other reagents. The bacterial enzymes, as well as pepsin, attack with some preference at the hydrophilic residues. Each of these enzymes can be used effectively in empirical fashion to split a limited number of bonds in intermediate-size peptides. Usually certain bonds in a given peptide are more susceptible to any one of those enzymes than other bonds, and definite fragments result.

The enzyme thermolysin has been reported to split with some selectivity at the amino end of leucine and isoleucine and may also prove useful for specific cleavage of viral proteins (Matsubara et al., 1965).

Trypsin, chymotrypsin, and the bacterial enzymes (usually 2–10% of the weight of the substrate) are used at 37°C and at pH 8, and pepsin in 10^{-2} M HCl (pH 2). When dealing with at least 0.1 μmole of peptide, the digestion can be performed in a pH stat using 0.1 N NaOH or preferably 0.1 N NH$_4$OH to maintain the pH. The alkali consumption is then an indication of the rate and extent of digestion, which can be stopped at any desired stage of partial digestion. Alternatively to the use of the pH stat, ammonium bicarbonate (0.1 M) represents a useful buffer, since its freshly prepared solutions are at pH 7.8, and it can be removed by freeze drying.

Many proteins are rather resistant to enzymatic digestion and must be denatured to expose sensitive sites that often lie protected within the interior of the chain (see Section II,C,1). An additional difficulty is that some proteins are insoluble in the aqueous media used for enzymatic digestion, particularly if they have been isolated, as is often the case, under denaturing conditions. However, most proteins are soluble in 8–10 M urea (provided precautions have been taken to prevent chemical crosslinking; see Section II,C,1–3), and once dissolved, often remain in solution even after considerable dilution of the urea. Trypsin and chymotrypsin, though inactive in 8 M urea (pH 7.8), are both fully active in 2 M urea at room temperature (Harris, 1956). The following procedure takes advantage of these facts (Rodbell and

Frederickson, 1956; Katz *et al.*, 1959). A solution of protein (5–10 mg/ml) in 8 M urea is diluted to 2 M urea with 0.1 M ammonium bicarbonate (or with water, if a pH stat is to be used to maintain pH 8). Some proteins may precipitate upon dilution of the urea, but these usually are dissolved during the course of digestion. Digestion is initiated by adding 2.5 mg crystalline trypsin (2.5% in water freshly prepared) per 100 mg of protein. Digestion is carried out for 90 minutes at temperatures of 25°–37°C. When digesting very small volumes, phenol red (20 μg/ml) can be used as internal indicator, since it does not interfere with subsequent analysis and serves as a convenient marker during the mapping procedure. At the end of tryptic digestion in 2 M urea, the urea is removed by adsorbing the peptides on a small column, 0.8 $\times$ 5 cm, of Dowex 50-X2, 100 mesh, in the hydrogen form. Exhaustive washing of the column with glass-distilled water removes the urea. However, certain acidic peptides (e.g., acylated peptides) may be eluted with the urea under those conditions. Typically amphoteric peptides are eluted with 4 M NH₄OH. For satisfactory separation of peptides, the final mixture should be free of salts, and it is for this reason that a volatile buffer and ammonia are preferred, which can be removed by evaporation in a vacuum desiccator. The peptides are redissolved in a small volume of dilute ammonia for mapping.

2. Specific Chemical Cleavages

N-Bromosuccinimide and related compounds have been shown to split peptide chains at the carboxyl end of tryptophan and to a lesser extent of tyrosine, but the quantitative aspects of this reaction leaves much to be desired. Cyanogen bromide treatment of proteins, on the other hand, has proved a very valuable method, since it splits with good specificity at methionine residues, transforming the methionine into C-terminal homocysteine lactone (Gross and Witkop, 1962). Since most proteins contain only a few methionine residues, this method splits proteins into a few large fragments, which can subsequently be digested with trypsin. Alternatively, big tryptic peptides containing methionine can be secondarily degraded with cyanogen bromide.

A 30- to 40-fold molar excess of CNBr over methionine is weighed in glass-stoppered vials and added to the protein dissolved in 0.1 N HCl or, preferably, in 50–80% formic acid. The reaction mixture is held at 25°–30°C for about 24 hours, then diluted with water and lyophilized. The residue is taken up in water with dropwise addition of 0.1 N NaOH until all is in solution at or about pH 8, and the resulting fragments are separated by Sephadex, DEAE-cellulose column chromatography, or gel electrophoresis.

Another useful tool consists in heating the protein, or preferably smaller fragments, in dilute acid (pH 2, 0.01 N HCl). This leads to a release of aspartic acid residues (Partridge and Davis, 1950; Tsung and Fraenkel-Conrat, 1965). Asparagine is deamidated and more slowly released; few other bonds are broken at a time when over 70% of the aspartic acid is released. The fragments from both sides of the aspartic residues are separated chromatographically, as usual.

The search for new procedures for selective cleavage is quite active, but not all methods that are proposed are found to live up to expectations when applied to a new protein by an investigator other than the originator. One of these methods that has not yet been "checked out" independently is the specific cleavage at proline residues by means of sodium in liquid ammonia (Wilchek et al., 1965).

After a protein has by combinations of the methods listed been reduced to peptides containing, hopefully, 10 residues or less, this mixture must be resolved before the amino acid-sequence analysis of each peptide can be tackled.

B. Separation of Peptides

Enzymatic degradation or selective chemical cleavage gives an array of more or less definite peptide fragments. Elucidation of the amino acid sequence of the parent chain ideally requires isolation in high yield and characterization of each peptide fragment. Because of the wide range of peptides that could possibly be encountered, each protein and protein digest presents its own peculiarities and special difficulties, and no generally successful formula for resolution of peptide mixtures can be put forward.

1. Ion-Exchange Chromatography

The most successful means for preparative resolution of peptide mixtures has been the use of ion exchangers in combination with pH, salt, and organic-solvent gradients. The automatic amino acid analyzer affords a practical route to preparative resolution of peptides containing up to 20–25 amino acid residues. Dowex 50-X2 (Hirs et al., 1956) and Dowex 1-X2 (Rudloff and Braunitzer, 1961) have been successfully used to resolve mixtures of up to about 20 peptides. A very desirable feature of ion-exchange resins is their ability to handle reasonably large amounts of material. Thus preparative columns of Dowex 1 and Dowex 50 (2.5 × 150 cm) are capable of resolving 200–600 mg or more of hydrolyzate. Phosphocellulose, with an even higher capacity, has been reported capable of handling similar loads on columns of only 2.4 × 25 cm (Canfield and Anfinsen, 1963).

Since peptides are usually amphoteric, they can be adsorbed on cation exchangers under conditions sufficiently acidic to protonate essentially all of their amino and carboxyl groups. The adsorbed peptides are then eluted by gradually increasing the salt concentration or pH. For example, a peptide mixture in 0.2 M pyridine acetate buffer at pH 3.5 will be adsorbed to a column of Dowex 50 equilibrated against the same buffer and the peptide components eluted successively and roughly in order of their respective net electrical charges, starting with the least basic, by a linear gradient obtained by gradual addition of 1 M pyridine acetate at pH 5.0.

In contrast, elution from an anion exchanger such as Dowex 1 with an alkaline pH decreasing to acid and/or increasing salt concentration yields the most basic peptides first. Besides volatility, the use of pyridine-containing buffers also has the advantage of reducing the danger of bacterial decomposition of peptides during their isolation. Ammonia, pyridine, collidine, or trimethylamine, and formic or acetic acids are most commonly employed for preparing volatile buffers. Gradients of almost any desired profile can be generated with a multichambered device called the Varigrad (Peterson and Rowland, 1961).

The particular buffers and gradients to resolve any particular mixture of peptides must generally be determined empirically. For such exploratory analytical work, 1–2 mg of digest may be fractionated on the automatic amino acid analyzer on small columns, e.g., 0.9 × 17 cm (Jones, 1964). Preparative columns of the same height and 2–3 cm in diameter can then be used when satisfactory conditions for resolution have been established. Since some very large peptides might fail to be eluted from ion-exchange resins, it is advisable to determine recoveries of material applied to the column. The number, height, and elevation of peaks on preparative columns may be monitored with the aid of a stream divider by passing a portion of the effluent stream through the reaction chamber of the amino acid analyzer while collecting the remaining portion of the stream in a fraction collector. Alternatively, when volatile buffers are employed, aliquots of the collected fractions may be dried in a vacuum oven overnight at 70°–80°C and analyzed after alkaline hydrolysis by ninhydrin (see Section II,A,2) or by the Lowry procedure.

Lowry peptide analysis. The Lowry procedure gives a rough measure of the size of the peptide and insures detection of peptides that in the intact form give a low ninhydrin color. For detection of peptides by the Lowry procedure (Lowry *et al.*, 1951) 10–100 μg of peptide is mixed with 1.0 ml of a reagent freshly prepared by mixing 50 ml of 2% Na_2CO_3 in 0.1 N NaOH with 1.0 ml of 0.5% $CuSO_4 \cdot 5H_2O$ in 1% sodium citrate. The mixture is allowed to stand for 10 minutes or more at room temperature, then 0.1 ml of Folin-Ciocalteau phenol reagent (commercially available), diluted with water to 1 N acid, is added with rapid mixing, and the absorbancy at 750 mμ is measured after 30–120 minutes. Though not strictly quantitative nor proportional to the amount of material (because the color yield varies somewhat for different peptides, depending on their content in aromatic amino acids and other factors), the method is nevertheless very useful for rough estimations of peptide amount because of its sensitivity and ease of routine application.

For direct amino acid analysis selection of a single peak tube is advocated. For preparative purposes, all tubes under a peak are pooled. The peptide material is recovered by lyophilizing to remove solvents and volatile buffer and the residue is dissolved in 1–2 ml of water. Insoluble peptides may often be dissolved by adding a little ammonium hydroxide or ammonium carbonate. The purity of peptides in the respective fractions may be estimated (1) by amino acid analysis (integral ratios are expected for pure peptides), and (2) by one- or two-dimensional chromatography or electrophoresis on paper or on thin layers (see Section IV,B,4).

2. Gel Filtration (see Section III,B)

As mentioned earlier, some large peptides may not be eluted from ion-exchange resins, and it may be advantageous to fractionate a peptide digest by gel filtration prior to ion-exchange chromatography. Very large peptides are then customarily broken down by further enzymatic or chemical treatment to small fragments more amenable to resolution on columns or paper, and further characterization.

Of the two different materials presently available for gel filtration, polyacrylamide and crosslinked dextran (Sephadex), the latter is more widely used. Sephadex G-10 and G-25 are best adapted to resolving typical peptide mixtures, though G-50 or gels with even larger pore sizes may occasionally be useful for resolving very large fragments. Sephadex gels appear to discriminate between peptide fragments primarily on the basis of size (Stepanov et al., 1961), with the exception of those containing aromatic residues, particularly tryptophan. The latter peptides evidently interact with the gel and elute more slowly than would be expected on the basis of their size. This effect is, however, largely prevented by the use of aromatic solvents such as phenol–acetic acid–H$_2$O (1 : 1 : 1) (Synge and Youngson, 1961) or acetic acid–pyridine–water (60 : 15 : 25) (Porath and Lindner, 1961). Peptides, especially in small amounts, when passed through Sephadex in distilled water may also be bound, but this effect is overcome by working with volatile buffers of moderate ionic strength (0.02–0.1 M). The absorption effect is most marked for basic peptides and probably is due to the presence of ionized carboxyl groups in the gel.

3. Paper Chromatography and Electrophoresis (Mapping)

Methods of chromatography and/or electrophoresis have proved to be very useful techniques for checking the purity of peptide fractions from ion-exchange or gel-filtration columns. They have also been employed as micropreparative purification techniques, but they have several limitations in this regard. As stated, the elution of small amounts of peptides, particularly large ones, from paper is far from quantitative, and the background of amino acid contamination from paper is very difficult to remove. Finally, the small amounts that can be fractioned by two-dimensional use of paper barely allow for amino acid analysis, but rarely suffice for further purification or proof of purity by other methods.

Fifty to 500 μg of a peptide or peptide mixture are applied to a strip of Whatman 3 MM filter paper and developed with butanol–acetic acid–water (4 : 1 : 5), dried, and developed with ninhydrin. Peptides rich in aromatic amino acids often move very slowly in this solvent and may be speeded up by addition of various amounts of pyridine to the above solvent (e.g., butanol, acetic acid, water, pyridine, 30 : 6 : 24 : 20). For micropreparative work the peptides to be eluted for further analysis are separated on washed filter paper and located by light staining with 0.01% ninhydrin in acetone, or by spraying only narrow guide strips. They may be eluted from the paper with 0.1 N NH$_4$OH or 1–5% pyridine in water. Any filter paper fibers are removed by centrifugation and the supernatant solution dried under a current of air or nitrogen. Recoveries are usually of the order of 50–80%.

A two-dimensional combination of electrophoresis and chromatography has proved very useful for resolution of even rather complex mixtures of peptides. Tryptic digests of different proteins can be resolved by this technique to give characteristic and usually unique patterns of peptide spots called "peptide maps" or "fingerprints" (Ingram, 1958).

A widely used technique capable of separating as many as 80 peptides on a single sheet of filter paper has been described by Katz et al. (1959). In this procedure, 1–2 mg of hydrolyzate (together with a little phenol red, which serves as a marker) in 20–40 μl of distilled water is applied to an 18½ $\times$ 22½ inch sheet of Whatman 3 MM filter paper and dried in a cool airstream. The sample is chromatographed 16 hours or more in a solvent consisting of n-butanol, acetic acid, and water (4 : 1 : 5, v/v/v). (The solvent separates into two phases. The upper turbid phase is filtered to clarify it and is used as the developing solvent within 24 hours for most reproducible results.) The paper is then dried in an oven at 70°C.

After chromatography and just before electrophoresis, 0.1 μmole of arginine is added to the origin line (parallel to the direction of chromatography) at a point just beyond the phenol red spot. Arginine serves as the electrophoretic reference standard. The paper is then moistened with buffer [pyridine, acetic acid, and water (1 : 10 : 289) pH 3.7], avoiding the origin line, which is moistened by the movement of buffer inward from both sides. This procedure washes material at the origin into a thin line. After blotting excess buffer, the paper, cooled by immersion in a bath of Varsol, which is itself cooled by water circulated through the coils, is subjected to electrophoresis in the same buffer at an applied voltage of 2000 V for about 75 minutes, when arginine should reach the top of the paper. The paper is then removed, dried, and stained by dipping in 1% ninhydrin in acetone and allowed to stand overnight at room temperature.

Somewhat simpler in manipulation are methods where electrophoresis is performed first (e.g., pH 6.4 pyridine–HAc–H$_2$O, 10 : 0.4 : 90), followed by chromatography in butanol–acetic acid–water or pyridine–isoamyl alcohol–water (35 : 35 : 30). Besides the Varsol-type tanks, electrophoresis can conveniently be performed on cooled plates such as the Pherograph (Brinkmann Instruments Co.).

4. Thin-Layer Chromatography (Mapping) with Silica Gel

Thin-layer chromatography, because of its great sensitivity, is a useful technique, particularly in those instances where the available material is scarce. An additional advantage is a considerable saving of time compared to paper chromatography. The various techniques and applications of thin-layer chromatography are reviewed in the books by Randerath (1963) and Stahl (1964).

The method is usually carried out on thin, even layers of a substrate (such as silica gel, cellulose, polyacrylamide, Sephadex, or any other suitable material) spread on sheet glass cut into standard sizes, generally 10 × 20 cm for single-dimensional work, 20 × 20 cm for two-dimensional work. The plates are thoroughly cleaned first in hot detergent water and, if necessary, with 1% KOH in methanol; they are finally well rinsed with distilled water and air dried prior to spreading the thin layer. The following procedure (Wieland and Georgopoulos, 1964) gives good peptide maps with 200–300 μg of hydrolyzate. The thin layers are formed from silica gel with a starch binder, which forms an exceptionally rugged and durable layer. To prepare the plates, 25 gm of silica gel S (commercially available from C. A. Brinkmann, Westbury,

New York) is suspended in 70 ml of boiling water, briefly heated to nearly boiling to dissolve the starch, deaerated with the aid of a water pump to remove bubbles from the gel, and spread on clean 20×20 cm glass plates in a layer 0.37 mm thick with the aid of a prewarmed spreader (Brinkmann). After allowing 20 minutes for the layers to gel, the plates are dried in a vertical position for 30 minutes at 110°C, then cooled to room temperature and used either immediately or stored in a closed desiccator without a drying agent.

Two hundred to 300 μg of peptide dissolved in 10 μl of water or dilute aqueous ammonia is applied as a spot 3–4 mm in diameter to a corner of the plate 2 cm from the lower edge and 7 cm from the anode side. The sample is applied in a cool stream of air in order to keep the spot as small as possible. A small spot of aqueous 1% ammonium picrate marker is then applied just below the sample spot.

For electrophoresis the plate is sprayed as evenly as possible with a buffer composed of pyridine–acetic acid–water (100 : 4 : 896, v/v/v) pH 6.4, taking care not to get it too wet (just glistening). Excess buffer is gently blotted from the surface with filter paper, avoiding the origin. The ends of the plate are then connected to the electrode vessels with filter paper laid 1 cm wide across either end of the plate. A sheet of dialysis tubing folded over the plate end of the paper wicks suppresses siphoning of buffer between the electrode vessel and the thin layers. A thick glass plate cover laid over the paper wicks anchors the leads and suppresses evaporation during electrophoresis. Electrophoresis is carried out on a cooled surface at about 50 V/cm (40 mA) until the picrate spot has moved about 5 cm (about 40 minutes). The plate is then dried 30 minutes at 110°C and chromatographed at right angles to the direction of electrophoresis.

The plate is positioned in 1 cm of solvent containing pyridine–acetic acid–n-butanol–water (40 : 14 : 68 : 25, v/v/v/v). Chromatography is carried out in a tightly closed solvent-saturated vessel lined with filter paper. When the solvent reaches the upper edge the plate is removed, dried 40 minutes at 110°C, and chromatography is repeated. After drying as above, the plate is sprayed with ninhydrin (1.2 gm of ninhydrin, 30 ml of 2 N acetic acid, 350 ml of n-butanol, and 600 ml of methanol). The peptide spots are developed by drying at 110°C or by storing in the dark at room temperature after blowing the vapor from concentrated aqueous ammonia over the plate.

5. Other Methods of Peptide Separation

Another technique that may prove very useful for the detection and resolution of peptides is electrophoresis on polyacrylamide gels. This combined use of gel filtration and electrophoresis has been applied to analysis of the peptide fragments from β-galactosides treated with cyanogen bromide (Steers et al., 1965). Because the analytical method as generally employed (cf. analytical polyacrylamide electrophoresis) relies on the insolubility of a peptide–dye complex, it might be anticipated that the value of this method will be limited to detection of only rather large peptides; the minimum size of peptides detectable by this technique has not yet been established. Nevertheless, electrophoresis on polyacrylamide, especially in conjunction with urea and other suitable solubilizing agents, may be expected to be especially suited for the study of very large peptide fragments, which are not readily resolved by ion-exchange methods.

Countercurrent distribution (Craig and Craig, 1950) has proved useful in studies on the peptides of TMV protein (Gish et al., 1958).

C. Amino Acid- and Peptide-Sequence Analysis

The methods of amino acid-sequence analysis of peptide fragments of viral proteins are in principle the same as those discussed in Section II,B. The most useful single tool is probably the phenyl isothiocyanate method of stepwise degradation from the amino end.* The paper-strip technique is advocated for longer peptides, while shorter oligopeptides may be more conveniently handled in solution. The second most useful procedure may be the use of carboxypeptidase. Partial acid hydrolysis is also frequently a convenient tool. If the N-terminus is determined by FDNB, and the C-terminus is given by the mode of obtaining the peptide (arginine or lysine in tryptic peptides, tyrosine or phenylalanine in many chymotryptic peptides), then isolation and analysis of two or three small fragments obtained by random acid treatment frequently allow the complete sequence to be reconstructed.

To establish the order of fragments in larger peptides, as well as in the original protein chain, requires the use of more than one method of fragmentation. This is best illustrated by a short hypothetical chain:

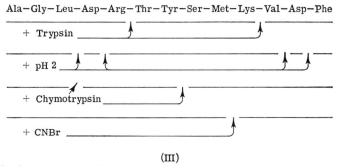

Ala−Gly−Leu−Asp−Arg−Thr−Tyr−Ser−Met−Lys−Val−Asp−Phe

+ Trypsin

+ pH 2

+ Chymotrypsin

+ CNBr

(III)

* See the footnote on p. 58.

The composition of the two or three fragments obtained by the specific action of each of the four methods listed unequivocally defines the order of the fragments, and only tripeptide sequences remain to be determined after this series of degradations, separations, and analyses of fragments.

The same principle approach of isolating overlap peptides serves to establish the linear arrangements of tryptic fragments in full-size proteins. Chymotrypsin is a convenient enzyme to obtain many fragments, and electorphoretic separation of all basic peptides is likely to supply the overlap sequences required to align the original tryptic peptides.

If disulfide groups were present in the original virus protein, then the problem remains, which pairs of the aminoethylcysteines (or carboxymethylcysteines, as the case may be) were originally linked to each other. This is best established by digesting the nonmodified proteins with pepsin and isolating the sulfur-containing peptides. Each of these must then be oxidized with performic acid, and the amino acid composition of each half-cystine peptide should identify the location of the crosslinkage on the previously determined amino acid-sequence map of the oxidized chain.

V. Renaturation of Virus Proteins and Reconstitution of Viruses

It has been known for many years that the protein of the TMV can be separated from the RNA under conditions that allowed its recovery in seemingly native form. The native state of proteins has been variously defined; one of the definitions is that it is the ability of the protein to perform its function. Degradation of the virus by alkali (pH 10.5) and by 67% acetic acid, both at 0°C, was shown to give protein preparations that under suitable conditions were able to aggregate in typically helical manner to rods indistinguishable from the original virus. If intact RNA was added, virus rods were formed that showed all the properties characteristic of natural TMV particles, namely, infectivity, stability, enzyme resistance, etc. (Fraenkel-Conrat and Williams, 1955; Fraenkel-Conrat and Singer, 1957, 1959). Thus the protein was native.

Studies on the ability of the protein to bind ^{3}H indicated that many protons were irreversibly bound if the virus, split either by acetic acid or by alkali in the presence of ^{3}H$_2$O, was then brought back to neutrality by dialysis against water containing the same concentration of ^{3}H$_2$O. The renatured protein did not lose its ^{3}H content upon prolonged exposure to H$_2$O at pH 5–8. This proton binding was independent of an additional quantity of ^{3}H fixed upon reconstitution of the protein with RNA to form virus at pH 7 (Fraenkel-Conrat, 1965).

Thus, it appears that the act of disaggregation leads to a conformational disturbance of the subunit peptide chain and that this loss of conformation is freely reversible (see Anderer et al., 1964). This is more dramatically demonstrated by dissolving the protein in 10 M urea or 0.1 N NaOH, conditions that are generally accepted as denaturing (Anderer, 1959). Native functional protein can be recovered even after this, and the yet stronger denaturing action of 5 M guanidine salts at pH 9, if autoxidation of the sulfhydryl group is prevented by the addition of mercaptoethanol (about 1%). Renaturation of TMV protein is achieved by dialysis against pH 6–7 phosphate buffer (0.02 M), or by passage through a G-25 Sephadex column equilibrated with this buffer. If denatured protein precipitates quickly upon dialysis, as it does, for instance, after guanidine denaturation, then the material may be redissolved in 8 M urea and treated with 1% mercaptoethanol for an hour at 25°C. The product usually remains soluble and becomes renatured upon a subsequent second step of dialysis against buffer.

Thus, it appears that the peptide chain conformation of this virus protein is a consequence of its amino acid sequence, a conclusion that has in recent years been arrived at with several enzyme and other proteins. It is of obvious biological consequence that the sole functions of the invading virus are to induce the host cell to replicate its RNA and allow its message or information to be translated into the linear sequence of 158 amino acids, and that from this stage on the maturation of the virus particle proceeds as a thermodynamically favored and spontaneous process in vivo, as it does in vitro.

While one is tempted to assume that such principles will have general validity, no similarly definitive evidence for the renaturability of other virus proteins has yet been reported, nor has it been possible to reconstitute viruses other than TMV and its strains from their nucleic acid and protein components in infective form.

Attempts to substitute other nucleic acids or other proteins than the homologous pair have met with variable success. RNA and protein obtained from different strains of TMV usually combine to typical virus rods, although the more distant the strain relationship, as gaged by the protein composition, the poorer the yield of stable virus (Fraenkel-Conrat and Singer, 1957, 1959; Holoubek, 1962).

The RNA of the phage MS2 gives TMV-like rods with TMV proteins that are predominantly 60% of the length of TMV, in accordance with the fact that MS2 RNA has a molecular weight of 1.1×10^6, 55% of that of TMV RNA (Sugiyama, 1966). The yields of this mixed virus were quite variable and in many experiments negligible. Thus the negative results obtained in single experiments with other natural (nonviral) RNA samples cannot be regarded as proof that these could not also interact with TMV protein. It may be that a minor factor that is as yet not sufficiently controlled is required for the initiation of the cocrystallization of non-TMV RNA with TMV protein.

When a variety of synthetic polynucleotides were tested for their ability to combine with TMV protein, only poly-A, poly-I, and mixed polymers rich in purines formed stable viruslike rods (Fraenkel-Conrat and Singer, 1964). It may thus be supposed that among the three nucleotides passing through each protein subunit there must be at least one purine to achieve a stable linkage. In surveying the amino acid sequence of TMV protein, as transcribed into codons, this condition can be met for all but one pair of amino acids, 12 and 13 in the coat protein chain, which according to present knowledge must contain at least five pyrimidines in a row.

REFERENCES

Akabori, S., Ohno, K., and Narita, K. (1952). *Bull. Chem. Soc. (Japan)* **25**, 214.
Akabori, S., Ohno, K., Ikenaka, A., Harnna, I., Tsugita, A., Sugae, K., and Matsushima, T. (1956). *Bull. Chem. Soc. (Japan)* **29**, 507.
Akers, G. B. (1964). *Biochemistry* **3**, 723.
Anderer, F. A. (1959). *Z. Naturforsch.* **14b**, 642.
Anderer, F. A., and Handschuh, D. (1963). *Z. Naturforsch.* **18b**, 1015.
Anderer, F. A., Kratky, O., and Lo, R. (1964). *Z. Naturforsch.* **19b**, 906.
Andrews, P. (1964). *Biochem. J.* **91**, 222.
Anfinsen, C. B., and Haber, E. (1961). *J. Biol. Chem.* **236**, 1361.
Aronsson, T., and Grönwall, A. (1957). *Scand. J. Clin. & Lab. Invest.* **9**, 338.
Bailey, J. L., and Cole, R. J. (1959). *J. Biol. Chem.* **234**, 1733.
Beeman, W. W., Kaesberg, P., Anderegg, J. W., and Webb, M. B. (1957). *In* "Handbuch der Physik" (S. Flügge, ed.), Vol. 32, p. 321. Springer, Berlin.
Benson, J. B., and Patterson, J. A. (1965). *Anal. Chem.* **37**, 1108.
Blackburn, S., and Lowther, A. G. (1951). *Biochem. J.* **48**, 126.
Boulton, A. A., and Bush, I. E. (1964). *Biochem. J.* **92**, 110.
Brakke, M. K. (1955). *Arch. Biochem. Biophys.* **55**, 175.
Britten, R. J., and Roberts, R. B. (1960). *Science* **131**, 32.
Burns, D. A., and Pollak, O. J. J. (1963). *J. Chromatog.* **11**, 559.
Canfield, R. E., and Anfinsen, C. B. (1963). *J. Biol. Chem.* **238**, 2684.
Choules, G. L., and Zimm, B. H. (1965). *Anal. Biochem.* **13**, 336–344.
Cleland, W. (1963). *Anal. Biochem.* **3**, 480.
Cohn, E. G., and Edsall, J. T. (1943). "Proteins, Amino Acids and Peptides," pp. 370–381. Reinhold, New York.
Colloms, M. (1966). *Federation Proc.* **25**, 590.
Craig, L. C., and Craig, D. (1950). *In* "Techniques in Organic Chemistry" (A. Weisberger, ed.), Vol. III, Part 1, p. 171. Wiley (Interscience), New York.

Cramer, R., and Svensson, H. (1961). *Experientia* **17**, 49.

Craven, G. R., Steers, E., and Anfinsen, C. B. (1965). *J. Biol. Chem.* **240**, 2468.

Crestfield, A. M., Moore, S., and Stein, W. H. (1963). *J. Biol. Chem.* **238**, 622.

Davis, B. J. (1964). *Ann. N.Y. Acad. Sci.* **121**, 404.

de Duve, C., Bartlett, J., and Beaufay, H. (1959). *Progr. Biophys. Biophys. Chem.* **9**, 326.

Determan, H. (1962). *Experientia* **18**, 430.

Duesberg, P. D., and Rueckert, R. R. (1965). *Anal. Biochem.* **11**, 342.

Eckert, E. A., Rott, R., and Schäfer, W. (1964). *Virology* **24**, 434.

Edman, P. (1951). *Acta Chem. Scand.* **4**, 277 and 283.

Edman, P. (1953). *Acta Chem. Scand.* **7**, 700.

Edman, P., and Begg, G. (1967). *European J. Biochem.* **1**, 80.

Fazekas de St. Groth, S., Webster, R. G., and Datyner, A. (1963). *Biochim. Biophys. Acta* **71**, 377.

Fraenkel-Conrat, H. (1954). *J. Am. Chem. Soc.* **76**, 3606.

Fraenkel-Conrat, H. (1955). *J. Biol. Chem.* **217**, 373.

Fraenkel-Conrat, H. (1957). *Methods Enzymol.* **4**, 247.

Fraenkel-Conrat, H. (1965). *Proteins* **3**, 99–151.

Fraenkel-Conrat, H., and Sherwood, M. (1967). *Arch. Biochem. Biophys.*, in press.

Fraenkel-Conrat, H., and Singer, B. (1957). *Biochim. Biophys. Acta* **24**, 540.

Fraenkel-Conrat, H., and Singer, B. (1959). *Biochim. Biophys. Acta* **33**, 359.

Fraenkel-Conrat, H., and Singer, B. (1964). *Virology* **23**, 354.

Fraenkel-Conrat, H., and Williams, R. C. (1955). *Proc. Natl. Acad. Sci. U.S.* **41**, 690.

Fraenkel-Conrat, H., Mohammad, A., Ducay, E. D., and Mecham, D. K. (1951). *J. Am. Chem. Soc.* **73**, 625.

Fraenkel-Conrat, H., Harris, J. I., and Levy, A. L. (1955). *Methods Biochem. Anal.* **2**, 359–425.

Frist, R. H., Bendet, I. J., Smith, K. M., and Lauffer, M. A. (1965). *Virology* **26**, 558.

Gish, D. T., Ramachandran, L. K., and Stanley, W. M. (1958). *Arch. Biochem. Biophys.* **78**, 433.

Glazer, A. N., and Wellner, D. (1962). *Nature* **194**, 862.

Goldberger, R. F., and Anfinsen, C. B. (1962). *Biochemistry* **1**, 401.

Gray, W. R., and Hartley, B. S. (1963). *Biochem. J.* **89**, 379.

Gross, E., and Witkop, B. (1962). *J. Biol. Chem.* **237**, 1856.

Gundlach, H. G., Stein, W. H., and Moore, S. (1959). *J. Biol. Chem.* **234**, 1754.

Hamilton, P. B. (1963). *Z. Anal. Chem.* **35**, 2055.

Hannig, K. Z. (1961). *Anal. Chem.* **181**, 244.

Harris, J. I. (1956). *Nature* **177**, 471.

Harris, J. I., and Hindley, J. (1961). *J. Mol. Biol.* **3**, 117.

Harris, J. I., and Hindley, J. (1965). *J. Mol. Biol.* **13**, 894.

Harris, J. I., and Knight, C. A. (1952). *Nature* **170**, 613.

Harris, J. I., and Knight, C. A. (1955). *J. Biol. Chem.* **214**, 215.

Hersh, R. T., and Schachman, H. K. (1958). *Virology* **6**, 234.

Hirs, C. H. W. (1956). *J. Biol. Chem.* **219**, 611.

Hirs, C. H. W., Moore, S., and Stein, W. H. (1956). *J. Biol. Chem.* **219**, 623.

Hjertén, S. (1962). *Arch. Biochem. Biophys.* **99**, 466.

Hjertén, S. (1964). *Biochim. Biophys. Acta* **79**, 393.

Hjertén, S., Jerstedt, S., and Tiselius, A. (1965a). *Anal. Biochem.* **11**, 219.

Hjertén, S., Jerstedt, S., and Tiselius, A. (1965b). *Anal. Biochem.* **11**, 211.

Holoubek, V. (1962). *Virology* **18**, 401.

Ingram, V. M. (1958). *Biochim. Biophys. Acta* **28**, 539.

Johansson, B. G., and Rymo, L. (1962). *Acta Chem. Scand.* **16**, 2067.

Johansson, B. G., and Rymo, L. (1964). *Acta Chem. Scand.* **18**, 217.

Jones, R. T. (1964). *Cold Spring Harbor Symp. Quant. Biol.* **29**, 297.

Jovin, T., Chrambach, A., and Maughton, M. A. (1964). *Anal. Biochem.* **11**, 351.

Kanarek, L., Bradshaw, R. A., and Hill, R. L. (1965). *J. Biol. Chem.* **240**, PC2755.

Katz, A. M., Dreyer, W. J., and Anfinsen, C. B. (1959). *J. Biol. Chem.* **234**, 2897.

Kawanishi, B. Y., Iwai, K., and Ando, T. (1964). *J. Biochem. (Tokyo)* **56**, 314.

Kielley, W. W., and Harrington, W. F. (1960). *Biochim. Biophys. Acta* **41**, 401.

Klainer, S. M., and Kegeles, G. (1955). *J. Phys. Chem.* **59**, 952.

Koenigsberg, W., and Hill, R. J. (1962). *J. Biol. Chem.* **237**, 2547.

Kostka, V., and Carpenter, F. H. (1964). *J. Biol. Chem.* **239**, 1799.

Kupke, D. W. (1960). *Advan. Protein Chem.* **15**, 57.

LaBar, F. E., and Baldwin, R. L. (1962). *J. Phys. Chem.* **66**, 1952.

Laver, W. G. (1964). *J. Mol. Biol.* **9**, 109.

Levy, A. L. (1954). *Nature* **174**, 126.

Levy, A. L. (1955). *Methods Biochem. Anal.* **2**, 360.

Levy, A. L., and Chung, D. (1953). *Anal. Chem.* **25**, 396.

Light, A., Glazer, A. N., and Smith, E. C. (1960). *J. Biol. Chem.* **235**, 3159.

Lowry, O. H., Rosebrough, N. J., Farr, A. L., and Randall, R. J. (1951). *J. Biol. Chem.* **193**, 265.

McMeekin, T. L., Groves, M. L., and Hipp, N. J. (1949). *J. Am. Chem. Soc.* **71**, 3298.

Maizel J. V. (1963). *Biochem. Biophys. Res. Commun.* **13**, 483.

Maizel, J. V. (1964). *Ann. N.Y. Acad. Sci.* **121**, 382.

Maizel, J. V. (1966). *Science* **151**, 988–990.

Martin, R. G., and Ames, B. N. (1961). *J. Biol. Chem.* **236**, 1372.

Matsubara, H., Singer, A., Sasaki, R., and Jukes, T. H. (1965). *Biochem. Biophys. Res. Commun.* **21**, 242.

Mazur, R. H., Ellis, B. W., and Cammarata, P. S. (1962). *J. Biol. Chem.* **237**, 1619.

Merigan, T. C., Dreyer, W. J., and Berger, A. (1962). *Biochim. Biophys. Acta* **62**, 122.

Moore, S. (1963). *J. Biol. Chem.* **238**, 235.

Moore, S., and Stein, W. H. (1954). *J. Biol. Chem.* **211**, 907.

Morris, C. J. O. R. (1964). *J. Chromatog.* **16**, 167.

Narita, K. (1958). *Biochim. Biophys. Acta* **28**, 184.

Narita, K., and Ishii, J. (1962). *J. Biochem. (Tokyo)* **52**, 367.

Ornstein, L. (1964). *Ann. N.Y. Acad. Sci.* **121**, 231.

Partridge, S. M., and Davis, H. F. (1950). *Nature* **165**, 62.

Perlmann, G. E. (1966). *J. Biol. Chem.* **241**, 153.

Peterson, E. A., and Rowland, J. J. (1961). *J. Chromatog.* **5**, 330.

Piez, K. A., and Morris, L. (1960). *Anal. Biochem.* **1**, 187.

Porath, J. (1960). *Biochim. Biophys. Acta* **39**, 193.

Porath, J., and Flodin, P. (1959). *Nature* **183**, 1657.

Porath, J., and Lindner, E. B. (1961). *Nature* **191**, 69.

Raftery, M. A., and Cole, R. D. (1963). *Biochem. Biophys. Res. Commun.* **10**, 467.

Randerath, K. (1963). "Thin Layer Chromatography." Academic Press, New York.

Raymond, S. (1962). *Clin. Chem.* **8**, 455.

Raymond, S. (1964). *Science* **146**, 406.

Reisfeld, R. A., Lewis, V. J., and Williams, D. E. (1962). *Nature* **195**, 281.

Richards, E. G., and Schachman, H. K. (1959). *J. Phys. Chem.* **63**, 1578.

Riordan, J. F., Wacker, W. E. C., and Vallee, B. L. (1965). *Nature* **208**, 1209.

Rodbell, M., and Frederickson, D. S. (1956). *J. Biol. Chem.* **234**, 562.

Rudloff, V., and Braunitzer, G. (1961). *Z. Physiol. Chem.* **323**, 129.

Rueckert, R. R. (1965). *Virology* **26**, 345.

Rydon, H. N., and Smith, P. W. (1952). *Nature* **169**, 922.

Ryle, A. P., and Sanger, F. (1955). *Biochem. J.* **60**, 535.

Sanger, F. (1945). *Biochem. J.* **39**, 507.

Sanger, F. (1949). *Biochem. J.* **45**, 563.

Schachman, H. K. (1957). *Methods Enzymol.* **4**, 32–103.

Schachman, H. K. (1959). "Ultracentrifugation in Biochemistry." Academic Press, New York.

Schachman, H. K. (1963). *Biochemistry* **2**, 887.

Scharff, M. D., Maizel, J. V., and Levintow, L. (1964). *Proc. Natl. Acad. Sci. U.S.* **51**, 329.

Schoellmann, G., and Shaw, E. (1963). *Biochemistry* **2**, 252.

Schram, E., Moore, S., and Biswood, E. J. (1954). *Biochem. J.* **57**, 33.

Schroeder, W. A., Shelton, J. R., Shelton, J. B., Cormick, J., and Jones, R. T. (1963). *Biochemistry* **2**, 992.

Seto, J. T., and Hokama, Y. (1964). *Ann. N.Y. Acad. Sci.* **121**, 640.

Sjøquist, J. (1953). *Acta Chem. Scand.* **7**, 447.

Smithies, O. (1959). *Advan. Protein Chem.* **14**, 65.

Smithies, O. (1965). *Science* **150**, 1595.

Smyth, D. G., Stein, W. H., and Moore, S. (1962). *J. Biol. Chem.* **237**, 1845.

Stahl, E. (1964). "Thin Layer Chromatography." Academic Press, New York.

Stark, G. R., Stein, W. H., and Moore, S. (1960). *J. Biol. Chem.* **235**, 3177.

Steere, R. L., and Akers, G. K. (1962). *Nature* **194**, 114.

Steers, E., Craven, G. R., and Anfinsen, C. B. (1965). *J. Biol. Chem.* **240**, 2478.

Stepanov, V., Handschuh, D., and Anderer, F. A. (1961). *Z. Naturforsch.* **16b**, 626.

Sugiyama, T. (1966). *Virology* **28**, 488.

Summers, D. F., Maizel, J. V., and Darnell, J. E. (1965). *Proc. Natl. Acad. Sci. U.S.* **54**, 505.

Svedberg, T., and Pedersen, K. O. (1940). "The Ultracentrifuge." Oxford Univ. Press (Clarendon), London and New York.

Swan, J. M. (1957). *Nature* **180**, 643.

Synge, R. L. M., and Youngson, M. A. (1961). *Biochem. J.* **78**, 31P.

Szybalski, W. (1960). *Experientia* **16**, 164.

Tanford, C. (1961). "The Physical Chemistry of Macromolecules." Wiley, New York.

Tiselius, A. (1937). *Biochem. J.* **31**, 1464.

Trautman, R., and Crampton, C. F. (1959). *J. Am. Chem. Soc.* **81**, 4036.

Tsugita, A. (1962). *J. Mol. Biol.* **5**, 284.

Tsung, C. M., and Fraenkel-Conrat, H. (1966). *Biochemistry* **5**, 2061.

Tsung, C. M., and Fraenkel-Conrat, H. (1965). *Biochemistry* **4**, 793.

van Holde, K. E., and Baldwin, R. L. (1958). *J. Phys. Chem.* **62**, 734.

Weil, L., and Seibles, J. S. (1959). *Arch. Biochem. Biophys.* **84**, 244.

Whitaker, J. R. (1963). *Anal. Chem.* **35**, 1950.

White, F. H., Jr. (1960). *J. Biol. Chem.* **235**, 383.

Wieland, T., and Georgopoulos, D. (1964). *Biochem. Z.* **340,** 476.
Wieland, T., Duesberg, P. D., and Determann, H. (1963). *Biochem. Z.* **337,** 303.
Wilchek, M., Sarid, S., and Patchornik, A. (1965). *Biochem. Biophys. Acta* **104,** 616.
Williams, D. E., and Reisfeld, R. A. (1964). *Ann. N.Y. Acad. Sci.* **121,** Art. 873.
Yaoi, Y., Titani, K., and Narita, K. (1964). *J. Biochem.* **56,** 222.
Young, R. W., and Fulhorst, H. W. (1965). *Anal. Biochem.* **11,** 389–391.
Yphantis, D. A. (1964). *Biochemistry* **3,** 297.

2 Analysis of Lipid Components of Viruses*

David Kritchevsky and Irwin L. Shapiro

I. Introduction

The accurate chemical analysis of any naturally occurring material depends upon the isolation of this material in a pure form. Isolation and analysis of pure virus particles present a particularly difficult problem because of the minute size and the intimate association of the particles with host cellular material that may be of very similar chemical composition. In the field of virus research, the primary analytical interest has centered upon the nucleic acid composition. There is little available knowledge concerning the accurate total chemical composition of any virus particle.

Lwoff (1957) has defined true viruses as substances that contain either DNA or RNA, multiply by means of their nucleic acid, and possess no energy-generating enzymes. Certain viruses or classes of

* This work was supported, in part, by U.S. Public Health Service research grants HE-03299 and HE-05209 and Research Career Award HE-K6–734 from the National Heart Institute.

viruses are subject to inactivation by ether, suggesting that lipid in some form is essential for preservation of virion structure; this ether sensitivity may be found in both DNA- and RNA-containing viruses (Green, 1965). The function of lipids in viruses is probably structural; the lipids are part of a lipoprotein that is present in the cell membrane. Franklin (1962) has classified viruses according to the presence or absence of structural lipids. He has marshaled evidence to show that viruses with structural lipids are assembled at the cell surface and that the lipid is probably a cellular membrane. Among the viruses that possess peripheral structural lipids are myxoviruses, arborviruses, herpes, measles, avian tumor viruses, some mouse tumor viruses, rabies, and vesicular stomatitis. Hog cholera virus has also been shown to be sensitive to ether (Loan, 1964).

The literature on analysis of the lipids present in viruses has been slow in developing, not only because of the peripheral interest in this topic but also because of lack of sensitive micromethods that could be applied. In the last decade, the development of paper chromatographic methods for lipid analysis, followed by the availability of the simpler technique of thin-layer chromatography, have made possible the rapid, accurate analysis of small quantities of viral lipids. These methods, together with gas–liquid chromatography, also allow for identification of the fatty acids present in various lipid classes.

Although there is still relatively little information concerning the complete spectrum of viral lipids and their component fatty acids, these data should be forthcoming. Knowledge concerning changes in individual lipid components during cycles of viral replication and/or infection will assist in evaluation of mechanisms of viral growth and infection.

II. Lipid Methodology

A. GENERAL CONSIDERATIONS

Any assessment of the biological significance of a compound or a class of compounds ultimately depends upon the development of adequate methods for their extraction, isolation, and quantitation. Lipids, when compared with carbohydrates and proteins, are seen to possess certain unique physicochemical properties; they generally are nonpolar molecules, are insoluble in water, are easily susceptible to air oxidation, and are sensitive to temperature extremes. These properties have necessitated the evolvement of unique analytical techniques designed to isolate the lipid in a form nearly identical to that which it exhibits in its native milieu.

Thus, lipids are extracted from biological samples with organic solvents and are protected against oxidation by processing the extracts in a nitrogen atmosphere. After extraction, samples are then chromatographically fractionated by means of silicic acid placed into columns, spread onto glass plates, or impregnated on filter papers or by gas–liquid chromatography.

Discussions of these chromatographic techniques (Section B,1–4) will apply mainly to those types of lipids found in significant amounts in biological tissues, exclusive of the nervous system. Analyses of gangliosides, cerebrosides, and sulfatides, therefore, have not been touched upon in detail. Finally, since it would be impossible to document all pertinent references to lipid methodology, only those procedures most frequently used will be cited.

1. *Extraction Procedures*

Lipids may be extracted from biological samples with a variety of organic solvents. Chloroform–methanol (2 : 1, v/v) (Folch *et al.*, 1957) is the most commonly employed solvent system. One part of the tissue is extracted with 20 parts of the solvent mixture. After the extract is dried and concentrated to a small volume (not to dryness), the sample is suitably prepared for chromatographic fractionation.

Lipids have been extracted from influenza viruses (PR8, DSP, and Lee) (Frommhagen *et al.*, 1958; Kates *et al.*, 1961) and from avian BAI-strain virus (Rao and Beard, 1964) with this solvent system.

Another lipid extraction solvent system, less widely employed, is ethanol–ether (3 : 1, v/v) (Bloor, 1928). A solvent-to-tissue ratio of 30 : 1 is generally used. Lipids have been extracted from influenza virus A and B (Taylor, 1944; Graham, 1950) with this technique.

Lipids also have been isolated from mumps virus with diethyl ether–methanol (2 : 1) (Soule *et al.*, 1959), from Rous sarcoma virus with chloroform–ethanol (2 : 1) (Bather, 1957), or from equine encephalomyelitis virus with mixtures of acetone–alcohol (1 : 1) and benzene (Taylor *et al.*, 1943).

2. *Processing and Preservation of Lipid Extracts*

a. Processing of Extracts. When processing micro- and milligram quantities of lipids, it is a good precaution to wash all appropriate glassware with chloroform–methanol (2 : 1) or with suitable lipid solvents, since most commercial detergents contain lipid contaminants that may potentially interfere with analysis of individual lipid classes.

After extraction, the lipid material should be processed as quickly as possible, or properly preserved. Lipid extracts are susceptible to degradation by air, owing primarily to attack by molecular oxygen at the double bonds of fatty acids or to degradation by elevated temperatures. These degradative effects can be minimized by working under nitrogen and by using moderate temperatures whenever possible. Antioxidants also have been added to lipid extracts to prevent or retard oxidation. Hydroquinone (Mattson and Volpenhein, 1962) and 4-methyl-2,6-di-*tert*-butyl-phenol (BHT) (Wren and Szczepanowska, 1964) are often used. BHT appears to be a particularly good antioxidant because it can be added in a low concentration (0.005%) and, if so desired, can easily be removed from individual lipid fractions. Moreover, this compound apparently completely protects phospholipids from oxidation.

b. Preservation of Extracts. If a large number of virus samples are harvested, they may be lyophilized or frozen and stored under nitrogen in a vacuum desiccator at —20°C until extraction can be accomplished.

After the lipid extract is subfractionated into component lipid classes, fractions should be collected and concentrated as quickly as possible. Since it is often impractical to quantitate each of these samples in a single working day, they may be stored under nitrogen, in the cold, in Teflon-lined screw-cap vials; alternately, these fractions can be stored in a vacuum desiccator over phosphorus pentoxide in a nitrogen atmosphere. The most desirable procedure is storage of lipid fractions in sealed ampules under vacuum in a nitrogen atmosphere.

Further guidelines to the extraction, processing, and preservation of lipid extracts may be obtained from articles by Sperry (1955), Entenman (1957, 1961), Svennerholm (1964), Galanos and Kapoulas (1965), and Van Slyke and Plazin (1965), and from a book by Stahl (1965).

3. Purification of Solvents

Only solvents of analytical-grade purity should be used in the processing or chromatography of lipids. Redistillation of solvents is desirable; it often reduces the extent of oxidation of samples and, in general, improves chromatographic separation of lipid classes. Diethyl ether, in particular, should be tested for the presence of peroxides and should then be redistilled where indicated. Methods for purification of organic solvents can be found in books by Vogel (1956) and Bush (1961).

4. Preliminary Analysis of Lipid Extracts

Colorimetric analysis for free and/or total cholesterol (Sperry and Webb, 1950), for phospholipid phosphorus (Fiske and Subbarow,

1925; Bartlett, 1959), for total fatty acids (Albrink, 1959), or for total lipid (Castaldo *et al.*, 1964) can be performed directly on aliquots of the lipid extract.

Preliminary subdivision of the extract into a neutral lipid fraction and a phospholipid fraction can be achieved by (1) dialyzing a petroleum ether solution of the lipid in a thin rubber sac (van Beers *et al.*, 1958), (2) partitioning the extract in a binary solvent system composed of petroleum ether–87% ethanol (1 : 1) (Galanos and Kapoulas, 1962), (3) precipitating phospholipids from an acetone solution with magnesium chloride (Sinclair, 1930), or (4) shaking an ether solution of the lipid extract with silicic acid (Marks *et al.*, 1960).

However, further fractionation by column, by thin-layer, or by paper chromatography is necessary to subdivide neutral lipids into free fatty acids, mono-, di-, and triglycerides, cholesterol, and cholesterol esters and to subdivide phospholipids into lysolecithins, sphingomyelins, phosphatidyl serines, phosphatidyl ethanolamines, and lecithins.

B. CHROMATOGRAPHIC TECHNIQUES FOR FRACTIONATION OF LIPID
EXTRACTS

1. *Column Chromatography*

If more than 50 mg of the lipid extract is available, fractionation by column chromatography should be performed. Lipid mixtures have been chromatographed on a variety of solid supports. A number of mixtures of organic solvents have been used as elutriants. Separation of neutral lipid classes routinely has been achieved using silicic acid (Borgström, 1952; Fillerup and Mead, 1953; Hirsch and Ahrens, 1958) or Florisil (Carroll, 1961) supports. Lipids can be eluted from the column with mixtures of either petroleum ether and diethyl ether (Fillerup and Mead, 1953), diethyl ether and hexane (Carroll, 1961), or benzene and hexane (Horning *et al.*, 1960).

Neutral lipids can be subfractionated into six or seven major classes with this technique. An example of the type of separation attainable by Florisil chromatography (Carroll, 1961) is given in Fig. 1. Individual lipid classes were eluted from the Florisil column according to the schedule of solvent systems described in Table I.

More recently, Unisil (a specially hydrated preparation of silicic acid) has been employed as a solid support for column chromatography of lipids. This innovation has provided a more reproducible separation of lipid classes and has permitted attainment of more rapid flow rates. Unisil chromatography has been used for separation of the lipids of tissue-culture cells (Rothblat *et al.*, 1963) and of pleuropneumonia-

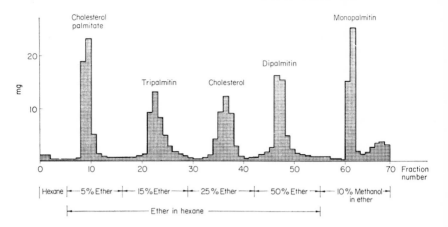

FIG. 1. Separation of lipid classes on a 30-gm column of Florisil. Ten milliliter fractions were collected. The column load consisted of 40 mg each of cholesterol palmitate, tripalmitin, cholesterol, 1,2-dipalmitin, and 1-monopalmitin. (After Carroll, 1961.)

TABLE I

ELUTION SCHEDULES FOR FLORISIL CHROMATOGRAMS[a]

Eluent	30-gm column (2.0 × 17.0 cm) (ml)	Eluting solvent	12-gm column (1.2 × 15.0 cm) (ml)
Hydrocarbons	50	Hexane[b]	20
Cholesterol esters	120	5% ether in hexane	50
Triglycerides	150	15% ether in hexane	75
Cholesterol	150	25% ether in hexane	60[c]
Diglycerides	150	50% ether in hexane	60[c]
Monoglycerides	150	2% methanol in ether	75
Free fatty acids	150	4% acetic acid in ether	75

[a] After Carroll, 1961.
[b] Purified Skellysolve B.
[c] It may be found more convenient to elute both cholesterol and diglyceride fractions with 140 ml of 25% ether in hexane.

like organisms (Smith, 1964), by means of the elution scheme of Horning *et al.* (1960).

Phospholipid classes may also be separated on silicic acid columns, with the use of various proportions of chloroform and methanol as elutriants (Hanahan *et al.*, 1957). Recently, more discrete separation of phospholipids on diethylaminoethyl- (DEAE) cellulose columns was reported (Rouser *et al.*, 1961b, 1963, 1964). Eleven fractions are obtained from the DEAE column using combinations of chloroform, methanol, acetic acid, and ammonia (Table II). If further subdivision of each neutral lipid and each phospholipid fraction is desired, thin-layer chromatography can be employed.

TABLE II

ELUTION OF ANEMONE LIPID FROM DEAE[a,b]

Fraction nos.	Solvent	Lipid class(es)	Weight (gm)	Total lipid (%)
7–15	C/M 9/1	Lecithin and nonionic lipid	0.17996	38.3
16–19	C/M 9/1	5 uncharacterized components	0.01314	2.8
20–42	C/M 7/3	Phosphatidyl ethanolamine and ceramide aminoethyl-phosphonate	0.06952	14.8
43–50	C/M 7/3	Primary ceramide aminoethyl-phosphate + phosphatidyl ethanolamine	0.07167	15.2
51–65	C/M 7/3	Uncharacterized ninhydrin-positive lipid	0.00995	2.1
66–81	CH$_3$OH	Uncharacterized lipid	0.02845	6.1
82–101	C/HAc 3/1	Pigments	0.00950	2.0
102–128	C/HAc 3/1 + 0.01 M NH$_4$Ac	Almost pure phosphatidic acid	0.01535	3.3
129–131	HAc	"Phosphatidyl serine" and uncharacterized lipid	0.04972	10.6
132–148	HAc	Pigments	0.00386	1.5
149–183	C/M 4/1 + 10 ml conc. aqueous NH$_3$ per liter	"Phosphatidyl inositol" and uncharacterized lipids	0.01310	2.8
			0.46422	99.5

[a] After Rouser *et al.*, 1963.
[b] C = chloroform, M = methanol, HAc = acetic acid, NH$_4$Ac = ammonium acetate.

2. Thin-Layer Chromatography

If less than 50 mg of a lipid extract is available, it is desirable to separate lipids by thin-layer chromatography (TLC). Alternately, this technique may be used as a tool to authenticate the homogeneity of lipid fractions obtained by column chromatography. TLC is a more convenient, more economical, and more rapid technique than column chromatography, since less solvent and much less time is required to achieve separations.

The most widely used adsorbent for thin-layer chromatography is silica gel G, a mixture of silicic acid containing calcium sulfate as a binder. The adsorbent is mixed with water (1 : 2, v/w) and spread in thin layers (250–1000 μ), using a commercially available spreader, onto 20 × 20 cm glass plates. After activation of the adsorbent layers in an oven at 110°–120°C, the plates are ready for use.

Practical approaches to the preparation of silica gel-coated plates may be obtained from books by Stahl (1965), Randerath (1963), Bobbitt (1963), Truter (1963), and Marini-Bettolo (1964). Review articles by Mangold (1961, 1964), Nichols (1964), Morris (1964), and Schlenk (1964) should prove helpful as guides to the separation of naturally occurring neutral lipids and phospholipids.

The best separation of neutral lipids is obtained on silica gel G-coated plates, using a combination of petroleum ether, diethyl ether, and acetic acid as developing solvents. The separation of a neutral lipid sample, using a mixture of petroleum ether–diethyl ether–acetic acid (90 : 10 : 1) (Malins and Mangold, 1960) as the mobile phase, is shown in Fig. 2. Mono- and diglycerides are not completely separated from cholesterol and free fatty acids, but suitable separation can be obtained by alteration of the solvent ratio.

A more discrete subdivision of individual neutral lipid fractions, particularly subfractionation of sterols, sterol esters, triglycerides, or fatty acid methyl esters, may be obtained using silica gel G adsorbents impregnated with silver nitrate (Morris, 1964).

Phospholipids remain at or near the origin when one uses petroleum ether–diethyl ether–acetic acid solvent systems. They may be eluted from the silica gel plates, reapplied to freshly coated plates, and fractionated by means of combinations of chloroform, methanol, and water as the mobile phase; or an aliquot of the lipid extract may be applied at the origin. Fig. 3 depicts the separation of a phospholipid mixture with chloroform–methanol–water (65 : 25 : 4) (Wagner, 1960; Wagner et al., 1961). Neutral lipids migrate to the solvent front if this solvent system is used. Equally or more effective unidimensional separations of phospholipids by TLC have been described by Skipski et al. (1962, 1963), Müldner et al. (1962), Nichols (1963), and Redman and Kelnan (1964).

If further subdivision into more discrete types of phospholipids is desired, the entire phospholipid sample or the individual fractions may be rechromatographed on silica gel G using two-dimensional chromatography (Skidmore and Entenman, 1962; LePage, 1964; Nichols, 1964). Alternately, two-dimensional TLC may be performed using layers of silicic acid impregnated with magnesium sulfate (Rouser et al., 1964).

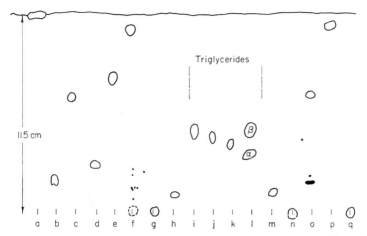

FIG. 2. Thin-layer adsorption chromatography of lipid classes on silica gel. Solvent: petroleum hydrocarbon–diethyl ether–acetic acid, 90 : 10 : 1, v/v/v. Development time: 40 minutes. Indicator: dichlorofluorescein. Amounts: 20 gamma, each. (a) Octadecene-9, (b) oleyl alcohol, (c) oleyl aldehyde, (d) oleic acid, (e) methyl oleate, (f) cholesteryl oleate, (g) monoolein, (h) diolein, (i) triolein, (j) trilinolein, (k) trilinolenin, (l) tricaproin (α) and tristearin (β), (m) cholesterol, (n) selachyl alcohol, (o) selachyl diolein, (p) oleyl oleate, (q) dioleoyl lecithin. (After Mangold, 1961.)

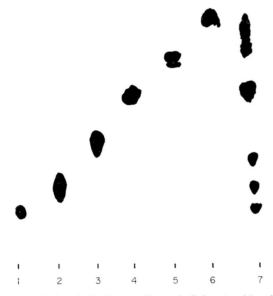

FIG. 3. Separation of phospholipids on silica gel. Solvent: chloroform–methanol–water, 65 : 25 : 4, v/v/v. Development time: 2 hours. Indicators: Rhodamin B and Dragendorff reagent. Amounts: 50–100 gamma each. (1) Lysolecithin, (2) sphingomyelin, (3) lecithin, (4) cephalin, (5) cerebroside, (6) cardiolipid, (7) mixture. (After Mangold, 1961.)

Lipids may be localized on thin-layer chromatograms with a variety of chemical reagents. The most commonly utilized chemical procedures involve (1) spraying the plate with sulfuric acid followed by charring or (2) exposing the plate to iodine vapor. The latter technique is rapid, nondestructive, and allows for reclamation of the compound after the iodine has sublimed. A list of those reagents most frequently employed to visualize lipids is given in Table III. Detailed descriptions of other color reactions that are used to detect lipids on thin-layer plates or on paper chromatograms have been described by Mangold (1961), by Ansell and Hawthorne (1964), and in previously cited references to TLC textbooks.

TABLE III

REAGENTS FOR DETECTION OF LIPIDS ON THIN-LAYER
OR PAPER CHROMATOGRAMS

Reagent	Type of lipid	Reference
Sulfuric acid (conc. or 50% aqueous)	All	Morris et al. (1961)
2′,7′-Dichlorofluorescein (0.2% in 96% ethanol)	All	Malins and Mangold (1960)
Iodine vapors	Unsaturated	Malins and Mangold (1960)
Ninhydrin (0.2% in n-butanol– aqueous acetic acid 10%, 95 : 5)	Aminophosphatides	Wagner et al. (1961)
Dragendorf reagent (a) 1.7 gm basic bismuth nitrate in 100 ml aqueous acetic acid (20%) (b) 40 gm potassium iodide in 100 ml water Reagent 20 ml of (a) plus 5 ml of (b) plus 70 ml water	Choline phosphatides	Wagner et al. (1961)

3. Gas–Liquid Chromatography

Gas–liquid chromatography (GLC) is now routinely employed to identify and often to quantitate a wider variety of compounds, including sterols and fatty acid methyl esters.

The primary chemical constituent of any lipid is the fatty acid. Analysis of the fatty acid spectrum of a total lipid extract or of individual lipid fractions, separated by column or thin-layer chromatography, can be achieved by GLC. Free fatty acids or individual lipid classes are converted to the fatty acid methyl esters by means of HCl–methanol (James, 1960) or BCl₃–methanol (Supina, 1964).

Separation of the resultant fatty acid methyl ester mixture is achieved by chromatography on coiled or U-shaped glass columns. These columns are packed with celite supports coated either with Apiezon L or M or with a polymer of ethylene glycol [poly(ethylene glycol adipate) or poly(ethylene glycol succinate)]. Columns are operated at temperatures between 180° and 200°C. A tracing of a series of peaks is obtained. Each peak may then be identified by comparison with reference standards. The relative absolute proportion of each fatty acid methyl ester is determined by measuring the area of each peak. This proportion is compared with a standard curve prepared for each fatty acid methyl ester. The separation of the fatty acids commonly found in biologic samples is illustrated by the GLC chart in Fig. 4.

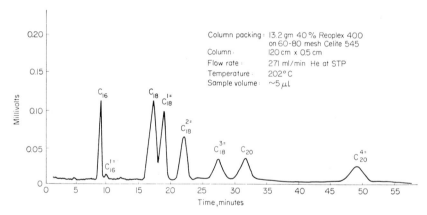

FIG. 4. Separation of mixture of fatty acid methyl esters containing methyl arachidonate. (After Orr and Callen, 1959.)

More information on detailed techniques and applications of GLC to the separation of fatty acid methyl esters can be obtained from review articles by James (1960, 1964), Supina (1964), and Horning and Vanden Heuvel (1963).

Analysis for sterols, including cholesterol, may also be achieved by GLC. Chromatographic separation has been achieved by means of a coiled column packed with a solid support composed of a diatomaceous earth preparation (Gas Chrom, Anakrom, or Chromosorb W), which is coated with dichlorodimethylsilane and finally with a silicone polymer (SE-30 or SE-52 is commonly used). The column is operated at temperatures between 200° and 250°C. Resolution and quantitation of such closely related sterols as cholesterol and desmosterol, which differ in structure by only one double bond, can be achieved by GLC. Review articles by Horning *et al.* (1963) and by Horning and Vanden Heuvel (1963, 1964) are useful references for the application of GLC to the separation of sterols.

4. *Paper Chromatography*

The use of paper chromatography (PC) for separation of lipids has largely been supplanted by the use of TLC. This technique, however, is still an equally useful analytical tool for several reasons. Paper chromatograms are easier to handle; radioactive compounds are more readily detected by autoradiography or by 2π-scanning (with greater sensitivity) than are the more fragile and thicker thin-layer plates. However, compared to TLC, PC does not have equal resolving power; less material can be analyzed; and more carefully controlled chromatographic conditions are required to achieve clear, reproducible separations.

Filter or glass fiber papers impregnated with silicic acid ordinarily have been used as supporting phases for the separation of neutral lipids and phospholipids into discrete classes. A more uniform silica

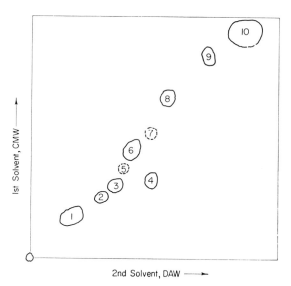

Fig. 5. Two-dimensional chromatogram of rat liver lipids. (1) Lysolecithin, (2) inositol phosphatide, (3) sphingomyelin, (4) phosphatidyl serine, (5) unidentified (possibly lysophosphatidyl ethanolamine), (6) lecithin, (7) unidentified (possibly cerebroside), (8) phosphatidyl ethanolamine, (9) cardiolipin, (10) combined neutral lipids. CMW = chloroform–methanol–water, 65 : 25 : 4; DAW = diisobutyl ketone–acetic acid–water, 40 : 25 : 5. (After Marinetti, 1965.)

gel-impregnated filter paper, which has higher resolving power and a higher loading capacity, has recently become available (Marinetti, 1965). The degree of resolution of phospholipids obtained on this support is shown in Fig. 5.

More specific applications of PC to the separation of lipids may be obtained from review articles by Marinetti (1962, 1964), Rouser *et al.* (1961a), and Hamilton and Muldrey (1961). Phospholipids of the lipid coat of influenza (Kates *et al.*, 1961) and mumps (Soule *et al.*, 1959) viruses have been analyzed using silicic acid-impregnated filter paper.

C. QUANTITATION OF LIPID CLASSES

After chromatographic fractionation of the lipid extract has been achieved, an estimate of the amount of each type of lipid may be obtained by colorimetry. A compilation of those colorimetric methods most commonly used for analysis of each type of lipid or for functional groups contained in the lipid is given in Table IV.

TABLE IV

METHODS FOR COLORIMETRIC ANALYSIS OF VARIOUS LIPIDS

Type of lipid	References
A. Neutral lipid	
1. Free cholesterol	Sperry and Webb (1950)
2. Total cholesterol	Sperry and Webb (1950); Mann Modification (Mann, 1961) of Zlatkis method (Zlatkis *et al.*, 1953)
3. Free fatty acids	Dole (1956); Albrink (1959); Duncombe (1963)
4. Glycerides (mono-, di-, and tri-)	Van Handel and Zilversmit (1957)
B. Phospholipids	
1. Phospholipid phosphorus	Fiske and Subbarow (1925); Bartlett (1959)
2. Phospholipid nitrogen	
a. Choline nitrogen	Dumas
b. Serine or ethanolamine nitrogen	Kjeldahl
3. Amino groups	Lea and Rhodes (1955)
4. Nitrogenous bases	
a. Choline	Wheeldon and Collins (1958)
b. Serine and ethanolamine	Collins and Wheeldon (1958)
C. Both phospholipids and neutral lipids	
1. Total fatty acids	Albrink (1959)
2. Lipid ester groups	Rapport and Alonzo (1955)

TABLE V

METHODS USED FOR ANALYSIS OF LIPIDS OF VARIOUS VIRUSES

Virus	Lipid-extraction technique	Chromatographic-fractionation technique	Lipids analyzed	Reference
Avian BAI (strain A)	Chloroform–methanol, 2:1	Thin-layer chromatography on silica gel G: neutral lipids separated with petroleum ether–diethyl ether–acetic acid, 90:10:1; phospholipids separated with chloroform–methanol–7 N ammonium hydroxide, 35:60:5	Neutral lipids; phospholipids	Rao and Beard (1964)
Equine encephalomyelitis	Acetone–alcohol, 1:1, benzene	None	Cholesterol; phospholipids; free fatty acids	Taylor et al. (1943)
Influenza (strains PR8 and Lee)	Ethanol–diethyl ether, 3:1	None	Cholesterol; neutral lipids; phospholipids	Taylor et al. (1942, 1943)
Influenza (strain PR8)	Ethanol–diethyl ether, 3:1	None	Phospholipids	Graham (1950)
Influenza (strains PR8, DSP, and Lee)	Chloroform–methanol, 2:1	Silicic acid microcolumn chromatography: lipids eluted sequentially with chloroform–hexane, chloroform–methanol	Cholesterol; triglycerides; phospholipids	Frommhagen et al. (1958)
Influenza (strains PR8, DSP, and Lee)	Chloroform–methanol, 2:1, or diethyl ether–ethanol, 1:2	Silicic acid microcolumn chromatography: lipids subfractionated using 10% methylene chloride in petroleum ether, chloroform, and methanol	Cholesterol; triglycerides; phospholipids	Frommhagen et al. (1959)

Virus	Extraction solvent	Method	Components	Reference
Influenza (Mel, 1935)	Chloroform–methanol 1 : 2	Silicic acid-impregnated filter paper: neutral lipids separated with n-heptane–diisobutyl ketone, 96 : 6; phospholipids separated with diisobutyl ketone–acetic acid–water, 40 : 25 : 5; gas–liquid chromatography: analysis of fatty acid methyl esters	Cholesterol; neutral lipids; fatty acid methyl esters	Kates et al. (1961)
Mumps	Diethyl ether–methanol, 2 : 1	Silicic acid-impregnated filter paper: phospholipids separated with diisobutyl ketone–n-butyl ether–acetic acid–water, 20 : 20 : 20 : 1, or diisobutyl ketone–acetic acid–water, 40 : 25 : 5, Silicic acid column chromatography: lipids eluted with increasing concentration of methanol in chloroform	Cholesterol; phospholipids; fatty acids	Soule et al. (1959)
Newcastle	Chloroform–ethanol, 2 : 1	None	Phospholipids	Cunha et al. (1947)
Rous sarcoma	Petroleum ether	Gas–liquid chromatography of fatty acids and methyl esters	Fatty acids	Bather (1957)
Sendai				Smirnova and Virkus (1964)
Sindbis	Chloroform–methanol, 1 : 1; chloroform	Silicic acid-impregnated filter paper; neutral lipids separated with n-heptane–diisobutyl ketone, 96 : 6; phospholipids separated with diisobutyl ketone–acetic acid–water, 40 : 25 : 5	Cholesterol; phospholipids	Pfefferkorn and Hunter (1963)

In addition to these methods, determination of the composition and relative proportion of fatty acids of each lipid class may be determined by GLC, as previously described in Section II,B,3.

Examples of the application of various techniques described above to the analysis of viral lipids is presented in Table V.

III. Applications of Existing Methodology to Lipid-Containing Viruses

A. MYXOVIRUSES

The most extensively studied of the lipid-containing viruses have been the myxoviruses, particularly the influenza group. The total lipid of PR8 virus is about 37% (Ada and Perry, 1954). Graham (1950) subjected several strains of influenza virus (PR8, DSP, and Lee) to ethanol–ether (3 : 1) extraction and determined phospholipid phosphorus only in the extract. Taylor (1944) subjected the PR8 and Lee strains of human influenza virus and a strain of swine influenza virus to two extractions: by alcohol–ether (3 : 1), then by petroleum ether. He analyzed the cholesterol as digitonide and the phospholipid as phosphorus and calculated the neutral lipid content by difference. His results showed that all three types of flu had similar lipid composition: total lipid 22–24%; phospholipid 10.7–11.3%; cholesterol 3.7–7.0%; and neutral lipid 5.1–7.7%. These results are in fairly close agreement with those obtained by more sophisticated methods of separation and analysis.

Frommhagen and his co-workers (1958, 1959) analyzed the lipids of three strains of flu (PR8, DSP, and Lee) and reported the lipid spectrum to resemble that of the host cell. They found 6–7% cholesterol and about 12% phospholipid, principally cephalin, sphingomyelin, and lecithin. Their analyses were carried out using an infrared spectroscopic technique developed by Freeman et al. (1957), coupled with silicic acid chromatography. Using paper chromatography for the analysis of the phospholipids of PR8, Armbruster and Beiss (1958) reported the presence of several cerebrosides. More recently, Kates et al. (1961) analyzed the phospholipids of influenza virus using chloroform–methanol extraction and chromatography on silicic acid-impregnated paper (Marinetti et al., 1958; Marinetti and Stotz, 1956) and found that the phospholipid (11–16% of the total) is primarily sphingomyelin (35%), lecithin (28%), and phosphatidyl ethanolamine (22%). The phospholipid separation was carried out using virus that had been grown in chick embryo. Comparison of the virus phosphatides with those present in the host indicated the presence of more lecithin and less sphingomyelin in the host than in the virus. When the phosphatides of influenza virus propagated in calf kidney cells were analyzed, the major phospholipids were found to be lecithin (36%), sphingomyelin (14%), phosphatidic acid (12%), and an unidentified compound (14%). The host cells contained much less of the phosphatidic acid and the unknown phospholipid than did the virus, but the quantities of lecithin and sphingomyelin were comparable. Using gas–liquid chromatography, the fatty acids of the viral lipids were determined for virus grown either in chick embryo or calf kidney cells. The predominant fatty acids in calf kidney-grown virus were palmitic (23%), oleic (21%), stearic (21%), linoleic (24%), and arachidonic (6%). This fatty acid spectrum is almost identical with that found in the host cell. Comparison of the fatty acids of chick embryo-grown virus with those of the host again showed very similar patterns, but the percentages of individual fatty acids were somewhat different: palmitic (32%), linoleic (9%), oleic (29%), stearic (13%), and arachidonic (6%).

Also found were appreciable quantities of plasmalogens, principally compounds containing palmityl and stearyl aldehydes. The pattern of plasmalogen aldehydes closely resembled that of the host cells.

Among the multiform myxoviruses, the most complete lipid analysis was carried out on mumps virus by Soule *et al.* (1959). Using Marinetti's technique of chromatography on silicic acid-impregnated filter paper, these workers found that the phospholipid fraction of this virus, which represents 7% of the total lipid content, is primarily sphingomyelin (60%), with lecithin (11%), phosphatidyl serine (10%), and phosphatidyl ethanolamines (19%) accounting for the remaining phosphatides. They were able to detect fatty acid, triglyceride, and free and ester cholesterol in their chromatograms, but did not quantitate these lipids. Newcastle disease virus has been reported to contain 27.2% total lipid and to have a high phospholipid content, but no more exact data are available (Cunha *et al.*, 1947). Sendai virus, after being subjected to purification by adsorption on red cells, differential centrifugation, and gel filtration, was extracted with petroleum ether and the fatty acids extracted after saponification of the lipid extract. Gas–liquid chromatography of the fatty acid methyl esters showed the fatty acids of Sendai virus to be palmitic (20.5%), stearic (30%), oleic (35%), and linoleic (14.5%) (Smirnova and Virkus, 1964).

B. ARBOVIRUSES

Of the arboviruses, the lipids of Eastern equine encephalomyelitis have been analyzed by Taylor *et al.* (1943). Extraction and direct analysis were used, and the total lipid (54%) was reported to contain phospholipid (35%), cholesterol (14%), and neutral fat (10%). Recently Hardy and Arbiter (1965) reported the presence of phospholipid-containing lipid inclusions in L cells infected with Venezuelan equine encephalomyelitis.

Pfefferkorn and Hunter (1963) reported on the phospholipid content of Sindbis virus. The principal phospholipids were lecithin (38%), phosphatidyl ethanolamine (25%), and sphingomyelin (25%).

C. Avian Tumor Viruses

Bather (1957) performed a chloroform–methanol (2 : 1) extraction on Rous sarcoma virus and found that it contained 42–44% lipid.

The lipids of avian myeloblastosis virus were determined gravimetrically after extraction of purified virus pellets serially by 80% methanol, chloroform–methanol (2 : 1), and ethanol. The total lipid content was found to be 35% (Bonar and Beard, 1959). In a more complete study, Rao and Beard (1964) followed extraction with thin-layer chromatography of the neutral lipids on silica gel G using petroleum ether–ethyl ether–acetic acid (90 : 10 : 1) as the developing solvent and phospholipids on the same adsorbent using chloroform–methanol–7 N ammonium hydroxide (35 : 60 : 5). Cholesterol accounted for 34% of the total lipid, neutral lipids for 5.3%, and the phospholipid classes as follows: lysolecithin 2.1%; sphinogomyelin 16%; phosphatidyl serine 7.4%; phosphatidyl ethanolamine 21% and lecithin 11%.

D. Other Viruses

No work has been done to elucidate the lipid composition of any of the other ether-sensitive viruses. Among the ether-resistant viruses, vaccinia virus has been shown to contain about 6% lipid (Hoagland et al., 1940). The lipid was obtained by extraction of the purified virus with alcohol–ether (3 : 1); the cholesterol (1.4%) and phospholipid (2.2%) content was determined chemically, and the neutral fat content (2.2%) by difference. The cholesterol could be removed by a second ether extraction. The resistance of this virus to ether suggests that the lipids are not an integral part of the cell surface.

The available literature relating to the lipid compositions of viruses is given in Table VI.

IV. Summary

The primary function of the lipids present in viruses seems to be to maintain the structural integrity of their membrane. These lipids

TABLE VI
LIPID CONTENT OF VIRUSES

Virus	Total lipid (%)	Neutral fat (%)[a]	Cholesterol (%)[a]	Phospholipids						Reference
				Total[a]	S[b,c]	L[b,c]	PS[b,c]	PE[b,c]	Other[b]	
Influenza										
PR8	23.4	5.1	7.0	11.3						Taylor (1944)
Lee	22.4	7.2	3.7	11.2						Taylor (1944)
Swine	24.0	7.7	5.7	10.7						Taylor (1944)
PR8	37.5									Ada and Perry (1954)
PR8	18–20	<1	6–7	11.5	36	15			49	Frommhagen et al. (1959)
DSP	18	<1	7	12						Frommhagen et al. (1959)
Lee	18	<1	5	11						Frommhagen et al. (1959)
Mel, 1935					35[d]	28	7	22	8	Kates et al. (1961)
Mel, 1935					14[e]	36	5	8	37	Kates et al. (1961)
Mumps				7	60	11	10	19		Soule et al. (1959)
Newcastle	27.2			17.5						Cunha et al. (1947)
EEE	54	9.6	13.8	35						Taylor et al. (1943)
Rous	42–44			22						Bather (1957)
Avian myeloblastosis	35	5.3	3.4		16	11	7	21	2	Bonar and Beard (1959); Rao and Beard (1964)
Vaccinia	5.7	2.2	1.4	2.2						Hoagland et al. (1940)
Papilloma	1.5									Beard et al. (1939); Taylor et al. (1942)

[a] Percent of total lipid.
[b] Percent of phospholipid.
[c] S, sphingomyelin; L, lecithin; PS, phosphatidyl serine; PE, phosphatidyl ethanolamine.
[d] Chick embryo-grown.
[e] Calf kidney-grown.

may also play an important role in the interaction of virus with host cells and in their agglutination of erythrocytes (Nicoli, 1965). With the availability of better methods of viral purification, it should be possible to obtain workable quantities of virus that are free of host–cell contamination. The present state of development of lipid methodology makes possible the separation and identification of all classes of viral lipids. The limiting factor is the availability of sufficient material.

References

Ada, G. L., and Perry, B. T. (1954). *Australian J. Exptl. Biol. Med. Sci.* **32,** 453.

Albrink, M. J. (1959). *J. Lipid Res.* **1,** 53.

Ansell, G. B., and Hawthorne, J. N. (1964). "Phospholipids: Chemistry, Metabolism and Function." Elsevier, Amsterdam.

Armbruster, Von O., and Beiss, U. (1958). *Z. Naturforsch.* **13b,** 75.

Bartlett, G. R. (1959). *J. Biol. Chem.* **234,** 466.

Bather, R. (1957). *Brit. J. Cancer* **11,** 611.

Beard, J. W., Bryan, W. R., and Wyckoff, R. W. G. (1939). *J. Infect. Diseases* **65,** 43.

Bloor, W. R. (1928). *J. Biol. Chem.* **77,** 53.

Bobbitt, J. M. (1963). "Thin-Layer Chromatography." Reinhold, New York.

Bonar, R. A., and Beard, J. W. (1959). *J. Natl. Cancer Inst.* **23,** 183.

Borgström, B. (1952). *Acta Physiol. Scand.* **25,** 101 and 111.

Bush, I. E. (1961). "The Chromatography of Steroids." Pergamon Press, Oxford.

Carroll, K. K. (1961). *J. Lipid Res.* **2,** 135.

Castaldo, A., Petti, L., and Ragno, I. (1964). *Rass. Med. Sper.* **11,** 201.

Collins, F. D., and Wheeldon, L. W. (1958). *Biochem. J.* **70,** 46.

Cunha, R., Weil, M. L., Beard, D., Taylor, A. R., Sharp, D. G., and Beard, J. W. (1947). *J. Immunol.* **55,** 69.

Dole, V. P. (1956). *J. Clin. Invest.* **35,** 150.

Duncombe, W. G. (1963). *Biochem. J.* **88,** 7.

Entenman, C. (1957). *Methods Enzymol.* **3,** 299.

Entenman, C. (1961). *J. Am. Oil Chemists' Soc.* **38,** 534.

Fillerup, D. L., and Mead, J. F. (1963). *Proc. Soc. Exptl. Biol. Med.* **83,** 574.

Fiske, C. H., and Subbarow, Y. (1925). *J. Biol. Chem.* **66,** 375.

Folch, J., Lees, M., and Sloane-Stanley, G. H. (1957). *J. Biol. Chem.* **226,** 497.

Franklin, R. M. (1962). *Progr. Med. Virol.* **4,** 1.

Freeman, N. K., Lindgren, F. T., Ng, Y. C., and Nichols, A. V. (1957). *J. Biol. Chem.* **227,** 449.

Frommhagen, L. H., Freeman, N. K., and Knight, C. A. (1958). *Virology* **5,** 173.

Frommhagen, L. H., Knight, C. A., and Freeman, N. K. (1959). *Virology* **8,** 176.

Galanos, D. S., and Kapoulas, V. M. (1962). *J. Lipid Res.* **3,** 134.

Galanos, D. S., and Kapoulas, V. M. (1965). *Biochim. Biophys. Acta* **98,** 278.

Graham, A. F. (1950). *Can. J. Res.* **28,** 186.

Green, M. (1965). *Am. J. Med.* **38,** 651.

Hamilton, J. G., and Muldrey, J. E. (1961). *J. Am. Oil Chemists' Soc.* **38,** 582.

Hanahan, D. J., Dittmer, J. C., and Warashine, E. (1957). *J. Biol. Chem.* **228,** 685.

Hardy, F. M., and Arbiter, D. (1965). *J. Bacteriol.* **89,** 1101.

Hirsch, J., and Ahrens, E. H., Jr. (1958). *J. Biol. Chem.* **233**, 311.

Hoagland, C. L., Smadel, J. E., and Rivers, T. M. (1940). *J. Exptl. Med.* **71**, 737.

Horning, E. C., and Vanden Heuvel, W. J. A. (1963). *Ann. Rev. Biochem.* **32**, 709.

Horning, E. C., and Vanden Heuvel, W. J. A. (1964). *In* "New Biochemical Separations" (A. T. James and L. J. Morris, eds.), p. 25. Van Nostrand, Princeton, New Jersey.

Horning, M. G., Williams, E. A., and Horning, E. C. (1960). *J. Lipid Res.* **1**, 482.

Horning, E. C., Vanden Heuvel, W. J. A., and Creech, B. G. (1963). *Methods Biochem. Anal.* **11**, 69.

James, A. T. (1960). *Methods Biochem. Anal.* **8**, 1.

James, A. T. (1964). *In* "New Biochemical Separations" (A. T. James and L. J. Morris, eds.), p. 11. Van Nostrand, Princeton, New Jersey.

Kates, M. A., Allison, A. C., Tyrrell, D. A. J., and James, A. T. (1961). *Biochim. Biophys. Acta* **52**, 455.

Lea, C. N., and Rhodes, D. N. (1955). *Biochim. Biophys. Acta* **17**, 416.

LePage, M. (1964). *J. Chromatog.* **13**, 99.

Loan, R. W. (1964). *Am. J. Vet. Res.* **25**, 1366.

Lwoff, A. (1957). *J. Gen. Microbiol.* **17**, 239.

Malins, D. C., and Mangold, H. K. (1960). *J. Am. Oil Chemists' Soc.* **37**, 576.

Mangold, H. K. (1961). *J. Am. Oil Chemists' Soc.* **38**, 708.

Mangold, H. K. (1964). *J. Am. Oil Chemists' Soc.* **41**, 762.

Mann, G. V. (1961). *Clin. Chem.* **7**, 275.

Marinetti, G. V. (1962). *J. Lipid Res.* **3**, 1.

Marinetti, G. V. (1964). *In* "New Biochemical Separations" (A. T. James and L. J. Morris, eds.), p. 339. Van Nostrand, Princeton, New Jersey.

Marinetti, G. V. (1965). *J. Lipid Res.* **6**, 315.

Marinetti, G. V., and Stotz, E. (1956). *Biochim. Biophys. Acta* **21**, 168.

Marinetti, G. V., Erbland, J., and Stotz, E. (1958). *J. Biol. Chem.* **233**, 562.

Marini-Bettolo, G. B., ed. (1964). "Thin-Layer Chromatography." Elsevier, Amsterdam.

Marks, P. A., Gellhorn, A., and Kidson, C. (1960). *J. Biol. Chem.* **235**, 2579.

Mattson, F. H., and Volpenhein, R. A. (1962). *J. Lipid Res.* **3**, 281.

Morris, L. J. (1964). *In* "New Biochemical Separations" (A. T. James and L. J. Morris, eds.), p. 295. Van Nostrand, Princeton, New Jersey.

Morris, L. J., Holman, R. T., and Fontell, K. (1961). *J. Lipid Res.* **2**, 68.

Müldner, H. G., Wherrett, J. R., and Cumings, J. N. (1962). *J. Neurochem.* **9**, 607.

Nichols, B. W. (1964). *In* "New Biochemical Separations" (A. T. James and L. J. Morris, eds.), p. 321. Van Nostrand, Princeton, New Jersey.

Nichols, B. W. (1963). *Biochim. Biophys. Acta* **70**, 417.

Nicoli, J. (1965). *Ann. Inst. Pasteur* **108**, 423.

Orr, C. H., and Callen, J. E. (1959). *Ann. N.Y. Acad. Sci.* **72**, 649.

Pfefferkorn, E. R., and Hunter, H. S. (1963). *Virology* **20**, 433.

Randerath, K. (1963). "Thin-Layer Chromatography." Academic Press, New York.

Rao, P. R., and Beard, J. W. (1964). *Natl. Cancer Inst. Monograph* **17**, 673.

Rapport, M. M., and Alonzo, N. (1955). *J. Biol. Chem.* **217**, 193.

Redman, C. M., and Kelnan, R. W. (1964). *J. Chromatog.* **15**, 180.

Rothblat, G. H., Martak, D. S., and Kritchevsky, D. (1963). *Proc. Soc. Exptl. Biol. Med.* **112**, 598.

Rouser, G., Bauman, A. J., Nicolaides, N., and Heller, D. (1961a). *J. Am. Oil Chemists' Soc.* **38**, 565.

Rouser, G., Bauman, A. J., Kritchevsky, G., Heller, D., and O'Brien, J. S. (1961b). *J. Am. Oil Chemists' Soc.* **38**, 544.

Rouser, G., Kritchevsky, G., Heller, D., and Lieber, E. (1963). *J. Am. Oil Chemists' Soc.* **40**, 425.

Rouser, G., Galli, C., Lieber, E., Blank, M. L., and Privett, O. S. (1964). *J. Am. Oil Chemists' Soc.* **41**, 836.

Schlenk, H. (1964). *In* "Fatty Acids, Their Chemistry, Properties, Production and Uses" (K. S. Markley, ed.), 2nd ed., Part 3, p. 2125. Wiley (Interscience), New York.

Sinclair, R. G. (1930). *J. Biol. Chem.* **88**, 575.

Skidmore, W. D., and Entenman, C. (1962). *J. Lipid Res.* **3**, 471.

Skipski, V. P., Peterson, R. F., and Barclay, M. (1962). *J. Lipid Res.* **3**, 467.

Skipski, V. P., Peterson, R. F., Sanders, J., and Barclay, M. (1963). *J. Lipid Res.* **4**, 227.

Smirnova, G. A., and Virkus, A. Yu. (1964). *Vopr. Virusol.* **9**, 417.

Smith, P. F. (1964). *J. Lipid Res.* **5**, 121.

Soule, D. W., Marinetti, G. V., and Morgan, H. (1959). *J. Exptl. Med.* **110**, 93.

Sperry, W. M. (1955). *Methods Biochem. Anal.* **2**, 83.

Sperry, W. M., and Webb, M. (1950). *J. Biol. Chem.* **187**, 97.

Stahl, E., ed. (1965). "Thin-Layer Chromatography." Academic Press, New York.

Supina, W. R. (1964). *In* "Biomedical Applications of Gas Chromatography" (H. A. Szymanski, ed.), p. 271. Plenum Press, New York.

Svennerholm, L. (1964). *J. Neurochem.* **11**, 839.

Taylor, A. R. (1944). *J. Biol. Chem.* **153**, 675.

Taylor, A. R., Beard, D., Sharp, D. G., and Beard, J. W. (1942). *J. Infect. Diseases* **71**, 110.

Taylor, A. R., Sharp, D. G., Beard, D., and Beard, J. W. (1943). *J. Infect. Diseases* **72**, 31.

Truter, E. V. (1963). "Thin Film Chromatography." Wiley (Interscience), New York.

van Beers, G. J., de Iongh, H., and Boldingh, J. (1958). *In* "Essential Fatty Acids" (H. M. Sinclair, ed.), p. 43. Butterworth, London and Washington, D.C.

Van Handel, E., and Zilversmit, D. B. (1957). *J. Lab. Clin. Med.* **50**, 152.

Van Slyke, D. D., and Plazin, J. (1965). *Clin. Chim. Acta* **12**, 46.

Vogel, A. I. (1956). "A Textbook of Practical Organic Chemistry," 3rd ed. Wiley, New York.

Wagner, H. (1960). *Fette, Seifen, Anstrichmittel* **62**, 1115.

Wagner, H., Hörhammer, L., and Wolff, P. (1961). *Biochem. Z.* **334**, 175.

Wheeldon, L. W., and Collins, F. D. (1958). *Biochem. J.* **70**, 43.

Wren, J. J., and Szczepanowska, D. (1964). *J. Chromatog.* **14**, 405.

Zlatkis, A., Zak, B., and Boyle, A. J. (1953). *J. Lab. Clin. Med.* **41**, 486.

3 RNA Virus RNA Polymerase: Detection, Purification, and Properties

J. Thomas August and Lillian Eoyang

I. Introduction

The replication of RNA viruses requires an enzymatic mechanism utilizing RNA as template. It has been assumed that such a reaction occurs in a manner analogous to that of DNA-directed nucleic acid synthesis, as depicted in the following:

$$
\begin{array}{c}
n \text{ APPP} \\
+ \\
n \text{ UPPP} \\
+ \\
n \text{ GPPP} \\
+ \\
n \text{ CPPP}
\end{array}
+ \text{ RNA} \rightleftarrows \text{ RNA} +
\left[
\begin{array}{c}
\text{AP} \\
| \\
\text{UP} \\
| \\
\text{GP} \\
| \\
\text{CP}
\end{array}
\right]_n
+ 4n \text{ PP}
$$

Such a system, utilizing RNA as template and ribonucleoside triphosphates as substrate, is not known to occur in uninfected animal, plant, or bacterial cells. It has been found, however, that infection with RNA-containing viruses results in the appearance of RNA polymerase activity formerly absent in extracts of the host cell (Astier-Manifacier and Cornuet, 1965; August et al., 1963; Baltimore and Franklin, 1962; Cline et al., 1963; Haruna et al., 1963; Ho and Walters, 1966; Horton et al., 1966; Lust, 1966; Plagemann and Swim, 1966; Weissmann et al., 1963; Wilson and Bader, 1965). Partially purified enzymes have been studied in several laboratories. Weissmann et al. (1964) obtained a fraction purified about 20-fold, with an activity of 1 mμmole UMP incorporated per milligram of protein per minute, from Escherichia coli Hfr 3000 infected with phage MS2. This fraction has been shown to catalyze the synthesis of parental-type RNA in a reaction that utilized RNA associated with the enzyme (Weissmann, 1965). August et al. (1965) obtained an RNA-dependent fraction with an activity of 40 mμmoles GMP incorporated per milligram of protein per minute and purified about 100-fold from E. coli K38 infected with su-11, an amber mutant of phage f2. The purified enzyme utilized many different types of RNA as templates to catalyze the synthesis of RNA resembling a complementary strand (Shapiro and August, 1965). Haruna and Spiegelman (1965), using E. coli Q-13 infected with phage Qβ, obtained a fraction catalyzing 0.4–1 mμmoles UMP incorporation per milligram of protein per minute in a reaction requiring Qβ-RNA as template and catalyzing the synthesis of infectious viral RNA (Pace and Spiegelman, 1966). The procedure described in this paper yields a 500-fold purified Qβ-RNA polymerase with an activity of 50–75 mμmoles GMP incorporated per milligram of protein per minute.

II. Detection

A. PREPARATION OF RNA PHAGE-INFECTED BACTERIA

1. Principle

The appearance of a phage-associated RNA polymerase activity in extracts of infected bacteria follows a temporal sequence after infection. Thus, to detect the presence of such an enzyme, the activity in uninfected bacteria should be compared with that of bacteria harvested at different times after infection. The presence of host enzymes may cause difficulty in the detection of a phage-associated enzyme and, as described below, precautions are necessary to avoid such interference. In this respect, a convenient host is E. coli Q-13, a mutant that contains low levels of polynucleotide phosphorylase and RNase I (Gesteland, 1966).

2. General Techniques

a. Media and Solutions. Several media may be used for the preparation of phage stocks (Watanabe and August, this volume). In these experiments, a medium was devised to be used for the preparation of phage stocks as well as of phage-infected bacteria for enzymatic studies. This medium (GC medium) has the advantage that it can be autoclaved in complete form, reducing excessive manipulation and thus the possibility of contamination.

The GC medium contains the following (per liter): 1.21 gm of Tris, 5.0 gm of NaCl, 1.0 gm of NH_4Cl, 0.052 gm of $Na_2HPO_4 \cdot 7H_2O$, 0.1 gm of $MgSO_4$, 10 gm of casamino acids, 10 ml of glycerol, and 2.5 ml of 1.0 M HCl. Prior to infection with RNA bacteriophage, 1.0 ml of 1 M $CaCl_2$ must be added per liter.

Hard agar contains (per liter) 10 gm of Difco Bactotryptone, 8 gm of NaCl, 1 gm of glucose, and 10 gm of Difco agar. After the agar has melted, 1.5 ml of 1 N NaOH and 2 ml of 1 M $CaCl_2$ per liter are added. Petri dishes are filled with about 30–35 ml of hard agar that has been sterilized and cooled to 45°–50°C. After the agar has hardened, the covered plates are inverted and allowed to dry at room temperature for 24–48 hours. The plates may then be stored for 1–2 weeks at 4°C.

Soft agar contains (per liter) 10 gm of Difco Bactotryptone, 8 gm of NaCl, 1 gm of glucose, and 6 gm of Difco agar. After the agar has melted, 1.5 ml of 1 N NaOH and 2 ml of 1 M $CaCl_2$ per liter are added. Soft agar is stored at 4°C in tightly stoppered 100-ml bottles.

Diluent used for titering RNA phage suspensions contains (per liter) 0.01 M Tris at pH 7.5, 0.001 M $MgCl_2$, 0.1 M NaCl, and 10 mg of gelatin.

Lysing solution contains (per 100 ml) 10 mg of lysozyme, 0.01 M EDTA at pH 7.5, and 1 M Tris at pH 7.5.

b. *Preparation of Cultures.* A single colony of bacteria is transferred into a flask containing GC medium. The flask is aerated at 37°C until the bacteria reach a concentration of $3–5 \times 10^8$ cells per milliliter. (It is convenient to estimate bacterial concentration by absorbance at 660 mμ.) To check for phage contamination, an aliquot of the culture is plated by the agar-layer method (Adams, 1959). This culture is also used as plating bacteria to confirm the cell's ability to act as host for RNA phage infection. Cultures stored at 4°C remain viable for approximately 1 week.

c. *Preparation and Assay of Phage.* The RNA phage infects only male strains (Hfr and F+) of *E. coli.* Both plating and inoculating bacteria must be in the early logarithmic phase of growth ($3–5 \times 10^8$ cells/ ml), since RNA bacteriophages may not adsorb to bacteria grown to stationary phase or grown at temperatures below 31°C, presumably because under these conditions the bacteria become F⁻ phenocopies (Lederberg *et al.,* 1952).

Phage titer and host range are determined by plaque formation utilizing the agar-layer method (Adams, 1959). After the top agar has hardened, the plates are inverted and incubated at 37°C with good aeration for 12–25 hours.* Plates should be examined during the first 24 hours, since the plaques may become obscure. The plaque size and morphology may differ depending on plating conditions.

Phage stocks are prepared by infecting bacteria in early exponential growth with a single plaque. A convenient procedure is to inoculate 500 ml of medium in a 2-liter flask with a bacterial concentration of approximately 5×10^9 bacteria. The culture is incubated at 37°C with maximum aeration. At a density of $3–5 \times 10^8$ cells/ml, the bacteria are infected with a single plaque. After incubation for 4–6 hours, lysis is completed by the addition of lysing solution, 0.05–0.10 volumes, and chloroform (1%, v/v). This lysate is used without further purification for the preparation of infected cells. The lysate may be stored at 4°C but should be titered prior to use, since there may be a loss in infectivity with time. Phage titer is determined by plaque formation and the agar-layer method (Adams, 1959).

3. Preparation of Phage-Infected Bacteria

Detection of phage polymerase activity is conveniently performed in the following manner. Six 2-liter flasks, each containing 500 ml of medium, are inoculated with 2.5×10^{10} bacteria. The flasks are incubated at 37°C with maximum aeration until the bacterial concentration reaches $3–5 \times 10^8$ cells per milliliter. Calcium chloride, 0.5 ml 1 M, is added to each flask. RNA phage are then added at a multiplicity of infection of 20–40 to all but one flask. Incubation with vigorous aeration is continued, and flasks are removed at timed intervals, such as 5, 10, 20, 30, and 40 minutes. Immediately upon removal from the incubator, each flask is cooled to 10°C in a Dry Ice–acetone bath and stored at 4°C until all samples are collected. The bacteria are harvested by centrifugation, and the cell pellets are stored at −20°C until time of use. The uninfected culture should be plated to check for contamination. Moreover, a sample of one of the infected cultures should be assayed for infective centers by the agar-layer method to verify that the conditions were appropriate for infection. The results of infection at various time intervals with different RNA bacteriophage are shown in Fig. 1.

4. Preparation of Cell-Free Extracts

Cold alumina (Alumina A-301, Aluminum Company of America), equal to twice the weight of bacteria, is added to each of the frozen

---

* It should be emphasized that good aeration is necessary. Plaque formation is known not to occur when a large number of plates are placed in a closed oven.

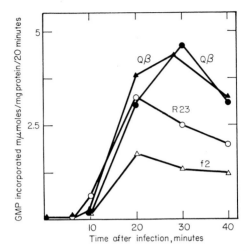

FIG. 1. Phage RNA polymerase activity following infection with RNA bacterio-phage. *E. coli* Q-13 was grown and infected with various RNA bacteriophage, as described in the text. The preparation of cell-free extracts and assay of phage RNA polymerase activity are also described in the text.

bacterial pellets. The bacteria are disrupted by grinding with a mortar and pestle for approximately 10 minutes until the mixture assumes a smooth, moist, and sticky consistency. The paste is then suspended in 4 volumes of a buffer solution containing 0.05 M Tris-HCl at pH 7.2, 0.005 M MgCl$_2$, 0.005 M 2-mercaptoethanol, and 0.001 M EDTA in 20% (v/v) glycerol. The suspension is centrifuged at 10,000 g for 5 minutes to remove the alumina and then at 30,000 g for 10 minutes. The supernatant (crude extract) is decanted. This crude extract usu-ally contains approximately 15–20 mg/ml protein, and 5–20-μl aliquots are used to assay for viral RNA polymerase activity.

B. ASSAY OF RNA VIRUS RNA POLYMERASE

1. *Principle*

The assay measures the incorporation of acid-soluble ribonucleotides into acid-insoluble material.* Other enzymatic reactions known to in-corporate ribonucleotides are inhibited as follows: DNase is added to inhibit the DNA-dependent RNA polymerase reaction. Phosphoenolpy-ruvate and pyruvate kinase are added to inhibit the polynucleotide phosphorylase reaction. GTP is used as the labeled substrate to avoid

---

* This acid-insoluble material must also be characterized as RNA. Procedures that may be employed are described elsewhere (August *et al.,* 1965).

polyriboadenylate polymerase and adenylate–cytidylate pyrophosphorylase activity.

2. Materials

Materials were obtained from the following sources: unlabeled and ^{14}C-labeled ribonucleotides from Schwarz BioResearch, Orangeburg, New York; pyruvate kinase and 2-phosphoenolpyruvate (tricyclohexylammonium salt) from California Corporation for Biochemical Research, Los Angeles, California; Tris, "Trizma Base," from Sigma Chemical Co., St. Louis, Missouri; pancreatic deoxyribonuclease I, electrophoretically purified free of RNase, from Worthington Biochemical Corporation, Freehold, New Jersey.

The conductivity of distilled or deionized water used for the preparation of reagents was less than 0.1 ppm as NaCl.

3. Reagents

(1) 50% glycerol; (2) Tris-HCl buffer, pH 7.5, 0.5 M; (3) $MgCl_2$, 0.1 M; (4) 2-mercaptoethanol, 0.1 M; (5) phosphoenolpyruvate, 0.1 M; (6) pyruvate kinase, 100 μg per milliliter; (7) ^{14}C-GTP (2–5 $\times$ 10^6 cpm per micromole), 0.01 M; (8) ATP, 0.01 M; (9) UTP, 0.01 M; (10 CTP, 0.01 M; (11) DNase, 1 mg per milliliter; (12) trichloroacetic acid (TCA), 5%, containing 0.02 M sodium pyrophosphate.

4. Procedures

The assay mixture contains 0.05 ml of Tris, 0.03 ml of $MgCl_2$, 0.01 ml of 2-mercaptoethanol, 0.01 ml of phosphoenolpyruvate, 0.01 ml of pyruvate kinase, 0.01 ml of ^{14}C-GTP, 0.02 ml each of ATP, UTP, and CTP, 0.01 ml of DNase, 0.005–0.02 ml of enzyme, and 50% glycerol to a final volume of 0.25 ml. (Additional RNA need not be added to the incubation mixture when a crude extract is the enzyme fraction.) After incubation for 20 minutes at 37°C, the mixture is cooled in ice, and approximately 3 ml of cold TCA-pyrophosphate solution is added. The contents are filtered through a membrane filter (Millipore Type HA, pore size 45 μ, diameter 25 mm) and washed four times with about 1-ml volumes of the TCA-pyrophosphate solution. The filter is glued to a planchet and dried by gentle heating. [A convenient glue is the Borden's cement (Elmer's Glue-all), but this glue, when not dry, will initiate a discharge in windowless gas-flow counters.] The acid-insoluble radioactivity is measured in a windowless gas-flow counter. [The radioactivity may also be measured by placing the filters in vials containing phosphor (3 gm of 2,5-diphenyloxazole and 100 mg of 1,4-bis-2-(5-phenyloxazolyl)benzene per liter of reagent-grade toluene) and counted in a liquid-scintillation spectrophotometer.] Reaction mixtures acidified immediately after the addition of all the components or those lacking enzyme serve as blanks.

The mμmoles GMP incorporated may be calculated from the specific activity of the labeled substrate. One unit of activity is defined as the incorporation of 1 mμmole per 20 minutes at 37°C. The specific activity of the enzyme, mμmoles per 20 minutes per milligram of protein, must be calculated in order to compare extracts from infected and uninfected bacteria.

III. Purification

A. GENERAL TECHNIQUES

1. Materials

Materials were obtained from the following sources: Alumina A-301, Aluminum Company of America; Dextran 500, Pharmacia Fine Chemicals, Inc., New York, New York; polyethylene glycol (Carbowax 6000), Union Carbide Chemicals Co., New York, New York; glycerol, "spectroquality reagent," Matheson, Coleman and Bell, Norwood, Ohio; ammonium sulfate, "special enzyme grade," Mann Research Laboratories, Inc., New York, New York; Tris, "Trizma Base," Sigma Chemical Co., St. Louis, Missouri; DEAE,* "Cellex-D High-capacity," Bio-Rad Laboratories, Richmond, California; hydroxylapatite, Hypatite C, Clarkson Chemical Co., Inc., Williamsport, Pennsylvania.

The conductivity of distilled or deionized water used for the preparation of reagents was less than 0.1 ppm as NaCl.

Qβ-RNA is obtained from lysates prepared as previously described. The phage are purified as described elsewhere (Watanabe and August, this volume). The suspension of purified phage is mixed with an equal volume of phenol (the phenol is redistilled and immediately prior to use washed twice with 0.1 M potassium phosphate, pH 7.5) in a glass-stoppered test tube and the tube is rolled gently at room temperature for about 10 minutes. The phases are separated by centrifugation at 15,000 g for 5 minutes. The top layer is removed and the RNA precipitated with the addition of 2 volumes of 95% ethanol. The precipitate is collected and dissolved in 0.02 M Tris-HCl at pH 7.5. The RNA is

---

* DEAE-cellulose was prepared in the following manner. "Cellex-D," 100 gm. was suspended in 4 liters of 0.5 N HCl, filtered through cheesecloth and washed with water until a pH of 4.0 was reached. It was then suspended in 4 liters of 0.5 N NaOH, filtered, and washed with water until the pH and absorbancy (260 mμ) of the effluent wash was that of water.

again precipitated with ethanol to remove traces of phenol and dissolved in Tris buffer as before. The stock solution of RNA is stored at $-70°C$. Small aliquots diluted to 0.5 μmoles/ml in 0.02 M Tris-HCl at pH 7.5 are prepared for use in the enzyme assay. (To protect against denaturation, the RNA is stored in small aliquots at $-70°C$. Each aliquot, when used as a working solution, is stored at $-20°C$ and is carefully removed only long enough to make the appropriate additions to the incubation mixtures.) The size of the RNA should be determined, since the Qβ-RNA polymerase reaction requires intact Qβ-RNA. [The size may be determined by sedimentation analysis (Haruna and Spiegelman, 1965).]

2. Reagents

(1) Qβ-RNA, 0.5 μmoles per milliliter in 0.02 M Tris at pH 7.5. [Nucleic acid concentrations are expressed in terms of total nucleotide ($\epsilon_{m\mu} = 8600$).] (2) Buffer solutions containing 0.05 M Tris at pH 7.2, 0.005 M MgCl$_2$, 0.005 M 2-mercaptoethanol, and 0.001 M EDTA (standard buffer) and the same components in 20% glycerol as well as 50% glycerol. (The pH of the buffer solution was determined at the stated concentration at 4°C.) (3) One hundred grams of Dextran 500, 20% (w/w), was added to 400 ml of H$_2$O and mixed until dissolved. (4) One hundred and fifty grams of polyethylene glycol, 30% (w/w), was added to 350 ml of H$_2$O and mixed until dissolved.

3. Assay

The assay materials, reagents, and procedure are the same as described in Section II,B except that 0.002 ml of Qβ-RNA is added to the incubation mixture prior to the addition of enzyme.

B. ISOLATION OF THE Qβ-RNA POLYMERASE

1. Principle

Isolation of the RNA phage RNA polymerase has been impeded in large measure by the lability of the phage polymerase activity in extracts of cells infected with f2, MS2, or R-17 phages. Considerable progress has been made, however, by using phage Qβ, apparently because the Qβ-RNA polymerase has greater stability. Nevertheless, care in avoiding protein denaturation must be exercised throughout the purification procedure, and the use of glycerol as a stabilizing agent is therefore recommended. With crude enzyme fractions, the reaction may be markedly inhibited by RNase or other inhibitors, and fractions should be assayed at more than one level to determine that incorporation is linear with the amount of protein added. The following procedure has been used thus far only in preparing extracts from *E. coli* infected with phage Qβ.

2. Growth of Infected Cells

Preparation of phage-infected extracts is carried out as previously described but in larger quantity. With a mixing speed of 300 rpm, 1 liter of culture per 2-liter flask may be prepared, with a yield of approximately 0.8 gm (wet weight) of cells per liter. Alternatively, large-scale cultures may be grown in carboys or 50- or 100-liter fermentors. Sufficient aeration to maintain a generation time for Q-13 of 35 minutes has been found to be satisfactory. The medium is inoculated with bacteria from a fresh culture in logarithmic growth to achieve an initial concentration of approximately 5×10^7 bacteria per milliliter. Incubation is at 37°C. When the bacteria have reached a concentration of 3–5×10^8 per milliliter, $CaCl_2$ and Qβ (multiplicity of infection 20–40) are added. Incubation and maximum aeration are continued for 20 minutes. The culture is then cooled to 10°C within 10 minutes, either by addition of ice or external cooling. Rapid cooling is important to avoid loss of enzyme activity. The cells are harvested by centrifugation and stored at -20°C. Because of their fragility, the packed cells are not washed. The yield of cells is 0.6–0.8 gm wet weight per liter.

3. Purification Procedure

Unless otherwise stated, all operations are carried out at 0°–4°C. The purification procedure and results of a typical preparation are summarized in Table I.

TABLE I

PURIFICATION OF THE Qβ-RNA POLYMERASE

Fraction	Protein (mg/ml)	Specific activity (units/mg)	Units (mμmoles/20 minutes)	Yield (%)
1. Crude extract	22	2.2	9200	100
2. High-speed super-natant	15	2.4	7200	78
3. Ammonium sulfate	16	13	8500	92
4. DEAE-cellulose	10	100	7000	76
5. Hydroxylapatite	0.66	1200	1050	11

a. Crude Extract. The frozen Qβ-infected cells, 50 gm, and cold alumina, 100 gm, are ground with a mortar and pestle until the mixture becomes smooth, sticky, and moist. The paste is suspended by mixing, and gradual addition of 200 ml of a buffer solution containing 0.05 M Tris-HCl at pH 7.2, 0.005 M MgCl$_2$, 0.005 M 2-mercaptoethanol, and 0.001 M EDTA in 20% glycerol. The suspension is centrifuged at 30,000 g for 10 minutes. The supernatant solution, 210 ml, is retained (crude extract).

b. *High-Speed Supernatant.* The crude extract is centrifuged in the Spinco No. 30 rotor at 30,000 rpm for 2 hours, and the supernatant solution, 202 ml, decanted (high-speed supernatant).

c. *Liquid Polymer and Ammonium Sulfate Fractionation.* To 200 ml of the high-speed supernatant are added with mixing 23.4 ml of 20% (w/w) Dextran 500, 62 ml of 30% (w/w) polyethylene glycol, and 66 gm of NaCl. [The final concentrations (by weight) of Dextran 500 and polyethylene glycol are 1.6% and 6.4%, respectively (Albertsson, 1962).] Mixing is continued for 1 hour, after which the suspension is centrifuged at 15,000 g for 5 minutes. The supernatant solution (phase top, 250 ml)* is removed and dialyzed for 2 hours against 4 liters of the standard buffer solution in 20% glycerol (phase top dialyzed, 310 ml). (The conductivity of a 5 × 10^4 dilution of the dialyzed phase top must be less than 1.3 ppm as NaCl.) The dialyzed phase top is brought to 35% saturation with the addition of 60 gm of ammonium sulfate. After being mixed for 10 minutes, the suspension is centrifuged at 10,000 g for 5 minutes. The lower phase is removed with a pipet, taking care to avoid contamination with the interface or upper phase. The lower phase (285 ml) is then adjusted to 55% saturation with 33.6 gm of ammonium sulfate. The suspension is mixed for 10 minutes and then centrifuged in the Spinco No. 30 rotor at the 30,000 rpm setting for 15 minutes. The supernatant is discarded and the precipitate dissolved in 15 ml of the standard buffer solution containing 20% glycerol (ammonium sulfate, 20 ml). (The ammonium sulfate fraction is stable for at least 3 days. The purification to this point is completed in 1 day. It should also be noted that this fraction is often greatly inhibitory when amounts in excess of 1–2 μl are used to measure the activity.)

d. *DEAE Fraction.* The ammonium sulfate fraction is dialyzed against 1 liter of standard buffer for 1–2 hours until the conductivity of a 5 × 10^4 dilution is less than 0.1 ppm as NaCl. The dialyzed fraction is then applied to a 3 × 12 cm column of DEAE-cellulose, previously equilibrated with 800 ml of standard buffer. The column is then washed with 100 ml of 0.1 M Tris-HCl, 400 ml of 0.2 M Tris-HCl, 300

---

* The phase top and phase top dialyzed are often greatly inhibitory when amounts in excess of 1–2 μl are used to measure the activity.

ml of 0.25 M Tris-HCl, 400 ml of 0.3 M Tris-HCl, and 100 ml of 0.5 Tris-HCl, all pH 7.5 and containing 0.005 M MgCl$_2$ and 0.005 M 2-mercaptoethanol. A flow rate of 5 ml per minute is maintained by slight pressure, and fractions of 100 ml are collected. All of the fractions except that of the 0.1 M Tris eluate are concentrated by the addition of solid ammonium sulfate to 55% saturation. The precipitates are collected by centrifugation at 30,000 g for 10 minutes and dissolved in 5 ml of standard buffer in 20% glycerol. The enzyme activity appears in the final 0.25 M and 0.3 M Tris eluate fractions. (The bulk of the DNA-dependent RNA polymerase is found in the 0.5 M Tris eluate.) Fractions with a specific activity greater than 50 are pooled (DEAE-cellulose). (With some batches of DEAE-cellulose, the enzyme has eluted slowly in the 0.2 M effluent with comparable results in terms of recovery and purification.)

e. Hydroxylapatite Fraction. The DEAE fraction is dialyzed for 1–2 hours against 1 liter of standard buffer until the conductivity of a 5×10^4 dilution is less than 0.1 ppm as NaCl. The dialyzed fraction is then applied on a 1.5×4.5 cm column of hydroxylapatite previously equilibrated with 100 ml of standard buffer. The column is then washed with 40 ml of 0.15 M ammonium sulfate, 40 ml of 0.20 M, 40 ml of 0.30 M, 40 ml of 0.4 M, and 20 ml of 0.5 M, all in standard buffer. Fractions of 40 ml are collected and concentrated by addition of solid ammonium sulfate to 70% saturation. The precipitates are collected by centrifugation at 30,000 g for 10 minutes and dissolved in 0.5 ml of standard buffer in 20% glycerol (hydroxylapatite). Two fractions are eluted, both of which must be added to the reaction mixture to obtain maximum activity, one in the 0.15–0.2 M ammonium sulfate eluate and the other in the 0.3–0.5 M eluate. The first fraction, which is completely inactive when assayed alone, contains RNase II, but may be heated at 60°C for 20 minutes to inactivate this RNase. The second fraction, assayed alone, contains approximately 10% of the activity obtained when the two fractions are combined.

IV. Properties of the Qβ-RNA Polymerase

A. GENERAL PROPERTIES

1. Stability

At $-20°C$ the purified fraction has been stable in the standard buffer solution containing 20% glycerol for at least 2 months. The enzyme is very heat sensitive, however, and loses one-half the original activity within 10 minutes at 37°C.

2. Contamination with Other Enzymes

The purified fraction (hydroxylapatite fraction) is completely free of other nucleotide polymerase activities, specifically the DNA polymerase, DNA-dependent RNA polymerase, polynucleotide phosphorylase, or polyriboadenylate polymerase. No *E. coli* RNase I or RNase II activity can de detected by their respective assays (Singer and Tolbert, 1965).

B. REACTION REQUIREMENTS

1. pH Optimum

The pH optimum in 0.1 *M* Tris-HCl buffer is 7.5–8.0. Enzyme activity is inhibited by equivalent concentrations of potassium Tris-maleate buffer, potassium phosphate, potassium maleate, potassium gutarate, or ammonium gutarate buffers.

2. Effect of Metal Ions and Other Reagents

Maximum incorporation is obtained in the presence of 12–16 mM $MgCl_2$. Ten to 20% of this incorporation is obtained in the presence of 4–20 mM $MnCl_2$. The reaction is markedly sensitive to the addition of other divalent metal ions, being almost completely inhibited by 2 mM $CaCl_2$, $NiCl_2$, $CdSO_4$, $CuSO_4$, $ZnSO_4$, or $CoSO_4$. Phosphate is also inhibitory, the activity being reduced by 50% in the presence of 0.02 M potassium phosphate at pH 7.5. The activity is less affected by certain monovalent metal ions, there being 37% inhibition in 0.16 M NaCl and no inhibition in 0.16 M KCl.

Increased activity is not obtained by the addition of polyamines, but rather the reaction is progressively inhibited by increasing concentrations, 0.8, 4.0, and 8.0 mM, of putrescine, spermine, or spermidine.

3. Nucleotide Requirement

The reaction with Qβ-RNA is dependent on the addition of all of the four ribonucleotides, ATP, UTP, GTP, and CTP, the K_s for each being 1–2 $\times$ 10^4 M. In the absence of any one or more of these substrates in the standard reaction there is no significant incorporation. However, in a reaction utilizing poly C (*vide infra*), GTP alone serves as the substrate.

4. Template Requirement

With purified enzyme, the reaction is completely dependent on the addition of RNA. This requirement is markedly specific, utilizing Qβ-

RNA only among those preparations from natural sources that have been tested. Furthermore, the $Q\beta$-RNA must be intact, as may be determined by sedimentation analysis (Haruna and Spiegelman, 1965). The K_s for $Q\beta$-RNA is approximately 1×10^{-6} M. The template requirement is also satisfied by poly C and a variety of copolymers containing cytidylate.

ACKNOWLEDGMENTS

We wish to acknowledge the receipt of *E. coli* Q-13 from Dr. W. Gilbert and of the RNA bacteriophage $Q\beta$ from Dr. S. Spiegelman.

This work was supported in part by grants from the National Institutes of Health (GM-11301 and GM-11936) and the National Science Foundation (GB-5082). Dr. J. T. August is recipient of an Investigatorship of the Health Research Council of the City of New York under contract I-346. This is Communication No. 72 from the Joan and Lester Avnet Institute of Molecular Biology, Albert Einstein College of Medicine, New York, New York.

REFERENCES

Adams, M. H. (1959). "Bacteriophages." Wiley (Interscience), New York.
Albertsson, P.-Å. (1962). *Arch. Biochem. Biophys. Suppl.* 1, p. 264.
Astier-Manifacier, S., and Cornuet, P. (1965). *Biochem. Biophys. Res. Commun.* 18, 283.
August, J. T., Cooper, S., Shapiro, L., and Zinder, N. D. (1963). *Cold Spring Harbor Symp. Quant. Biol.* 28, 95.
August, J. T., Shapiro, L., and Eoyang, L. (1965). *J. Mol. Biol.* 11, 257.
Baltimore, D., and Franklin, R. M. (1962). *Biochem. Biophys. Res. Commun.* 9, 388.
Cline, M. J., Eason, R., and Smellie, R. M. S. (1963). *J. Biol. Chem.* 238, 1788.
Gesteland, R. F. (1966). *J. Mol. Biol.* 16, 67.
Haruna, I., and Spiegelman, S. (1965). *Proc. Natl. Acad. Sci. U.S.* 54, 579.
Haruna, I., Nozu, K., Ohtake, Y., and Spiegelman, S. (1963). *Proc. Natl. Acad. Sci. U.S.* 50, 905.
Ho, P. P. K., and Walters, C. P. (1966). *Biochemistry* 5, 231.
Horton, E., Lui, S. L., Martin, E. M., and Work, T. S. (1966). *J. Mol. Biol.* 15, 62.
Lederberg, J., Cavalli, L. L., and Lederberg, E. M. (1952). *Genetics* 37, 720.
Lust, G. (1966). *J. Bacteriol.* 91, 1612.
Pace, N. R., and Spiegelman, S. (1966). *Proc. Natl. Acad. Sci. U.S.* 55, 1608.
Plagemann, P. G. W., and Swim, H. E. (1966). *J. Bacteriol.* 91, 2327.
Shapiro, L., and August, J. T. (1965). *J. Mol. Biol.* 11, 272.
Singer, M., and Tolbert, G. (1965). *Biochemistry* 4, 1319.
Weissmann, C. (1965). *Proc. Natl. Acad. Sci. U.S.* 54, 202.
Weissmann, C., Simon, L., and Ochoa, S. (1963). *Proc. Natl. Acad. Sci. U.S.* 49, 407.
Weissmann, C., Borst, P., Burdon, R. H., Billeter, M. A., and Ochoa, S. (1964). *Proc. Natl. Acad. Sci. U.S.* 51, 890.
Wilson, R. G., and Bader, J. P. (1965). *Biochim. Biophys. Acta* 103, 549.

4 Immunological Techniques for Animal Viruses

Jordi Casals

I. Introduction

A. Classification of the Immunological Techniques

The basis for the immunological techniques employed in the study of animal viruses is the same as for all other microorganisms, namely, an antigen–antibody reaction. Invasion, either in nature or artificially induced, of a competent host by a virus antigen results in production of an antibody that can react with the antigen that gave rise to it, or with related antigens, in a variety of ways. It is precisely the manner of visualization of the reaction that results in the different types of tests or techniques.

Combination of the antibody with the antigen may be observed by the fact that some of the biological properties of the antigen have been altered. Thus, the virus antigen is no longer capable of inducing lesions or disease in a usually susceptible host or system, appearing as though the virus has been destroyed or neutralized, neutralization test, or the host protected as a result of immunization, challenge test. Another biological change induced by the antibody consists in the inability of the virus to react with receptors on the surface of some types of erythrocytes, bringing about their agglutination or their adsorption onto the surface of cells grown in cultures infected by the virus. These tests are designated, respectively, the hemagglutination-inhibition (HI) test and the hemadsorption-inhibition test.

In another approach an attempt is made to visualize the actual antigen–antibody complex. The formation of an aggregate or lattice results in particles of a larger size than those of either reagent. Such aggregates tend to settle out of solution and precipitate, and the test thus originated is a precipitation test. There are, however, only few instances with animal viruses in which precipitates can be observed without special devices. Usually the reaction is noted by trapping and accumulating the precipitate in a semisolid medium, which allows diffusion of the uncombined reagents but not of the aggregate, immunodiffusion tests. Or one of the reagents, usually the antigen, is first caused to be adsorbed onto the surface of certain particles or cells that, following contact and reaction with the antibody, will agglutinate and sediment, resulting in an agglutination test.

An antigen–antibody complex can also be detected if one of the reagents, the antibody, is tagged or conjugated with a substance that has physical properties easily observable by means other than visible light; the fluorescent-antibody technique is rapidly becoming increasingly applied to animal virology, both as a diagnostic tool and as a means for basic studies on localization of antigens in the cell. The use of radioactive isotopes tagged to one of the reagents, while having at present limited application, is a method that may be useful in the future.

A third type of technique extensively used in the serological study of animal viruses is the complement-fixation (CF) test. Viral antigen–antibody aggregates share with other such nonviral aggregates the property of combining with the complement. There is no difference between this test as used with viral agents or their soluble products and its use in general microbiology; any differences reside almost uniquely in the nature of the antigens and their preparation.

B. General Principles and Applications

The immunological techniques are used to detect and identify either the antigen or the antibody; when the antigen is the unknown, it is necessary that reference-typing antisera be available and, conversely, to settle the presence and identity of antibodies, reference antigens are required.

1. *The Diagnostic Problem*

Often the diagnostic problem is not, strictly speaking, the identification of an entirely unknown reagent originating in nature but rather the detection of the presence or absence of a known system, such as the progression and distribution of a given virus experimentally inoculated to an animal or in a cell culture; or whether a certain schedule of immunization results in development of antibodies in a given species and at what rate. In these instances, the diagnostic problem is simple in that, barring contaminants, only one antigen and one immune serum, with the necessary controls, need be considered. In other instances, however, when a real diagnostic problem is involved, such as when a viral isolate from man or lower animals in nature is submitted for identification, or when a serum of similar origins is to be analyzed for the presence of antibodies, then the problem of immunological identification becomes extremely complex owing to the large number of viruses known, which at present is well over 400 (Table I). Even if the identification is to be limited to a given group—enteroviruses, arthropod-borne viruses—the number of serotypes against which the unknown is to be matched is large. A requisite for a laboratory that has a diagnostic function is a collection of reference reagents, viruses, antigens, and immune sera, as complete as possible within its specialized domain.

2. *Immunological Cross-Reaction*

Whether the unknown is the antigen or the antibody there is a circumstance that further complicates the diagnostic problems, namely, the existence of immunological cross-reactions among different viruses. Viruses may share antigens with one another; consequently the immune response of a host being directed against all the antigenic constituents of a virus will give rise to an immune serum that will react not only with the infecting or injected agent but, to a certain extent, with all those agents that share antigens with it. The immune response is particularly deceiving in cases of superinfections in nature, when, as has been noted with influenza viruses, exposure to late or recent strains results in development of antibodies not only against them but mainly against the strain that first infected the host (Francis, 1959) ; or, as observed experimentally in the arboviruses, when inoculations of two different viruses of an antigenic group in succession results in antibodies against all the viruses of the group (Casals, 1961).

While cross-reactions among viruses may, on the one hand, complicate a diagnostic problem, they can, on the other, be of considerable assistance in solving it. Generally the degree of serological overlap between viruses depends, among other reasons, on the type of test used, some agents cross-reacting widely in one test and less so or not at all in another. This fact often permits placement of an isolate in one of the large divisions or subdivisions of the animal viruses by means of one test and its specific identification by means of another. An adenovirus (Ginsberg, 1962) and a reovirus (Rosen, 1960a) can be serologically identified as such by means of the CF test using a single serum, while the specific serotype is decided by neutralization or HI tests. An arbovirus belonging in groups A or B can be placed in either group with relative ease by means of the HI test and specifically identified within the group by CF or neutralization tests.

3. *Prime Strains*

A diagnostic difficulty converse to that deriving from cross-reactions among viruses owes to the existence of variation resulting in prime strains (Melnick, 1957). A prototype immune serum may fail to react by neutralization test with a given strain of this particular serotype if the strain happens to be a prime strain; on the other hand, the antiserum against the prime strain reacts equally well with both prime and prototype. In the CF test, however, prime and prototype strains cross-react amply. Prime strains illustrate a situation in which a specific diagnosis may be missed owing to a lack of cross-reactivity between strains; they are also an additional example of viruses that cross-react fully in one test and only partially in another.

4. *Virus Classification*

A virus is submitted for immunological identification usually after it has been propagated serially in a laboratory system; on occasion, however, the antigen is diagnosed in the original, natural material. Diagnosis of rabies virus infection by the fluorescent-antibody technique applied to the salivary glands of the naturally infected animals (Goldwasser *et al.*, 1959) is now a common practice; Japanese encephalitis has been identified in a fatal human case by preparing a complement-fixing antigen with the victim's brain tissue (Sabin, 1947); and typing of polioviruses can be done concomitantly with their isolation. With these and similar exceptions, however, the problem confronting a serologic diagnostic laboratory is to identify an established virus rather than to isolate it.

The proper application of immunological methods to the identification of animal viruses requires the knowledge of some of the properties of the viruses other than the serological; this knowledge, in turn, can be used as a basis for classification. While the use of new principles— type of nucleic acid, symmetry, envelope, size—for the classification of viruses is described elsewhere (Vol. 4), the adoption at this point of a grouping based in part on those principles will facilitate the critical and proper use of the immunological techniques.

TABLE I

GROUPS OF ANIMAL VIRUSES

Name	Number of serotypes[a]	Remarks
Adenovirus	45	28 of human origin, common CF antigen
Arbovirus	190–200	About 20–22 antigenic groups and many ungrouped
Herpesvirus	15	Some share antigens
Myxovirus	27+	Some viruses have subtypes; antigens shared among some of the types
Papovavirus	4–10	Number varies depending on criteria for analysis
Picornavirus	156	Little antigenic cross-reaction
Poxvirus	6+	Large number are of lower animal origin
Reovirus	3	Common CF antigen

[a] The number of distinct serotypes is, in most groups, approximate.

Table I summarizes the current known animal viruses and their distribution in families or groups, classified on the basis of some of their basic, structural properties. Exceptions to this criterion for grouping are the arboviruses, which are classed together by a common biological characteristic rather than by chemical and physical properties. Regardless of the grounds for the establishment of the large divisions, the basis for deciding on the individuality of a given isolate is always serological. On this basis, the number of presently recognized serotypes within the animal viruses can be conservatively estimated at around 450. This number includes only viruses that can affect higher vertebrates—birds and mammals—which alone are considered in this chapter.

In the orderly process of identification an agent is first placed in one of the larger groups or divisions, next in an antigenic group or type and, finally, established either as a new isolate of an old virus or as a new virus. While placement of a virus in some of the larger divisions can be done by serological methods—adenoviruses, reoviruses—it is based usually on properties other than serological.

a. *Isolation.* The circumstances of isolation are useful in giving an early orientation. Granted that viruses belonging in several different groups (Table I) may be found in a given secretion, excretion, or organ and that viruses of one of the groups may turn up in several distinct locations, the fact remains that it is more likely that adenoviruses, myxoviruses, and picornaviruses rather than arboviruses will be isolated from throat washings and swabs; enteroviruses and reoviruses will most often be recovered from feces and rectal swabs; and one expects to isolate herpes, herpes zoster, and smallpox from typical vesicles. From organs at postmortem the CNS will yield arboviruses, polioviruses, rabies, or herpes, while isolations of influenza viruses or other myxoviruses are unlikely. On investigation of extrahuman sources, arthropod's tissues will ordinarily yield arboviruses rather than other viruses. Isolations taking place during the course of an epidemic or epizootic can often be channeled in the right direction by virtue of the clinical manifestations, signs, and ecological considerations.

b. *Type of Propagation.* An important factor in facilitating recognition is the host animal or tissue culture in which the isolate has been established and the type of lesions it produces; propagation in a particular system may serve to eliminate the likelihood that the isolate belongs in a given group. Thus propagation in an animal host—mouse, guinea pig—would indicate that the isolate is not an adenovirus; multiplication in monkey or human kidney cell cultures with or without clear cytopathic effect but with hemadsorption of guinea pig erythrocytes is likely to be due to a myxovirus; multiplication in tissue cultures with formation of multinucleated cells or syncytia will be indicative of some of the myxoviruses.

c. *Susceptibility to Ether or Sodium Deoxycholate.* A very important property, one that is easy to determine and that allows the placement of an agent in some groups or families while completely eliminating the others from further consideration, is the resistance or susceptibility of viruses to the action of ether or sodium deoxycholate (Andrewes and Horstmann, 1949; Theiler, 1957). This property is linked with the presence of an envelope with essential lipids, one of the basic criteria for viral classification (Lwoff *et al.,* 1962). The ether test is performed by preparing a suspension of virus, to which is added diethyl ether (20%, v/v); the mixture is kept at 4°C for 18–20 hours, with shaking at intervals, after which the suspension is titrated for virulence at the same time as a sample of the same viral suspension kept without ether. A resistant virus shows no loss of infective titer; in fact, it may increase somewhat by the action of sodium deoxycholate (Theiler, 1957). Resistant viruses are adenoviruses, papovaviruses, picornaviruses, and reoviruses. Susceptible viruses are arboviruses, herpesviruses, and myxoviruses. Poxviruses appear to be divided, some reported as sensitive, others as susceptible.

d. Other Characterization Procedures. Additional steps in the family characterization include determination of symmetry, size, and arrangement of capsomeres (Horne, 1963) and determination of nucleic acid type by investigating, for example, the effect of 5-fluoro-2-deoxyuridine or 5-bromo-2-deoxyuridine on viral multiplication in tissue cultures, multiplication of DNA viruses being inhibited by these compounds while that of RNA viruses is not (Hamparian *et al.,* 1963). These physical and biochemical procedures are described elsewhere in this treatise.

5. Immunological Identification

Once a virus has been placed in one of the large divisions (Table I), the process of specific identification is continued and concluded by means of immunological techniques. Placement in a division has the advantage of limiting considerably the extent of the immunological testing required, since it is assumed that viruses belonging in one family as defined by Lwoff *et al.* (1962) will not belong in a different one antigenically.

The type of immunological test used depends in part on the stage of the identification. In fact, there are occasions when immunological tests are used for placing a virus in a family before its structural properties are determined. This may be because it is not practical to conduct the physical and chemical determinations necessary; or the family is probably heterogeneous with respect to those properties, as appears to be the case with the arbovirus group, although not much work has been reported along these lines. In some cases, as has been noted with the adenoviruses and reoviruses, an immunological property is so characteristic of the family that its presence is considered proof for inclusion.

Within some of the divisions listed in Table I there exist subdivisions variously designated as antigenic groups, types, or subgroups.

These subdivisions are either based exclusively on common antigenic constituents shared by the different agents, as with the arboviruses and influenza viruses, or the viruses share antigenic constituents in addition to having other determining properties, such as some of the subdivisions in the picornaviruses, foot-and-mouth disease viruses (Shahan, 1962), or the poxviruses (Downie and Dumbell, 1956; Woodroofe and Fenner, 1962).

After the family and the subdivisions have been settled, the final step in the identification is the determination of the specific serotype, either by matching an existing type or failing to do so by establishing a new one. It is possible to carry the characterization of an agent even beyond the stage of serotype determination by means of a finer analysis using adequate, sensitive techniques; the result is the detection of antigenic variants of which abundant examples have been described, for example, influenza (Jensen and Francis, 1953a), poliomyelitis (McBride, 1959; Plotkin et al., 1961), arboviruses (Casals, 1964; Clarke, 1964), and echoviruses (Melnick, 1957).

It is evident from the preceding paragraphs that depending on the stage of serologic identification, the type of test—and of immune reagent—will vary. That technique will be used that gives the wider antigenic coverage or cross-reactivity when the problem is to place an agent in a family, for inclusiveness of the test is the reason for its use at this stage. Then, in descending order of extent of overlap, tests or techniques will be used that can place the agent in an antigenic group, type, or subgroup and, finally, match it with a specific serotype. This gradation in serologic tests does not necessarily apply to all the groups listed in Table I; however, even where it is only partially operative, it is of considerable help.

6. *Properties of Virus Groups in Choice of Immunological Tests*

Some of the properties of the different groups of animal viruses determine the choice of immunological tests and reagents to be used; for this reason a brief description is given of pertinent ones.

A. Adenoviruses. All adenoviruses thus far known have a common complement-fixing antigen, except the avian adenolike strain. As a result, the most useful single procedure for placing an agent in the family or for diagnosing adenoviral infection is the CF test; one single human convalescent serum suffices as reference (Ginsberg, 1962). Hemagglutination-inhibition and neutralization tests are type specific; when cross-reactions occur (Rosen et al., 1962), they are much less marked than the homologous ones.

b. Arboviruses. There is no known antigenic constituent common to all the arboviruses. There are, however, antigens shared by some of the viruses, as a consequence of which they can be assembled in antigenic groups (Casals, 1957). By definition an antigenic group is made up of all the viruses that show a relationship by any immunological technique; on occasion, however, a virus from a group shows a distant relationship with a virus or viruses from another. While, strictly speaking, these groups should thereby be combined into one, there are practical reasons for maintaining them as separate. There are now 21 or 22 groups (Casals and Clarke, 1965), each with from 2 to 35 viruses; in addition, about 50 viruses are ungrouped.

The relative degree of overlap noted in each group varies with the test used, particularly with the *in vitro* tests. The gradation of overlap given by the different tests is not uniform in all the groups, consequently, a test that is used for grouping with one group may be used for specificity determination with another. Furthermore, since considerable cross-reactivity is observed in some tests between distinct agents, quantitative comparison of the strain under investigation with different serotypes is more to be advised in this family than in others.

The procedure generally followed to characterize an arbovirus consists in attempting to place it in an antigenic group by HI and CF tests using an antigen prepared with the unknown virus and polyvalent-group sera. With a minimum number of polyvalent sera, ideally one for each group, it should be possible to place the unknown agent in one of the groups or to decide that it belongs among the ungrouped, thereby limiting subsequent investigation to the pertinent sector.

The nature and degree of cross-reactivity vary within the groups and determine the particular type of test to be used at each step. As an example, viruses in groups A and B show the most overlap by HI, less by CF, and least of all by the neutralization test by the intracerebral route of inoculation, preferably in newborn mice or in tissue cultures (Casals, 1963; Price *et al.*, 1963; Porterfield, 1961). Therefore, HI test is advised for grouping these viruses and the other tests for type-specific determination.

c. Herpesviruses. This group of large DNA-containing, ether-sensitive viruses (Andrewes, 1962) has about 15 distinct serotypes, 4 of which are of human medical interest, herpes, B virus, varicella-zoster, and human cytomegaloviruses. On the basis of biological behavior in tissue cultures, a division into two subgroups has been suggested (Melnick *et al.*, 1964). There is no common antigenic constituent known to link the entire group; it appears, however, that the six members of one of the subgroups, particularly herpes, B virus, and pseudorabies, show a relatively close antigenic relationship by CF test,

less so by neutralization test. In general, however, to include immunologically a virus in this group it will be necessary to have recourse to
immune reagents prepared with each of the distinct viruses; hence inclusion in the group and determination of serotype go hand in hand.
Any of a number of tests has been used, CF, neutralization, and, particularly with herpes virus, fluorescent-antibody technique (Biegeleisen
et al., 1959).

   d. *Myxoviruses.* From a serological diagnostic viewpoint this is a
complex group. Some of the viruses, such as influenza A, show much
antigenic variation while others, such as mumps and measles, show little; in addition, a fairly large number of agents originating in lower
animals, the avian leukoses group, has not been as yet sufficiently investigated serologically.

   By definition myxoviruses (Andrewes et al., 1955; Andrewes, 1962)
contain RNA, have a medium to large size, and are ether susceptible.
Many have the capacity to cause hemagglutination of erythrocytes of
various animal species and hemadsorption in tissue cultures; blocking
of these actions by immune sera has given a most useful tool for antigenic studies of the agents.

   There are between 20 and 30 serotypes in this family, depending on
the criteria adopted for classification and on the uncertainty with respect to the typing of some of the agents deriving from lower animals.
Following Andrewes (1962), three subgroups are included in the family: influenza, paramyxoviruses, and other myxoviruses.

   The influenza subgroup includes three distinct, immunologically
quite unrelated viruses, A, B, and C; each has a type-specific, soluble
CF antigen common to all the strains of that virus or type. Within
each of the three types, groups or families of strains occur specifically
separable by HI, neutralization, or CF with the viral rather than the
soluble antigen, the degree of separation between groups or among
strains of a group varying widely, depending on epidemiologic circumstances but also on the method of study. Francis (1959) stated that by
selective procedures differences can be shown between almost any two
strains (Jensen, 1957).

   Within the paramyxovirus subgroup are included (Andrewes, 1962)
parainfluenza types 1, 2, 3, and 4, mumps, Newcastle disease virus
(NDV), and myxovirus Yucaipa. Diagnostic interpretations of antigenic studies are complicated in this subgroup by two facts. First, there
is a community of antigenic components among several of the serotypes in the subgroup, particularly mumps, NDV, and some of the parainfluenzas; however, these common antigens are not shared by all the
types in the subgroup, hence they cannot be used as a certain basis for

inclusion. The second complexity derives from the existence of strains isolated from lower animals, mouse, pig, monkey, and cow, which are related to one or another of the parainfluenzas, but still are antigenically separable from them; the question is whether they are to be considered as distinct viruses or not.

Among the remaining myxoviruses or presumed myxoviruses, there exist certain antigenic associations that result in serological groups. These relationships, more marked in some instances than in others, are detected mainly by neutralization and CF tests. Among these relationships are measles, canine distemper, and rinderpest (Warren, 1960) with, as far as is known, a single type of measles, while there may be some variation with the other two viruses; respiratory syncytial virus (Coates et al., 1963), with two serotypes separable by neutralization test; and the group of the avian leucoses, including lymphomatosis, erythroblastosis, and Rous sarcoma virus. Rabies is now considered a myxovirus; no variation of strains capable of causing diagnostic problems has been reported nor has any relationship between this and any other virus been found. Finally, among the myxoviruses are also included an additional six to eight viruses of lower animals, among which are the hog cholera complex and African swine fever virus. None of these is antigenically related to the preceding ones.

As a consequence of the sharp antigenic separation shown by some of the members of this family, as well as the presence of partial cross-reactions shown by others, it is evident that a specific diagnosis of a myxovirus may present considerable complications. It seems evident that in the end a typing serum against each of the 20–30 presently known members of this family is required to establish a specific antigenic diagnosis; this without going into the possible study of strain specificity.

The type of test to be used with these agents varies with the agent. With influenza viruses, the CF test with soluble antigen is recommended; with parainfluenzas, mumps, and NDV, hemadsorption and hemadsorption-inhibition tests are easily performed. Rabies has been diagnosed most effectively by means of the fluorescent-antibody technique (Goldwasser et al., 1959).

e. *Papovaviruses.* The group so designated by Melnick (1962) consists of DNA-containing viruses, with cubic symmetry, small size, and resistance to ether (Virus Subcommittee, 1963). On the whole, the agents in the group have had little participation as cause of disease of man or domestic animals. These viruses are of considerable interest, however, in that they are in general endowed with oncogenic properties, either in the original species from which they were isolated, or, more commonly, in hosts other than their natural ones (Melnick, 1962). In addition, these agents are not infrequently encountered in the course of studies with other viruses, as contaminants in tissue cultures or experimental animals. Their serological recognition is therefore important. The group when first described consisted of four viruses, Shope's rabbit papilloma, human wart papilloma, mouse polyoma, and simian vacuolating agent SV40; subsequently about six other viruses were added to the group.

Owing to the sharp antigenic demarcation and lack of distinct variants, specific diagnosis of some of the agents of the group, such as polyoma and SV40 viruses, should offer no difficulties by means of standard procedures, HI, neutralization, and CF tests. Diagnosis of other viruses, such as human papilloma, is, on the other hand, handicapped by lack of a suitable or dependable system for experimental propagation.

f. Picornaviruses. Following the scheme of the International Committee on Nomenclature (Virus Subcommittee, 1963), viruses in this group are characterized by the presence of RNA in their virion, small size, cubic symmetry, and resistance to ether. Based on these properties, included in this group are not only over 100 agents of human origin and about 40 from lower animals but also some plant viruses.

On the basis of biological considerations, this family has been divided into several subgroups. While these considerations are not seemingly grounded on known physicochemical properties and in some ways are irrelevant, the subdivisions are nevertheless worth keeping at this time, since knowledge concerning them facilitates the path to a specific diagnosis. The group and its subdivisions are given in Table II.

Application of immunological tests to the study of the group presents great complexity because of the large number of viruses involved. Since, with rare exceptions, the serological reactions of all the members are sharply specific and therefore there are no antigens common to the members of any of the subdivisions, no stepwise process of identification, such as is applied to some of the other viral families, is possible with this group. Whatever the procedure used, each serotype has to appear in the matching process, either by inoculating animal donors of immune sera with multiple antigens or by having each individual specific serum present in the serum pools (Schmidt *et al.*, 1961; Lim and Benyesh-Melnick, 1960) devised to facilitate and expedite the identification. Even assuming that only the viruses of human origin are considered, their number is over 100 and will probably increase, particularly among rhinoviruses; this alone is a large enough number against which to type an unknown isolate. But the fact remains that the viruses of lower-animal origin cannot be left out of consideration, if for no other reason than because some of the species from which they derive are sources of tissue culture cell systems used in the study of agents of more immediate interest; hence, such viruses can appear as contaminants in those systems. Furthermore, the use of mice as experimental animals makes it necessary to be constantly on the alert for possible contamination of materials with encephalomyocarditis and murine encephalomyelitis viruses. It is therefore obvious that means to identify each of the picornaviruses must be available at a specialized diagnostic center.

TABLE II

PICORNAVIRUS GROUP[a]

Subdivisions	Number of serotypes	Remarks[b]
Human origin		
Enteroviruses		
Polioviruses	3	Pathogenic for monkeys and simian and human TC
Coxsackie viruses A	24	Pathogenic for mice
Coxsackie viruses B	6	Pathogenic for mice and simian and human TC
ECHO viruses	30	Pathogenic for simian TC
Rhinoviruses	53[c]	
Lower animal origin		
Porcine enteroviruses	9	Includes Teschen and Talfan viruses
Bovine enteroviruses	7	
Simian enteroviruses	7	
Feline enteroviruses	1	
Avian enteroviruses	1	
Murine encephalomyocarditis	1	
Murine encephalomyelitis	2	
Foot-and-mouth disease	7	
Swine vesicular exhanthem	4	
Equine respiratory virus	1	

[a] Based on Andrewes, 1962, and on criteria adopted by the International Enteroviruses Study Group, 1963.

[b] Characteristic pathogenicity of majority of strains.

[c] Hamparian et al., 1964.

Certain biological properties are useful, since their detection can reduce the number of serological tests to be performed with viruses of human origin. The majority of rhinoviruses require for their isolation either embryonic human kidney cell cultures or human diploid cells (H types) in roller cultures at 33°C and pH 6.8–7.3; others, the M types, can be isolated in monkey kidney cells under similar conditions. In general, members of this subgroup do not do well at 37°C and pH 7.6 or higher, conditions that are favorable for the enteroviruses. Rhinoviruses are easily inactivated at pH 3–5, while enteroviruses withstand the treatment under similar conditions. The rhinoviruses are almost exclusively isolated from the nose and throat, while enteroviruses are isolated also from feces or rectal swabs. Finally, while it is possible to adapt the H strains to cells other than the human embryonic or diploid, such as HeLa cells, both H and M strains can be propagated only in tissue cultures. The enteroviruses can be grouped, with few exceptions, in the four subdivisions shown in Table II on the basis of pathogenicity of strains for monkeys, mice, HeLa cell cultures, and monkey kidney cultures.

If the biological properties enumerated place an isolate in a subdivision, serological typing can proceed with a substantially reduced number of immune sera. There are hardly any diagnostic difficulties arising from cross-reactivity among serotypes, particularly with the human serotypes. A positive reaction at the reasonably expected titer with a typing serum in any of the standard tests is diagnostic. There is evidence of cross-reaction between polioviruses types 1 and 2 by CF and neutralization tests. Among Coxsackie viruses, crossings with human sera, less so with those of experimentally immunized animals, have been observed between several type A viruses, but hardly any with type B agents. ECHO viruses types 1 and 8 share antigenic constituents between them, and types 12 and 13 do so to a lesser extent. With the rhinoviruses (Hamparian et al., 1964) studied by neutralization test with guinea pig immune sera, strict specificity is the rule; in fact, specificity occurs even with human sera from adults who may have had broad experience with other serotypes of these agents.

A diagnostic difficulty that may arise with echoviruses by neutralization test owes to the presence of prime strains. Since for the identification of echoviruses the neutralization test is widely, almost exclusively, used, prime strains could be missed. However, they share CF antigens with the prototype, so that with this test antisera against the prototype can be used for typing prime strains. Prime strains have been reported with ECHO viruses types 1, 4, 5, 6, and 8.

An additional aid to the identification of enteroviruses of human origin follows from the fact that some of them agglutinate human O erythrocytes and one of them chicken erythrocytes (Goldfield et al., 1957; Rosen and Kern, 1961). The viruses thus acting are Coxsackies A7, 20, 21; and 24; Coxsackies B1, 3, and 5; and ECHO viruses 3, 6, 7, 11, 12, 13, 19, 20, 21, 24, and 29.

g. *Poxviruses.* In this group are included a fairly large number of viruses causing pox diseases in various animal species. While the number described reaches almost 20 or 25, the fact remains that within each of the four or five subgroups the different agents are very closely related serologically by all types of tests, with the result that each can be considered, on antigenic grounds, either as made up of distinct but closely related viruses or as an individual virus with a number of antigenic variants. The viruses in the group are of the DNA type, with helical symmetry and a lipid envelope (Andrewes, 1962). With respect to ether sensitivity, some members are reported to be partly or completely ether sensitive while most are ether resistant. These viruses are large (200–300 mμ) and are described as brick shaped. Placement in this family is not difficult, since the viruses derive from pathologic conditions of man or animals that are rather typical and characteristic. In addition, their large size, easily detectable by simple centrifugation or filtration, as well as the pocks shown on chorioallantoic membranes of embryonated hen's eggs, facilitate their preliminary identification.

There are included in the group the following subgroups: (1) variola-type viruses, including smallpox, alastrim, vaccinia, cowpox, ectromelia, and monkey and rabbit poxes; (2) avian poxviruses, canary pox, fowlpox, and pigeon and turkey poxes; (3) a group of poxviruses of mammals other than group 1, including poxes of horse, goat, sheep, swine, and camel; also pustular dermatitis of sheep and bovine lumpy skin disease; (4) a group including rabbit myxoma and rabbit and squirrel fibromas.

All of the agents in each of subdivisions 1, 2, and 4 are closely related antigenically within the subdivision, so that a single serum for each subdivision would suffice for the diagnosis; there are no cross-reactions between the subdivisions. The serological relationships among the members of subgroup 3 are not clearly defined; cross-reactions between some of the members of the subgroup and some of those in subgroup 1 have been reported (Andrewes, 1962), mainly by CF and agar-gel precipitation.

h. Reoviruses. This group consists of three serotypes having a common CF antigen, but separable by neutralization and HI tests. The agents have been isolated from man, especially children with diarrhea or mild respiratory infections, and from a variety of domestic, wild, and laboratory animals. The fact that mice can be affected by at least one of the reoviruses, type 3, or murine hepatoencephalitis is to be borne in mind when using this experimental animal. All strains of each type are undistinguishable serologically, whether isolated from man or lower animals. Owing to the ease of diagnosis by CF, these agents do not represent a major diagnostic problem. In addition to the common antigen, reoviruses as a family are characterized by presence of RNA, cubic symmetry, medium size, and resistance to ether.

i. Other Viruses. The preceding groups include most of the recognized animal viruses experimentally propagated. A few additional ones, however, that do not seem to fit in any of the groups must not be overlooked in the course of immunological tests; among these agents are lymphocytic choriomeningitis, rubella, Chang's lipovirus (1964), and several "slow viruses" (Gajdusek *et al.*, 1965).

C. Preparation of Biological Reagents: Immune Sera and Antigens

Immune reagents—sera and ascitic fluids—are used in all immunological tests; antigens, as understood in this section, are used in *in vitro* tests, particularly CF and HA tests.

1. *Immune Reagents*

Reference sera for viral serotypes are described as immune, hyperimmune, or convalescent. Often these designations are employed to indicate that the donor animal has been inoculated, respectively, once or twice, many times, or once with ensuing illness with recovery followed by antibody development. On other occasions, the terms "immune" and "hyperimmune" are used to indicate, respectively, a serum with low or moderate titer as contrasted with one having a high titer.

It is generally observed that repeated inoculations of a virus suspension to an animal result in a serum differing in its reactivity from a serum deriving from an animal inoculated only once with an antigen that does not multiply and cause disease. The former has a higher titer, a stronger capacity to combine with the antigen *in vitro*, and, when pertinent, greater and more extensive cross-reactivity with related viruses. The greater immunological reactivity of the host animal in the course of the secondary immune response is desirable as a means of increasing the antibody yield; it results, however, in sera that are less specific within the antigenic group concerned.

The extent of cross-reactivity shown by experimentally produced immune sera is also influenced by the time elapsed between vaccination and bleeding. In the early phase of a primary immune response the antibodies are particularly specific, while later the specificity declines.

The overlap among related viruses given by a serum depends also on the test used. Thus, as already stated, all adenoviruses are related by CF test, but not by neutralization or HI tests; a similar situation occurs with the reoviruses. In some groups of arboviruses a serum cross-reacts widely by HI and less by CF, while in other groups the converse is true.

A factor to consider in the preparation of immune reagents is the existence of nonspecific serological reactions that may appear as a result of the vaccinating procedure. These reactions particularly affect the CF test and relate ordinarily to the development of organ-specific antibodies or antibodies against the tissues or proteins present in the medium in which the viruses are propagated. These reactions have not been found to affect either the neutralization or HI tests, but can interfere with precipitin tests in agar gel. The simplest way to prevent such complications is to use a homologous system for the preparation of sera, i.e., to immunize with the virus propagated in tissue or proteins from the same species to which the serum donor belongs, particularly when repeated inoculations are given. If this is not possible, then the number of injections and the mass of foreign material is to be reduced to a minimum; or, preferably, a convalescent serum is prepared by means of a single injection of a high dilution of an infectious agent in order that the extraneous materials thus diluted will no longer be antigenically active.

The use of convalescent sera from natural sources, man or lower animals, as typing sera is not without risk of complications. While the current infection is undoubtedly well diagnosed and recognized, the past experience of the individual with other related or unrelated viruses is, at best, vague. As a consequence, when using such sera apparent cross-reactions may be detected or diagnostic false starts can be made. Perhaps a similar objection could be made to the use of wild and domestic animals brought into the laboratory when adult— monkeys, horses, pigs—to be used as subjects for immunization. While in these instances pretesting of the sera against the agents with which the animals are to be immunized is done, it is nevertheless impractical to test each animal against all families of viruses; hence, unexpected serologic results must be carefully investigated before they are accepted.

The use of adjuvants, substances incorporated in the vaccinating antigen, with the result that the host's response is at a higher titer and longer lasting, is now widespread. The most commonly employed are Freund's adjuvants (Freund and McDermott, 1942). They are commercially available in two types, complete, consisting of mineral oil, a heat-killed mycobacterium, and an emulsifying agent; and incomplete, lacking the mycobacterium.

The use of immune ascitic fluid as a substitute for serum has received a great deal of attention in the last few years, particularly when typing antibodies are produced in mice, as is often the case with arboviruses. The mice are immunized as though for the preparation of an immune serum, and at the opportune time the ascitis-producing material is inoculated and the fluid obtained by paracentesis. The antibody titers in the serum and fluid from a mouse are similar, but the yield of fluid is 10–50 times greater.

The manner of preservation or storage of immune reagents is of considerable importance. In many laboratories sera are held at −20°C in an electric deep freezer, often in plastic tubes containing to begin with 8–9 ml; when needed, the serum is thawed out and replaced. This way of handling alters the properties of the sera in the neutralization test by destroying accessory factors (Morgan, 1945; Whitman, 1947); repeated freezing and thawing of a serum over a period of time may also damage antibodies through protein denaturation. The harmful effect of preservation of a serum at an inadequate temperature may not be observable over relatively short periods of time, but it would affect the performance of a reagent when kept for several years. Preferably, sera should be stored at a temperature not higher than −60°C in small amounts in sealed ampules or lyophilized, since then they can be held at 4°C.

A feature of the use of immune sera that has acquired increasing importance with the growing number of serotypes is the development of methods whereby the extent of testing required for identification is reduced. This problem has become particularly acute with enteroviruses, arboviruses, rhinoviruses and adenoviruses. There are basically two methods that have been developed, the one to be used depending on the extent of the natural cross-reactions among the serotypes involved.

When, as with the enteroviruses, there are practically no cross-reactions among the viruses involved with the test used—the neutralization test—it is profitable to prepare specific sera for each serotype and mix them in pools according to predetermined schemes. A given serum appears in more than one pool; the total number of serotypes determines the number of sera in each pool, as well as the number of pools and the combinations required. The goal of these pools is to achieve a specific diagnosis, with a single test, on the basis of the pattern of reaction obtained when the unknown strain, tested against all the pools, reacts with one or more of the pools (Lim and Benyesh-Melnick, 1960; Schmidt et al., 1961). This method has also been applied to the rhinoviruses (Hamparian et al., 1964).

With the arboviruses, the problem has been approached in a different way, by taking advantage of the natural cross-reactions that led to the development of the concept of antigenic groups (Casals, 1961). By inoculating an animal in succession with several viruses of a group, sera can be obtained that react with all the members of the group, particularly by HI, and, by increasing the number of viruses in the immunizing course, by CF and neutralization tests as well. With these group-polyvalent sera unknown viruses can easily be placed in their corresponding group and, through the use of less cross-reacting sera, in a subgroup or complex; in this manner specificity tests need only be done with a few viral systems. This method allows placing a virus in a group with much less effort. With the ungrouped viruses, which now number between 40 and 50, no pool scheme has been devised, mainly because the CF test, which is mostly used for their typing, can be easily performed even with that number of specific sera.

Typing sera for the animal viruses are prepared in monkeys (*M. mulatta*), mice, guinea pigs, and rabbits; other animals, hamsters, white rats, chickens, goats, pigs, and horses, are also used but less frequently. Illustrative schedules of vaccination will be given with viruses of different groups; the number of variations is practically limitless.

a. For Enteroviruses in Monkeys. The following procedure (Wenner *et al.*, 1954; Kamitsuka *et al.*, 1961) has been used extensively and satisfactorily for preparation of type-specific antisera. Monkeys are pretested to determine that antibodies against enteroviruses are absent; vaccination is done with virus emulsified in an adjuvant. The virus is used in the form of infected monkey kidney tissue culture fluid or as a 10 or 20% suspension of infected newborn mouse tissue—torso and limbs—in physiological salt solution with strains of coxsackieviruses that do not cause cytopathic effects (CPE) in tissue culture. The adjuvant consists of 1 part of Arlacel A and 9 parts of standard mineral oil (Bayol F). Equal volumes of virus suspension and adjuvant are mixed by means of an electric mixer, in the cold; the mixture thickens rapidly. With a 20- or 22-gage needle the emulsion is injected into the calf muscles of each leg in 2-ml amounts, four times at 2-week intervals; 2 weeks after the last injection the monkeys are bled. The neutralizing titers of these sera against 100 TCD_{50} of homologous virus range between 1 : 1000 and 1 : 10,000, while those against similar amounts of heterologous viruses are usually less than 1 : 16. Most of these sera have also been satisfactory for typing strains by CF (Schmidt and Lennette, 1961), with the exception of those prepared with the mouse tissue suspensions.

b. For Rhinoviruses in Guinea Pigs. Ketler *et al.* (1962) prepared type-specific sera against 53 viruses in guinea pigs. The viruses are propagated in cultures of the WI-26 strain of human diploid cells, HeLa cells, or green monkey kidney cells. Culture fluids containing between 10^3 and $10^{5.5}$ TCD_{50} per 0.2 ml are treated once with fluorocarbon-113 and emulsified with an equal amount of an adjuvant consisting of 1 part Arlacel A and 9 parts Drakeol. The guinea pigs are inoculated with 1 ml intramuscularly twice, at 6-week intervals, and bled 2 weeks after the second injection. The reported titers of these sera in the neutralization test against 200–2000 TCD_{50} of the homologous strain are 1 : 20–1 : 640.

c. *For Adenoviruses in Rabbits.* Specific typing antisera prepared in rabbits (Rosen, 1960b) are used in the HI and neutralization tests. The supernatant fluids of HeLa or KB cell cultures infected with the virus are freed of the cells and debris by centrifugation at 2000 rpm for 15 minutes, at the time when the cells show advanced CPE; rabbits are given 3 or 4 weekly intravenous injections of the fluid, 1 ml each time, for a period of about 3 weeks and are bled 10 days after the last injection. Somewhat better titers are obtained by freezing and thawing the cell cultures repeatedly, removing the debris by low-speed centrifugation as before, sedimenting the virus by centrifugation at 40,000 rpm for 1–2 hours in an angle-head centrifuge, and emulsifying the pellet in Freund's adjuvant. Three intramuscular injections, each 1 ml, are given at weekly intervals and the rabbits are bled 2 weeks after the last inoculation.

d. *For Parainfluenza Viruses and Reoviruses in Guinea Pigs.* Typing sera for these agents are prepared mainly in guinea pigs using the intranasal route. Since many of these animals may have naturally acquired antibodies against these viruses, they must be pretested, and only those free from antibodies are used (Cook *et al.*, 1959). For immunization, the guinea pigs are placed under light ether anesthesia, and 0.1 ml of infected, undiluted tissue culture fluid is instilled into each nostril; since these viruses multiply in the guinea pig, although without producing overt disease, a high infective titer in the tissue culture fluid is not essential. Following inoculation, the guinea pigs are kept in isolation to avoid spread of the virus to other animals and to prevent their contamination with other reoviruses or parainfluenza viruses. After 2–3 weeks for the reoviruses, the animals are sample bled and tested by HI; if they have satisfactory titers, about 1 : 160 or better with the homologous antigen, 1 : 10 or less with heterologous ones, the animals are bled. With parainfluenza it is recommended that all animals be bled 3–4 weeks after instillation, and a pool is made with the sera of those that have the highest CF titers. In general, the homologous titers against both viral particle antigen "V" and soluble "S" antigen are of the order of 1 : 80–1 : 2560, with heterologous crossings of less than 1 : 10. These sera are also specific by neutralization and HI tests.

e. For Arboviruses in Mice; Immune Ascitic Fluids. The white mouse is the most universal experimental host for the propagation of arboviruses at present known, and the CF technique is much used in the study of these viruses. To forestall nonspecific reactions that would interfere with that test, a homologous system must be used, i.e., the vaccinated animal species must be the same as that which supplies the inoculum. To prepare antisera with arboviruses, repeated injections are often needed. Since, in addition, the CF antigens generally derive from murine tissues, it should be understandable why the mouse is used for the production of immune sera even though the yield per animal is small.

The numerous schedules of immunization differ in detail but can be reduced to two, depending on the type of serum desired: (1) multiple injections of vaccinating antigen with a view to preparing a serum with the highest possible homologous titer and, with grouped viruses, pronounced cross-reactivity, these sera to be used particularly for grouping; and (2) one or two injections of antigen in order to have a serum with maximum specificity within the group, these sera to be used for serotype diagnosis. The following are illustrative examples.

A virus is intracerebrally inoculated into newborn mice 1–5 days old. When sick, the brain tissue is harvested and made into a 10% suspension in 0.9% NaCl. This stock suspension is preferably used freshly made, although it can be kept for a few weeks at −60°C. Mice 4–6 weeks old are selected for immunization. Since a number of arboviruses can kill mice of this age on intraperitoneal inoculation in dilutions of 10^{-1}, 10^{-2}, or even higher, inactivated suspensions are used in such cases for the primary inoculation, to be followed by injections of fully active material. Inactive suspensions are prepared by one of the following methods: (1) Commercial Formalin is added to the 10% stock suspension of virus to a final concentration of 0.5%; this preparation is kept in a glass-stoppered flask at 4°C for a week, at which time it is ready for use. (2) Beta-propiolactone is added to the 10% stock virus suspension at a final concentration of 0.1 or 0.2%; the suspension is heated at 37°C in a water bath for 1 hour and used.

For preparation of multiple-injection sera, the donor mice are intraperitoneally inoculated on days 1 and 3 with 0.3 ml of an inactivated suspension or, if known not to be lethal, of the 10% stock, active virus, in saline. On days 15, 20, and 25, the mice are given, by the same route, 0.3 ml of a 10% virus suspension in saline, freshly prepared or held at −60°C for not longer than 2 or 3 weeks. On day 32 or 33 the mice, under ether anesthesia, are bled by cardiac puncture using a 26-gage needle one quarter of an inch long attached to a 1-ml tuberculin syringe. With some practice 10 ml of serum can be obtained from a group of 40 mice with no more than 8 or 10 mice lost. A second sample of serum can be obtained by giving the surviving mice another injection of virus on day 50 or 55 and bleeding them 7 or 8 days later. Additional inoculations and bleedings can be attempted, but it becomes increasingly harder to bleed the animals successfully.

Sera obtained after five injections have shown with most arboviruses CF titers of 1 : 64–1 : 256 or higher and HI titers, when an antigen is available, of 1 : 1280–1 : 5120 or higher; the neutralization indexes of these sera by mouse intracerebral inoculation test as a rule have values of 100–100,000. Sera obtained after 6 or 7 injections have somewhat higher titers and show more pronounced cross-reactions.

Immune sera of this type, as well as with similarly good CF and neutralizing potency, can be prepared for a greater variety of viruses other than arboviruses that can be propagated in mice, among which are lymphocytic choriomeningitis, rabies, herpes, reovirus type 3 (mouse hepatoencephalitis), mouse polioencephalitis, mouse encephalomyocarditis, Coxsackie viruses A and B (substituting torso and legs for brain tissue as source material), and poliovirus type 2 (MEF 1 strain).

When immune sera are desired with a minimum of cross-reactivity while still having, in many instances, high homologous titers, the schedule of vaccination consists of only one or two injections prior to bleeding. Thus a schedule frequently used consists of an intraperitoneal injection of 0.3 ml of a 10% or a 10^{-2} virus suspension, inactivated or fully virulent, followed by a second similar injection of active virus between days 18 and 22. Bleeding by cardiac puncture under ether anesthesia is done 6 or 7 days after the second injection.

Immunization of mice and guinea pigs can be done with a number of arboviruses, by giving a single intracerebral injection (0.03 ml for mice, 0.1 ml for guinea pigs) of active virus in a dilution of 10^{-2} or 10^{-3} in 0.9% NaCl under anesthesia and bleeding the animals 7 or 8 days later and again 20 or 22 days after the single inoculation. These sera can have high titers, particularly by HI and neutralization tests, and show marked specificity within the corresponding antigenic groups. The procedure is limited to arboviruses that do not kill the hosts following inoculation, but lead, presumably, to viral multiplication. Sera of a similar type have also been obtained with rabbits and monkeys.

While preparation of immune sera in mice is generally satisfactory, it has the serious drawback that the amounts obtainable are limited; the possibility of substituting immune ascitic fluid for serum has been investigated. Munoz (1957) first noted that mice repeatedly inoculated by the intraperitoneal route with Freund's adjuvant and a protein produced large volumes of ascitic fluid containing antibodies against the protein. Various materials, in addition to Freund's adjuvant, have been used to stimulate peritoneal exudate, chiefly sarcoma 180 (Herrmann and Engle, 1958), heat-killed staphylococcus (Lieberman *et al.*, 1959), and a slow-killing strain of sarcoma 180, strain 180/TG (Sartorelli *et al.*, 1965). Generally, the titers of antibodies in the serum and fluid of a mouse are similar. With arboviruses, the mice are vaccinated as for the preparation of an immune serum with five or six injections; depending on the schedule and on the material used for production of ascites, this material is mixed with the viral antigen, either in each injection or in the first and last, or, in the case of sarcoma cells, at the end of the immunizing course only. As soon as the mice show conspicuous swelling of the abdomen, usually 4–10 days after the effective inoculation, the fluid is withdrawn by peritoneal paracentesis. When using staphylococcus or adjuvants the mice develop pronounced peritoneal adhesions, which makes extraction of the fluid time consuming. For extraction an 18- or 20-gage needle, 1 or 1½ inches long, mounted on a 5- or 10-ml syringe is used; ascites production continues in an animal for many days after it first appeared, consequently repeated tapping is indicated. Amounts of fluid obtained vary considerably from one animal to another, but average yields per mouse repeatedly tapped can be as high as 20–50 ml.

2. *Viral Antigens*

This designation is applied here to preparations derived from tissues infected with a virus and used for the identification and study of the virus and antibodies against it in *in vitro* tests, chiefly CF and HI tests. In some cases the antigen can be obtained from the infected host with no manipulation other than that required for harvesting it, for example, when the antigen is an infected allantoic fluid. In other instances the source material has to be subjected to certain procedures that are necessary either to obtain the antigen or to improve it vastly. Often the techniques used remove inhibitors of, or substances interfering with, the antigenic activity, or, by disrupting cell membranes, larger amounts of antigen are released; or, by concentrating antigens that are present and active but in small amounts, make usable otherwise inactive preparations. In general, preparations employed as HA antigens can also be used as CF antigens, with the exceptions noted later.

a. Antigen from Embryos. Newcastle disease virus is an illustration of the simplest method to obtain an antigen from embryonated hen's eggs. Nine- to 11-day-old embryos are inoculated into the allantoic cavity with 0.2 ml of dilution 10^{-2} or 10^{-3} of an allantoic fluid infected with a laboratory-established strain. The eggs are incubated at 36°C for 2 or 3 days; when the embryos are moribund they are chilled to reduce bleeding and the allantoic fluids are harvested. This fluid is the antigen; by HA test the titers range from 1 : 320 to 1 : 2560 and by CF test from 1 : 2 to 1 : 16. The antigen is preserved at —60°C in sealed glass ampules.

A similar procedure supplies HA antigens for the influenza viruses. With strains on primary isolation amniotic fluid is preferable, while later allantoic fluids or pools of both fluids are used. With mumps virus, CF antigens can also be easily obtained from infected chick embryos, using allantoic fluid as viral or "V" antigen; to obtain the soluble or "S" antigen, the allantoic membranes are made into a 20% suspension in 0.9% NaCl, centrifuged at 20,000 rpm for 30 minutes, and the supernatant used.

b. Antigen from Tissue Cultures. Infected tissue cultures are a source of antigen for many animal viruses. The fluid is collected at the time when the cell sheets show advanced destruction and is used as an HA antigen, with no more than low-speed centrifugation to free it from cellular debris. To prepare CF antigens from infected cultures, often the sedimented cells or the entire culture are frozen and thawed several times in order to increase the yield of antigen by causing further cellular disruption. The debris are removed by centrifugation as before. These antigens can be stored at —20°C or lower temperatures.

Hemagglutinating antigens of this type are prepared for adenoviruses (Rosen, 1960b; Zuschek, 1961) using HeLa and KB cells and harvesting the fluids 5–7 days after infection; for CF antigens the fluids are harvested 2 days later and, by combining them with the frozen and thawed cells, titers between 1 : 8 and 1 : 32 are obtained. In a similar manner CF antigens are obtained for respiratory syncytial and measles viruses (Coates *et al.*, 1963) grown in Hep-2 cell cultures.

Antigens for enteroviruses and reoviruses are generally derived from rhesus monkey kidney tissue cultures (Black and Melnick, 1954; Goldfield *et al.*, 1957; Lahelle, 1958; Rosen and Kern, 1961) in medium 199 without serum, or, if necessary, with 5% chicken serum, in order to minimize agglutination of human erythrocytes used in the test. With the reoviruses, the antigen has both CF and HA activity, the latter with titers between 1 : 4 and 1 : 256, the former with somewhat lower titers.

Not all the enteroviruses agglutinate red cells, there being at present only 18 or 20 known to do so, among which are 4 Coxsackies A, 3 or 4 Coxsackies B, and 11–13 ECHO viruses. The capacity to agglutinate depends on temperature of incubation following addition of cells, either 4° or 37°C, and the pH of the medium, some viruses being active at a pH near 5.8, others at pH 7.4. Erythrocytes from a newborn, obtained from the umbilical cord, are generally more sensitive than those from an adult.

With enteroviruses that propagate exclusively or preferentially in newborn mice, antigens are prepared by other methods (see Section I,C,2d).

c. Antigens Obtained by Cell Disintegration. Antigens from tissue cultures are sometimes best obtained by disintegrating the infected cells by physical means. With parainfluenza viruses types 1–4, both HA and CF antigens are prepared (Chanock *et al.,* 1961a; Dick and Mogabgab, 1961) by growing the agents in rhesus monkey tissue cultures. For types 1, 2, and 3, fluid and cells are harvested after 5 or 6 days incubation, and for type 4 after 6–10 days incubation. The cells are thoroughly disintegrated by treatment for 10 minutes at 10 kc in a Raytheon oscillator at 0°C. The suspensions, centrifuged at 2000 rpm for 15 minutes, constitute the antigens; they can be preserved in the frozen state.

d. Antigens from Mouse Tissues. Antigens for the arboviruses are generally prepared from tissues of infected newborn mice, usually brain but also blood serum and liver. Embryonated hen's eggs and tissue cultures have also been employed for the purpose, but the mouse has the advantage that it can be used with nearly all, if not all, these viruses, and the antigens have higher titers. Some of the methods used for the arboviruses are also employed successfully for the preparation of CF antigens with viruses from other groups propagated in newborn mice: mouse encephalomyocarditis, mouse polioencephalitis, reovirus type 3 (mouse hepatoencephalitis), lymphocytic choriomeningitis, rabies, herpes, and poliomyelitis type 2 (strain MEF 1). Complement-fixing antigens can be prepared with Coxsackie viruses of type A, which multiply better in suckling mice than in tissue cultures, and with some of type B, using muscle tissue—torso and legs—from infected newborn mice as source material and some of the methods described in this section.

Preparation of antigens from infected animal organs often requires treatment to eliminate anticomplementary and nonspecific effects in the CF test or inhibitory and nonspecific properties in the HA test. Not all arboviruses yield a HA antigen by the known methods, but with

hardly an exception all give CF antigens. Since brain tissue is generally the source material, the following methods are described as apply
to that tissue.

Mice 1–5 days of age, intracerebrally inoculated with the virus, are
killed by etherization when sick or at the selected time after inoculation; their brains are harvested with forceps and scissors or by aspiration (Strome, 1953) and held in a precipitate's dish or wide-mouthed
tube at −60°C until processed. To harvest blood, cardiac puncture
under anesthesia is used or, with large numbers, the anterior chest wall
and heart are cut open with a pair of sharp scissors and the blood allowed to drop into a test tube. Harvesting of the liver presents no difficulties; to harvest muscular tissue, the head, skin, feet, and viscera
are eliminated, keeping only the torso and legs.

(i) *Alkaline aqueous extraction.* A 10 or 20% suspension of brain tissue
is made in borate–saline buffer pH 9.3 (see Section III,C) using a
homogenizer with an overhead drive and a side port at the bottom
through which the homogenate may be removed without opening the
vessel. The supernatant after centrifugation at 10,000 rpm in a preparatory angle-head centrifuge is the antigen. This simple method yields HA
antigens for numerous arboviruses, particularly those of group B,
especially when followed by treatment with protamine sulfate. Aqueous
extraction with 0.9% NaCl to make a 10% suspension of tissue, followed
by centrifugation at 2500 rpm for 30 minutes, gives good CF antigens,
especially if the suspension is alternately frozen and thawed four or five
times, using solid CO_2 in alcohol, before centrifugation (Casals and
Palacios, 1941).

(ii) *Sucrose–acetone extraction.* Brain tissue is homogenized in
4 ml per gram of a chilled 8.5% solution of sucrose; the homogenate
is added dropwise with mechanical stirring to 20 ml of acetone, analytical reagent grade, per milliliter of homogenate. The mixture is centrifuged at 1500 rpm for 5 minutes, the supernatant is discarded, and
to the sediment is added a volume of new acetone equal to that first
used. The bottles containing the suspension are held for 1 hour in an
ice water bath, after which the sediment is easily dispersed by means
of a motor-driven plunger. The suspension is centrifuged as before, the
supernatant discarded, and the sediment dried under an oil-pump
vacuum. After 2–4 hours the sediment is dry and to it is added a volume of 0.9% solution of NaCl equal to 0.4 the volume of the homogenate. The rehydrated extract after 1 hour or overnight at 4°C is centrifuged in a preparatory angle-head centrifuge at 10,000 rpm for 1
hour. The supernatant, which is the antigen, is kept lyophilized and is

usable in both the HA—if the virus has this activity—and the CF tests (Clarke and Casals, 1958).

(*iii*) *Acetone extraction.* The method is used mainly for preparation of HA antigens from mouse serum, although it can also be used with brain and other tissues. The serum, diluted 1 : 3 or 1 : 4 in distilled water, is added dropwise through a small-gage needle to 20 volumes of acetone, referred to the diluted serum, and kept in motion by stirring with a motor-driven rod. Following centrifugation at 1500 rpm for 5 minutes, the sediment is reextracted twice with a similar volume of acetone as before. After the last extraction, the dry residue is dissolved in a volume of borate–saline buffer pH 9, equal to 5 times the initial volume of serum. Since the residue dissolves completely, no centrifugation is necessary. If this procedure is used for brain or liver, the extracted material is resuspended in a volume of 0.9% NaCl equal to 2 or 3 times the weight of the tissue initially used, and after standing overnight at 4°C, the suspension is centrifuged at 10,000 rpm for 1 hour.

(*iv*) *Protamine sulfate treatment.* This treatment, first used for partial purification of viral preparations (Warren *et al.*, 1949), is used to improve HA antigens, particularly by broadening the pH range of their activity and improving the sedimented pattern. However, since it has different results on different viruses and is in cases harmful rather than beneficial, the treatment must first be tried on a small sample of a preparation. Its use is not recommended for antigens in the CF test, since protamine sulfate makes them anticomplementary and lowers their titer. Protamine sulfate is prepared in a 0.9% NaCl solution at a concentration of 50 mg/ml of the saline solution for use with the organic solvent-extracted antigens or with the 20% unextracted tissue antigens or 25 mg/ml when used with the 10% tissue aqueous antigens. The solution is prepared shortly before use. To the antigen chilled in an ice water bath is added 0.1 volume of the protamine solution. The mixture is held in the ice water bath for 30 minutes, with occasional shaking, and then centrifuged in the cold for 15 minutes at 2500 rpm. The clear supernatant is the antigen.

(*v*) *Additional methods.* Additional methods for preparing antigens from infected, whole animal tissues differ in detail from the ones described; owing to some special features the following two are mentioned.

From torsos and legs. Complement-fixing antigens for the Coxsackie viruses that propagate in newborn mice can be prepared (Contreras *et al.*, 1952) by harvesting the torso and legs when the animals show signs of illness, usually 2 or 3 days after inoculation. The material is homogenized in an electrically driven blender for 3 minutes with two short intermissions, using 10 ml of 0.9% NaCl solution for each mouse. The suspension is centrifuged at 1500 rpm for 10 minutes, and to each 10 ml of the supernatant is added 4 ml of diethyl ether. After vigorous shaking the mixture is kept overnight at 4°C, after which the aqueous phase is collected, the residual ether in solution evaporated under vacuum, and the antigen used or stored at −20°C.

Extraction with fluorocarbon. Extraction of tissues with a fluorocarbon derivative, Arcton 63, has been used for preparation of HA antigens with arboviruses (Porterfield and Rowe, 1960). A 10% suspension of infected mouse brain tissue is made in borate–saline buffer at pH 9. This suspension is added to an equal volume of Arcton 63 and the mixture is shaken by hand for 2 minutes. The material is centrifuged, either immediately or preferably after standing overnight at 4°C, at 10,000 rpm for 1 hour. The supernatant is the antigen.

II. Neutralization Test

Virus and serum are mixed or brought in contact under specified conditions and inoculated to a susceptible host. In the absence of antibodies, the host shows lesions, disease, death, or failure to be infected when challenged by another viral agent that would ordinarily do so. If antibodies are present, the host suffers no such reactions. With manifestations capable of quantitation, the extent is diminished; the host is protected or the virus is neutralized.

This test has been used with the animal viruses longer than other serological tests and its result is generally taken as the final, decisive criterion for identification of the serotype of a viral isolate. It is considered to be the most universally specific of the various tests in use. Certain observed facts, however, place definite qualifications on the specificity as well as on the interpretation of the test's results.

A number of basic principles of the test derived from investigations by, among others, Andrewes and Elford (1933) and Dulbecco et al. (1957). Andrewes and Elford formulated one of the first principles of virological serology with their "percentage law," which states that, with an excess of antibody, when virus is added to antibody the percentage of virus surviving or escaping neutralization is the same regardless of the amount of virus added. Dulbecco et al. (1957), in their study on the kinetics of the reaction, showed that with a small amount of antibody the proportional rate of virus inactivation remained constant during the inactivation of most of the virus. They also observed hat with different concentrations of serum the rate of virus disappearance was directly proportional to the concentration of antibody, and that the logarithm of the percentage of original virus remaining active was inversely proportional to the length of incubation. The same authors, studying the question of dissociation of the virus–antibody complex, found evidence of only a slight degree of dissociation with dilution, even though numerous studies in the past appeared to show that animal viruses were easily reactivated by dilution of neutral mixtures. Finally, they detected a nonneutralizable fraction of the virus. This fraction was not genetically distinct nor was it inherently nonneutralizable (Mandel, 1960).

Additional studies bearing on the basic properties of the test have been reported by Tyrrell and Horsfall (1953), Rubin and Franklin (1957), Mandel (1960), and Westaway (1965). While a complete description of these studies is not indicated here, there are at least two aspects of the reaction that are of considerable importance in the practical use of the test, as follows.

The practical basis of the neutralization test is that the mixture of antibody and virus on inoculation fails to induce lesions or disease in a susceptible host system. It is a matter of fact, however, that a given serum may neutralize a virus to a variable degree and that a mixture of virus and serum may appear infective or not depending on the susceptible host employed. This occurs even though in some instances the virus has, seemingly, similar infective titers for the different hosts used. The neutralization of influenza A virus by an immune serum illustrates the influence of the host on the outcome of the test (Tyrrell and Horsfall, 1953). When a given serum–virus mixture is inoculated into mice by the intracerebral or intrapulmonar route, higher protection is noted than when the same mixture is inoculated into the allantoic cavity or into the chorioallantoic membrane of embryonated eggs. Generally, higher antibody titers are obtained in less sensitive hosts; a possible explanation is that in any serum–virus mixture there remains a small proportion of uninactivated virus (Dulbecco et al., 1957). If the host is highly susceptible, the small amount of virus will suffice to overcome the host over a series of increasing dilutions of virus, while with a less susceptible host this residue will not be effective.

The outcome of a neutralization test may even differ in the same animal species or tissue culture depending on route of inoculation in the former and criterion for evaluation in the latter. With arboviruses inoculated into mice, it is an old and common observation (Olitsky and Harford, 1938; Lennette and Koprowski, 1944) that a serum that gives hardly any protection when the mixture is inoculated intracerebrally will give solid protection on intraperitoneal injection. Similarly, with several cell cultures, particularly rhesus monkey kidney cells, the metabolic-inhibition test with poliovirus (Salk *et al.*, 1954) has proved more sensitive for the detection of neutralizing antibodies than the observation of CPE on monolayers in fluid cultures (Sabin, 1956, 1957).

The criterion generally accepted, based on extensive observations, that the neutralization test is specifically diagnostic requires qualification. In general, cross-reactions between related viruses are more pronounced by CF or HI tests than by neutralization test. However, as the numbers of serotypes in the different groups—picornaviruses, arboviruses—have grown, it has become increasingly apparent that overlaps by neutralization test occur, and that neutralization of a virus by a typing-reference serum without a quantitative comparison with the homologous systems is not adequate for an identification. This reasoning applies especially to the results of immunological surveys. The capacity of a serum to neutralize a virus is not necessarily proof of previous exposure of an individual to that virus, particularly in cases where successive exposure to several members of an antigenic group may result in wide cross-reactivity, as with influenza and arboviruses.

Consequently, in the interpretation of the results of neutralization tests, two important criteria must be considered in order to minimize the risk of erroneous interpretations: (1) The degree of protection afforded by a serum varies considerably, depending on the technique, particularly the host, route of inoculation, relative purification of the viral suspension, and availability of accessory factors. (2) From the fact that a serum neutralizes a virus it could be concluded that the donor has had previous contact with this virus when in reality he may have been exposed to other, related viruses.

A. ELEMENTS OF THE TEST

The elements involved in the test are, first, the virus, the serum or other immune reagent, and the host system. Second, the outcome of the test is influenced by the accessory factors and conditions under which the test is performed, including incubation of the serum–virus mixture and route or manner of inoculation.

1. *Serum or Immune Reagent*

The serum or immune reagent can be the unknown, for instance, when antibodies are determined in a serum against reference viruses, mainly as an aid to the diagnosis of a current illness and in surveys to determine the immune status of a population. Conversely, the immune reagent contains known antibodies and is used as reference to identify a viral isolate. In other instances both serum and virus are specifically known and the problem is a quantitative determination, such as finding out the efficacy of a procedure of vaccinaton through the development of antibodies. The preparation of immune sera and ascitic fluids is described in Section I,C,1; for accessory factors, see Section II,B,1,c.

2. Virus Preparations

In a standard neutralization test the virus consists in extracts of infected tissues, the fluid phase of tissue cultures, or fluids from embryonated eggs. The virus stock is inoculated into the host of choice, and previous experience with the agent decides the optimum time to harvest.

Infected fluids from tissue cultures or embryonated eggs and infected sera are used directly or after centrifugation at low speed to eliminate debris. Tissue extracts from whole animals, usually brain and also liver and carcass from mice, are prepared by weighing the tissue and making a 10 or 20% suspension in a diluent (see Section II, B,2,a), using an electrically driven homogenizer, tissue grinder, or mortar and pestle. The suspension is centrifuged at about 2000 rpm for 15 or 20 minutes, and the supernatant fluid, pipeted off, constitutes the virus. To minimize losses of infectivity owing to heat inactivation, the viral suspension is held at 4°C in an ice water bath.

It has been observed that more effective neutralization of a virus by a serum is achieved when the tissue extracts are partially purified. It would seem that tissue debris contain a noninfective antigenic mass capable, however, of combining with antibody in the serum, thus diverting it from neutralizing active infectious virus. Consequently, elimination of tissue constituents by a procedure that does not affect the infectious titer of the virus is advised. The simplest method is centrifugation in a preparatory angle-head centrifuge at speeds of 6000–10,000 rpm for 1 hour. With a number of viruses the suspension can be cleaned by treatment and precipitation of tissue proteins with protamine sulfate (Warren et al., 1949), as described in Section I,C,2.

The infected fluids or tissue extracts that constitute the virus preparations employed in the test are used freshly made, or, if the viruses can stand the procedure with no loss of infectivity, they can be lyophilized and held at —20°C or shell frozen in sealed glass ampules and held at —60°C or lower temperatures.

3. Host System

The host employed is primarily determined by the infectious and lethal capacity of the virus and next by the convenience of use and availability, provided that the host results in tests sufficiently sensitive and accurate. For special purposes, sensitivity and accuracy may be needed or desired even at the cost of ease of performance. In essence the serum–virus mixtures are inoculated to animals, embryonated eggs, or cells in tissue cultures.

a. Animals. Albino Swiss mice of uniformly susceptible stocks are the host generally used for tests with viruses that are pathogenic for mice; they are used as newborn, i.e., from a few hours old to 5 or 6 days old and as weanlings or young adults 3–6 weeks of age. Only a few other animal species are routinely used at present, in special circumstances, for example, newborn hamsters and half-day-old chicks. This is due to the fact that in some instances the use of tissue cultures has replaced the use of animals other than mice, for example, monkeys in poliomyelitis or rabbits in vaccinia. For reasons to be explained later, inoculation of mice in the neutralization test is done by one of two routes, intracerebral or intraperitoneal. The neutralization test in mice is used particularly with the arboviruses.

b. Embryonated Eggs. Embryonated hen's eggs are used and the route of inoculation, age of the embryo, and temperature of incubation depend on the virus. Particularly used in the study of pock-producing viruses such as the variola-vaccinia, herpes, and mumps group, they are gradually being replaced by tissue cultures. An important use of embryonated eggs is in the neutralization test with influenza viruses. The outcome of the test is decided by the detection of hemagglutinins in the allantoic fluid of the inoculated eggs rather than by lesions or death of the embryo.

c. Tissue Cultures. Animal viruses that propagate in the laboratory exclusively, or nearly so, in tissue cultures—ECHO viruses, rhinoviruses, parainfluenza viruses, and adenoviruses—obviously require these cultures for performing neutralization tests. With other viruses, while it is possible to propagate them in the laboratory by inoculation of animals or embryonated eggs, neutralization tests are nevertheless performed in tissue cultures for reasons of simplicity, accuracy, economy, and work output. Among these viruses are polioviruses, some Coxsackie viruses, reoviruses, and poxviruses.

The selection of cell type and conditions of incubation, such as temperature, concentration of CO_2 in the atmosphere, whether rotary or stationary cultures, composition of the growth and maintenance media, including pH, frequency of changes of supernatant fluid, and other details are determined by the properties of each virus.

There are basically two types of tissue cultures used in the neutralization test (Table III), fluid and overlaid cultures. In the former, the cells and the virus infecting them grow in contact with a fluid phase, in which the virus, when released by the cells, diffuses and spreads freely. The effect of the virus on the cells can be observed either as lesions—cytopathic effect (CPE), change of pH in the

TABLE III
NEUTRALIZATION TEST

Host system	Route of inoculation or type of test	Viruses with which more generally used
Animal		Arboviruses, rabies
Mouse	Intracerebral	
	Intraperitoneal	
Hamster, chick, etc.		
Embryonated hen's eggs	Various routes	Influenza, mumps, herpes
Tissue cultures	Fluid-phase cultures	
	CPE	ECHO viruses, adenoviruses,
	Metabolic inhibition	rhinoviruses, and polioviruses
	Hemadsorption	Myxoviruses
	Interference	Rubella
	Overlaid cultures	All, mostly for special purposes
	Plaque neutralization	rather than routine diagnosis
	Plaque reduction	
	Plaque inhibition	
	Plaque suppression	

medium—or by hemadsorption. Some viruses fail to grow in a visible way in tissue culture, producing neither CPE nor pH change nor hemadsorption; however, they can inhibit the multiplication of a second virus on the cells that they first infected. This interfering action can be suppressed by antibodies against the first virus, thus the multiplication of the second virus is an indication of neutralization of the first one.

The second type of neutralization test, using overlaid cultures, is based on the fundamental observation of Dulbecco (1952) that viruses which grow in a cell culture under a cover that prevents their spread give rise to plaques; each plaque is theoretically produced by an infective unit or virus particle. Plaque counting is the most accurate method for titration of viruses. Since formation of plaques by viruses can be inhibited by neutralization of the virus, the plaque neutralization test is, in turn, of extreme sensitivity. This method is not generally used for routine survey purposes or identification problems because it is time consuming and exacting; but it is widely applied in the study of basic properties, where accuracy and sensitivity are essential, particularly with regard to such questions as antigenic comparison between similar viruses, detection of antigenic variants, analysis of viral populations, and study of the kinetics of the neutralization test.

B. NEUTRALIZATION TEST TECHNIQUES

1. *General Observations*

a. Dilution. Regardless of host system and route of inoculation, a test can be carried out using either increasing dilutions of virus and a constant amount of serum, usually undiluted, or serum in dilutions, with a constant amount of virus determined by a previous titration. In general, the method of undiluted serum combined with dilutions of virus is used in tests conducted with mice, while the method of serum dilutions and constant amount of virus is more generally employed with tissue culture tests.

The use of serum dilutions in a test seems to permit a more accurate determination of the strength of a serum in that it actually titrates it. The reason the method is not generally used with mice is that the reproducibility of the titrations of the amount of virus is less accurate in mice than in tissue cultures, thus making comparisons between the results of different tests less satisfactory with the former. In addition, in mice irregularities in the titrations occur when the serum is diluted, consisting in spotty deaths over several serial dilutions. Finally, on diluting the serum beyond a certain point, there may occur a sharp bend in the slope of the curve of neutralization, owing probably to diluting out of the accessory factors. These are presumably less effective in tissue cultures and do not alter the result of the *in vitro* test.

b. Incubation. The serum–virus mixture is generally incubated prior to inoculation, even though there is no complete agreement concerning its need or efficacy. The temperature and length of incubation vary with different agents; a major consideration is that the virus must be able to withstand the conditions of incubation with little or no loss in titer and another is that these conditions result in the greatest increase in sensitivity of the test with no increase of inspecificity. The temperatures of incubation are 37°, 22°, and 2°C, or incubator, room, and refrigerator temperatures, and the length, respectively, 1–2 hours, 2–4 hours, and 6 hours to overnight.

c. Labile Factors. An element that influences the result of the neutralization tests is an accessory factor (Morgan, 1945; Whitman, 1947) or labile factors easily inactivated by heat at 56°C, by preservation of the serum for long periods of time at 2°–4°C or even at lower temperatures, and whose action, when inactivated, can be in part restored by the addition of fresh normal serum from the same or other species. This factor, as well as the one described by Sabin (1950) in connection with dengue viruses, are potentiating factors, in that they are without effect on the virus in the absence of neutralizing antibodies. A different heat-labile factor (Ginsberg and Horsfall, 1949) acts by inhibiting nonspecifically several myxoviruses in the absence of neutralizing antibody.

Potentiating accessory factors are effective mainly in neutralization tests by intracerebral inoculation in mice and much less so by the intraperitoneal route. Individual sera vary considerably in the contents of this factor. Since, in addition, the efficacy of the factor diminishes rapidly with storage, misleading results may be obtained when testing serial samples from the same individuals.

There is no general agreement on how to handle the question of the accessory factors and nonspecific neutralizing substances. Heating all sera at 56°C for 30 minutes has been advocated, but this may result in destruction of antibodies in low titer and make for a less sensitive test. On the other hand, the use of freshly drawn serum is not always possible, in addition to being hazardous owing to the inhibitors. In some laboratories a supply of normal serum from rhesus monkey, rabbit, or guinea pigs previously tested to determine absence of antibodies is kept at −60°C or lower temperatures in small aliquots. The serum is incorporated in the diluent, when needed for a test, in proportions from 10 to 50%. Often simply nothing is done about these factors, and the sera are used after variable periods of storage at −20°C or lower temperatures, without inactivation and without addition of fresh serum.

2. Description of Methods

a. Tests in Mice. These are used particularly with the arboviruses. The serum–virus mixtures are inoculated either intracerebrally or intraperitoneally, the former giving higher specificity than the latter when dealing with antigenically related agents. For reasons indicated earlier, the method of constant serum and varying virus dilutions is generally used. There is great diversity of detail in the distinct procedures advocated and the choice is often empirical.

(*i*) *Mice* (See Section II,A,3,a). Age of the mice is very important; for the intracerebral test mice are generally used when 3–4 weeks old.

However, there are many viruses that propagate only in newborn mice, in which case mice of uniform age in days, 1–6, depending on the virus, must be used; the litters are randomized. With the intraperitoneal test, in general only newborn mice are used, except with viruses that are pathogenic by this route for older mice.

(*ii*) *Diluent.* Numerous diluents are used; their common characteristic is that they contain an amount of protein to prevent rapid inactivation of the virus. A diluent often used consists of a 10% solution of normal rabbit serum heated at 56°C for 30 minutes in physiological salt solution (0.16 M NaCl). The serum is pretested to ascertain that it has no antibodies against the viruses under study. Another diluent found most suitable for work with arboviruses consists of 0.75% bovine plasma albumin (Armour, fraction V) in 0.05 M phosphate-buffered saline pH 7.2. This diluent is filtered through a Millipore pad of 0.45 μ average pore diameter to eliminate bacterial contaminants.

(*iii*) *Serum.* This is in constant amount. For handling of accessory factors, see Section II,B,1,c.

(*iv*) *Virus.* When the virus suspension—infected brain, other tissues, or serum—is prepared freshly, a pool from several mice is advisable to minimize individual differences in titer. For the preparation and preservation of stock suspensions, see Section II,A,2.

With either a fresh suspension of virus or an ampule of the stock preparation, a 1 : 50 (or 2×10^{-2}) dilution of original infected tissue is prepared. From it, increasing 10-fold dilutions are made until a dilution is reached that, from previous experience with the virus, will be two decimal dilutions higher than the anticipated infective titer. Dilutions in the necessary amounts are made in test tubes of a convenient size; to minimize loss of virus titer owing to thermal inactivation, the rack with the tubes is kept in an ice-water bath during the manipulations.

(*v*) *Test.* The test consists of a comparative titration of the virus in the presence of each of the unknown sera and of a control serum. The latter is a serum from the same animal species supplying the test sera and known to be negative. It is not usually necessary to include for each serum all dilutions of virus from the lower dilution, 10^{-2}, to one or two beyond the anticipated titer, which can on occasion be 10^{-8} or 10^{-9}, since this can result in a cumbersome test; experience should serve as a guide. For the control serum and with sera with which low neutralizing capacity is expected, only four or five dilutions are used, with one or two above the anticipated end point; with sera expected to be positive, the dilutions used need not go above the end point.

To carry out the test, in a rack or racks are placed as many sets of tubes as there are sera to be tested and controls. The tubes are arranged in columns that will have the same dilution of virus and in rows that will have aliquots of a given serum. Using a 1-ml pipet, 0.3 ml of the virus dilutions is added to each column in descending order, beginning with the highest one. Next, using a fresh pipet for each serum, 0.3 ml of a serum is added to each of the tubes of the corresponding row, including the one with the control. The mixtures that now contain virus in dilutions from 10^{-2} up and serum diluted 1 : 2 are shaken well by hand and incubated at the selected conditions, which most often are 37°C in a water bath for 1 hour. Following incubation, the racks are placed in ice water baths during the course of the inoculation.

All the mixtures in a row corresponding to a serum are inoculated, beginning with the highest dilution of virus, before starting with the next serum; the control serum or sera is inoculated last. In a test by the intracerebral route, 0.03 ml is inoculated to weaned or adult mice, 0.02 ml to newborn ones, under ether anesthesia using a 0.25-ml tuberculin-type syringe and a 26- or 27-gage needle one-quarter inch long. For the intraperitoneal test, the volume injected is either 0.1 ml or 0.025–0.05 ml, depending on the age of the mice. With the larger volume it may be necessary to increase the volume of reagents mixed. Whether the test is by the intracerebral or intraperitoneal route, six or eight mice are inoculated with each virus dilution.

(*vi*) *Result and interpretation.* With rare exception the appraisal of a test is based on death or survival of the inoculated animals. When mice die outside the anticipated time, for example, a few hours after inoculation or much after the expected average survival time (AST), such deaths are considered to result from nonspecific causes and are omitted from the calculations. Checking the cause of death for specificity may be indicated in some instances but is not generally done.

The titer of the virus in the presence of each serum and of the control serum or diluent is calculated (see Section II,C) and the different titers of the virus with the control and with a serum are a measure of the neutralizing activity of the latter. It is expressed as either its neutralization index (NI) or its log NI.

(*vii*) *Simplified version.* A simplified version of the test is often used for immunological surveys of populations. As the number of sera is large, it is not practical to do a complete titration of the virus in the presence of each one. Instead, a screening test is done that consists of testing each serum against only one dilution of virus. From previous titrations the virus dilution is anticipated to contain between

100 and 200 50% lethal doses (LD_{50}). A complete titration of the virus is included; usually six mice are used with each serum, and depending on the number of survivors, the serum is considered positive, questionable, or negative.

b. Tests in Embryonated Hen's Eggs. The development and wide application of tissue culture methods have resulted in a decrease in the use of neutralization tests based on inoculation of embryonated eggs. Important details, such as length of incubation of the eggs before they are used, depend on the route of inoculation selected, which, in turn, is determined by the virus and purpose of the test. Every effort should be made to use eggs from flocks free from known viral and other infections.

In most of the methods described, the mixture of virus and serum is incubated at 37°C for a period of time, usually 1 hour, before inoculation. Generally, dilutions of serum are employed with the virus maintained constant. Determination of viral action on the embryo as a measure of the activity of a serum is made by one of several indexes: (1) direct observation of the embryo's death; (2) formation of pocks on the chorioallantoic membrane; and (3) agglutination of erythrocytes by the allantoic or amniotic fluid.

(i) Embryo's death. Observations of the embryo's death is often the basis of the test used with Newcastle disease virus. Sera are inactivated at 56°C for 30 minutes, diluted in increasing 2-fold dilutions from 1 : 2 to 1 : 512, using phosphate-buffered saline as diluent. A dilution of virus-infected allantoic fluid is made that is calculated to yield 1000–10,000 LD_{50}. Serum dilutions and virus are mixed in equal volumes, incubated at 37°C in a water bath for 1 hour, and 0.2 ml of each mixture inoculated in the allantoic cavity of five embryonated eggs on the tenth or eleventh day of incubation. The titer of the serum is calculated on the basis of the survival of embryos.

(ii) Formation of pocks. With viruses, such as herpes and vaccinia, that on multiplication on the chorioallantoic membrane produce local lesions or pocks, the neutralizing capacity of a serum is based on the effect it has on pock formation. With herpesvirus, for example, a stock is prepared and stored at −60°C that consists of a 10% suspension of infected chorioallantoic membrane in phosphate-buffered saline pH 7.2 containing 10% normal rabbit or horse serum. The infective, pock-forming titer is determined once and for all by titrating in 10-fold dilutions on the chorioallantoic membranes of 10- or 12-day-old embryos. In the neutralization test proper, a dilution producing approximately 100 pocks per 0.05 ml is used. This fixed dose of virus is mixed with an equal volume of each of a series of increasing 2- or 4-fold

dilutions of serum. Controls, consisting of the fixed dose of virus mixed with a known negative serum and with a positive one diluted so that it completely neutralizes the virus, are part of the test. Following incubation at 37°C for 1 hour, the mixtures are inoculated onto the surface of the chorioallantoic membrane of 10- to 12-day-old embryos (for embryonated egg techniques, see elsewhere in this treatise). The eggs are incubated for 48 hours, at which time the membranes are harvested, fixed in 0.5% Formalin, and the pocks counted on a dark surface. Difficulties in accurate readings and reproducibility of pock counts are not unexpected. The number of pock-forming units per unit volume in the stock used is determined by actual titration, and the neutralizing titer of a serum for the dose of virus used is calculated as the highest dilution that reduces the pock count by 50–80% relative to the control serum.

(iii) *Test for agglutinating activity.* Testing of the amniotic or allantoic fluids for agglutinating activity on suspensions of erythrocytes is done with mumps and influenza viruses, among others. As an illustration, with mumps (Gotlieb *et al.,* 1953) a stock consisting of infected allantoic fluids is prepared, pretested for titer, and stored at −60°C or lower temperatures. For a test, serum in dilutions is mixed with an equal volume of a virus dilution containing between 1000 and 10,000 50% infective doses (ID_{50}) per 0.1 ml; after incubation for 1 hour at 37°C or 18 hours at 4°C, the mixtures in 0.2 ml amounts are inoculated into the allantoic cavity of six 8-day-old embryos. Six to 7 days after incubation at 37°C, the individual allantoic fluids are harvested and tested for the presence of hemagglutinins for either chicken or guinea pig erythrocytes (see Section III). The absence or presence of agglutination serves as an indication of whether neutralization has occurred or not; the titer of the serum is calculated in the standard way.

c. *Tests in Tissue Cultures.* The tissue culture techniques are described elsewhere in this treatise; only details that apply directly to the neutralization test are given in this section.

The use of tissue cultures in the neutralization test is so extensive and there are so many variations in detail that it is possible here to describe only a few representative methods. The method of constant virus mixed with dilutions of serum is used far more often than with the mouse neutralization test, since it has been found more useful in demonstrating significant increases of antibody between acute- and convalescent-phase sera than the method of constant serum–virus dilutions. Sera are universally inactivated at 56°C for 30 minutes to destroy heat-labile virus inhibitors; since the efficacy of accessory factors remains largely undetermined in the tissue culture test, no attempt is made to replace them. The diluent for virus, serum, or a substitute for either is the same maintenance medium used in the cell cultures.

(i) *Methods based on direct observation of CPE.* The cell monolayers are either under a fluid phase or under an overlay of nutrient agar; the latter is the method of plaque formation and its inhibition.

Monolayers in fluid phase. This is probably the type of tissue culture neutralization test most extensively used with animal viruses. The following was recommended as most suitable for the enteroviruses (Committee, 1957) and is based largely on investigations by Melnick (1955).

Monkey (*M. mulatta*) kidney cells in primary cultures are used, grown in a medium consisting of Hanks' balanced salt solution, 86.7%; 5% lactalbumin hydrolyzate, 10%; calf serum, 2%; and $NaHCO_3$ and antibiotics in solution. Before use the medium is substituted by a maintenance medium, either medium No. 199 or Melnick's M-E medium, containing Earle's balanced salt solution, 86%; 5% lactalbumin hydrolysate, 10%; 7.5% $NaHCO_3$, 3%; and antibiotics in solution.

The virus consists of infected fluid harvested when the tubes or bottles show extensive CPE, kept at $-70°C$ in sealed ampules. Increasing serial 5-fold dilutions of serum are prepared and mixed in 0.5 ml volume with a similar one of a virus dilution calculated to contain 100 TCD_{50} per 0.1 ml. The mixtures are incubated at 37°C for 2 hours and added in 0.2-ml amounts to four tubes of cell monolayers. With the test is included a titration of the virus, mixed with diluent instead of serum. The cultures are incubated at 37°C, observed daily, and the results recorded 3–4 days later and again 7–8 days after inoculation. The two readings are done in order to detect a possible subsequent breakthrough by late virus action that could indicate the presence of an antigenically related system.

Simultaneous inoculation of cells and virus. Inoculation of the tubes with the viral suspension immediately after seeding the cells, rather than 2 or more days later when the monolayer has been formed, is the basis of the metabolic-inhibition test. However, the procedure has also been employed using as criterion of viral multiplication the observation of CPE in the monolayers as they appear following incubation. The method has been applied to adenoviruses (Grayston *et al.*, 1956) and to arboviruses (Kunz *et al.*, 1964). With the former, the virus propagated in HeLa cells is used in a test at a dilution that contains 100 TCD_{50} per volume employed. The serum in dilutions and the virus are mixed in equal amounts, 0.25 ml of each, the mixtures are held at room temperature for 30 minutes, and 0.1 ml of each mixture is inoculated into two or four tubes, each containing a freshly prepared suspension of 100,000 HeLa cells in 1 ml of maintenance medium. The tubes are incubated at 37°C in the standard stationary tissue culture rack and inspected daily. Neutralization is indicated by absence or reduction of CPE when compared with its extent in the control tubes with no immune serum.

Monolayers under agar overlay; plaque-neutralization test. There are different ways in which the test is applied to the detection of antibodies (Porterfield, 1964): neutralization, reduction, suppression, and inhibition plaque tests.

In the plaque-neutralization test, the serum and virus are mixed, incubated, and the residual infectivity of the mixture determined by plaque titration. Ordinarily the serum is used in 2- or 4-fold dilutions against a constant amount of virus. The titer of the serum is expressed by the highest dilution that reduces the plaque count by an arbitrarily selected standard, 50, 80, or 90%. This is a very sensitive but laborious method that gives accurate and precise results; it has been applied to enteroviruses, arboviruses, myxoviruses, and vaccinia.

In the plaque-reduction test, the monolayers in Petri dishes or bottles are infected first with a given dose of virus and next overlaid with agar in which have been incorporated serial dilutions of the test serum. No plaques appear with a high amount of antibody; where there is no antibody or where it is diluted beyond an effective range, the anticipated number of plaques appear, and the dilution of serum that reduces the number by the adopted criterion determines its titer. The serum has to be effective not against the virus first introduced but against the more numerous particles that follow from the multiplication of the one first introduced. As a result, the test has been less sensitive than the preceding one. Furthermore, the reading at and near the end point is not easy, the action of the serum appearing either as a delay in the formation of plaques or as a diminution in their size. In addition, the time of reading may introduce a source of error, for plaques may be present one day that were not seen the day before. This requires the setting of an arbitrary time for reading the test, usually when plaques first appear in the controls.

In the plaque-suppression test (Melnick, 1960), the serum in dilutions is incorporated in the agar overlay, as in the reduction test, and the infecting virus is placed on the surface of the agar in a filter-paper disc impregnated with a given number of plaque-forming units. The virus can also be deposited as a thin film of fluid, later removed, or it can be incorporated in a second layer of agar. The amount of virus that produces a countable number of plaques is determined first, and as usual the serum dilution that reduces the number by the selected percentage decides its titer. Owing to the fact that there are difficulties in reproducing a countable number of plaques, the test is ordinarily done with a large excess of virus (Melnick, 1960) and taking as an end point the dilution that suppresses all plaque formation.

The plaque-inhibition test is extensively used because it is technically easier to perform than the others, although probably not as sensitive as the plaque-neutralization test (de Somer and Prinzie, 1957; Farrell and Reid, 1959; Porterfield, 1961). The cell monolayers are infected with a fixed dose of virus producing confluent plaques; after allowing for viral adsorption, the cell sheet is overlaid with agar. The serum in dilutions is applied to the surface of the agar, either in the form of impregnated filter-paper discs or "fish spine" electrical insulation beads that have been dipped in the serum. Serum diffuses through the agar and inhibits the formation of plaques around the discs or beads; neutralization is evidenced by the presence of a circular zone of healthy cells that have taken on the neutral stain, while beyond, the infected cells appear with unstained, confluent plaques. Under certain standard conditions, Porterfield (1964) found that with arboviruses the area of the zone of inhibition is proportional to the logarithm of the concentration of serum.

Numerous variations in detail exist among the reported plaque-neutralization tests. Because of their more general application, the main details of two types, a neutralization and an inhibition test, are described here.

A plaque-neutralization test extensively used with the enteroviruses is the following (Hsiung and Melnick, 1957; Wallis et al., 1962): Monkey kidney cell cultures are grown in stoppered 3-ounce prescription bottles in the medium described in Section II,B,2,c,(i). When the cells make a confluent monolayer and are ready to use, the growth medium is removed, the cell sheet washed with saline or maintenance medium without serum, and the monolayers inoculated with the serum–virus mixtures. These have been prepared by mixing equal volumes of a constant amount of virus that from previous determinations is estimated to contain 100 plaque forming-units per 0.1 ml and serial increasing 2-fold dilutions of serum. The mixtures are incubated at 37°C for 1 hour and 0.2 ml is inoculated into each of two bottles, care being taken to distribute the inoculum evenly over the cell sheet. After allowing a period of 2 hours at 37°C for adsorption, the monolayers are covered with agar. This overlay consists of a mixture of equal parts of a nutrient overlay solution, which, in addition to cell nutrients, contains sodium bicarbonate, neutral red, and antibiotics, and of melted (46°–47°C) 3% agar. The overlay is held at 46°–47°C while being added to the bottles, 10 ml each, which are then kept at room temperature for 1 hour on a horizontal surface to insure even spreading and solidification. The bottles are inverted and incubated at 37°C in the dark to prevent photodynamic inactivation of the virus by the neutral red. The plaque counts at each serum dilution are compared with those in the control bottles without serum. In the test recommended for enteroviruses, a 90% reduction is taken as the lower limit of significance, and the highest dilution of serum that gives it represents the titer of the serum.

The inhibition test for arboviruses developed by Porterfield (1960, 1964) is as follows: A cell monolayer of chick embryo fibroblasts is established by trypsinization of the embryo's tissue suspension; the cells are counted in a hemocytometer and diluted in growth medium to give $5–6 \times 10^6$ cells per milliliter. The cell suspension, after removing large aggregates, is dispensed on either Petri dishes 60 mm in diameter in 8-ml amounts or on 250-mm square glass trays in a volume of 150 ml. The cells are then incubated 16–18 hours at 35°C. After overnight incubation, the growth medium is removed and replaced by a suitable virus dilution, 1 ml for the dish or 15 ml for the tray. The virus is allowed to adsorb during 2 hours at 35°C, with occasional rocking to insure even distribution. Following adsorption, the fluid is removed and the cell sheet is overlaid with agar medium, 6 ml for the dish or 100 ml for the tray. For this process the agar is melted, then cooled at 42°C, added to the infected cell cultures, and allowed to harden. "Fish spine" beads, sizes 2 or 3, dipped in the serum are placed on the agar surface, and the cultures are incubated at 35°C in incubators with trays of water to prevent evaporation until plaques appear. Sera that contain antibodies against the virus cause a zone of plaque inhibition surrounding the bead; the diameter of the zone is read to the nearest millimeter. The antibody titer of a serum is expressed in terms of the size of the zone of inhibition in millimeters under standard conditions or as a ratio between this value and that given by a reference serum, the antibody contents of which have been determined by another method. For details concerning preparation of diluents and media, see Porterfield (1964).

(*ii*) *Tests based on observation of pH changes of the medium; metabolic-inhibition test.* Cells in suspension actively metabolizing in a medium that contains glucose produce acid; if there is in the solution phenol red, the color changes from red to yellow with falling pH values. Multiplication of a virus with destruction of cells is manifested by the color remaining red, indicating inhibition of metabolism. If to the system is added a mixture of virus and serum that has antibodies against it, the cells, being undamaged, will metabolize normally, as in the uninoculated tubes; consequently, the color will turn yellow. If the serum has no antibodies, the color remains red, since there are no cells that metabolize. The metabolic-inhibition test has practical advantages, particularly when applied to large-scale surveys (Salk et al., 1954). It is simpler to carry out than the test on monolayers because cells and serum–virus mixtures are inoculated at the same time and because results can be read by naked-eye inspection, thus eliminating time-consuming microscopic examination of large numbers of tubes. Furthermore, the test can be more sensitive for detection of antibodies than the test based on observation of CPE. Various cells have been used, rhesus monkey kidney, chick embryo fibroblasts, HeLa, and human amnion, among possibly others. The test has been applied to enteroviruses, adenoviruses, influenza, herpes, and arboviruses.

As first applied to polioviruses and described by Salk et al. (1954) and modified by Schmidt and Lennette (Schmidt, 1964), one of the techniques consists of the following steps: Primary rhesus monkey kidney cell cultures are prepared in 200-ml flasks; after 5–6 days incubation at $36°–37°C$, when the monolayers are confluent, the medium is removed and the cell sheets washed with phosphate-buffered saline. To the monolayers is added a cell-dispersing agent, 10 ml of either 0.25% trypsin solution or Versene, diluted 1 : 3000. The standard procedure for preparing cell suspensions from monolayers is then followed. The dispersed cells are sedimented by low-speed centrifugation and resuspended to a concentration of 80,000 per milliliter in a metabolism medium consisting of horse serum (inactivated at $56°C$ for 30 minutes), 2 ml; medium No. 199 in Hanks' balanced salt solution (the latter containing the glucose and phenol red), 94.5 ml; 2.8% $NaHCO_3$, 3 ml; and penicillin and streptomycin (20,000 units and 20,000 μg, respectively, per milliter), 0.5 ml.

The sera to be tested, inactivated at $56°C$ for 30 minutes, are diluted in increasing 2-fold dilutions from 1 : 8 to 1 : 2048; from one to three tubes are used for each dilution. The diluent for the serum, as well as for the virus, consists of Hanks' balanced salt solution (BSS), 72 ml; medium No. 199 in Hanks' BSS, 25 ml; 2.8% $NaHCO_3$, 2.5 ml; and 0.5 ml of antibiotics solution, as in the metabolism medium. To 0.25 ml of the serum dilutions is added 0.25 ml of a virus suspension containing, from previous determinations, 100 TCD_{50}. Controls, including serum with no virus, a virus titration without serum, and known positive sera, one with high and one with low titers, are used in the test. The serum–virus mixtures are incubated at room temperature for 30–60 minutes. To each tube is then added 0.25 ml of the cell suspension that contains 80,000 cells per milliliter. The metabolic activity of the cells is also titrated by introducing in tubes different quantities of cells, 40,000, 20,000, 10,000, and 5000, without serum or virus. To all of the tubes, containing now a total volume of 0.75 ml, is added a seal of 0.5 ml of paraffin; the test is incubated at $36°-37°C$ for 5 or 6 days. The reading is done by comparison to color standards, a pH of 7.4 or higher indicating viral activity, a pH of 7.2 or lower showing metabolizing cells, hence no virus action. The titer of a serum is given by the highest dilution that inhibits viral action or preserves cell metabolism.

(iii) *Tests based on observation of hemadsorption.* Certain viruses that multiply in tissue cultures cause a minimum of observable CPE, which makes their detection difficult; parainfluenza viruses are notable in this respect. Work with these agents has been considerably facilitated by the hemadsorption reaction, which Vogel and Shelokov (1957) discovered with influenza viruses. In this reaction, when erythrocytes from chickens or guinea pigs are added to a monolayer of infected cells, they remain attached to the surface of the cells; since the reaction can be specifically inhibited by immune serum, it is used for titrating antibodies.

With parainfluenza viruses (Chanock *et al.*, 1961a,b), a stock from a pool of infected tissue culture fluids is prepared and stored at $-60°C$. The sera, inactivated at $56°C$ except when tested for type 2 antibodies, which are labile, are diluted in 2- or 4-fold dilutions in Hanks' BSS with 0.5% gelatin. The stock virus is diluted, using the same diluent, to an estimated amount of 100 TCI_{50} per 0.1 ml, 10 TCI_{50} when using type 1 virus. Serum and virus mixed in equal volumes are incubated for 1 hour at room temperature, and 0.2 ml of each mixture is inoculated into each of two or three monkey kidney cell cultures; a simultaneous titration of the virus in the absence of serum is carried out. After 3 days incubation at $33°-35°C$ for types 1, 2, and 3, and 5 days for type 4, infection is determined by hemadsorption. The cultures are drained, washed with BSS, and 1 ml of a 0.1% suspension of guinea pig erythrocytes added to each tube. Types 1–3 are held in a horizontal position for 0.5 hour at $4°C$ (type 4 is kept at $25°C$), then turned to let free erythrocytes run off, and observed under the microscope. Complete inhibition of hemadsorption indicates neutralization, and the titer of a serum is calculated in the standard manner.

(iv) *Tests based on interference.* Certain viruses that propagate in tissue cultures with no visible lesions or induction of hemadsorption can, nonetheless, be detected by the fact that their propagation interferes with the CPE of a second virus subsequently added to the cultures. The interference can be prevented by immune sera, resulting in the interference–neutralization test.

As there are two infective systems involved, in addition to the other variables, and the balance between them needs careful adjustment, the test is not practical for large-scale serological surveys. It has been used with rhinoviruses (Hitchcock and Tyrrell, 1960) until conditions developed that resulted in CPE (Tyrrell and Parsons, 1960), with rubella (Parkman *et al.*, 1962), strains of dengue (Buescher, 1963), and Crimean hemorrhagic fever (Chumakov, 1965) viruses.

With rubella (Parkman *et al.*, 1962; Cabasso and Stebbins, 1965), a stock pool is prepared in African green monkey kidney (GMK) cell cultures and stored at $-65°C$ in sealed glass ampules. For the neutralization test, the serum inactivated at $56°C$ for 30 minutes is diluted in Hanks' BSS in increasing 2-fold dilutions, beginning at 1 : 2 or 1 : 4. To a volume of the serum dilutions is added an equal volume of virus, diluted so as to have an estimated 10–20 interfering doses per 0.1 ml on the basis of previous titrations. After 1 hour at $22°$ or $37°C$, 0.2 ml of the mixture is inoculated into two or four tubes with GMK monolayers that are incubated at $35°C$ in stationary racks or a roller drum; a titration of the virus seed used is included. After 5–9 days incubation, the fluid medium is removed and replaced with fresh medium containing the challenge virus, about 10,000 TCD_{50} of ECHO virus 11. Within 2–3 days the challenge virus shows typical CPE in the tubes that contained no rubella virus, i.e., those with sera having antibodies.

An interference–neutralization test that combines, in addition, hemadsorption has been described as the hemadsorption-negative plaque test (Marcus and Carver, 1965). While not suited to routine studies, the test offers possibilities for the search for new types or classes of noncytopathic and nonhemadsorbing viruses. In the test with rubella virus, this is grown in monolayers of GMK cells in 60-mm Petri dishes; 3–4 days later the medium is removed and Newcastle disease virus is (NDV) added. After allowing for attachment of NDV, about 60 minutes at $37°C$, a suspension of bovine erythrocytes is introduced, and adsorption is carried out at $4°C$ for 20 minutes. Rubella virus-infected cells appear at first as hemadsorption-negative discrete areas or plaques; with longer incubation before adding NDV, these areas cover the entire surface of the monolayer. The formation of hemadsorption-negative plaques is prevented by a rubella immune serum.

C. Calculation of Titration End Points

In HI and CF tests 2-fold dilutions of the reagents, serum or antigen, are generally used, and since no multiple determinations are made, the estimation of the end point presents no difficulties. By selecting a criterion for reading the test, the titer of a serum or antigen is expressed by the highest dilution that fulfills that criterion, with no attempts made to interpolate.

In the neutralization test, particularly with mice using varying virus and constant serum, serial 10-fold dilutions are the rule, as well as from six to eight animals per dilution. Since the dilution interval is relatively large and the outcome is seldom either death or survival (or whatever criterion is used) of all the animals in every dilution, the estimation of a reasonably accurate end point requires certain simple computations on the numerical results.

An end point based on a 100% reaction is unadvisable, since it is much affected by small chance variations. It has become the rule in animal virology to use 50% end points, i.e., the titer of a virus suspension is defined as the dilution at which 50% of the animals inoculated die, if that is the criterion adopted. The notation used to indicate it is LD_{50}, for 50% lethal dose.

A method universally employed for end-point computations is that described by Reed and Muench (1938); one of its merits is that by accumulating deaths and survivals—or reactors and nonreactors—occurring over the entire range of dilutions, the method uses in the calculations all the animals in the titration rather than only those in the dilutions adjacent to the end point. While each dilution has few animals, the statistical effect of the computation is as though all the animals were accumulated around the end point.

1. Calculation of 50% End Point in Virus Titrations

For purposes of illustration, the result of a titration in mice is given and arranged in the manner used for the calculations in Table IV.

It is assumed that animals that died at a given dilution would also have died had they been inoculated at lower dilutions. Hence column "c" is added from the bottom, and the subtotal for each dilution is entered in column "e" as the accumulated number of mice dying at this and higher dilutions. Conversely, mice surviving at a given dilution would have survived at the higher ones, therefore the accumulation in column "f" of the animals surviving, column "d," is carried out by adding the figures in the latter from the top. In this instance, the 50% mortality is between dilutions 10^{-4} and 10^{-5} and, by inspection,

TABLE IV

COMPUTATION OF THE 50% END-POINT TITER OF A VIRUS BY
THE REED AND MUENCH METHOD[a]

Dilution of virus a	Mortality ratio b	Died c	Survived d	Accumulated		Mortality	
				Deaths e	Survivals f	Ratio g	% h
10^{-2}	6 : 6	6	0	20	0	20 : 20	100
10^{-3}	6 : 6	6	0	14	0	14 : 14	100
10^{-4}	5 : 6	5	1	8	1	8 : 9	89
10^{-5}	3 : 6	3	3	3	4	3 : 7	43
10^{-6}	0 : 6	0	6	0	10	0 : 10	0

[a] Dilution factor = 10; log dilution factor = 1.

closer to the latter. The formula for the proportional distance (PD) of the 50% end point from the dilution, 10^{-4}, giving next above 50% mortality is

$$PD = \text{\% mortality at dilution next above 50\%} - 50\% / \text{\% mortality at dilution next above 50\%} - \text{\% mortality at dilution next below 50\%} \quad (1)$$

Since the dilutions increase in a logarithmic scale, the real value of the PD is obtained by multiplying the value given by Eq. (1) by the logarithm of the dilution factor. In 10-fold dilutions, the log is 1 and the operation is disregarded; in 2-fold dilutions the log is 0.3; in 4-fold, 0.6, etc.

In the example, the PD distance from dilution 10^{-4} is

$$PD = 89 - 50/89 - 43 = 0.8 \quad (2)$$

and the 50% end-point titer is $10^{-(4+0.8)}$, or $10^{-4.8}$.

2. *Calculation of the 50% End-Point Titer of a Serum in a Neutralization Test*

In titrations of sera against constant amount of virus, dilutions of serum are often 2- or 4-fold rather than 10-fold; the results are arranged as above, and the computation is done in a similar manner except that the direction of the accumulations of deaths and survivals is reversed.

In the example in Table V, the PD of the 50% end point from the dilution next below the 50% mortality, 1 : 16 or $10^{-1.8}$, is:

TABLE V

COMPUTATION OF THE 50% END-POINT TITER OF A SERUM
BY THE REED AND MUENCH METHOD[a]

Dilution of serum a		Mortality ratio b	Died c	Survived d	Accumulated			
					Deaths e	Survivals f	Mortality Ratio g	Mortality % h
Undiluted	10^0	0 : 6	0	6	0	18	0 : 18	0
1 : 4	$10^{-0.6}$	0 : 6	0	6	0	12	0 : 12	0
1 : 16	$10^{-1.2}$	2 : 6	2	4	2	6	2 : 8	25
1 : 64	$10^{-1.8}$	4 : 6	4	2	6	2	6 : 8	75
1 : 256	$10^{-2.4}$	6 : 6	6	0	12	0	12 : 12	100
1 : 1024	$10^{-3.0}$	6 : 6	6	0	18	0	18 : 18	100

[a] Dilution factor = 4; log dilution factor = 0.6.

$PD = 50\% - \%$ mortality at dilution next below $50\%/\%$ mortality at dilution next above $50\% - \%$ mortality at dilution next below (3) $50\% \times \log 4$

or

$$PD = 50 - 25/75 - 25 \times 0.6 = 0.5 \times 0.6 = 0.3 \qquad (4)$$

Therefore the titer of the serum is:

$$10^{-(1.2+0.3)} = 10^{-1.5} = 1/10^{1.5} = 1:32 \qquad (5)$$

3. Finding the Difference between Two Titers

In a test with constant serum and virus in dilutions, the neutralizing effect of a serum is expressed by the "neutralization index," which is determined by computing the LD_{50} titers of the virus in the presence of a control serum or diluent and in the presence of the test serum. By subtracting the exponent of the latter from that of the former—disregarding the negative signs—is obtained a number that represents the logarithm of the neutralization index. The neutralization index of a serum is, therefore, the ratio between the titers of the virus in the presence of this serum and in the presence of a control diluent or serum; it is expressed by the notation "NI," or, if using logarithmic notation, by "log NI." As an illustration, if the LD_{50} titer of a virus in the presence of the test serum is $10^{-3.1}$ and in the presence of the control serum $10^{-7.4}$, the NI of the serum is

$$NI = 10^{-3.1}/10^{-7.4} = 10^{7.4}/10^{3.1} = 10^{(7.4-3.1)} = 10^{4.3} = 20,000 \qquad (6)$$

and the logarithm of the NI is log NI $=$ log $20,000 = 4.3$.

The Reed and Muench formula is also used with tests in tissue cultures, using as criteria CPE, metabolic inhibition, or plaque formation. With the latter, reduction values in the number of plaques produced by a given dilution of virus by 50, 80, or 90% are used in the computations. On the subject of end-point calculations, see Kärber (1931), Cutchins et al. (1960), and Lorenz (1962).

4. Significance of Observed Differences in Titers

The neutralizing effect of a serum is given by a difference between titers. To evaluate properly the difference it is necessary to know the experimental error or expected variation of titrations of a virus or serum.

The accumulated experience in neutralization tests is that, in general, multiple simultaneous titrations of a virus suspension done in 10-fold dilutions can easily vary by a factor of 10, or log $10 = 1$. Consequently, it is generally accepted that values of neutralization indexes of less than 10, or whose log is less than 1, are not significant; values between 10 and under 50, or logs between 1 and 1.6, as questionable; and values of 50 or greater, log 1.7 or more, as significant.

In serum titrations it is hardly possible to show, reproducibly, differences in titers between sera unless they are as great as or greater than given by two consecutive steps in the dilution; therefore, using 2-fold dilutions, only 4-fold or greater ratios are considered significant.

III. Hemagglutination (HA) and Hemagglutination-Inhibition (HI) Tests

Hemagglutination, first observed with influenza viruses (Hirst, 1941), has since been noted with agents from practically all groups. A virus or antigen derived from it adsorbs to erythrocytes through receptor sites on their surface and agglutinates them. This action can be specifically inhibited by antibodies, and since the reaction is easily performed, HA and its inhibition are extensively employed for identification of viral isolates and titration of antibodies.

The HA reaction is extremely simple in concept. A suspension of red cells is brought in contact with a preparation that contains antigen and with one without antigen. As the red cells sediment by gravity, in the presence of antigen they do so in the form of large clumps or, once settled, they appear as a continuous sheet or layer that covers the entire surface of the bottom of the test tube. In the absence of antigen the cells sediment in the shape of a tightly packed button that gathers in a small area. This is the pattern method of observing agglutination (Salk, 1944).

Another procedure for observing agglutination is based on the fact that agglutinated cells sediment at a faster rate than unagglutinated ones; therefore, agglutination can be titrated by estimating the red cells left behind in suspension at definite times rather than by observing the sedimented cells. By using adequate standards and precision of measurements (Levine et al., 1953), very accurate titrations can be made by this method, designated the sedimentation method. However, since it is technically far more exacting than the pattern method, it is used only for special studies.

While simple in essence, the HA and HI tests can be somewhat complex in execution because of limitations imposed by the range of agglutinable red cells, conditions of pH and temperature under which the reactions occur, existence of nonspecific inhibitors in sera and in the infected tissues or fluids from which the antigens are prepared, and presence of nonviral agglutinins in sera and tissue extracts.

As a diagnostic test, HI is used for identification of new isolates and for determination of the presence of antibodies, either as an aid to the specific diagnosis of a current illness or for surveys. With some viruses, antibodies detected by HI are similar in specificity to those found by neutralization test. With influenza and parainfluenza viruses, both neutralizing and HI antibodies are specific for the subtype or group of strains, or even for a strain, while CF antibodies are type inclusive; similarly, with reoviruses and adenoviruses, the HI and neutralizing antibodies are type specific, while the CF ones are common to the group. With other agents a different situation prevails; thus, with groups A and B arboviruses the HI antibodies show a more pronounced overlap than the CF ones, and these, in turn, are less type specific than neutralizing antibodies determined by the intracerebral test in newborn mice. Therefore, the information obtained with the HI test needs to be evaluated in view of the viruses under study. (For passive agglutination, see Section VII,B.)

A. PRELIMINARY HANDLING OF SOME REAGENTS

For the preparation of antigens, see Section I,C,2.

1. Erythrocytes

Thus far only erythrocytes from mammals and birds are used. Viruses differ in the number of species whose red cells they agglutinate; some have a narrow range limited to one species, or even only to individuals of that species, while other viruses are active with erythrocytes from several kinds of animals. Vaccinia virus agglutinates only red cells from particular chickens, and mouse encephalomyelitis (GD7 strain) only human cells; on the other hand, arboviruses are effective in various degrees on red cells from mammals—man, rhesus monkey, guinea pig, sheep, mouse—and birds—goose, chicken, and pigeon. When several kinds of red cells are agglutinated, one is usually better than the rest and is selected.

Red cells from the following animals are generally used: with adenoviruses of group 1, rhesus or grivet monkey, of groups 2 and 3, rat; with arboviruses, goose; with enteroviruses, human O, except for Coxsackie virus A7, with which cells from selected chickens are required; with myxoviruses, for influenza A and B, parainfluenza 1–4, and Newcastle disease, human O, chicken, and guinea pig, while with influenza C and mumps only chicken cells, and with measles, cells from rhesus, patas, or grivet monkeys; with reoviruses, human O or bovine cells; with vaccinia, cells from selected chickens, the same ones that react with Coxsackie A7; with mouse polyomavirus, guinea pig erythrocytes; with mouse encephalomyocarditis, sheep cells; and with mouse encephalomyelitis (GD7 strain), human O cells.

The concentration of the suspension of red cells influences the outcome of the test in that there is an inverse relation between the concentration and the agglutinating titer of an antigen. In addition, the aspect of the sedimented pattern varies, and is more easily read or interpreted at intermediate concentrations of cells than at extreme ones. For these reasons, the selected concentration is usually as low as possible but compatible with the good performance of the test. The concentrations vary in the different systems, ranging between 0.25 and 1% of packed cells in the suspensions as added to the other reagents, which represents a final concentration of cells in the test between 0.12 and 0.33%. In general, mammalian cells are used at slightly higher concentrations than avian cells because they sediment more slowly than the latter; by increasing their number the time needed for sedimentation is shortened. The desired concentration is achieved either by sedimenting the red cells at low speed in a centrifuge and measuring volumes of packed cells or by determining the optical density of the suspension by means of a spectrophotometer under standardized conditions.

Two alternate procedures are used for preparation of erythrocytes.

a. Erythrocytes for Immediate Use. The animal is bled using a sufficient amount of 5% sodium citrate to yield a 1 : 5 mixture with blood. The cells are washed three times in 0.9% NaCl and the third washing is done in a graduated centrifuge tube and the cells sedimented at 1500 rpm for 10 minutes. The cells are resuspended in 9 volumes of 0.9% NaCl, thus obtaining a 10% by volume stock suspension, which is kept at 4°C for no more than 5 or 6 days. From the stock suspension, the working suspension at the desired concentration is made in saline.

b. Erythrocytes Able to Be Stored. Erythrocytes collected as described above have a tendency to hemolyze, shrink, and lose reactivity when kept for more than a few days. The following method (Clarke and Casals, 1958) minimizes these difficulties and allows cells to be kept in good condition for at least 2 weeks.

The animal is bled into a syringe containing 1.5 ml of acid–citrate–dextrose (for chemical reagents, see Section III,C) per 8.5 ml of blood. The cells are washed four times with dextrose–gelatin–Veronal (DGV), the first time by adding 1 volume of blood to 2.5 volumes of DGV and subsequently with 3 volumes for 1 of original blood; centrifugation at 1500 rpm is done at 4°C. After the final washing the cells are resuspended in 3 volumes of DGV (original blood volume) and standardized by determining the optical density (OD) of the suspension, which is directly proportional to the cell count.

For standardization, after removing a small amount, the volume of the original suspension is measured; the small amount is diluted 1 : 40 in 0.9% NaCl. The OD of this diluted suspension is measured in a photoelectric spectrophotometer at a wavelength of 490 mμ in tubes with an internal diameter of 10 mm. Knowing the volume of the original suspension and the OD of its 1 : 40 dilution, one can determine how much further the original suspension must be diluted in DGV to give any desired concentration as follows:

$$\text{Final volume} = \text{Initial volume} \times \text{observed OD/desired OD}$$

Since the observed OD is that of the original suspension diluted 40 times, the adjustment to final volume is made with due consideration to this dilution factor.

It is practical to adjust the volume of the original suspension so that a 1 : 40 dilution gives an OD of 0.450, the suspension containing then 8–10% by volume of red cells, depending on the species supplying them. The adjusted standardized suspension is kept at 4°C and constitutes the stock suspension; from it are prepared the working suspensions as needed, by dilution at the desired OD in virus-adjusting diluents (VAD) or other diluents. For work with arboviruses using plastic trays, the suspension generally used has an OD of 0.750, or a dilution of 1 : 23 of the stock.

2. *Adjustment of pH*

With the majority of hemagglutinating viruses the reaction is not closely dependent on the pH of the medium, provided that the pH is not very far removed from neutrality. With most of the viruses the reaction occurs with no change in titer at pH values between 6.0 and 8.5. As a consequence, not much attention is paid to this variable in the described methods, and as diluent for all reagents in the test either a 0.9% solution of NaCl or 0.01 M phosphate-buffered saline at pH 7.2, is used.

There is an exception, however, represented by the arboviruses, with which HA with the known systems is extremely dependent on pH. Most of these viruses agglutinate only at a narrow pH range, so that the effective zone for many is no wider than 0.3 or 0.4 pH unit; the overall zone of pH activity is limited to values between 5.8 and 7.2 or 7.4, and the optimal zone for nearly all lies between 6.0 and 7.0. At the same time, the agglutinating antigens of these viruses are unstable unless kept at high pH values, in the neighborhood of 9.0; consequently, in order to carry out the reaction between an antigen kept at pH 9.0 and cells at a pH between 6.0 and 7.0, it is necessary to bring the system to the low pH at the time when the cells are added. Adsorption to the red cell receptors takes place very rapidly and with it agglutination. To perform the test, the cells are suspended in phosphate buffers (see Section III,C), designated VAD, of such composition that by mixing them with an equal volume of the antigen and serum diluent (borate–saline buffer, pH 9.0) the mixture has the desired pH in the range 5.8–7.6.

3. Dependency on Temperature

The temperature of incubation following addition of the red cells to the system is 4°, 22° (room temperature), or 37°C. With most viruses, the temperature is either indifferent or not too critical, leading at most to a slight difference in titers of an antigen when the mixture is incubated at the various temperatures. If possible or advisable, temperatures of 22° or 37°C are preferred because sedimentation occurs at a faster pace and often the patterns, both positive and negative, are sharper. With some viruses, however, a definite temperature must be used; influenza C, mouse encephalomyelitis (GD7), and mouse encephalomyocarditis agglutinate only at 4°C, and if the agglutinated cells are brought to a higher temperature, deagglutination occurs rapidly.

The length of time required after adding the cells to the antigen for the test to be readable is determined by the sedimentation in the erythrocyte control tubes or wells; it varies with the type of cell, their concentration, and the temperature. With mammalian cells at low concentration and 4°C incubation, it takes 4–8 hours before the controls settle; with avian cells at standard concentration (around 0.4%) and 37°C, the controls settle in about 1 hour.

4. Nonspecific Inhibitors in Serum

Nonspecific inhibitors of HA are present in some of the source materials used for preparation of antigens; the methods used (Section I, C,2) are, in part, designed to eliminate them. Inhibitors in sera and immune ascitic fluids must also be eliminated if the test is to be used for specific titration of antibodies.

Some of the methods summarized here (a to e) were developed for removal of inhibitors against influenza, parainfluenza, and NDV; others (f and g), were first developed for arboviruses. While it is possible that the kaolin method removes early-appearing antibodies of low titer, it has, nevertheless, proved practical and applicable to many species of animal sera. Spence (1960) advocated its use with influenza virus, and it has also been applied to adenoviruses, enteroviruses, reoviruses, and measles. Methods *a* to *e* have been tested, comparatively, with influenza viruses (Ananthanarayan and Paniker, 1960), with the conclusion that no one technique was universally applicable for all types of serum against all strains.

a. Heating at 56°C for 30 Minutes. This simple procedure has been used with only moderate success.

b. Receptor-Destroying Enzyme Treatment (RDE). RDE from *Vibrio cholera* is obtained from cultures in peptone broth incubated at 35°–37°C for 24 hours; following centrifugation of the culture the supernatant is adjusted to pH 7 with 0.1 M NaOH and sterilized by filtration. The preparation can be kept fully active for 1 year at 4°C. To treat the serum, 1 volume of it is mixed with 5 volumes of RDE, the mixture incubated at 37°C for 18 hours, and then heated at 56°C for 1 hour; the volume is made up with saline to give a final dilution of 1 : 10.

c. Periodate Method. One volume of serum is mixed with 2 volumes of $M/90$ KIO$_4$ and kept at room temperature for 15 minutes or for 12 hours at 4°C. Two volumes of 1% glycerol in saline or phosphate-buffered saline is added and the mixture is heated at 56°C for 30 minutes; the volume is made up with saline to a final serum dilution of 1 : 10.

d. Trypsin method. Crystalline trypsin having a strength of 2000 units per milligram is added to serum, 8 mg/ml, and the mixture heated at 56°C for 30 minutes; the serum is then diluted to 1 : 10 for use in the test.

e. Trypsin and Periodate Method. One volume of serum is mixed with 0.5 volume of trypsin and heated at 56°C for 30 minutes; 1.5 volumes of $M/90$ KIO$_4$ is then added and the mixture held at room temperature for 15 minutes, after which 1.5 volumes of 1% glycerol in saline or buffered saline is added and allowed to act at room temperature for an additional 15 minutes. The serum dilution is adjusted to 1 : 10, with the usual diluent.

f. Kaolin Method. Kaolin must be acid washed; an approximate 25% suspension is made by adding, with constant mechanical stirring, 25 gm of the powder to 100 ml of borate–saline at pH 9.0. This preparation keeps indefinitely at 4°C. For treatment, to 1 volume of serum is added 4 volumes of borate–saline and 5 volumes of kaolin suspension; the mixture is held at room temperature, with occasional shaking, for 20 minutes and centrifuged at 2500 rpm for 30 minutes. The supernatant serum, diluted approximately 1 : 10 at pH 9.0, is adsorbed with the pertinent red cells to remove natural agglutinins before using it in a test.

g. Acetone Treatment. The serum is diluted 1 : 4 or 1 : 5 in distilled water and added dropwise to 10–15 volumes, referred to the diluted serum, of chilled acetone; the mixture is centrifuged immediately at 2500 rpm for 10 minutes, preferably in the cold, and the clear supernatant is discarded. The sediment is reextracted, with an amount of acetone similar to that used before for 10 minutes with occasional shaking, and again centrifuged as before. The sediment is now dried by means of a vacuum pump. The dry residue is dissolved in 10 volumes, referred to the original undiluted serum, of borate–saline. This solution represents serum diluted 1 : 10 and at pH 9.0 and is ready for red cell adsorption.

5. Removal of Natural Agglutinins

Sera from various species have natural agglutinins for some of the erythrocytes used in the HA test; since, by causing a nonviral agglutination, they interfere with the test, they have to be removed. This is done by adsorption of the sera with packed red cells of the species used in the test; for serum diluted 1 : 10, adsorption is done with 0.1 ml of cells per 5 ml of serum at 4°C in an ice water bath for 10–20 minutes.

B. TECHNIQUES FOR THE TESTS

The pattern method having been adopted as a general procedure for observation of HA, a vessel—test tube or molded depressions on a plastic tray—is selected that has a regular bottom surface free from imperfections and with a curvature that favors deposition of agglutinated cells so that they can be easily distinguished from sedimented unagglutinated ones.

Test tubes 75 × 13 mm or 100 × 13 mm can be used; for several reasons, however, plastic trays seem preferable. Various models of disposable and nondisposable trays are commercially available. Models in which the capacity of the cavity is 1.3–3 ml are used for a test in which the total volume of the combined reagents is 0.6–1 ml. In other models the wells have a capacity of 0.2–0.3 ml and are used in a test in which the reagents are delivered in the form of drops from calibrated pipets, specially tooled spiral loops, or 18-gage hypodermic needles mounted on a glass tube with a rubber bulb to control the flow (Fulton and Dumbell, 1949; Takatsy *et al.*, 1954; Sever, 1962). In this test, the total volume is represented by 3 or 4 drops, with a total volume of 0.075–0.2 ml. Disposable trays have the advantage of eliminating washing, which may present difficulties owing to etching of the surface with continuous use and to film deposits of nonremovable material that can interfere with tests with the more delicate antigens. The microtests result in considerable savings of the amounts of reagents and, from the manner in which these are diluted and delivered, also saving of time.

The total volume of the combined reagents in a test does not seem to alter the results provided that the relative proportions of the reagents remain constant. In the HA test, only antigen and red cells participate; but, since in its serological application the HA test is a preliminary step to the HI reaction, in which there is, in addition, a serum, the total volume used in a test is established to include serum, antigen, and red cells. If either of the former two is left out, the serum in the titration of an antigen or the antigen in the determination of nonspecific agglutination by the serum, an equal volume of diluent is substituted for the missing reagent.

In many macrotests the volumes used are 0.2 or 0.25 ml each of serum, antigen, and erythrocytes suspension; in others the volumes are 0.2 ml each of serum and antigen and 0.4 ml of the cell suspension. With the microtest the corresponding volumes are 1 drop—0.025 or 0.05 ml—for each reagent, serum, antigen, and cell suspension; or 1 drop for serum and antigen and 2 drops for the red cells.

With the exception of the arboviruses, HA is not influenced by moderate shifts of pH near neutrality; as a consequence the method for carrying out the test is simple. Once the cell species and concentration and temperature of incubation are chosen, dilutions of antigen are made in saline or buffered saline, distributed in tubes or trays, and red cells suspended in the same diluent are added and the test is incubated. With arboviruses accurate adjustment of pH is required.

Two illustrative methods are described.

1. *Method for Influenza Viruses*

A method used for influenza viruses can be given as a model for tests that require no pH adjustment. To titrate an antigen, serial increasing 2-fold dilutions are made in saline, beginning with 1 : 10 and distributed in a 0.2-ml volume; 0.2 ml of diluent is added in place of serum and then 0.4 ml of a 0.5% suspension of chicken or human O erythrocytes. The tubes or trays are held at the required temperature—22°C for types A and B, 4°C for type C—and the result read 1–2 hours later, as soon as the cell control has settled. The titer of the antigen, under the conditions of the test, is determined by the highest dilution giving complete agglutination. This dilution is said to contain 1 hemagglutinating unit in the volume used.

For the HI test, the antigen is first titrated and the dilution that contains 4 units per 0.2 ml is determined. The sera, treated as indicated in Section III,A,4, are diluted in serial increasing 2-fold dilutions, beginning at 1 : 10, using the same diluent as for the antigen and cells. The serum dilutions are distributed in 0.2-ml amounts; to them is added 4 units of antigen in a 0.2-ml volume, and the mixtures are incubated at room temperature for 30–60 minutes. Several controls are included: serum alone in dilution 1 : 10 to determine efficacy of removal of nonspecific agglutinins; an antigen control that consists of an amount of antigen similar to that added to the sera; and a known positive serum and a known negative serum, in dilutions. At the end of the incubation of the serum–antigen mixtures, the antigen control is titrated by diluting it in 2-fold dilutions to ascertain that it has retained its power under the conditions of incubation. The red cells, 0.4 ml of a 0.5% suspension, are now added to all the tubes or wells, and when the cell-control tubes have settled the test is read.

2. Method for Arboviruses

The procedure with the arboviruses requires pH adjustment. Titration of an antigen from a new virus or of a new batch from an established one is done at various pH values to determine the active range and titer. Using as diluent borate–saline with 0.4% bovine plasma albumin (BS–BPA), serial 2-fold dilutions are made in a master set of test tubes, beginning with 1 : 10 or higher, in 2- or 3-ml volumes. Dilutions are distributed in 0.2-ml (or 1-drop) amounts in tubes or trays, as required, in descending order; six to eight sets of dilutions are thus prepared. To each tube is added 0.2 ml (or 1 drop) of BS–BPA diluent, bringing the volume to 0.4 ml (or 2 drops). The tubes or wells in a row, each row representing a titration, receive goose erythrocytes suspended at optical density 0.750 in virus-adjusting diluents (VAD) that will give a series of pH values between 6.0 and 7.4 at 0.2 intervals; the amount of red cell suspension added is 0.4 ml (or 2 drops). Tubes with diluent in place of antigen are included as cell controls at each pH. The test is incubated at either 37° or 22°C until the cells have settled in the control tubes. These titrations show the pH range of activity as well as the optimal pH to use; ordinarily the latter is in the middle of the usable range, which can be relatively wide, i.e., a similar titer appears at several consecutive pH values, or sharp with the titer of an antigen falling off rapidly at pH values close to the optimal. Only the selected pH is used in subsequent titrations of an antigen.

In the HI test, sera are tested against one or several antigens, depending on the purpose of the test. In serological surveys in certain areas of the world it is not unusual to use as many as 15 or 20 antigens. When multiple antigens are used, master dilutions of each serum are made in BS–BPA, in test tubes, beginning at 1 : 10 and increasing serially in 2-fold steps for 6–10 dilutions. These are distributed in as many sets of tubes or rows of wells as there will be antigens in the test, in either 0.2-ml or 1-drop amounts. To each set of dilutions is added an antigen so diluted in BS–BPA that 0.2 ml (or 1 drop) contains 8 units. Controls consisting of each serum at the first dilution, without antigen, and antigens as added to the test, i.e., 8 units, are included. The mixtures are incubated at either 4°C for 18 hours or at 22°C for 3 hours. At the end of this incubation, the antigen controls are diluted out serially in order to titrate them at the end of the incubation period. Red cells suspended in VAD's at the required pH for each antigen are added, 0.4 ml (or 2 drops). Incubation is done as for the antigen titration, either at 37° or 22°C.

C. Chemical Reagents and Other Supplies

All reagents are prepared in glass-distilled or demineralized water (formulas from Clarke and Casals, 1958).

1. Acid–Citrate–Dextrose (ACD)

This solution is prepared as follows: Sodium citrate ($NaC_6H_5O_7 \cdot 2H_2O$) 11.26 gm, citric acid ($H_3C_6H_5O_7 \cdot 2H_2O$) 4 gm, dextrose 11 gm, and water to 500 ml. The solution is sterilized by autoclaving for 10 minutes at 10 lb pressure.

2. Dextrose–Gelatin–Veronal (DGV)

Veronal (barbital) 58 gm, gelatin 0.6 gm, sodium Veronal (sodium barbital) 0.38 gm, $CaCl_2$ (anhydrous) 0.02 gm, $MgSO_4 \cdot 7H_2O$ 0.12 gm, NaCl 8.5 gm, dextrose 10 gm, and water to 1000 ml.

The Veronal (barbital) used is crystallized once by chilling a saturated solution of USP barbital in hot ethyl alcohol. The sodium veronal is prepared from USP barbital by making a saturated solution of the latter in ethyl alcohol at room temperature and precipitating the sodium salt by gradually adding, with stirring, an alcoholic solution of NaOH (1.5–2.0 M) until the suspension is alkaline. The crystals are collected on a Buchner funnel and dried.

The DGV solution is prepared by dissolving the Veronal and gelatin in 250 ml of water and heating. This solution is combined with the other reagents and remaining water; it is sterilized by autoclaving for 10 minutes at 10 lb pressure.

3. Borate–Saline (BS) at pH 9.0

This solution is 0.05 M borate–0.12 M NaCl and is prepared from the following concentrated stocks: (1) 1.5 M NaCl, NaCl 87.675 gm, water to 1000 ml; (2) 0.5 M boric acid, H_3BO_3 30.92 gm, distilled water to 1000 ml; (3) 1 M sodium hydroxide, NaOH 58.5 gm, water to 1000 ml. For BS of pH 9, 80 ml of (1), 100 ml of (2), and 24 ml of (3) is diluted to 1000 ml in water.

4. Borate–Saline with Bovine Plasma Albumin (BS–BPA) at pH 9

A 4% stock solution of bovine albumin (Armour fraction V) is made in BS at pH 9; since the albumin may lower the pH value somewhat, it is adjusted to 9 with 2 M NaOH. The working solution for the test is a 1 : 10 dilution of this 4% stock in BS pH 9; the concentration of albumin is, therefore, 0.4%.

5. Virus-Adjusting Diluents (VAD)

These are 0.15 M NaCl–0.2 M phosphate diluents. The following stock solutions are prepared: (1) 1.5 M NaCl; (2) 2 M dibasic sodium phosphate, Na_2HPO_4 (anhydrous) 283.96 gm, water to 1000 ml; (3) 2 M monobasic sodium phosphate, $NaH_2PO_4 \cdot H_2O$ 276.02 gm, water to 1000 ml. With these, 10 times diluted stocks are prepared: (a) 0.15 M NaCl–0.2 M Na_2HPO_4, by mixing 100 ml of (1), 100 ml of (2), and water to 800 ml; (b) 0.15 M NaCl–0.2 M NaH_2PO_4, by mixing 100 ml of (1), 100 ml of (3), and 800 ml of water. To have working VAD with pH values ranging 5.75–7.4, the diluted stocks are mixed in the proportions tabulated here.

pH	a	b
5.75	3	97
6.0	12.5	87.5
6.2	22	78
6.4	32	68
6.6	45	55
6.8	55	45
7.0	64	36
7.2	72	28
7.4	79	21

It must be stressed that the pH values shown are those resulting from mixing equal parts of BSB–BPA and the corresponding VAD. It is necessary to ascertain the pH of the mixture and make adjustments, usually very slight.

6. *Phosphate-Buffered Saline (PBS)*

This is a 0.15 M NaCl–0.005 M phosphate diluent, pH 7.2; it is prepared by dissolving NaCl 8.5 gm, Na_2HPO_4 (anhydrous) 0.56 gm, and KH_2PO_4 0.14 gm in water to a volume of 1000 ml.

7. *Plastic Trays and Dropping Pipets*

Plastic trays of several models are supplied by various manufacturers: Linbro Chemical Co., New Haven, Connecticut; Cooke Engineering Co., Alexandria, Virginia; Prestware, Ltd., South Down Works, Kingston Road, Raynes Park, London, S.W. 20.

Dropping pipets for microtests can be easily and economically prepared as follows: 18-gage, 2-inch long hypodermic needles are cut off near the tip to eliminate the bevel. This is done by holding the needle in a collet on a lathe and cutting it by means of a small grindstone in a Handee grinder. The needle is attached to a glass connector from a blood transfusion set, and a 1-ml rubber bulb is used for aspirating the solutions and controlling the delivery of drops. An 18-gage neeedle delivers 40–42 drops per milliliter.

Specially calibrated pipets and diluting wire loops for microtests are also available commercially.

IV. Complement-Fixation (CF) Test

A. General Considerations

The property that antigen–antibody complexes have of combining with complement constitutes the basis for a serological test. By mixing in a test tube complement and two distinct antigenic systems, the first one being the variable under investigation and the second a constant consisting of sheep erythrocytes and an antisheep antibody (hemolysin), the second system acts as an indicator through which the reaction, positive or negative, given by the first is visualized. As one of the effects of complement on the sheep erythrocyte–antisheep antibody complex is hemolysis, absence of hemolysis in the tube indicates that there was no free complement, hence that it had been adsorbed by the first system. When a known positive antigen was used, this result shows that the serum had antibodies against it, and when a known positive serum was employed, that the antigen was effective.

While almost exclusively used, the direct hemolytic complement-fixation test is not the only type; others exist, for example, indirect hemolytic complement fixation and conglutinating complement fixation. Because their use in animal virology is restricted, these tests will not be described here. In this section the designation complement-fixation (CF) test is used—as it is in general—as equivalent to direct hemolytic complement-fixation test.

Certain applications of the test were mentioned in Section I, such as detection of antigens common to several or all members of a type or group (influenza A, influenza B, reoviruses, adenoviruses, some of the arboviruses groups, etc.). This reaction is thus much used for group placement in the identification of viral isolates. With other agents, such as arboviruses of group A and Coxsackie viruses, the relative specificity of the reaction obtainable with immune sera produced in experimental animals serves for purposes of specific identification.

An area in which this test is extensively used is in the diagnosis of a large number of viral infections of man. Circulating antibodies detectable by CF appear to be the result of a recent or relatively recent infection, mostly associated with clinical manifestations; their rate of development is slower than that of neutralizing or HI antibodies. As a result, the test is useful as an aid to the diagnosis, since, by testing two specimens of serum, one taken early in the acute phase of the disease and the other 2 or 3 weeks later, it is possible to detect a significant rise in the titer of antibody, 4-fold or greater, more often than with other serological tests. An added reason for the use of the CF test with this type of clinical studies is that it is relatively simple to perform, technically dependable, and well adjusted to large numbers of specimens. With infections caused by a virus that belongs in a group of antigenically related agents, no specificity can always be anticipated in the diagnosis, but at least the group in which the infecting agent falls can be ascertained.

As a tool for conducting serological surveys in a population, the CF test is not of much help, because, in general, CF antibodies are short-lived in the host after clinical infections and of low titers in asymptomatic ones. Therefore, at a given time it is to be anticipated that only the individuals in a population having had a recent contact will be positive. If used in a survey, the CF test should be used as an adjunct to neutralization or HI tests, the latter two showing the overall extent of the infections, the former the recent ones.

Anticomplementary effect, a property that some sera and antigens have to combine with or destroy complement, and nonspecific reactions such as given by some tissue extracts, exudates, and bacterial filtrates, which in the presence of normal or antigenically unrelated sera make complexes capable of fixing complement—although neither serum nor extract is anticomplementary—constitute the two main causes of error and sources of difficulty in interpreting the CF test.

The best, most reliable method for eliminating anticomplementary and nonspecific reactions of antigens and sera is to purify them by eliminating the interfering substances. The methods used for preparation of antigens (Section I) in great part eliminate substances that have anticomplementary and nonspecific actions. Among the methods are extraction with organic solvents, centrifugation, filtration, and adsorption. Removal of anticomplementary action from sera is often impossible, in which case the sera can be used only at a higher dilution than that at which they act inspecifically or they are not fit for the test. Sera that have a moderate degree of anticomplementary or nonspecific effect can often be cleaned by heating at temperatures slightly higher than that required for inactivation of complement, the optimal temperatures varying with the donor species (see Section IV,B,3). Centrifugation of the heated sera in an angle-head centrifuge at 15,000–18,000 rpm for 30 minutes further improves them. Other procedures are precipitation with acetone or adsorption with kaolin or Sephadex. Addition of 1 part of fresh guinea pig serum to 4 parts of the given serum followed by heating at 60°C has also been recommended.

When using sera from animals experimentally immunized, care must be exercised, in order to reduce nonspecific reactions, not to inoculate an animal with infected tissues from the species that is used as source material for preparation of the antigen, unless the same species supplies the serum, infected tissues, and antigen.

While the essentials of the test are constant, the details on how to carry it out show great variation, involving volume of the reagents, vessel or container, incubation of the first phase, amount of complement, criterion for end-point hemolysis, concentration of erythrocytes, composition of the diluent, etc. Some of the details are important, such as amount of complement, criterion for end-point hemolysis, and incubation of the first phase; others, such as volume of reagents and container, are less so and depend to a considerable extent on individual choice or expediency.

In general and for routine use in diagnostic laboratories, the end point for hemolysis is taken at the 100% hemolysis. This is considered a far less sensitive and accurate end point than that determined by 50% hemolysis. However, reading of a test on the latter basis can be done accurately only by using color standards or photometers and in test tubes, not by the microtest on trays. Furthermore, since 5 units of complement are ordinarily employed with the 50% end point, and this amount of complement is close to 2 units in the 100% hemolysis test, there is, in fact, little difference between the two.

The total volume of the combined reagents used in the test has evolved, particularly in recent years, toward the use of microtests, with the measurement and delivery of the reagents being done in terms of drops, in a manner similar to the HI test. In various described tests, the total volume varies between 1.5 ml and 0.15 ml; it appears to be of no consequence in determining the outcome, provided the relative proportions of the reagents remain constant. In the CF test as usually carried out there are basically 6 equal units of volume to consider; 1 each is taken by the serum and the antigen, 2 by the complement, and 2 by the hemolytic system (1 volume of hemolysin and 1 of erythrocyte suspension). The volume unit varies from 0.25 ml to 0.025 ml (1 drop). Tests in which the volume unit is 0.1 ml or greater are done in tubes, and those with smaller volumes on plastic trays similar to the ones used in HA tests. When in a test a reagent is left out, the missing volume is made up with diluent.

B. TECHNIQUES FOR THE TEST

No useful purpose would be served by giving several versions that differ in detail; the illustrative techniques to be described have evolved in our laboratory in studies with arboviruses and other viruses and incorporate methods from other sources as well.

1. Diluent

The diluent used is a veronal buffer (Mayer et al., 1946). By recrystallizing the Veronal and preparing the sodium salt as described (Section III,C) the diluent can be used without autoclaving or aging. The formula of the 5 times concentrated buffer is: Veronal (diethyl barbituric acid, barbitone) 5.75 gm; sodium Veronal (sodium barbiturate) 3.75 gm; magnesium chloride ($MgCl_2 \cdot 6HO_2$) 1.68 gm; calcium chloride ($CaCl_2$) 0.28 gm; and distilled water to 2000 ml. For use in the test the stock is diluted by adding 4 volumes of distilled water to 1 volume; the pH of the diluted buffer is 7.3–7.4.

2. Antigen

Preparation of antigens is described in Section I,C,2.

3. Serum

Sera are inactivated or heated in order to destroy complement that may be present; heating also eliminates moderate anticomplementary or nonspecific effects. The optimal temperature of inactivation, based on observation, varies somewhat with the different species (Casals and Palacios, 1941): for guinea pig sera, the usual 56°C is satisfactory;

human and mouse, 60°C; rabbit, hamster, and rhesus monkeys, 63°–65°C, all for 20 minutes, and, with the higher temperatures, after dilution to 1 : 4. Experience shows the proper temperatures of inactivation of sera from other animal species; however, 60°C seems to be adequate for most.

4. Complement

Lyophilized complement of consistently high titer and good quality is commercially available. While its titer for a given lot remains unchanged over more than 1 year, titrations of complement must be included in every test. Since in accurate titrations the amounts of complement in the serial tubes are by design very close, a gradation of hemolysis is noted over several adjacent places in the series. Because the unit of complement is defined as the smallest amount giving complete hemolysis (or 50% hemolysis), the estimate of the degree of hemolysis must be accurate. This can hardly be done in plastic trays with a micromethod; therefore, even when using this method, the preliminary titration of complement is done in tubes with at least 0.6 ml final volume of reagents.

5. Sheep Erythrocytes

Stabilized and standardized red cells are also commercially available as a 10% suspension and have been found consistently satisfactory. If no such supply is available, sheep are bled in Alsevers' solution. The concentration of cells used in the test is 2.5% of packed cells. This concentration, when diluted 10-fold, has an OD of 0.450 in the Coleman spectrophotometer at a wavelength of 490 mμ. In other described tests the cell concentrations used vary from 0.4% in microtests to 2–3% in macrotests.

6. Hemolysin

Commercial preparations of antisheep hemolysin in 50% glycerol are available. While a titer is given for such preparations, it is necessary to retitrate it in the system used. The titer remains unchanged for years if kept at 4°C. The titration determines the minimal hemolytic dose (MHD) or amount, which under the conditions of the test completely hemolyzes the sheep cells in the presence of 3–4 units of complement. An excess of hemolysin must be avoided to prevent agglutination of the cells before hemolysis occurs.

Titration of hemolysin is done as follows. Amboceptor is diluted to 1 : 100, then in 2-fold steps to 1 : 12,800 or higher. To a series of 100 × 13 mm test tubes is introduced, in descending order, 0.1 ml of each dilution. To all tubes is then added 0.1 ml of the cell suspension and 0.4 ml of complement, diluted so that, judging from previous titrations, it contains 3–4 units. The tubes are incubated at 37°C for 30 minutes. The highest dilution giving complete hemolysis is the MHD, and in a test three MHD's are used. The titration of hemolysin is done only once for the particular lot.

7. Container or Vessel and Volume

Test tubes, 100×13 mm, with a total volume of 0.6 ml are used for titrations of hemolysin and preliminary titrations of complement. Disposable plastic trays with 96 wells, each with a capacity of 2.5 ml, or smaller ones with a capacity of about 0.3 ml and a total volume of 0.15 ml, are used for the test in general.

8. Test

The test is based on the 100% hemolysis end point. A preliminary titration of complement is carried out to determine the unit or smallest amount that completely hemolyzes the red cells; in the test 1.8–2 units are used, depending on circumstances.

a. *Titration of Complement.* Lyophilized complement is rehydrated and diluted to a working dilution or stock, in the current system, 1 : 50. A series is prepared in test tubes by adding decreasing amounts of the working stock and increasing amounts of diluent, as follows:

Complement, 1 : 50, in ml:	2.0	1.6	1.4	1.2	1.0	0.8	0.7	0.6	0.4
Diluent, in ml:	1.0	1.4	1.6	1.8	2.0	2.2	2.3	2.4	2.6

This series constitutes the master set of complement dilutions and is used for both preliminary and final titrations.

For the preliminary titration, beginning with the smallest amount of complement to the right, 0.3 ml of each mixture is measured into test tubes, followed by 0.1 ml of diluent. In this manner a series is obtained in which the amounts of working stock of complement (1 : 50), are, from left to right, 0.2 ml, 0.16 ml, 0.14 ml, etc., down to 0.04 ml, and the volume of fluid in each tube is 0.4 ml.

A 2.5% suspension of sheep erythrocytes and a dilution of hemolysin (usually 1 : 500) that contains three MHD's per 0.1 ml are prepared. Equal volumes of these are mixed, held at room temperature for 15 minutes, and 0.2 ml of the mixture added to the tubes of the titration. After shaking well the mixture is incubated in a water bath at 37°C for 30 minutes. A tube with the hemolytic system alone is included as a control of cell stability.

Following incubation the titration is read, and the smallest amount causing complete hemolysis is the unit of complement. In the test, between 1.8 and 2 units are used; as an illustration, if in a titration the unit is 0.1 ml, 0.18–0.2 ml will be used; the decision is based on previous experience with the type of reagents used in the particular test, whether the antigens and sera tend to be anticomplementary or, on the contrary, to promote complement action. If in this illustrative example it is decided to use 1.8 units or 0.18 ml of the working stock, the dilution of this stock is adjusted so as to have the required amount of complement in 0.2 ml.

b. *Test Proper.* The test proper is carried out on disposable plastic trays (see Section IV,B,7) with all measurements being made in terms of 1 drop instead of 0.1 ml. The drop, delivered through a squarely cut 18-gage hypodermic needle (Section III,C), has a volume very close to 0.025 ml.

Dilutions of the sera and antigens required are made in master sets of test tubes. Depending on the purpose of the particular test, the format varies, but there are basically three types.

(*i*) *Determination of the titer of an antigen and of relationships between viruses.* In this case simultaneous dilutions of sera and antigen are used—the so-called box or checkerboard titration. In general, antigen and sera are diluted in increasing 2-fold dilutions, beginning at 1 : 4.

(*ii*) *Identification of an antigen.* The antigen has already been tested with the homologous antiserum, is known to be positive, and its titer has been determined. The problem is to identify the antigen by testing it against typing sera of known titers. The usual pattern to follow is to test the problem antigen at two or three dilutions, representing, respectively, 2, 8, and, if the titer is high enough, 32 units, against typing sera in 2-fold dilutions beginning at 1 : 4 or 1 : 8 and following with six or eight dilutions, depending on titer. By thus including various amounts of antigen, it is often possible to reach a specific diagnosis even with viruses with which cross-reactions occur, but at lower levels than the homologous one.

(*iii*) *Determination of antibodies in a serum against reference antigens.* This may have as object to aid in the diagnosis of a current illness, to investigate viral relationships, or to test the efficacy of an immunizing vaccine or schedule. Dilutions of serum of 1 : 4–1 : 8 up are tested against a constant amount of one or various antigens representing 4–16 units.

Whatever the pattern of a given test, controls consisting of a normal antigen, i.e., uninfected source material treated as for preparing an antigen, and normal sera, or, better yet, preinfection or preimmunization serum from the individual, must be included.

The test is carried out by distributing the serum dilutions in 1-drop amounts (or, in general, 1 volume). Titrated complement, 1.8–2.0 units, in 2 drops, is added next, followed by 1 drop of antigen. The mixtures are placed in the cold at 4°C for 18 hours and care is taken to cover the wells to prevent evaporation.

Along with the test proper, final titrations of complement are also held at 4°C overnight. These titrations constitute a determination, under the actual conditions of the test, of the anticomplementary effect of each of the antigens and sera used as well as a titration of the complement alone. The antigens and sera are used in these titrations only at the highest concentration at which they appear in the test. The final titrations are done in the following manner.

From the master set of complement dilutions (see Section IV,B,8,a), 3 drops of each amount from 0.04 ml to 0.2 ml are delivered into columns of wells in a tray; each column consists of as many spaces as there are sera and antigens to be tested plus one. Then to each row is delivered 1 drop of a serum or antigen, and to the last row, 1 drop of diluent. In this fashion a series of titrations of complement similar to the preliminary one is obtained, each in the presence of a different reagent in addition to the one with complement alone.

After 18 hours at 4°C the trays with the test and final titrations of complement are held at room temperature for 15 minutes. At this time are prepared a dilution of hemolysin containing 3 MHD's in 1 drop and a 2.5% suspension of sheep erythrocytes; equal volumes of these are mixed and also held at room temperature for 15 minutes. Two drops of the mixture are added to each well and the trays are placed in the warm room at 37°C immediately to minimize agglutination before hemolysis takes place; after 30 or 40 minutes, the result is read. Following a usual notation, complete hemolysis is recorded as 0, no hemolysis as 4, with intermediate values ±, 1, 2, and 3. The titer of a serum or antigen is determined by the highest dilution that gives a 3 or better fixation.

9. Partial Hemolysis Test

As an illustration of a test in which partial, 50% end-point hemolysis is used as well as color standards for its estimation, see Laboratory Branch Complement Fixation (LBCF) test (Communicable Disease Center, 1962).

V. Fluorescent-Antibody (FA) Techniques

The FA techniques are used as a routine, sensitive diagnostic method with a few animal viruses. Their main application is, however, as a procedure for determining the location of viral antigens in the infected cell and the site in the cell at which the elaboration of antigens is completed. With these techniques it is also possible to follow infection of individual cells in sections or cell cultures when no abnormality is as yet otherwise seen.

The basis of the entire methodology (Coons *et al.*, 1941) is that antibodies in sera when conjugated with fluorescent substances retain combining sites free to react with antigens, and the resulting antigen–antibody complex is visualized by fluorescence (for a detailed account, see Chapter 10 of this volume; also Coons, 1958).

Both the direct and the indirect techniques are used in studies with animal viruses. The former is mainly applied to particular diagnostic problems, for instance, detection of rabies virus in brain tissue, where a single labeled antiserum suffices. The indirect method is preferred in other instances when the problem is to determine the presence of antibodies in sera, against one or several viruses; to label each serum might be a large task, but with the indirect method only one labeled antiserum for each animal species involved is required.

Staining of complement fixed by the antigen–antibody complex formed *in situ* represents a further simplification in that only one labeled serum, antiguinea pig serum, suffices; for technical reasons this type of test seems to have had only limited application.

In its use with animal viruses, perhaps more than with other applications, the main difficulty with the FA test is the presence of nonspecific adsorption of the dye by tissue constituents not related to the antigenic reaction, thus creating difficulties of interpretation. Ways have been devised to eliminate nonspecific adsorption, and the success of conjugation of the dye with the serum is measured by the efficacy of the attempts.

It is to be noted that the immune sera, both that directed against the viral antigen as well as the one directed against the specific serum used in the indirect test, must have high reacting titers; also that the conjugated serum for the indirect test must be prepared using as antigen not whole serum from the species supplying the antiviral serum but that fraction only in which the antibodies are located, the globulins; similarly, only the globulin fraction of the immune serum in the direct test is used in the conjugate.

The labeling compound generally used is fluorescein isothiocyanate, which under the fluorescence microscope gives a brilliant yellow-green color; the optimal ratio, by weight, of fluorescein to protein for conjugation is given variously as 1 : 20, 1 : 40, and 1 : 50. Conjugation requires an alkaline medium and holding the mixture overnight at 4°C. Commercial preparations of a number of conjugated sera for use in the indirect test are available.

The main details of various methods described (Coons and Kaplan, 1950; Goldstein et al., 1961; Liu, 1964; Johnson, 1964; Wood et al., 1965) for the preparation of the fluorescent antibody are as follows.

For the direct method, the animal is immunized with the virus according to the selected schedule. The serum globulins are precipitated by half saturation with ammonium sulfate, the precipitate taken up in water, introduced in a cellophane bag, and dialyzed against numerous changes of phosphate buffer at pH 7.0 until no trace remains of ammonium ion. The globulin fraction is now ready for conjugation.

To prepare a serum directed against the serum protein of another animal species for use in the indirect method, for example antihuman rabbit immune serum, the globulins in human serum are precipitated by half saturation with ammonium sulfate and used for immunization of rabbits following a schedule known to result in high-titered antibodies. In turn, the globulin fraction of the rabbit antihuman serum is precipitated with half saturation with ammonium sulfate and conjugated.

Conjugation is carried out under conditions that insure the optimal ratio of fluorescein isothiocyanate to globulin. The protein concentration of the globulin solution is determined; the pH of the solution is adjusted to 8.8–9.0 by means of sodium carbonate–sodium bicarbonate buffer and the fluorescein added, 1 mg per 50 mg of globulin (Johnson, 1964) or 1 mg per 20 mg of globulin (Liu, 1964), after which conjugation is completed by holding overnight at 4°C. Excess, unconjugated fluorescein is removed either by dialysis against phosphate buffer or by passing the conjugate through a column of Sephadex G-50, which retains the free fluorescein while allowing the conjugated protein through. The conjugate is stored in small amounts at −20°C or lower temperatures.

For best results, fluorescent conjugates are adsorbed with powdered tissues before they are used, in order to remove nonspecific background staining. The selection of tissues for adsorption is empirical; as a rule, liver tissue from mice or monkeys is employed. The tissue, suspended in saline by means of a homogenizer, is repeatedly extracted with acetone and kept as a dry powder; when required, a sample of the conjugate is adsorbed with the powder.

An improved method for preparation of the fluorescein–serum conjugate with little or no nonspecific staining is described by Goldstein *et al.* (1961) and modified by Wood *et al.* (1965). The method requires preparation of a chromatographically homogeneous antibody globulin for coupling with the dye; following coupling the conjugate is subjected to fractionation on a diethylaminoethyl- (DEAE)-cellulose column. The fractionation removes both the overcoupled globulin fraction that gives brilliant but nonspecific staining as well as the undercoupled fraction that gives poor staining and sensitivity. The method, in addition, does away with the need for adsorption with powdered tissue.

The specimens for examination are of various types: frozen sections of unfixed tissues made with a microtome placed in a cryostat at $-20°C$, 6–8 mμ thick and collected on clean slides; tissue culture cells grown on cover slips in Leighton tubes; imprint smears of tissues, such as brain or liver; and smears of nasal secretions or exudates.

Fixation is done as a rule by immersion in acetone for 10 minutes at room temperature, or longer, from 4 hours to overnight, at 4° or $-20°C$. The tissue is then allowed to dry for some minutes at 37°C and is ready for staining.

In the direct method, following fixation, staining is done by dropping with a pipet a sufficient amount of the conjugate on the specimen and keeping it for 30 minutes at room temperature or at 37°C; the slides are next rinsed for 10 minutes at room temperature with phosphate buffer, mounted with buffered glycerol and a cover slip, and examined.

In the indirect method, after fixation, the specimen is first treated with the unlabeled antiserum for 30 minutes at room temperature, rinsed with buffered saline for 10 minutes, after which the antiglobulin conjugate is added and allowed to react for another 30 minutes at room temperature; final rinsing and mounting is done as in the direct method.

Examination of the specimens with the fluorescence microscope is done using ultraviolet light deriving, as a rule, from a high-pressure mercury vapor arc, various types of which are commercially available; also available are different types of exciter filters that cut all wavelengths in the visible range—above 4200 Å. A barrier filter between the objective and eyepiece to suppress wavelengths in the ultraviolet range—under 4200 Å—completes the system.

The applications of the FA technique to various basic studies are numerous. It has been of particular help in the study of the development and appearance of viral antigens in the host cell and in determining the site of probable completion and maturation of the viral particle. It has also facilitated the antigenic comparison between related agents such as influenza strains within a type and of different serotypes in the arbovirus groups. In the diagnostic field, the FA method demonstrated the presence of rabies antigens in smears of brain tissue and salivary glands of infected animals (Goldwasser *et al.*, 1959) and is now a standard laboratory procedure for rabies diagnosis; with other viral infections, however, its practical value requires confirmation. Other suggested diagnostic applications are in herpes (Biegeleisen *et al.*, 1959), influenza (Liu, 1961), smallpox (Murray, 1963), rubella (G. C. Brown *et al.*, 1964), and respiratory syncytial virus (Schieble *et al.*, 1965).

VI. Immunodiffusion

Immunodiffusion is a technique by which the result of a precipitin reaction is visualized by conducting the test in a semisolid medium. As they diffuse against each other, the reactants precipitate at the zone of optimal proportions; the precipitate appears as a readily visible whitish, opalescent line, or lines in complex systems, that remains stabilized. Various jelling agents can be used, but, as a rule, agar is the most commonly utilized, particularly with animal viruses.

The modern use of immunodiffusion derives from the work of Oudin (1946), Ouchterlony (1948), and Elek (1948); its application to studies with animal viruses ensued and rapidly expanded. Of the different types of immunodiffusion (Crowle, 1961), the one generally used in virological studies is the two-dimensional radial double diffusion in plates. A combination of this method with electrophoresis resulted in a sensitive analytical method, immunoelectrophoresis (Grabar and Williams, 1955). An additional development, consisting in the use of a radioactive-tagged reagent, radioimmunoelectrophoresis, increased further the sensitivity of the method by recording a reaction not visible to the naked eye.

A. DOUBLE DIFFUSION

The double-diffusion plate system is commonly used for qualitative tests, but it can be easily adapted to antibody titration (Clarke, 1964). In essence, an agar gel is prepared using a concentration of 0.7–1.5% and as liquid phase either distilled water or phosphate buffer pH 7–7.4; a preservative is added to prevent bacterial contamination. It is particularly important to maintain a constant temperature and a humid atmosphere during the entire procedure in order to prevent artifacts. The size, shape, and placement of the depots of reactants vary with the particular problem and with personal predilection; cups or wells in the gel are made with a cutter on puncher and are used as reservoirs.

This technique has been used successfully with representative viruses of most if not all groups (Table I). The main applications have been to the study of antigenic variation of viruses and to the determination of antigenic relationships among them; these two areas are of great consequence in taxonomy. The technique has also been applied to the investigation of the distinct components in complex viral antigens and to the study of their nature. Illustrative instances of these applications are in influenza (Jensen and Francis, 1953b), smallpox (Gispen, 1955), myxomatosis and fibromatosis (Fayet *et al.*, 1957), foot-and-mouth disease and vesicular stomatitis (F. Brown and Crick, 1957), adenoviruses (Pereira, 1960), and arboviruses (Clarke, 1964).

Application to diagnosis of clinical infections has been attempted with several viruses. Dumbell and Nizamuddin (1959) described a simple and rapid diagnostic procedure with smallpox using as antigens suspended scrapings and fluids from lesions or suspensions of scabs from patients as well as materials from infected embryonated hen's eggs. With known positive sera, precipitation lines appeared in 2 hours. With enteroviruses (Schmidt and Lennette, 1962), the test can be used successfully for early diagnosis of Coxsackie virus infection of man; while the test requires concentrated antigens, the use of a microtechnique and adequate screening permits routine use. The same authors found, in addition, that the test gave fewer heterotypic reactions than the CF test and that it detected a higher proportion of significant antibody rises than the neutralization test.

As an illustration, the method employed by Clarke (1964) is outlined here, since it embodies a number of recent improvements.

Ordinary glass microscope slides, 3×1 inch, are used as carriers. In order to prevent subsequent seepage, they are pretreated with a thin layer of 0.2% agar in water and dried. The agar is dissolved in water to give a 2% concentration and mixed in the molten state with borate-buffered NaCl to give a final concentration of 1% agar in 0.05 M NaCl–0.05 M borate at pH 9; 0.01% final concentration of thiomersal is added as a preservative. The molten agar is pipeted onto the slide, 1 ml per square inch of surface, and allowed to harden for 2 hours or longer in a humidified chamber. A central well and a series of peripheral ones surrounding it, up to six, are cut using a plastic template and a fitted, hollow, stainless-steel cutter; the cut agar is aspirated through the cutter. The wells are 4 mm in diameter and about 2.5 mm apart. The wells are filled with the sera and antigens using a 0.25-ml tuberculin syringe fitted with a one-quarter inch long 27-gage needle. The reaction is allowed to proceed at room temperature in a humidified chamber until precipitation lines are observed, from a few hours to 1 or 2 days later; photographic permanent records are kept.

B. IMMUNOELECTROPHORESIS

Immunoelectrophoresis is a form of immunodiffusion in which electrophoretic fractionation of a reagent is produced first, then the fractions are brought in contact with the second reagent in the same medium in which electrophoresis was performed (Grabar and Williams, 1955; Grabar, 1959). A microtechnique is used in which the reaction is carried out on a glass microscope slide.

The technique, while still not extensively used in animal virology, offers valuable analytical possibilities. Pereira *et al.* (1959), for example, demonstrated the presence of three different antigens in adenovirus type 5, distinct from the virus particle itself. The method that they used, also applicable to other agents, consists in preparing on a glass slide a layer of 2% agar in 0.05 M borate–phosphate buffer at pH 8.5. The same buffer is used in the electrode baths and to moisten the lint-connecting strips between the slide and the electrode baths. Electrophoresis is carried out at room temperature for 7 or 8 hours, using a 20-mA current. The antigen, 0.1 ml, is placed in a well punched in the agar; the antiserum, placed in preformed side channels or troughs, is allowed to react, after electrophoresis of the antigen, at 4°C in a moist chamber for 5–6 days. The gel is washed, dried, stained with naphthalene black, and saved as a permanent record.

C. RADIOAUTOGRAPHY

A refinement and improvement of both immunodiffusion and immunoelectrophoresis is the combination of either with a radioactive reagent, resulting in radioimmunoelectrophoresis or radioautography. The antigen is tagged with a radioactive isotope, and following electrophoresis of the serum, the fractions are made to react with the labeled antigen to form the precipitation arcs or lines, in which the antigen accumulates. The slide is covered with an x-ray film that, after the necessary contact, records the radioactive lines. Thus not only a permanent record is obtained but certain reactions that might be otherwise unobserved are visualized by this procedure.

Radioimmunoelectrophoresis has been employed in the study of various antigen–antibody reactions, such as between insulin and insulin-binding antibodies (Miller and Owen, 1960). Similar applications have been recently extended to the field of animal viruses. Ainbender *et al.* (1965) have applied the technique to the investigation of the human immunoglobulins that react with poliovirus. In order to have a sensitive technique, it is necessary to concentrate and purify the immunoglobulins and to use large amounts of poliovirus. Certain improvements, particularly the introduction in the system of an antihuman rabbit immune serum, have facilitated the recognition of the immune fractions that react with the poliovirus antigens as well as increased the sensitivity of the test. In the method described (Ainbender *et al.*, 1965), microscope glass slides were covered with 1% agar in 0.025 M Veronal buffer at pH 8.6, and in them were cut the appropriate wells and troughs. Poliovirus type 1 was the antigen used, grown in HeLa cells in a medium containing sodium phosphate-^{32}P. The human sera under investigation were placed in one of the wells and subjected to electrophoresis, then a rabbit antihuman serum was placed in the trough and allowed to diffuse and react with the human serum proteins. After this, the tagged poliovirus was added to the same trough and incubated for 24 hours at room temperature. The slides were then washed for 48 hours in a 1% solution of sodium chloride. The slides were then dried and placed in contact with x-ray film for 1 week, after which the same slides were stained with amido black. In this fashion was obtained a radioautograph and a stained record of the same preparation. By combining in one slide the polio-immune human serum under investigation, a rabbit antihuman serum, and radioactive-labeled poliovirus, the latter was bound only by some of the human serum globulins, which can be easily recognized by the radioautograph and identified among the numerous precipitation arcs by the stained preparation.

VII. Other Tests

Most of the tests briefly described in this section have not been widely applied since they were first reported; others are very recent and there is not as yet sufficient evidence to appraise them.

A. PRECIPITATION OR FLOCCULATION TEST

Precipitation tests in fluid medium have been applied to several animal viruses. Their use, however, has not been extensive, owing in part to the need to prepare purified and concentrated antigens in order to obtain a visible reaction and in part to the development of precipitation tests in semisolid media, which have proved technically more reliable and sensitive. An improvement in the sensitivity of the precipitation in fluid medium has been obtained by labeling one of the reagents with a radioactive isotope. The labeled reagent in the precipitate or its removal from the supernatant can be measured with accuracy when a visible reaction is hardly noticeable.

1. *Precipitation or Flocculation in Fluid Medium with Visible Reaction*

This type of reaction has been observed with vaccinia (Ledingham, 1931), polioviruses (Smith *et al.*, 1956; Smith, 1958; Schmidt and Lennette, 1959), and influenza and other myxoviruses (Belyavin, 1957).

The following technique has been used for the myxoviruses (Belyavin, 1957). As source of antigen, allantoic fluid from infected embryonated hen's eggs was used. Since the crude fluid is not usable because of nonspecific inhibitors, a degree of purification and concentration was achieved by adsorption and elution on human or fowl erythrocytes for influenza types A and B; for Newcastle disease virus, in addition, sedimentation by high-speed centrifugation was employed; and for mumps, only the latter procedure. The sera were inactivated at 56°C for 1 hour. The reaction was carried out in Dreyer's tubes, in which were mixed 0.3 ml of serum in dilutions with 0.3 ml of antigen containing a standardized amount of virus. The mixtures were incubated in a water bath at 37°C. After 4–5 hours the flocculation was assessed by means of a low-power magnifying glass.

With polioviruses types 1, 2, and 3 (Schmidt and Lennette, 1959), a microflocculation technique was used, resulting in considerable saving of materials. The antigens were obtained from HeLa cell cultures infected with a virus and purified and concentrated by one of three methods: high-speed centrifugation of the fluid; precipitation by dialysis against McIlvaine buffer at pH 4.3, followed by resuspension at pH 8.0 to a volume 1 : 50 of the original; and dialysis against a large volume of distilled water and concentration by pervaporation. The sera, human and from experimental animals, were inactivated twice at 56°C for 30 minutes to eliminate nonspecific reactions.

The reaction was carried out by mixing equal volumes of antigen and serum in dilutions in a Dreyer tube and examining a hanging-drop preparation of the mixture under the microscope; or by mixing 1 drop of serum and 1 of antigen in a small well or depression on a special Pyrex plate, allowing the mixture to react at 37°C for 18 hours, with care taken to prevent evaporation, and examining the mixture microscopically under low power to detect flocculation.

In spite of their apparent simplicity, the technical problems presented by the flocculation techniques militate strongly against their use. Good titer antigens, particularly with polioviruses, are not easy to obtain, and the reading of the test is such that it is not practical for even moderately large volume of work. In addition, the presence of any particulate material in the sera renders them unusable.

2. Precipitation in Fluid Medium and Detection by Means of Radioisotopes

Clarke and Black (1955) used immune sera labeled with [131]I. By holding the amount of iodine at a low level, no change was detected in the immunological reactivity of the antibody. The test is simple in execution; the immune serum or globulin is iodized under the required conditions and allowed to react with the viral antigen at 4°C overnight. The antigen–antibody complex is sedimented by centrifugation in a preparatory high-speed angle-head centrifuge, and the radioactivity of the sediment is measured in a Geiger counter. The method failed to show conclusive reaction with two arboviruses and their corresponding antisera, but demonstrated specific combination between a strain of influenza virus and its antiserum.

A considerable improvement on previous attempts to use radiolabeled reagents in serological tests with animal viruses is the method of Gerloff et al. (1962), which they named radioisotope precipitation (RIP) test. In essence, the test consists in a primary reaction between labeled virus—in this particular instance, poliovirus type 2—and its specific antibody. Subsequent addition to the system of an immune serum directed against the gamma-globulin (AGG) of the animal species supplying the antipoliovirus serum results in a secondary reaction, precipitation, between the last two elements. A readily separable flocculate forms consisting of AGG, polio-immune, and nonimmune serum combined with the immune globulin. Although this is a complex mixture, the criterion of virus–antibody reaction is not the visible precipitate but the precipitation of radioactivity. Even though direct precipitation of a radio-labeled reagent appears to be a simpler procedure, it is less sensitive than the RIP test.

The components of the RIP test are: radio-labeled virus, serum being examined for viral antibodies, and rabbit serum containing AGG for the serum being examined. The virus—poliovirus type 2—grown in KB tissue cultures was labeled with [32]P. The labeled virus was purified and concentrated by elution from a DEAE-cellulose column and centrifugation or by centrifugation in a CsCl density gradient. The preparation was diluted to the required volume in 0.02 M phosphate buffer at pH 7.1, containing 5% calf serum and stored in sealed ampules at −70°C until used.

Human sera from persons vaccinated with polioviruses and immune monkey sera were successfully employed in the reaction. Rabbit serum containing antiglobulins for human and monkey sera was prepared by one of the standard procedures, i.e., fractionation of the latter in a DEAE-cellulose column in order to separate the AGG, which was then used for immunizing the rabbits. The amount of AGG used in the RIP test is not critical provided it is in excess or in optimal proportion.

The test is simple, can be completed in 2–3 hours, and proceeds as follows: The three components, labeled virus, serum, and AGG, are appropriately diluted in 0.02 M Tris–HCl buffer at pH 7.6 in 0.9% NaCl. One tenth of a milliliter of radio-labeled virus suspension and 0.25 ml of test serum are mixed in a small test tube and incubated at 37°C for 1 hour, after which 0.25 ml of AGG is added and the incubation repeated as before. The precipitate formed is packed by centrifugation. The supernatant fluid is transferred to a plastic planchet, and the precipitate, taken up in distilled water, to another. The specimens are dried and radioactivity is determined. Total radioactivity and percentage of radioactivity precipitated (PRP) are calculated; the latter is an indicator and measure of the amount of virus–antibody reaction that has taken place.

The test has been used for titration of antibodies in sera. Also, by exposing the serum to unlabeled virus first and then to the labeled one, the reaction of the serum with the latter is diminished or absent, whereby the test can be used for titration of unlabeled virus.

B. AGGLUTINATION

Antigens can be adsorbed onto the surface of inert particles and the antigen-coated particles agglutinated by immune serum, resulting in an easily observable reaction. This type of reaction has been applied to various immune systems, including animal viruses, with different degrees of success. A number of particles have been used, of which erythrocytes are the most readily available and have, in addition, a narrow and well-defined size range. Other particles used are collodion, bentonite, latex (polymerized styrene), and bacterial cells. The reversed sequence, adsorption of antibody on the particles and agglutination by the antigen, has also been tried.

With animal viruses the most generally used particles are erythrocytes, resulting in a test that, in order to distinguish it from the HA test (Section III), is often designated the passive agglutination test. The erythrocytes can be used either with no treatment preceding contact with the antigen or following previous treatment with certain chemicals, ordinarily tannic acid and formaldehyde.

Untreated red cells have been used in tests with Newcastle disease

(Burnet and Anderson, 1946) and Japanese encephalitis and dengue
(Hale and Pillai, 1960) viruses; more recently, the technique was described by Lim and Pong, (1964) again for Japanese encephalitis and
dengue viruses and for Langat virus. As reported by the latter, the test,
designated sensitized erythrocyte agglutination (SEA), essentially consisted in treating a suspension of goose or chick erythrocytes with a
HA antigen by mixing equal parts of a 4% cell suspension and antigen
at a pH at which the antigen is active. After 1 hour at 2°C the mixture
was centrifuged and the red cells washed in saline and resuspended to
a 0.5% concentration in phosphate buffer at pH 7.6. The serum in dilutions was distributed on the agglutination trays and an equal volume
of sensitized erythrocytes was added. The test was read after 1 hour at
room temperature or after 18 hours at 4°C in the cold room.

Treatment of erythrocytes with tannic acid (Boyden, 1951) render
them capable of adsorbing antigens from solutions; red cells thus
treated are agglutinated by the corresponding antisera. This finding
has been applied to several animal viruses with, in some instances,
encouraging results. The erythrocytes have, in some cases, been treated
with formaldehyde before exposure to tannic acid in order to preserve
them for longer periods of time. The technique has been used with
herpesvirus (Scott *et al.*, 1957), adenoviruses (Friedman and Bennett,
1957; Ross and Ginsberg, 1958), and polioviruses (McKenna *et al.*,
1958).

With adenoviruses (Friedman and Bennett, 1957), a 4% suspension
of sheep cells in buffered saline at pH 7.2 was mixed with an equal
volume of a 1 : 20,000 solution of tannic acid in the same diluent. After
30 minutes contact at room temperature the cells were centrifuged,
washed, and resuspended in buffered saline to a 2% concentration. The
antigen, consisting of fluid from HeLa cell cultures infected with the
virus, was mixed with the tannic acid-treated cells. After 30 minutes at
room temperature, the antigen had attached itself to the erythrocytes
and these were now ready for the test. In the test serum dilutions in
amounts of 0.2 ml were mixed with an equal volume of the antigen-
coated cells and held at room temperature until ready to be read.

Coating of inert particles with antibody and agglutination by the
antigen has been reported with hog cholera and vesicular stomatitis
(Segre, 1957). The inert material was a basic anion-exchange resin,
Amberlite IRA-400. The AGG fraction from hyperimmune sera was
used for coating the finely divided resin powder, and the antigen or
virus was titrated by mixing it in dilutions with a similar volume of a
constant amount of coated particles. An inhibition of agglutination for
testing sera was also developed with this system.

The general appraisal of the agglutination tests when applied to animal viruses is guarded. The tests are not easy to use, largely because of the marked tendency that treated cells have to agglutinate spontaneously in the absence of an immune serum; as a consequence, interpretation of a test in the absence of dependable controls is unreliable.

C. REACTION ON A SOLID SUPPORT

Precipitation reactions occurring in a solid support have been reported by Nezlin (1960) with influenza virus; Hodes *et al.* (1957) described a test with poliovirus and human sera. The latter was based on the fact that if a strip of filter paper is put in contact at one end with a suspension of poliovirus, this will spread up on the paper and distribute itself evenly. If at a given place the strip has been impregnated with antiserum, the upward progress of the virus is blocked. By marking 12 equal transversal divisions on a strip 12×175 mm, it was possible to deduct the relative strength of an immune serum by the progress achieved by the virus when the serum was placed on the third and fourth lower spaces. Testing was done by cutting the sections and introducing each in a tube with monkey kidney tissue culture cells. The test was recommended particularly for screening of large numbers of sera, since by testing only one of the paper sections near the middle of the strip it was possible to decide whether a serum was positive or negative using only one cell culture tube.

D. ELECTROADSORPTION

Monomolecular films of proteins transferred onto metalized glass slides react specifically with antisera (Rothen and Landsteiner, 1942). A test was recently described based on that observation (Mathot *et al.*, 1964), in which a reaction between arboviruses and their antisera was detected. The test consisted in placing a $1:10$ dilution of antigen in a Pyrex tube 8×60 mm. An electric current was applied to the solution by immersing in it two electrodes connected with a direct current power source gaged at 0.3 mA; the negative pole was connected to a chromium-plated slide, and a platinum wire to the positive one. The current was allowed through for 90 seconds, and the thickness of the material deposited on the slide was measured by means of an ellipsometer (Rothen, 1957) adapted to this type of work; the thickness was of the order of 25 Å. The slide was next immersed in a similar test tube containing diluted serum, inverting the polarity, i.e., the slide connected to the positive pole and the wire to the negative one. The same current was allowed through for 3–5 minutes, and the thickness of the deposited material was again measured. A distinctly greater increase in thickness was noted with homologous antigen–antibody combinations than with heterologous or control ones; the homologous reaction was often 2 or 3 times greater than the cross-reactions.

REFERENCES

Ainbender, E., Berger, R., Hevizy, M. M., Zepp, H. D., and Hodes, H. L. (1965). *Proc. Soc. Exptl. Biol. Med.* **119,** 1166.

Ananthanarayan, R., and Paniker, C. K. J. (1960). *Bull. World Health Organ.* **22,** 409.

Andrewes, C. H. (1962). *Advan. Virus Res.* **9,** 271.

Andrewes, C. H., and Elford, W. J. (1933). *Brit. J. Exptl. Pathol.* **14,** 367.

Andrewes, C. H., and Horstmann, D. M. (1949). *J. Gen. Microbiol.* **3,** 290.

Andrewes, C. H., Bang, F. B., and Burnet, F. M. (1955). *Virology* **1,** 176.

Belyavin, G. (1957). *J. Hyg.* **55,** 281.

Biegeleisen, J. Z., Jr., Scott, L. V., and Lewis, V., Jr. (1959). *Science* **129,** 640.

Black, F. L., and Melnick, J. L. (1954). *Yale J. Biol. Med.* **26,** 385.

Boyden, S. V. (1951). *J. Exptl. Med.* **93,** 107.

Brown, F., and Crick, J. (1957). *Nature* **179,** 316.

Brown, G. C., Maassab, H. F., Veronelli, J. A., and Francis, T., Jr. (1964). *Science* **145,** 943.

Buescher, E. L. (1963). Personal communication.

Burnet, F. M., and Anderson, S. G. (1946). *Brit. J. Exptl. Pathol.* **27,** 236.

Cabasso, V. J., and Stebbins, M. R. (1965). *J. Lab. Clin. Med.* **65,** 612.

Casals, J. (1957). *Trans. N.Y. Acad. Sci.* [2] **19,** 219.

Casals, J. (1961). *Bull. World Health Organ.* **24,** 723.

Casals, J. (1963). *Anais Microbiol., Univ. Brasil* **11A,** 13.

Casals, J. (1964). *J. Exptl. Med.* **119,** 547.

Casals, J., and Clarke, D. H. (1965). *In* "Viral and Rickettsial Infections of Man" (F. L. Horsfall, Jr. and I. Tamm, eds.), 4th ed., pp. 659–684. Lippincott, Philadelphia, Pennsylvania.

Casals, J., and Palacios, R. (1941). *J. Exptl. Med.* **74,** 409.

Chang, R. S. (1964). *J. Immunol.* **92,** 305.

Chanock, R. M., Bell, J. A., and Parrott, R. H. (1961a). *In* "Perspectives in Virology" (M. Pollard, ed.), Vol. II, pp. 126–139. Burgess, Minneapolis, Minnesota.

Chanock, R. M., Johnson, K. M., Cook, M. K., Wong, D. C., and Vargosko, A. J. (1961b). *Am. Rev. Respirat. Diseases* **83,** 125.

Chumakov, M. P. (1965). Personal communication.

Clarke, D. H. (1964). *Bull. World Health Organ.* **31,** 45.

Clarke, D. H., and Black, F. L. (1955). *Proc. Soc. Exptl. Biol. Med.* **89,** 391.

Clarke, D. H., and Casals, J. (1958). *Am. J. Trop. Med. Hyg.* **7,** 561.

Coates, H. V., Kendrick, L., and Chanock, R. M. (1963). *Proc. Soc. Exptl. Biol. Med.* **112,** 958.

Committee. (1957). *Am. J. Public Health* **47,** 1556.

Communicable Disease Center. (1962). *CDC* Laboratory Branch Training Manual, U.S. Dept. Health, Education and Welfare, Public Health Service.

Contreras, G., Barnett, V. H., and Melnick, J. L. (1952). *J. Immunol.* **69,** 395.

Cook, M. K., Andrewes, B. E., Fox, H. H., Turner, H. C., James, W. D., and Chanock, R. M. (1959). *Am. J. Hyg.* **69,** 250.

Coons, A. H. (1958). *Gen. Cytochem. Methods* **1,** 399–422.

Coons, A. H., and Kaplan, M. H. (1950). *J. Exptl. Med.* **91,** 1.

Coons, A. H., Creech, H. J., and Jones, R. N. (1941). *Proc. Soc. Exptl. Biol. Med.* **47,** 200.

Crowle, A. J. (1961). "Immunodiffusion." Academic Press, New York.

Cutchins, E., Warren, J., and Jones, W. P. (1960). *J. Immunol.* **85,** 275.

de Somer, P., and Prinzie, A. (1957). *Virology* **4,** 387.

Dick, E. C., and Mogabgab, W. J. (1961). *Am. J. Hyg.* **73,** 273.

Downie, A. W., and Dumbell, K. R. (1956). *Ann. Rev. Microbiol.* **10,** 237.

Dulbecco, R. (1952). *Proc. Natl. Acad. Sci. U.S.* **38,** 747.

Dulbecco, R., Vogt, M., and Strickland, A. G. R. (1957). *Virology* **2,** 162.

Dumbell, K. R., and Nizamuddin, M. (1959). *Lancet* **I,** 916.

Elek, S. D. (1948). *Brit. Med. J.* **I,** 493.

Farrell, L. N., and Reid, D. B. W. (1959). *Can. J. Public Health* **50,** 20.

Fayet, M. T., Mackowiak, C., Camand, R., and Leftheriotis, E. (1957). *Ann. Inst. Pasteur* **92,** 466.

Francis, T., Jr. (1959). *In* "Viral and Richettsial Infections of Man" (T. M. Rivers and F. L. Horsfall, Jr., eds.), 3rd ed., pp. 633–672. Lippincott, Philadelphia, Pennsylvania.

Freund, J., and McDermott, K. (1942). *Proc. Soc. Exptl. Biol. Med.* **49,** 548.

Friedman, M., and Bennett, C. R. (1957). *Proc. Soc. Exptl. Biol. Med.* **94,** 712.

Fulton, F., and Dumbell, K. R. (1949). *J. Gen. Microbiol.* **3,** 97.

Gajdusek, D. C., Gibbs, J. C., Jr., and Alpers, M. (1965). "Slow, Latent, and Temperate Virus Infections." Monograph No. 2, National Institute of Neurological Diseases and Blindness, Washington, D. C.

Gerloff, R. K., Hoyer, B. H., and McLaren, L. C. (1962). *J. Immunol.* **89,** 559.

Ginsberg, H. S. (1962). *Virology* **18,** 312.

Ginsberg, H. S., and Horsfall, F. L., Jr. (1949). *J. Exptl. Med.* **90,** 475.

Gispen, R. (1955). *J. Immunol.* **74,** 134.

Goldfield, M. S., Srihongse, S., and Fox, J. P. (1957). *Proc. Soc. Exptl. Biol. Med.* **96,** 788.

Goldstein, G., Slizys, I. S., and Chase, M. W. (1961). *J. Exptl. Med.* **114,** 89.

Goldwasser, R. A., Kissling, R. E., Carski, T. R., and Hosty, T. S. (1959). *Bull. World Health Organ.* **20,** 579.

Gotlieb, T., Bashe, W. J., Jr., Henle, G., and Henle, W. (1953). *J. Immunol.* **71,** 66.

Grabar, P. (1959). *Methods Biochem. Anal.* **7,** 1.

Grabar, P., and Williams, C. A. (1955). *Biochim. Biophys. Acta* **17,** 67.

Grayston, J. T., Johnston, P. B., Smith, M. E., and Loosli, C. G. (1956). *J. Infect. Diseases* **99,** 188.

Hale, J. H., and Pillai, K. (1960). *Ann. Trop. Med. Parasitol.* **54,** 236.

Hamparian, V. V., Hilleman, M. R., and Ketler, A. (1963). *Proc. Soc. Exptl. Biol. Med.* **112,** 1040.

Hamparian, V. V., Leagus, M. B., and Hilleman, M. R. (1964). *Proc. Soc. Exptl. Biol. Med.* **116,** 976.

Herrmann, E., and Engle, C. (1958). *Proc. Soc. Exptl. Biol. Med.* **98,** 257.

Hirst, G. K. (1941). *Science* **94,** 22.

Hitchcock, G., and Tyrrell, D. A. J. (1960). *Lancet* **I,** 237.

Hodes, H. L., Zepp, H. D., Henley, W. L., and Berger, R. (1957). *Science* **125,** 1089.

Horne, R. W. (1963). *Sci. Am.* **208**, 48.

Hsiung, G. D., and Melnick, J. L. (1957). *J. Immunol.* **78**, 128.

International Enteroviruses Study Group. (1963). *Virology,* **19**, 114.

Jensen, K. E. (1957). *Advan. Virus Res.* **4**, 279.

Jensen, K. E., and Francis, T., Jr. (1953a). *J. Exptl. Med.* **98**, 619.

Jensen, K. E., and Francis, T., Jr. (1953b). *J. Immunol.* **70**, 321.

Johnson, H. N. (1964). *In* "Diagnostic Procedures for Viral and Rickettsial Diseases" (E. H. Lennette and N. J. Schmidt, eds.), 3rd ed., pp. 356–380. Am. Public Health Assoc., New York.

Kamitsuka, P. S., Soergel, M. E., and Wenner, H. A. (1961). *Am. J. Hyg.* **74**, 7.

Kärber, G. (1931). *Arch. Exptl. Pathol. Pharmakol.* **162**, 480.

Ketler, A., Hamparian, V. V., and Hilleman, M. R. (1962). *Proc. Soc. Exptl. Biol. Med.* **110**, 821.

Kunz, C., Buckley, S. M., and Casals, J. (1964). *Am. J. Trop. Med. Hyg.* **13**, 738.

Lahelle, O. (1958). *Virology* **5**, 110.

Ledingham, J. C. C. (1931). *Lancet* **II**, 525.

Lennette, E. H., and Koprowski, H. (1944). *J. Immunol.* **49**, 375.

Levine, S., Puck, T. T., and Sagik, B. P. (1953). *J. Exptl. Med.* **98**, 521.

Lieberman, R., Douglas, J. O. A., and Humphrey, W. (1959). *Science* **129**, 775.

Lim, K. A., and Benyesh-Melnick, M. (1960). *J. Immunol.* **84**, 309.

Lim, K. A., and Pong, W. S. (1964). *J. Immunol.* **92**, 638.

Liu, C. (1961). *Am. Rev. Respirat. Diseases* **83**, 130.

Liu, C. (1964). *In* "Diagnostic Procedures for Viral and Rickettsial Diseases" (E. H. Lennette and N. J. Schmidt, eds.), 3rd ed., pp. 177–193. Am. Public Health Assoc., New York.

Lorenz, R. J. (1962). *Arch Ges. Virusforsch.* **12**, 108.

Lwoff, A., Horne, R., and Tournier, P. (1962). *Cold Spring Harbor Symp. Quant. Biol.* **27**, 51.

McBride, W. D. (1959). *Virology* **7**, 45.

McKenna, J. M., Zuscheck, F., and Frankel, J. W. (1958). *Proc. Soc. Exptl. Biol. Med.* **97**, 160.

Mandel, B. (1960). *Ann. N.Y. Acad. Sci.* **83**, 515.

Marcus, P. I., and Carver, D. H. (1965). *Science* **149**, 983.

Mathot, C., Rothen, A., and Casals, J. (1964). *Nature* **202**, 1181.

Mayer, M. M., Osler, A. G., Bier, O. G., and Heidelberger, M. (1946). *J. Exptl. Med.* **84**, 535.

Melnick, J. L. (1955). *Ann. N.Y. Acad. Sci.* **61**, 754.

Melnick, J. L. (1957). *In* "Cellular Biology, Nucleic Acids and Viruses" (O. V. St. Whitelock, ed.), Spec. Publ. No. 5, pp. 365–381. N.Y. Acad. Sci., New York.

Melnick, J. L. (1960). *Am. J. Public Health* **50**, 1013.

Melnick, J. L. (1962). *Science* **135**, 1128.

Melnick, J. L., Midulla, M., Wimberly, I., Barrera-Oro, J. G., and Levy, B. M. (1964). *J. Immunol.* **92**, 596.

Miller, H., and Owen, G. (1960). *Nature* **188**, 67.

Morgan, I. M. (1945). *J. Immunol.* **50**, 359.

Munoz, J. (1957). *Proc. Soc. Exptl. Biol. Med.* **95**, 757.

Murray, H. G. S. (1963). *Lancet* **I**, 847.

Nezlin, R. S. (1960). *Proc. Acad. Sci. USSR (English Transl.)* **131**, 676.

Olitsky, P. K., and Harford, C. G. (1938). *J. Exptl. Med.* **68**, 173.

Ouchterlony, O. (1948). *Acta Pathol. Microbiol. Scand.* **25**, 186.

Oudin, J. (1946). *Compt. Rend.* **222**, 115.

Parkman, P. D., Buescher, E. L., and Artenstein, M. S. (1962). *Proc. Soc. Exptl. Biol. Med.* **111,** 225.

Pereira, H. G. (1960). *Nature* **186,** 571.

Pereira, H. G., Allison, A. C., and Farthing, C. P. (1959). *Nature* **183,** 895.

Plotkin, S. A., Cohen, B. A., and Koprowski, H. (1961). *Virology* **15,** 473.

Porterfield, J. S. (1960). *Bull World Health Organ.* **22,** 373.

Porterfield, J. S. (1961). *Bull. World Health Organ.* **24,** 735.

Porterfield, J. S. (1964). *In* "Immunological Methods" (J. F. Ackroyd, ed.) pp. 341–362. Blackwell Scientific Publications, Oxford, England.

Porterfield, J. S., and Rowe, C. E. (1960). *Virology* **11,** 765.

Price, W. H., Parks, J., Ganaway, J., Lee, R., and O'Leary, W. (1963). *Am. J. Trop. Med. Hyg.* **12,** 624.

Reed, L. J., and Muench, H. (1938). *Am. J. Hyg.* **27,** 493.

Rosen, L. (1960a). *Am. J. Hyg.* **71,** 242.

Rosen, L. (1960b). *Am. J. Hyg.* **71,** 120.

Rosen, L., and Kern, J. K. (1961). *Proc. Soc. Exptl. Biol. Med.* **107,** 626.

Rosen, L., Hovis, J. F., and Bell, J. A. (1962). *Proc. Soc. Exptl. Biol. Med.* **110,** 710.

Ross, E., and Ginsberg, H. S. (1958). *Proc. Soc. Exptl. Biol. Med.* **98,** 501.

Rothen, A. (1957). *Rev. Sci. Instr.* **28,** 283.

Rothen, A., and Landsteiner, K. (1942). *J. Exptl. Med.* **76,** 437.

Rubin, H., and Franklin, R. M. (1957). *Virology* **3,** 84.

Sabin, A. B. (1947). *J. Am. Med. Assoc.* **133,** 281.

Sabin, A. B. (1950). *Bacteriol. Rev.* **14,** 225.

Sabin, A. B. (1956). *J. Am. Med. Assoc.* **162,** 1589.

Sabin, A. B. (1957). *In* "Cellular Biology, Nucleic Acids and Viruses" (O. V. St. Whitelock, ed.), Spec. Publ. No. 5, pp. 113–133. N.Y. Acad. Sci., New York.

Salk, J. E. (1944). *J. Immunol.* **49,** 87.

Salk, J. E., Younger, J. S., and Ward, E. N. (1954). *Am. J. Hyg.* **60,** 214.

Sartorelli, A. C., Fischer, D. S., and Downs, W. G. (1965). *J. Immunol.* **96,** 676.

Schieble, J. H., Lennette, E. H., and Kase, A. (1965). *Proc. Soc. Exptl. Biol. Med.* **120,** 203.

Schmidt, N. J. (1964). *In* "Diagnostic Procedures for Viral and Rickettsial Diseases" (E. H. Lennette and N. J. Schmidt, eds.), 3rd ed., pp. 78–176. Am. Public Health Assoc., New York.

Schmidt, N. J., and Lennette, E. H. (1959). *Am. J. Hyg.* **70,** 51.

Schmidt, N. J., and Lennette, E. H. (1961). *Progr. Med. Virol.* **3,** 1.

Schmidt, N. J., and Lennette, E. H. (1962). *J. Immunol.* **89,** 96.

Schmidt, N. J., Guenther, R. W., and Lennette, E. H. (1961). *J. Immunol.* **87,** 623.

Scott, L. V., Felton, F. G., and Barney, J. A. (1957). *J. Immunol.* **78,** 211.

Segre, D. (1957). *J. Immunol.* **78,** 304.

Sever, J. L. (1962). *J. Immunol.* **88,** 320.

Shahan, M. S. (1962). *Ann. N.Y. Acad. Sci.* **101,** 444.

Smith, W. (1958). *Progr. Med. Virol.* **1,** 280.

Smith, W., Sheffield, F. W., Churcher, G., and Lee, L. H. (1956). *Lancet* **II,** 271.

Spence, L. (1960). *Proc. Soc. Exptl. Biol. Med.* **103,** 425.

Strome, C. P. A. (1953). *Proc. Soc. Exptl. Biol. Med.* **84,** 287.

Takatsy, G., Furesz, J., and Farkas, E. (1954). *Acta Physiol. Acad. Sci. Hung.* **5,** 241.

Theiler, M. (1957). *Proc. Soc. Exptl. Biol. Med.* **96,** 380.

Tyrrell, D. A. J., and Horsfall, F. L., Jr. (1953). *J. Exptl. Med.* **97,** 845.

Tyrrell, D. A. J., and Parsons, R. (1960). *Lancet* **I**, 239.

Virus Subcommittee of the International Nomenclature Committee. (1963). *Virology* **21**, 216.

Vogel, J., and Shelokov, A. (1957). *Science* **126**, 358.

Wallis, C., Melnick, J. L., and Bianchi, M. (1962). *Texas Rept. Biol. Med.* **20**, 693.

Warren, J. (1960). *Advan. Virus Res.* **7**, 27.

Warren, J., Weil, M. L., Russ, S. B., and Jeffries, H. (1949). *Proc. Soc. Exptl. Biol. Med.* **72**, 662.

Wenner, H. A., Miller, C. A., Kamitsuka, P., and Wilson, J. C. (1954). *Am. J. Hyg.* **59**, 221.

Westaway, E. G. (1965). *Virology* **26**, 517.

Whitman, L. (1947). *J. Immunol.* **56**, 97.

Wood, B. T., Thompson, S. H., and Goldstein, G. (1965). *J. Immunol.* **95**, 225.

Woodroofe, G. M., and Fenner, F. (1962). *Virology* **16**, 334.

Zuschek, F. (1961). *Proc. Soc. Exptl. Biol. Med.* **107**, 27.

5 Serological Techniques for Plant Viruses

R. E. F. Matthews

Serological methods are not of such direct importance in the study of plant viruses as they are with animal viruses, where the immune response is an integral part of the individual organism's reaction to infection. Nevertheless, many plant viruses are immunogenic in the usual laboratory animals. Thus the sensitivity and specificity of serological tests can be used in a variety of ways for work with plant viruses. Appropriate serological tests, especially when used in conjunction with other techniques, have played an important part in the development of our knowledge of these viruses. For example, serological tests with antisera against complete virus have been used to establish the existence of noninfectious viruslike proteins in infected plants [e.g., turnip yellow mosaic virus (TYMV), Markham *et al.* (1948), Markham and Smith (1949), Matthews (1960); tobacco mosaic virus (TMV), Commoner *et al.* (1953), Jeener *et al.* (1954), Kleczkowski (1957), van Slogteren (1958); *Prunus* necrotic ringspot virus, Allen and Tremaine (1965)].

Gierer and Schramm (1956) used the fact that antibody protein does not combine with isolated RNA to provide supporting evidence in their demonstration that isolated TMV RNA is infectious. Fluorescent antibody methods have been used to study the intracellular distribution of TMV in tobacco tissues (e.g., Nagaraj, 1965) and to detect virus antigens in insect vectors (e.g., Sinha and Reddy, 1964). Serological tests can be used to study structural relationships between intact virus particles and the protein subunits or aggregates of subunits from which they are assembled (Aach, 1959; Rappaport *et al.*, 1965).

Like most other techniques, there are a number of general precautions that need to be borne in mind if the methods are to give useful results (see Section VII,A). Major limitations in the application of serological tests to plant viruses are (1) that many viruses are unstable and occur in low concentration in the host plant, and (2) that many host plants contain phenolic substances or other materials that precipitate proteins and make isolation of antigenically active virus difficult or impossible. Several accounts of serological methods applied to plant viruses and other plant materials have appeared (Matthews, 1957; van Slogteren and van Slogteren, 1957; Ball, 1961; Bawden, 1964).

I. The Preparation of Reagents

A. PREPARATION OF ANTIGENS

Wherever possible, purified preparations of plant viruses should be used for injection into animals to prepare antisera. Details of the methods used to isolate plant viruses are given elsewhere in this treatise.

1. Advantages of Purified Antigens

Purified virus preparations have the following advantages over crude extracts: (1) Host plant antigens are partially or completely eliminated, resulting in more specific antivirus sera; (2) host material toxic for the animal can be eliminated; (3) a known and reproducible amount of virus antigen can be used for injection; and (4) with viruses occurring in low concentration in the plant, a purified and concentrated preparation allows more antigen to be injected, giving antisera of higher antibody content.

2. Stabilization of Virus Antigens in Crude Extracts

With viruses that have not yet been purified, it is often possible to obtain antisera using crude extracts from infected plants. In the simplest procedure, expressed sap from infected plants is used for injection after a low-speed centrifugation to remove large particulate material and cell debris. With unstable viruses, it is often advisable or necessary to design a medium for extraction of the tissue that will assist in stabilizing the virus antigen and keep it in solution. The major factors to be considered are listed in the following paragraphs.

a. *pH.* Virus stability may be markedly dependent on pH and on the buffer salts used to maintain a particular pH.

b. *Reducing Conditions.* Many viruses are readily denatured by oxidation. The addition of reducing substances such as cysteine, sodium sulfite, or ascorbic acid may assist in the preservation of the virus. These additives also prevent the oxidation of phenols in the extract to quinones, which can combine with proteins. A newly developed reagent for sulfhydryl groups, dithiothreitol (Cleland, 1964), may prove useful for the stabilization of plant virus antigens.

c. *Salt Concentration.* The ionic strength of the medium and the kinds of ion present may markedly affect the stability of the virus antigen.

d. *Temperature.* Generally speaking, with unstable viruses it is advisable to prepare extracts at low temperatures (1°–4°C).

3. Partial Purification of Antigens

A number of procedures may be used to remove some or all of the host antigens and toxic substances from the crude extract.

a. *Freezing.* Freezing of the tissue before grinding may assist in the coagulation of much host material, but it should be remembered that many viruses do not withstand this treatment.

b. *Heating.* Heating to 55°C for 3–5 minutes in a water bath will coagulate much plant material, particularly ribosomes and chloroplast fragments, which can then be removed by low-speed centrifugation. However, much of the cytoplasmic protein and protein released from chloroplasts may remain in solution after such treatment.

c. *Dialysis.* Dialysis against an appropriately buffered salt solution may remove much low molecular weight toxic material such as is found, for example, in members of the Solanaceae.

d. *Fractionation on Sephadex.* The use of Sephadex columns for the isolation of viruses is described in detail elsewhere in this treatise. For the partial purification of viral antigens for injection, a grade of Sephadex with large pore size (G-200) is used. On passing an extract containing virus through such a column, the virus will come through the column after about 1 bed volume of eluting fluid has passed through. Small molecular weight compounds and many plant proteins will move through the column more slowly.

The above remarks apply to the preparation of virus antigens for injections into animals. The type of material containing virus that is used for *in vitro* tests with antisera will depend very much on the type of test used, the object of the test, and the stability of the virus concerned. For a simple diagnostic test such as slide agglutination, crude untreated plant sap may be sufficient. Generally speaking, however, the more purified the virus preparation the less chance there will be of interference by nonspecific effects such as precipitation of host proteins.

For viruses that are sufficiently stable, such as TMV, TYMV, and potato X, the crude expressed sap can be heated to 53°–55°C for 3–5 minutes. The copious precipitate is removed by low-speed centrifugation (say 2000 rpm for 5 minutes). The supernatant fluid can then be used fairly reliably for serological tests. However, on standing for a few hours, nonspecific precipitates usually appear. For viruses that will not stand heating, centrifugation at higher speed (say 10,000 rpm in a Spinco No. 40 rotor for 10 minutes) will give quite effective clarification, provided the serological tests are carried out at no higher than room temperature.

B. Preparation of Antisera

A variety of animals have been used for the preparation of antisera against plant viruses. These include chickens (Newton and Edwards, 1936), horses (van Slogteren and van Slogteren, 1957), guinea pigs (Chester, 1936), and mice (Marbrook and Matthews, 1966). Each of these have advantages in particular circumstances. For example, horses have been employed in Holland for the large-scale production of antisera for routine diagnostic testing for certain potato viruses. Rabbits have been most widely used because (1) they are usually readily available, (2) they are easily maintained and handled, (3) they are good producers of precipitating antibodies, and (4) they are large enough to produce a useful volume of serum. Mice have not been used widely in plant virus work, since their small size makes them more difficult to work with and they give very small volumes of serum. This second disadvantage has been minimized by the development of micromethods for titrating precipitating antibody and antigen, particularly immunodiffusion in agar gel (see Section III,C). Mice do not produce antibodies against plant viruses as effectively as rabbits (on a body weight basis), if TYMV can be taken as a typical example. Nevertheless, they have two advantages over rabbits in situations where it is necessary to take account of the variation in antigenic response between individual animals. It is relatively easy to breed and maintain large numbers of mice; and inbred mouse strains, which presumably give a more uniform response, are readily available. Here we will discuss the use of rabbits and mice for the preparation of antisera.

1. Rabbits

Animals should preferably be fairly large (about 2 kg), 9–24 months old, and have conspicuous marginal ear veins. Animals should be kept singly in suitable cages and should be marked in some way for identification (by tattooing on the inside of the ear, by a punch code, or by small numbered metal tags clipped through the ear). For intravenous injections and for bleeding, the animal may be held in a specially designed box (Matthews, 1957). Alternatively, it can be held firmly in a comfortable position by an assistant.

a. *Intravenous Injection.* A 1–2-ml hypodermic syringe, preferably the all-glass type, is used with a fairly short fine needle (one-half inch, size 22). The needle should be clean and sharp. The syringe is filled and any air bubbles expelled with the needle held uppermost. The ear is swabbed with 70% ethanol. This usually shows up the vein clearly. If it does not, the ear should be rubbed briefly to cause dilation of the veins.

Alternatively, the ear may be shaved. The vein that runs parallel to the outer margin of the ear and a few millimeters from it should be used. The needle is pointed toward the base of the ear, parallel to and at an angle of about 45° above the vein. The bevel face of the needle is uppermost. The needle is then inserted for a very short distance and then brought parallel to the surface of the ear as the needle is inserted a short distance into the vein. The contents of the syringe are then injected. Resistance to movement of the plunger indicates that the needle is not in the vein. Forced injection of fluid may cause damage to the tissues of the ear. After the injection is completed, the needle is gently withdrawn, while slight pressure is maintained over the point of entry with the thumb and forefinger of the left hand. This pressure is maintained for a short period after the needle has been removed to prevent bleeding. If an animal is to receive a series of injections, it is best to begin near the tip of the ear, giving each successive injection closer to the base.

b. Subcutaneous Injection. This is a simpler operation than intravenous injection and is usually carried out on areas of the back and flanks where the skin is loose. An area is swabbed with alcohol and the skin lifted with one hand while the needle, held more or less parallel to the body surface, is inserted near the base of the raised area and the fluid injected. About 0.5–1.0 ml can be given per site.

c. Intraperitoneal Injection. This is best carried out by two operators, one holding the animal by its legs, stretched to display the abdomen. If necessary, fur may be clipped from a small area. The needle, about size 17 and not too sharp, is inserted directly into the abdominal cavity, pulled back slightly, and the injection made. Up to about 5 ml can be given in one injection.

d. Use of Adjuvants. Adjuvants, developed to boost antibody production for use with other systems, are sometimes used with plant viruses. A mixture of mineral oil and lanolin is emulsified with the virus preparation and this emulsion used for subcutaneous injection. Use of a mechanical homogenizer is advisable to ensure thorough emulsification. One recipe is as follows: A 50 : 50 mixture of Shell mineral oil (Risella 17) and lanolin is prepared. An equal volume of this mixture is added to the antigen solution and shaken well. About 0.5–1.0 ml of this mixture is injected at about three subcutaneous sites. Some workers used heat-killed tubercle bacilli as a further constituent of the adjuvant mixture. This may cause severe reactions in the animal and should be avoided where possible in work with plant viruses.

e. Choice of Injection Procedure. Intravenous injection is usually the preferred method with purified plant virus preparations or with crude or partially purified preparations that do not cause marked toxic reactions. Some workers prefer a set of subcutaneous injections in adjuvant followed by a booster intravenous injection several weeks later. This is considered to give high-titer antisera. The injection schedules used by various workers vary widely, and there has been little systematic study of their efficiency for plant virus antigens.

One problem is that individual animals may vary widely in their response to a given antigen. Thus numbers of animals are needed in any comparative tests. There is some evidence that response to plant virus antigens may be genetically determined (Sobey, 1954). Fig. 1A shows the range of variation to be expected in rabbits in response to intravenous injection.

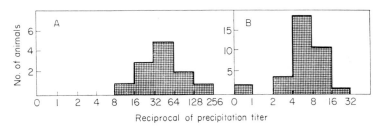

Fig. 1. Variation in antibody titers produced in rabbits and mice following a single injection: (A) 12 rabbits given an intravenous injection of 100 μg of TYMV nucleoprotein and bled after 3 weeks; (B) 37 C3H mice given a single intraperitoneal injection of 3 μg of TYMV nucleoprotein and bled after 3 weeks.

It is often considered that subcutaneous injections with adjuvant give a higher and longer-lasting antibody content in the serum for a given weight of antigen injected than do intravenous injections. However, Moorhead (1961) studied the use of water–oil emulsions and of phosphorylated herperidin solutions as adjuvants for intramuscular or subcutaneous administration of four relatively stable plant viruses. She found that the relative effectiveness of the various methods depends on the virus used. Our data for TMV and TYMV support this view (Fig. 2). The use of adjuvant appears to offer little advantage for TYMV.

The injection schedule chosen will depend on (1) the quantities of antigen available, (2) freedom of the preparations from toxic materials, and (3) the purpose for which the antiserum is to be used.

Where high-titer sera for routine work are required, with such viruses as TMV or TYMV, a series of 3–6 weekly injections of 1–10 mg of virus (the dose of antigen being increased with each injection) should give good sera. Alternatively, a set of three subcutaneous in-

jections of about 1 mg of virus could be used followed by an intravenous booster of 10 mg after 3 weeks. Where the amount of antigen
available is very limited and as high a titer as possible is desired,
it is preferable to give it in a series of smaller but increasing doses
at intervals of about 7 days rather than in one large dose.

If a crude virus preparation containing antigenic host constituents
is used, there may be little point in attempting to produce very high-
titer antisera, since correspondingly large volumes of crude host–
antigen preparations will be required to absorb out antibodies to host
constituents from the serum.

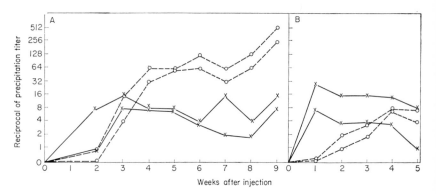

Fɪɢ 2. Comparison of intravenous injection and subcutaneous injection with adjuvant in rabbits. (A) TMV ×—× = 1 µg intravenous; ○--○ = 1 µg subcutaneous
in mineral oil and lanolin. (B) TYMV ×—× = 1 µg intravenous; ○--○ = 1 µg
subcutaneous in mineral oil and lanolin.

f. Bleeding. Since it is not usually necessary to obtain sterile sera
for plant virus work, the heart-puncture technique need not be used.
Adequate volumes of serum can be obtained by bleeding from the
marginal vein of the ear. For this the animal needs to be held by an
assistant or placed in a suitable box (Matthews, 1957) or a canvas
harness. The marginal vein of the ear is distended by rubbing a small
amount of xylene onto the tip of the ear with cotton wool. The vein
is swabbed with alcohol and a small transverse cut made in the vein
near the base of the ear with a sharp scalpel. For later bleedings,
successive cuts are made closer to the tip of the ear. Blood is collected
in a tube held beneath the ear. Bleeding is stopped by washing off
the xylene with ethanol and by applying gentle pressure over the
cut with a wad of cotton wool. (Up to about 40–50 ml of blood
can be taken on about three occasions within a week.) Blood is allowed
to clot for a few hours or overnight at room temperature or 37°C.

The serum is poured off and the remaining free blood cells removed by low-speed centrifugation.

2. Mice

a. General. For work with TYMV, we have used C3H mice maintained as a randomly bred population. Many other strains of mice are available, but no investigation has been made of the comparative merits of these for plant virus work.

Figure 1B illustrates the variability in the response of C3H mice to a single intraperitoneal injection of 3 μg of TYMV nucleoprotein. Using 10–100 μg, it is possible to obtain sera with precipitation endpoint titers of about 1 : 256.

b. Methods for Injection of Antigen. In experiments with TYMV, we have used three routes of injection. For intraperitoneal injection, virus in 0.2 ml of 0.14 M saline was administered with a tuberculin syringe using a 26-gage needle. For intravenous injection into the tail vein, a volume of 5 μl was used with a 28-gage needle and an Agla syringe. Injection into the hind foot pad was made with a 26-gage needle and an Agla syringe using a 5-μl volume.

With TYMV, there was no significant difference in levels of circulating precipitated antibody produced following administration of a single dose of 3 μg by the above three methods. The intraperitoneal method is simplest, and we use this routinely.

c. Bleeding. A mouse weighing 20 gm contains about 2 ml of blood. Up to about 1 ml of blood can be obtained from the jugular vein or by heart puncture by killing the animal. The operation is carried out under anesthesia (e.g., 0.25 ml of a 10 μg/ml solution of sodium pentobarbitone per 20 gm of mouse given intraperitoneally).

A series of bleedings may be made most simply from the caudal artery. The tip of the tail is cut off, and the blood collected in a 2-ml conical centrifuge tube. The clot is freed from the wall of the tube with a fine glass rod after standing about 1 hour at room temperature and allowed to retract on standing at 4°C. The coagulated blood is centrifuged, if necessary, at 2000 rpm for a few minutes. The serum is taken off with a silicone-treated Pasteur pipet or a Microcap disposable capillary pipet. Bleeding from the retroorbital sinus is used in some laboratories (e.g., Briody, 1959).

3. Storage of Sera

Rabbit sera are most simply stored frozen in small bottles containing 5–20 ml of serum. All the serum in a container should be thawed and mixed by shaking before a sample is withdrawn. If freezing cannot be used, a few drops of some antimicrobial agent such as phenol, thymol, or chloroform should be added to the serum. Under these conditions, the serum will slowly deteriorate. If an antiserum is to be used only for precipitation tests, it can be effectively stored at room temperature with a larger quantity of phenol (a tenth volume of a 10% aqueous solution of phenol is added slowly with stirring). Freeze-drying is a highly effective method of storage, particularly for transportation or for long-term storage. Mouse serum is best stored frozen in small tubes.

II. The Precipitation Reaction

The combination between an antigen and specific antibody protein may be demonstrated in a variety of ways. One of the most direct methods is to observe the formation of a visible specific precipitate between the antigen and antibody. The precipitin or precipitation reaction is the most widely used in work with plant viruses. The term "agglutination" is used when cells such as bacteria or cell organelles such as chloroplasts are clumped by reaction with specific antisera. "Precipitation" is the term used for the reaction with molecular antigens such as proteins and polysaccharides. Plant viruses are intermediate in size between these two classes, but the term "precipitation" is generally used with respect to them.

Plant virus antigens are polyvalent, i.e., each particle can combine with many of the much smaller antibody protein molecules. It is thought that most antibody molecules are divalent, i.e., have two specific reactive sites on their surface, allowing them to combine with two molecules of the antigen. In this way a lattice of antigen and antibody molecules may be formed, growing in size until a visible precipitate forms. The formation of this visible precipitate may be detected experimentally in a number of different ways, each of which has particular uses and limitations. In the most direct form of the test, virus and antiserum are mixed together in a small test tube; the mixture is then incubated under standard conditions and observed for the formation of a visible precipitate.

A. FACTORS AFFECTING TUBE PRECIPITATION

1. Presence of Salt

Specific precipitates do not form in a medium of low ionic strength. It is usual to carry out all tests in 0.14 M sodium chloride solutions.

2. *Temperature*

Within the range where the two reagents are stable, the higher the temperature the more rapidly will a specific precipitate form. With some viruses that are very stable, such as TMV, it is quite safe to incubate mixtures of virus and antiserum at 55°C. With most viruses, however, it is safer to incubate at 30°–37°C, and at even lower temperatures for the more unstable viruses. For example, TYMV preparations lose some of their RNA at 37°C and pH 7.0. With impure virus preparations, nonspecific precipitation is much more likely to occur at higher temperatures.

3. *pH*

Precipitation tests are usually carried out without the addition of buffers. The serum, unless highly diluted, holds the mixture at a pH near 7.0. However, specific precipitates will form over a range of pH values from about 6.0 to 9.0. With some unstable viruses it is preferable to use some pH value within this range other than 7.0.

4. *Efficiency of Mixing*

There are two aspects to the question of mixing the two reagents— initial mixing and continued stirring. The initial speed and efficiency with which the virus and antiserum are mixed may be important in determining the rate of precipitation. Mixing is particularly important where a strong virus solution is mixed with a weak or relatively highly diluted antiserum. Under these conditions, with poor initial mixing a specific precipitate may form and then redissolve on continued incubation. Rapid mixing can be achieved by using a hypodermic needle to squirt a given volume of one reagent into a tube containing the other. After initial mixing, continued stirring for a period will speed precipitate formation. This can be achieved by shaking manually or on a shaking machine, or by using convection currents set up using a water bath with temperatures somewhat above room temperature. Racks of tubes are placed in the water bath so that about half the contents are immersed in the heated water. This leads to convection currents in the fluid in the tube, giving continued mixing during incubation.

5. *Concentrations of Virus and Antiserum*

Both the relative and absolute concentrations of virus and antiserum are most important factors in determining the speed at which a precipitate forms, the amount of precipitate produced, and, indeed, whether or not a precipitate is formed at all. The formation of a specific precipitate may be inhibited by an excess of either reagent. For this reason, it is usually necessary to set up a series of mixtures containing different ratios of reagents to ensure that the absence of a precipitate is not due to an excess of one reagent.

B. Main Features of the Tube Precipitation Reaction

It is usual to make serial 2-fold dilutions in 0.14 M NaCl of one reagent and then add to each tube an equal volume of the other reagent at a constant dilution. The volume of each reagent used is usually 0.5 ml. The reaction of a virus with a particular antiserum is clearly delineated if a series of tests is made with 2-fold dilutions of both reagents in all combinations, under standard conditions of temperature and mixing. If the time for first visible precipitation to occur (using a $\times$ 8 hand lens) is noted for each combination, we can construct a two-way table for the antiserum, known as a precipitation diagram. Such a diagram for an antiserum to TYMV is shown in Fig. 3. This figure illustrates some of the more important features of the precipitation reaction.

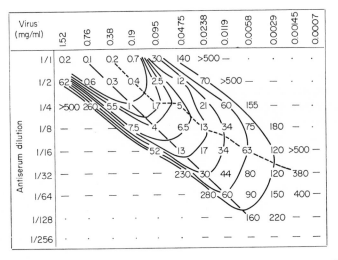

Fig. 3. Precipitation diagram of a rabbit antiserum against TYMV to illustrate various features of the precipitation reaction carried out in tubes. All practicable combinations of virus and antiserum in 2-fold dilution steps were tested. Figures in the table are the time in minutes for visible precipitation to first appear — = no precipitation after 24 hours; · = not tested. From Matthews (1957).

1. *Inhibition by Excess Antiserum*

In the top right of Fig. 3 no precipitation has occurred. This owes to inhibition of precipitate formation by excess antiserum.

2. *Inhibition by Virus Excess*

In the bottom left of Fig. 3 is another area in which no precipitation occurred. This owes to an excess of virus in the mixtures.

3. *The α-Optimum*

If we look, say, along the horizontal line of times for antiserum diluted to 1 : 4 in Fig. 3, we find that fastest precipitation took place with 0.19 mg/ml of virus. This tube is known as the α-optimum. The ratio of reagents at the α-optimum is constant for all antiserum concentrations. Thus we can draw a diagonal line connecting the α-optimum tubes. Because of this proportion, the α-optimum can be used to measure virus concentration or antibody concentration.

4. *Virus End Point*

The highest dilution of virus giving a visible precipitate in Fig. 3 is 0.00145 mg. This is known as the virus end point. Within the error imposed by the 2-fold dilution steps, this figure is constant for a given virus and can be used to estimate virus concentration. For TYMV it is about 1.0 μg. However, as discussed in Section V, with rod-shaped viruses the degree of end-to-end aggregation of virus particles can markedly affect the amount of virus at the end point. Increasing aggregation reduces the amount of virus needed for a visible precipitate. Inhibition by antiserum excess gives lower virus end points with dilutions of antiserum of less than 1 : 16 (with this particular serum). Thus to find the true virus end point it is necessary to test with a range of antiserum dilutions. Generally speaking, however, if a dilution of antiserum of 1 : 20 or greater is used, the true virus end point will be obtained. With very weak antisera it may not be possible to obtain the true virus end point, while with very strong antisera the true virus end point may be obtained even with undiluted antiserum.

5. *Titer of Antiserum*

The highest dilution of the antiserum that gives a visible precipitate is known as the antiserum titer and is a measure of the precipitating antibody protein in the serum. Note that in the region of excess virus the true antiserum titer is not obtained (Fig. 3). This feature is common to all virus antisera. For this reason, when measuring the strength of antisera by the dilution method it is necessary to use a dilution of virus within one or two dilution steps of the virus-dilution end point.

6. The β-Optimum

Looking at the vertical column of figures for virus at 0.0475 mg/ml in Fig. 3, we find that fastest precipitation took place with antiserum at 1 : 4. This tube is known as the β-optimum. The β-optimum tube for each vertical column is connected by a dotted line in Fig. 3. In this particular serum the ratio of reagents at the β-optimum is more or less constant. In the past many workers have used the β-optimum to measure virus or antiserum concentration. However, it is a most unreliable criterion, and with antisera of high titer it is useless.

7. Isochrones

The contour lines or isochrones in Fig. 3 are drawn in by inspection. These lines join points of equal time of precipitation and form a summary of the behavior of the particular antiserum under the particular conditions used.

8. The Composition of Specific Precipitates

The various "zones" of the precipitation reaction between virus and antiserum can be determined more precisely by chemical estimation of the amount of protein in the specific precipitates, combined with tests on the supernatant fluids for the presence of excess of either reagent.

A series of 2-fold dilutions of a virus preparation of known concentration is made and an equal volume of an antiserum dilution added to each antigen dilution. The mixtures are incubated under standard conditions (for example, 2 hours at 37°C, then overnight at 4°C). The precipitates are centrifuged down (about 2000 rpm for 5 minutes) and the supernatant fluids poured off and retained. The precipitates are washed by resuspension in 1.0 ml of 0.14 M NaCl and centrifuged again. The washing is repeated twice. The nitrogen content of the precipitates is then determined by a suitable micromethod (Kabat and Mayer, 1961). This nitrogen will include both antibody and virus nitrogen. If the virus nitrogen content of the original virus preparation is known, the antibody content of the precipitate can be determined by difference. This calculation can be applied only in those tubes where all the virus is precipitated. These tubes can be identified by tests on the supernatant fluids. Half of this fluid is put in each of two tubes, and a further small quantity of virus is added to one and of antiserum to the other. The tubes are then incubated under standard conditions and observed for further specific precipitates. The results for one such series of tests with TYMV are shown in Table I.

The zone of virus excess is indicated by precipitation with added antiserum and the zone of antibody excess by precipitation with added virus. Between these two zones lies a set of three tubes in which neither antibody nor virus was detected in the supernatant fluid. This is the equivalence zone in which all of both reagents precipitate.

For small spherical plant viruses, the tube in which maximum total precipitate forms and the tube in which precipitation is fastest lie close to the antigen-excess end of the equivalence zone. For rod-shaped viruses, these tubes may be well into the region of antigen excess, and their exact position is affected by the degree of aggregation of the virus preparation.

III. Modifications of the Precipitation Reaction

A. THE RING TEST

A small volume of undiluted or slightly diluted antiserum is placed in a small glass tube to give a column of antiserum about 5–10 mm high. Over this is carefully layered a roughly equal volume of fluid containing the virus antigen. The high density of serum allows a sharp boundary to be formed at the interface. Whitcomb and Black (1961) used higher dilutions of serum in the ring test. To maintain the density of the serum layer, they made dilutions in a mixture of 9 volumes of 0.14 M saline plus 1 volume of glycerin. The tube is kept at room temperature. With time, antibody diffuses into the virus solution and virus diffuses into the antiserum. Somewhere near the region of the boundary a zone of specific precipitate will form, provided both reagents are sufficiently concentrated. The question of optimal proportions is not a problem with the test carried out in this way. It is a useful quick test, but it is rather insensitive and can be wasteful of reagents unless narrow-bore tubes are used. Where there is any possibility of spontaneous precipitation of materials from the virus preparation, which would form a nonspecific zone of precipitate at the interface, a control test with normal serum should be set up.

B. AGGLUTINATION TESTS

1. With Untreated Extracts

When a drop of freshly expressed leaf sap from plants infected with viruses occurring in high concentration is mixed on a microscope

TABLE I

COMPOSITION OF SPECIFIC PRECIPITATES (VARYING AMOUNTS OF TYMV ADDED TO A CONSTANT AMOUNT OF ANTISERUM)[a,b]

(A) Virus nitrogen added (μg)	(B) Total nitrogen in precipitate (μg)	(C) Antibody nitrogen precipitated (B − A)	Ratio, antibody N/virus $N = C/A$ in precipitates	Tests on supernatant fluid with		Zone
				Added virus	Added antiserum	
760	82.5	—	—	—	++	Virus excess
380	394.0	—	—	—	++	
190	240.0	50.0	0.26	—	—	Equivalence
95	139.5	44.5	0.47	—	—	
47.5	91.0	43.5	0.92	—	—	
23.7	65.5	41.8	1.76	+	—	Antibody excess
11.9	39.6	27.7	2.33	+	—	
5.9	20.4	14.5	2.46	+	—	

[a] Matthews, 1957.

[b] +, a further precipitate forms; —, no precipitation.

slide with a drop of an antiserum, clumping of small particles of host material occurs. This may be seen with the naked eye, but is viewed more readily with a hand lens or low-powered microscope. Chloroplasts and chloroplast fragments are prominent in the clumped aggregates. This may well owe to the fact, recently shown by Nagaraj (1965) using microfluorescence methods, that TMV antigen accumulates around the periphery of chloroplasts. Munro (1954) described a simple slide agglutination test for field tests with potato virus X, in which drops of normal serum and antiserum are used. A mirror is used to provide a strong source of light, obviating the need for a microscope. The slide agglutination test is less reliable than tests using virus preparations from which much of the spontaneously precipitating host material has been removed. It is also much less sensitive than tube precipitation tests or precipitations in agar gel.

Various modifications of the slide agglutination test have been developed, particularly by workers in Holland and Germany. For example, Stapp and Bercks (1948) used wafers of paper impregnated with an antiserum against potato virus X as a simple method for distributing antiserum to potato-breeding farms. The antiserum is spread on thin white paper and dried in a desiccator at room temperature. Wafers 4 mm square are cut from the dried sheets. Similar wafers are prepared with normal serum. A wafer of each sort is placed, one at each end, on a microscope slide. A drop of 0.14 M NaCl is added to each wafer, followed by a drop of the expressed sap to be tested. The slide is incubated at room temperature for 20 minutes and then examined for agglutination in the drop under a microscope with dark field at a magnification of $\times$ 50.

2. Van Slogteren's Method

A major problem with using small drops of reagents on a microscope slide is that drying out may occur unless high humidity is held during incubation. This problem is overcome in the method of van Slogteren (1955), who covered small droplets with paraffin oil. The inner surface of a clean dry Petri dish is coated with Formvar by pouring into it a 1% solution of poly(vinyl formaldehyde) in chloroform, and then pouring it out again. The thin film is allowed to dry for several hours. This treatment gives a hydrophobic surface. The Petri dishes used should be as free as possible from optical flaws. The Petri dish is placed on a piece of paper ruled with 8 $\times$ 8 mm squares. Small drops of the test fluids are mixed on the dish at one corner of each square, using finely drawn Pasteur pipets. Drops must be covered with paraffin oil before they dry. Agglutination reactions are observed using a hand lens or $\times$ 60 magnification with a microscope and direct illumination. This procedure is one of the most useful modifications of the precipitation reaction developed so far for large numbers of tests. It has been widely used for indexing work with various potato viruses. For further details, see van Slogteren (1955) and van der Veken *et al.* (1962).

3. *Bentonite Flocculation Test*

In this test (Bozicevich *et al.*, 1963) the globulin fraction of the antiserum (prepared by ammonium sulfate precipitation), or the antigen, is adsorbed to bentonite. In testing for viruses in crude extracts, the antibody is adsorbed to the bentonite. This reagent is stable for several months at room temperature. A small volume (0.1 ml) of virus extract is mixed on a ringed microscope slide with 0.05 ml of antibody-sensitized bentonite. Flocculations can be observed after 20 minutes. Bozicevich *et al.* (1963) give details for the method. They found it to be rapid, sensitive, and specific. TMV could be detected at 0.015 μg in 0.1 ml; Southern bean mosaic virus at 0.03 μg; and tobacco ringspot virus at 0.05 μg. Scott *et al.* (1964) applied this method to routine testing of potato tubers for infection with certain viruses.

C. Precipitation Reactions in Gels

Over the past few years the use of serological precipitation tests carried out in gels has become widespread. These tests are based on the early work of Oudin (1946, 1952), Ouchterlony (1948, 1958), and Grabar (Grabar and Williams, 1953; Grabar *et al.*, 1956). The great advantage of this type of test is that mixtures of antigenic molecules and their corresponding antibodies may be physically separated either because of differing rates of diffusion in the gel or differing rates of migration in an electric field (in immunoelectrophoresis) or by a combination of these factors.

In early work, immunodiffusion tests were carried out in small tubes (i.e., in one dimension). Reactants were arranged so that only one diffused (single diffusion) or both diffused (double diffusion). However, this type of test has been largely superseded by double-diffusion tests in two dimensions. These tests can be carried out on a macro scale in, for example, a Petri dish. However, substantial savings in the quantities of antigen and antibody required and in time can be achieved by the use of standard 76 $\times$ 26 mm microscope slides. This discussion will be confined to the use of such slides. For a general account of all methods, see Ouchterlony (1962). (Reprints of this valuable review are available from LKB-Produkter AB, P.O. Box 12220, Stockholm 12, Sweden.)

1. *Double-Diffusion Tests on Microscope Slides*

A 1% solution of a high-quality agar of low ion content (e.g., Difco special Agar Noble or Ionagar No. 2) is used. This gives a water-clear gel without further treatment. The 1% agar solution in the appropriate buffer is heated to 92°C in a water bath to ensure that the agar goes fully into solution. The solution is then allowed to cool to 60°C. Sodium azide is added with stirring to give a final azide concentration of about 0.1%. The azide prevents growth of microorganisms in the agar. Choice of buffer salts and pH will depend on the stability and behavior of the virus or virus protein used. In order that the specific precipitation take place, the pH should be between 6.0 and 9.0 (preferably between 7.0 and 8.0). For example, with TYMV we use 0.14 M Tris-HCl buffer at pH 7.2 as the only addition apart from sodium azide.

It is most important that the agar be of very even thickness (about 1–2 mm). Clean microscope slides should be laid on a level surface and surrounded by a low wall of appropriate height. Holders for preparing six slides at once are provided in the LKB apparatus. Alternatively, a wall made of two layers of slides can be provided to contain the agar. The agar is dispensed at a temperature of about 48°C. An appropriate volume is pipeted onto the slides. The surface of the agar should not be touched after pouring.

Antigen and antiserum can be applied to the agar either in wells or in discs of filter paper. The filter paper procedure is simpler, but the use of wells gives greater precision. Holes are punched at appropriate sites in the agar with a suitable punch. The cut discs of agar are removed with a suction pipet. If care is taken not to move the agar layer on the slide, no leakage of reagents under the agar takes place. As a precaution against such leakage, slides can be given a thin coating of agar before pouring the 2-mm layer. A few drops of liquified 3% agar in distilled water is rubbed over the clean glass. The agar is then dried at about 80°C. Alternatively, the slides can be "siliconized." For reproducible results it is important that the geometric relationship of the wells cut in the agar be standardized and that their walls be vertical. This is achieved by using a template consisting of a metal block holding several punches in the required arrangement. A suitable general purpose arrangement is to have one central well surrounded by four to eight wells on a circle. A variety of templates are available with the LKB apparatus.

As an alternative to punched wells small circles of filter paper (about 2 mm in diameter) can be used. When positioning the discs, an outline of the required positions for the filter paper is drawn in India ink on a piece of cardboard and placed under the slide. Discs are wetted with the appropriate reagent and placed on the agar. The major difficulties with this method are: (1) the accurate and reproducible positioning of the filter paper discs and strips; (2) the difficulty of ensuring that discs of the same size always take up the same amount of reagent; and (3) the danger of deforming the agar while placing the discs.

When using wells punched in the agar, reagents are pipeted into appropriate wells and the slides are incubated under conditions designed to eliminate evaporation from the slides. Time and temperature of incubation will depend on the particular tests to be made. Many plant viruses are unstable at 37°C over a period of hours at pH values near 7.0. For this reason, it is preferable to incubate at 18°–20°C. At this temperature precipitation bands have usually developed in 24 hours. Slides may then be placed at about 4°C for 1–3 days to allow any further precipitation to develop.

2. Immunoelectrophoresis on Microscope Slides

Using similar methods to prepare the agar-coated slides, the antigen or mixture of antigens can be made to undergo electrophoretic migration in the gel along the long direction of the slide. Antiserum is then placed in a trough parallel to the path of migration and a microdiffusion test carried out as described above. Critical factors in immunoelectrophoresis are the pH of the buffer used, total ionic strength in the agar, and temperature control during the electrophoresis run.

Because of the subsequent precipitation reaction, choice of pH is limited to the range of about 6.0–9.0, as noted above for immunodiffusion. Many plant viruses have isoelectric points below pH 6.0, so that they will show some migration in buffers in this pH range. The strength of the buffer must be a compromise between the need to have a buffer strong enough to eliminate local variations in pH and the need to keep ionic strength low to avoid excessive conductivity and thus heating in the agar. For example, two buffers that give satisfactory results with TYMV are:

Phosphate, pH 7.4   6.4 gm Na_2HPO_4
                          1.3 gm NaH_2PO_4
                          H_2O to 1 liter

Barbital, pH 8.2   15.85 gm sodium barbital
                          23 ml 1.0 N HCl
                          H_2O to 1 liter

The slides are connected to buffer vessels by means of short filter paper wicks (3 MM) cut to the width of the slide and laid on the agar. The problem of temperature control can be overcome as follows (Markham, personal communication, 1965): A piece of one-quarter inch brass plate is cut to take three microscope slides. This plate is fixed to two vertical pieces of one-quarter inch brass plate about 2 inches high to act as legs. This brass table is placed in an ice bath with the buffer vessels on each side. To prevent electrochemical changes, the brass is given a thin coat of Vaseline or vacuum grease. The vessel containing the ice water should be of as small a volume as possible, with an airtight lid to minimize evaporation from the agar during the run.

A simple power supply giving 0–260 V dc with up to 100 mA can be constructed. A potential gradient of 3–6 V/cm is usually employed. The time required will vary with the particular materials used, but will usually be in the range of 0.5–4.0 hours. The antigen solution can be applied in a well or with a paper disc, as for immunodiffusion. The position of the antigen depot should be halfway along the slide if the direction of migration is unknown or if components migrate in both directions. If all components of interest migrate only in one direction, the depots are placed near one end of the slide. Usually two antigen depots can be used per slide, with the antiserum depot lying longitudinally between them.

After the electrophoresis run the antiserum is placed in the longitudinal well. This well is cut, but the agar is not removed until after the electrophoresis step, and the slide is incubated as for immunodiffusion.

Besides the net charge on the antigen, the temperature, and current used, other factors such as endosmosis affect the actual rate of migration of the antigen. A marker protein of known mobility (or dye such as bromphenol blue) can be added as a reference for comparison between different runs.

3. *Immunoosmophoresis*

Ragetli and Weintraub (1964) reported the application of immunoosmophoresis to plant viruses in crude extracts or in purified solutions. In this technique the virus solution is placed in a well in a thin layer of agar and the antiserum and another well 2 cm away. The agar contains buffer pH (6.8–7.6). An electric field is applied parallel to the line connecting the wells. Provided the virus particle has an appropriate net negative change, it will migrate toward the antiserum well, while antiserum moves from its well due to endosmosis. This migration leads to the formation of visible specific precipitation bands in the agar within about 60 minutes. For suitable viruses, this modification of immunoelectrophoresis may be of value in routine testing.

4. *Recording of Results for Immunodiffusion and Immunoelectrophoresis*

a. Visual Observation of Fresh Slides. Here lighting is the critical factor. Slides must be viewed by light scattering against a dark background when specific precipitates show up as whitish zones or lines. Various devices can be constructed to give effective lighting (e.g., Crowle, 1961, p. 258).

b. Staining. Staining increases sharpness and clarity of the bands, and if slides are subsequently dried, gives a permanent record. Before staining takes place it is essential to leach out the unprecipitated proteins. This is normally done by standing the slides in a 1% sodium chloride solution for 24 hours followed by rinsing for 1 hour in distilled water. Slides are immersed in the aqueous staining solution (commonly amido black 10B; Crowle, 1961) for about 10 minutes. Excess stain is removed (by soaking in 2% acetic acid for amido black 10B) for about 6–24 hours. Slides can be dried slowly by placing them in a small airtight box at room temperature for several days. Slow drying gives better preservation of the shape of the agar.

c. Photography. Either stained or unstained slides can be photographed. The latter are best photographed by oblique lighting against a black background. Various devices can be used (Crowle, 1961, p. 261). The simplest way to record a stained slide is to use the slide itself as a negative in the enlarger.

Many plant viruses contain a high percentage of RNA. One can take advantage of this fact to obtain a photographic record of bands of precipitate containing virus (Thompson, 1964). To use this procedure it is necessary (1) to have a source of ultraviolet light filtered to give wavelengths predominantly near 260 mμ (2) to use quartz microscope slides, as employed for fluorescence microscopy; or it may be possible to strip the agar from the glass and place it directly on the photographic paper. However, reducing materials in the agar will fog the photographic film. (3) To use buffers that do not absorb in the ultraviolet region. Barbital buffers are no good for this reason. In a comparative test using TYMV as antigen, ultraviolet photography was no more sensitive than observation with dark-background illumination.

d. The Use of Radioautography. With viruses such as TMV and TYMV that can be labeled with ^{35}S, radioautography can be used to record precipitation bands. After the immunodiffusion is completed, the slide is washed, dried, placed on an x-ray film separated from it by a sheet of thin polythene (10 μ), enclosed in black paper, and left for a few days or weeks before the film is developed.

Tables II and III show the results of a series of immunodiffusion tests using ^{35}S-labeled TYMV as antigen and a TYMV antiserum with both reagents tested over a wide range of dilutions. Table II shows those combinations of dilutions giving precipitin bands visible by dark-background illumination. Table III records the bands visible on an x-ray film after the slides had been exposed for 10 days.

The radioautographic method is much more sensitive than observation of visible precipitation bands. The TYMV used had 200 counts

TABLE II

PRECIPITATION DIAGRAM USING THE AGAR DIFFUSION METHOD[a,b]

Antiserum dilution	TYMV (μg/ml)							
	100	50	25	12.5	6	3	1.5	0.75
1 : 1	X	X	X	X	X	X	0	0
1 : 2	X	X	X	X	X	X	0	0
1 : 4	X	X	X	X	X	X	0	0
1 : 8	X	X	X	X	X	X	0	0
1 : 16	0	?	X	X	X	X	0	0
1 : 32	0	0	0	X	X	X	0	0
1 : 64	0	0	0	0	0	?	0	0

[a] TYMV antigen and antiserum. Precipitin bands observed with dark-background illumination.
[b] X, visible band; 0, no band; ?, doubtful.

TABLE III

PRECIPITATION DIAGRAM USING THE AGAR DIFFUSION METHOD[a]

Antiserum dilution	TYMV (μg/ml)										
	100	50	25	12.5	6	3	1.5	0.75	0.37	0.18	0.09
1 : 1	X	X	X	X	X	X	X	X	X	X	0
1 : 2	X	X	X	X	X	X	X	X	X	X	0
1 : 4	X	X	X	X	X	X	X	X	X	X	0
1 : 8	X	X	X	X	X	X	X	X	X	X	0
1 : 16	X	X	X	X	X	X	X	X	X	X	0
1 : 32	X	X	X	X	X	X	X	X	X	X	0
1 : 64	X	X	X	X	X	X	X	X	X	X	0
128	?	X	X	X	X	X	X	X	X	X	0
256	0	0	0	?	X	X	X	X	X	X	0
512	0	0	0	0	?	X	X	X	X	X	0
1024	0	0	0	0	0	0	?	X	X	0	0
2048	0	0	0	0	0	0	0	0	0	0	0

[a] Same set of immunodiffusion tests as Table II. Precipitin bands recorded by radioautography.

per minute of ^{35}S per μg of virus (measured at about 5% efficiency). Had more highly labeled TYMV been used, and had the x-ray film been exposed for a longer period, much higher dilution end points could have been obtained. Thus under appropriate circumstances radioautography may be a very sensitive method for estimating antibody or antigens.

In Tables II and III there are no indications of inhibition of precipitation by excess antiserum. Inhibition by excess antigen occurs as it does with tube precipitation tests (see Fig. 3).

5. *Interpretation of Immunodiffusion and Immunoelectrophoresis Patterns*

Space does not permit a detailed discussion of the different types of precipitation patterns. Their interpretation is discussed in detail by Ouchterlony (1962) and Crowle (1961). Here it will be sufficient to emphasize four points.

1. Diffusion of the virus antigen in the agar gel is strongly dependent on the size and shape of the virus. For small spherical plant viruses, the methods are satisfactory. Long rods may diffuse slowly or not at all. Intact TMV diffuses slowly in agar, but the method has not been successful with some other rod-shaped viruses (van der Veken *et al.*, 1962). Rate of diffusion in agar gels has been used to provide estimates of the size of plant virus antigens (e.g., Tremaine and Willison, 1961).

2. Breakdown or aggregation of virus may occur during a run unless temperature, pH, and possibly ionic conditions are carefully controlled. For example, a proportion of TYMV particles lose their RNA at pH 7.0 at 37°C (Lyttleton and Matthews, 1958).

3. An imbalance in the ratio of antigen to antibody gives rise to multiple bands from a single antigen. Such an imbalance can readily be produced with those plant viruses that can be isolated in relatively large amounts. It is always advisable to run a preliminary diffusion test with a range of antigen–antiserum ratios.

4. The immunodiffusion method is so sensitive that minor impurities that do not interfere with tube precipitation tests may give spurious results. The most likely host material to contaminate a virus preparation is fraction I (chloroplast) protein. Large amounts of this material are present in many leaf extracts. Fraction I protein tends to precipitate (and aggregate irreversibly) below about pH 6.2 (Singer *et al.*, 1952). Traces of this material may well carry through in many of the procedures used to isolate plant viruses (van Regenmortel, 1963, 1964).

6. *General Comments on Immunodiffusion*

Immunodiffusion carried out on microscope slides in agar is now the method of choice for many applications with plant viruses. For laboratories beginning work in this field, the immunodiffusion apparatus and accessories marketed by LKB-Produkter, Sweden, is very satisfactory, particularly their gel punches and templates and the apparatus designed to produce slides with a standardized coating of agar. However, their immunoelectrophoresis apparatus has been designed primarily for the separation of serum components and as such is not perfectly adapted for use with plant viruses and other plant materials. A particular deficiency is the lack of a cooling system.

Immunodiffusion has been carried out in a variety of media besides agar. These include pectin, alginates, and acrylamide gels. Space does not permit detailed consideration of these. However, mention should be made of the recent development of immunodiffusion on cellulose acetate membranes. This may find a useful application with plant viruses. Accessories for the method are available commercially from the Millipore Filter Corporation, Bedford, Massachusetts.

D. Factors to Be Considered in Routine Tests for Virus Infection

A common application of serological tests (usually some variant of the precipitation reaction) is in testing plants for freedom from infection with a particular virus. A number of different situations arise here and these will be considered separately.

1. Nucleus Stocks of Vegetatively Propagated Plants

When a search is being made for virusfree individuals of vegetatively reproduced plants, such as potatoes and bulbs, to serve as nucleus stocks for virusfree clones, it is necessary to test individual plants as thoroughly as possible. Inoculation to indicator host plants will detect much smaller concentrations of virus, but serological tests may reveal symptomless strains of the virus. The most sensitive available serological tests should be used.

2. Checking Large Numbers of Plants for Freedom from Infection

This situation arises when virusfree stocks of a vegetatively reproducing plant have been multiplied up to a commercial scale. All plants cannot be tested, but the more that can be tested the more reliable will be the result. Thus a compromise must be reached between rapidity of a test and its reliability. It is in this situation that various modifications of the precipitation reaction designed for simplicity and speed have proved valuable (Section III,B).

Where the expected proportion of infected plants is low, and where the serological test being used is sufficiently sensitive, it should be possible to test groups of plants by mixing samples of tissue, say from 10 plants for one test, thus increasing the significance of the results from a given number of tests. An elementary treatment of the statistical considerations involved in testing large numbers of plants is given by Matthews (1957).

3. Testing Moderately Large Groups of Plants in Which the Level of Infection Is Unknown

This situation may arise in breeding for resistance to a virus when progeny of crosses are tested for infection following inoculation. A similar situation occurs when survey information is needed, for example, on levels of infections in different localities. Here group testing is not applicable and plants selected at random should be tested individually. Rapid slide agglutination or droplet agglutination methods can be used.

IV. Other Types of Serological Tests

A. COMPLEMENT FIXATION

This type of test is widely used with animal viruses. It has found only limited use with plant viruses, mainly because of the presence of interfering substances in many crude or partially purified plant extracts and because of the number of reagents required.

Complement is a nonspecific mixture of factors present in fresh unheated serum. Complement must be present for the lysis of red blood cells to occur when they are mixed with an anti-red cell serum. Combination between a virus and its antibody does not require complement, but if complement is present, it will be "fixed" or bound by the antigen–antibody complex.

Complement fixation is an indirect two-stage test for combination between viral antigen and antibody. In the first stage the virus antigen is mixed with its antiserum, which has previously been heated to 56°C to inactivate its complement. An appropriate standarized amount of fresh guinea pig serum is also present in the mixture. The mixture is then incubated. If the antigen and specific antibody are present, they will combine, and the added guinea pig complement will be fixed in the process. If no such combination takes place, no antibody will be fixed.

The second stage of the test is to determine whether or not the complement has been fixed. The indicator system used is a suspension of sheep red blood cells and a rabbit antisheep red cell antiserum (heated to inactivate its complement). If all the complement has been fixed in the first stage, no lysis of the red cells will occur. If no complement has been fixed in the first stage, then full lysis of the cells, with release of hemoglobin, will occur if appropriate quantities of reagents have been used.

Zones of optimal fixation of complement occur, and tests must be carried out over a range of ratios of reagents. Appropriate controls without the virus antiserum must be included to test for nonspecific binding of complement by materials in the antigen preparation. The complement-fixation method appears to be no more sensitive than the precipitation reaction, at least for some plant viruses (Matthews, 1957). Details of the method are given by Kabat and Mayer (1961), and its use with plant viruses is illustrated by Moorhead (1959) and Wright and Hardy (1961).

B. ANAPHYLAXIS

An animal that has been injected with an antigen may react to a second injection with the same or a related antigen with symptoms known collectively as anaphylactic shock. The pattern of such symptoms varies with animal species. Guinea pigs are particularly sensitive. Anaphylaxis *in vivo* is not widely used. In a more sensitive form of the method, the uterine horns of a sensitized guinea pig are removed and placed in a bath of Ringer's solution attached to a kymograph. On addition of the appropriate antigen, rapid contraction of the uterine muscle occurs, followed by a slow relaxation. This will occur only once for a given antigen and piece of tissue. The work of Chester (1936) illustrates use of the method with plant viruses, but it has been used very little in recent years.

C. NEUTRALIZATION OF INFECTIVITY

A specific antiserum will prevent infection when mixed under appropriate conditions with a virus inoculum. For animal viruses this method is very sensitive and is widely used. It is not so generally useful with plant viruses. First, infectivity measurements with plant viruses are much less sensitive, and less reliable, than those now available for many animal viruses. Second, serum is a reasonably "natural" medium for animal viruses and their hosts. With plants, nonspecific effects of serum both on the virus and on the susceptibility of the host may interfere with tests unless such factors are carefully controlled. Normal rabbit serum reduces the number of local lesions produced in *Nicotiana glutinosa* by TMV if present in the mixture at concentrations greater than 10^{-3} ml/ml (Rappaport and Siegel, 1955).

The inactivation by specific antibody protein involves the protein coat of the virus and, at least for TMV, the infectivity of the virus is not irreversibly destroyed. Partial recovery of infectivity of TMV can be obtained by dilution of the reaction mixture or by digestion of the antibody protein with proteolytic enzymes. Rappaport (1961a) obtained complete recovery of the infectivity of TMV by bringing inactive specific precipitates to pH 2.0. Under these conditions, the antibody is dissociated and the virus can be isolated by centrifugation and resuspension of the pelleted material at pH 7.0. Rappaport *et al.* (1964) showed that TMV that had had part of its protein coat stripped off with Duponol C was still inactivated by a purified anti-TMV globulin preparation, suggesting that the remaining protein coat was still important during infection.

In considering the use of neutralization of infectivity for plant virus work, the following factors must be considered: (1) The test is limited to virus host combinations giving a good local lesion assay. (2) Appropriate controls using normal serum or normal serum fractions must be included in the infectivity assays. The sera compared must be of comparable age and stored in the same way. (3) Nonspecific effects of serum on the virus and on the sensitivity of the host plant can be reduced by using the γ-globulin fraction of the serum or more highly purified antibody protein preparations (Rappaport, 1961a). (4) Active nucleases are present in serum and will rapidly destroy the infectivity of any exposed viral ribonucleic acid.

D. HEMAGGLUTINATION

If red blood cells are suitably treated with tannic acid, they will then nonspecifically adsorb protein antigens. Such cells with the antigen attached to their surface can then be incubated with antiserum. Specific combination between the antigen and antibody will result in agglutination of the red cells (Boyden, 1951). The method has not yet been widely used with plant viruses.

Saito and Iwata (1964) tested the method with purified barley stripe mosaic virus (BSMV) and found it to be specific and highly sensitive. In their procedure, 1 volume of a 3.5% suspension of sheep red blood cells was mixed with an equal volume of 0.005% tannic acid in 0.14 M NaCl and incubated at 37°C for 10 minutes. The cells were then sedimented and washed once with 1 volume of saline buffered at pH 7.2 with a Veronal buffer. One volume of 3.5% suspension of the tanned cells was mixed with 4 volumes of 0.1 M saline (at pH 5.0 with phosphate buffer) and 1 volume of a 0.05% solution of purified BSMV. This mixture was held at room temperature for 15 minutes. The cells were then sedimented and washed once in the medium used for making serum dilutions (0.5% normal rabbit serum in Veronal-buffered saline). Cells were resuspended in the same medium to give a 3.5% suspension.

Serial dilutions of antiserum were made (0.5 ml volumes), and 0.05 ml of the tanned virus-sensitized red cell suspension was added to each. Readings were made after 3 hours at room temperature or after an overnight period at 5°C. A positive agglutination pattern consisted of a relatively uniform thin layer of cells covering the bottom of the tube. A negative pattern consisted of a more compact sedimentation of the cells, sometimes forming a ring at the bottom of the tube.

Saito and Iwata (1964) found that the most important factor in the test was the pH of the mixture in which the tanned cells were incubated with virus. For BSMV, this was pH 5.0. The other important factors that must be controlled to prevent nonspecific hemagglutination or hemolysis are the concentration of tanned cells (3.5%) and normal rabbit serum (0.5%) in the incubation mixture. Saito and Iwata found the hemagglutination titer for a BSMV antiserum to be 10,000 times higher than the complement-fixation titer. They also found that the method could be used to detect as little as 10^{-8} gm of purified BSMV.

V. The Quantitative Estimation of Viruses

Serological tests provide rapid and convenient methods for the estimation of plant viruses. The main advantages of such tests are: (1) the specificity of the reaction allows virus to be measured in the presence of host materials or other impurities; (2) measurements can be made on very small amounts of virus; (3) results are obtained in a few minutes or hours compared with days for infectivity assays; (4) the methods give an answer that is directly proportional to virus concentration over a wide range of concentrations; (5) serological tests are particularly useful with viruses that have no good local lesion host; (6) antisera can be stored and standard tests made over quite long periods.

The main limitations of serological tests are: (1) they measure the virus protein antigen, not the amount of infective virus. This fact may, of course, be used to advantage in some situations. (2) Infectivity measurements are usually about 10 times as sensitive as the precipitation reaction carried out in tubes. However, certain modifications of the test may require much less material than infectivity tests. (3) With rod-shaped viruses, end-to-end aggregation of virus particles can occur. Variation in the degree of aggregation can markedly affect the results of some of the assay methods described below. (4) The major deficiency of serological tests is that so far they can be applied only to a limited number of plant viruses.

Antisera to be used for virus estimations are best produced in rabbits, where a fairly large volume of serum can be obtained. It is worthwhile trying to produce an antiserum of high titer. This allows high dilutions of the serum to be used, thus reducing or avoiding nonspecific inhibitory effects of serum at low dilutions and allowing more tests to be made from a given volume of serum. Where a fairly large volume of a stock antiserum has been prepared for routine use, it is well worthwhile to prepare a precipitation diagram as in Fig. 3 if tube precipitation tests are to be used or as in Table II if gel diffusion tests are to be used. Such diagrams allow rapid calculation of appropriate dilutions and quantities of reagents needed for various purposes.

A. Precipitation End-Point Methods

1. *In Tubes*

Antisera should be used at a dilution of at least 1 : 16. Serial 2-fold dilutions (0.5-ml volumes) of the virus samples to be compared are made in 0.14 M saline. An equal volume of the diluted antisera is added to each tube, and the contents are mixed by shaking and incubated at 30°–37°C for a few hours, followed by an overnight period at about 4°C. The highest dilution of each sample to give a visible precipitate is noted. With the small spherical plant viruses this method gives reproducible results. For example, with TYMV, the dilution end point (within the error of the 2-fold dilutions steps) is about 1 μg of virus in 0.5 ml. However, with rod-shaped viruses, the more aggregated the preparation the less virus required to give a visible precipitate.

2. *By Gel Diffusion*

This is a very useful micromethod for the small spherical plant viruses. A row of wells is cut in the agar on the microscope slide with a trough for the antiserum dilution. Serial 2-fold dilutions of the antigen (about 7-μl volumes) are placed in the wells. For TYMV, this method can detect about 0.1 μg of virus, using visual assessment of precipitation bands. (See Section III,C,4 for other methods of assessment.) This method is probably of much less value for most rod-shaped viruses, where aggregation and poor diffusion in the agar may cause difficulties.

B. α-Optimal Proportions

As noted in Section II, the position of the α-optimum is fairly strictly proportional to the dilution of reagents. This is the basis of its use as a quantitative test. A series of 0.5-ml volumes of 2-fold dilutions of virus is set up. The antiserum, 0.5 ml, at a constant dilution is added to each tube, beginning with the most dilute virus sample, and the contents are mixed as rapidly as possible. The first tube to give a visible precipitate is noted as the α-optimum. If the antiserum has been titrated with virus of known absolute concentration, the α-optimum result can be converted into approximate weight of virus per milliliter. The antiserum solution used should be sufficiently dilute so that a number of tubes do not all produce precipitates at once.

With rod-shaped viruses, the position of the α-optimum may be greatly affected by the degree of aggregation in the preparation. Coprecipitating host constituents are more likely to affect the position of the α-optimum than the virus end-point determination. The α-optimum cannot be used to compare strains of virus that are not fairly closely related serologically.

When the dilution of antiserum can be arranged so that the fastest tube precipitates in about 20–30 minutes, a $\sqrt{2}$-fold dilution series may give added precision. The more dilute the initial virus concentration, the more dilute the antiserum must be to give an α-optimum. Very dilute virus preparations may not give an α-optimum. The virus end-point method would then be used.

The α-optimum proportions method gives an answer much more rapidly than the end-point method. This is often an advantage when the serological test is used as an adjunct in some other experimental procedure. However, it requires more virus and antiserum than the end-point method.

C. Time Taken for Precipitation

The time taken for visible precipitation can be used as an estimate of virus concentration for spherical viruses (Matthews, 1957). A constant dilution of antiserum is chosen such that time at the α-optimum is about 1 minute. Serial 2-fold dilutions of a standard virus preparation are then tested against the antiserum dilution. Minimum times for precipitation are recorded under standard conditions of mixing, temperature, and volume. A water bath with windows and suitable lighting (Matthews, 1957) is almost essential for this type of test. All mixtures that precipitate within 30–40 minutes are recorded. Mixtures in the antigen-excess region are not used as times, since these tend to be more variable. For the preparation of a standard time curve, the mixtures are set up twice, say, and the mean times are plotted on a logarithmic scale against virus dilution. The points should lie on a straight line. An unknown virus sample can then be tested over a range of 2-fold dilutions under the standard conditions and the data plotted. From the displacement of the lines along the concentration axis it is possible to calculate the relative concentration of two virus preparations with considerable precision or to determine absolute concentration if a standard virus preparation of known concentration is used.

Whitcomb and Black (1961) and Whitcomb (1964) adapted this timing procedure to giving quantitative data with the ring test for wound tumor virus, thus using much less material. Appearance of the zones of specific precipitate were observed in a darkened air-conditioned room using a narrow light beam with a heat filter.

D. Amount of Specific Precipitate

The amount of virus in specific precipitates can be measured in several ways—by total nitrogen determinations, by isolation and estimation of the nucleotides from the virus ribonucleic acid, or by radioactivity measurements. These methods give precise estimates of virus concentration that are unaffected or not greatly affected by the degree of aggregation of rod-shaped viruses.

1. By Nitrogen Determinations

An appropriate constant amount of antiserum is added to a series of dilutions of a virus preparation of known nitrogen content determined as indicated in Section II,B,8. A standard curve for the antiserum is then prepared that relates virus concentration to total nitrogen in the specific precipitate. To estimate the virus in an unknown sample, the same volume of the same dilution of antiserum is added to an equal volume of the virus preparation and incubated under the standard conditions. From the amount of nitrogen in the washed precipitate the amount of virus can be determined by reference to the standard curve. The supernatant fluid is tested with added antiserum to ensure that the unknown mixture was in the region of antiserum excess or the equivalence zone. This method is liable to error where virus in crude plant extracts is used, since some nonvirus material containing nitrogen usually precipitates during the incubation.

2. By Estimation of Virus Nucleotides

The specificity of both serological and chromatographic procedures can be combined to give a useful micromethod for estimating virus in suitable plant extracts (Matthews, 1954). The virus in a clarified plant extract is quantitatively precipitated by the addition of excess antiserum. The specific precipitate is washed with 0.14 M NaCl, dried, and hydrolyzed with a small volume of 1 N KOH at room temperature for 24 hours. The mixture is then subjected to chromatography on filter paper, using a solvent system that moves the four ribonucleotides in a compact group down the paper. The nucleotides are then located eluted from the paper and estimated spectrophotometrically. This gives an estimate of the virus RNA in the original sample. For further details, see Matthews (1957). The method as so far developed should be used with caution if both ultraviolet absorption and radioactivity measurements are to be made, since with ^{32}P at least contaminating radioactivity may be associated with the isolated nucleotides. The method should be capable of considerable refinement now that nucleotides can be isolated and estimated in very small amounts following suitable thin-layer chromatography.

E. LIGHT SCATTERING

When antibody combines with virus particles to form aggregates larger than the single virus particles in solution, light scattering by the solution is increased. This property can be used to follow the kinetics of antibody virus interaction and can be used to measure virus antigen. Turbidity can be measured by increase in absorbance at 650 mμ using a standard spectrophotometer. Bradish and Crawford (1960) made a detailed study by measuring light scattering of the interaction between TMV and tomato bushy stunt viruses and their respective rabbit antisera. Details of the method are given by these workers. An appropriate light-scattering apparatus must be available, and rather large volumes of solution are required (5 ml or more). However, in terms of concentration, the method is useful down to virus concentrations of about 1 μg/ml.

F. HEMAGGLUTINATION

The hemagglutination method of Saito and Iwata (1964), described in Section IV,D, should prove to be a very useful method for estimating virus antigens down to very low levels, at least for virus preparations that have been purified sufficiently to remove interfering factors from the plant extracts.

VI. *The Estimation of Antibody Concentration*

In work with plant viruses the antibody content of sera is not frequently of interest, as it naturally is with animal viruses. Nevertheless, in preparing antisera for estimating virus antigens or for routine tests for virus infection it is useful to know the relative strength of sera used. In using some serological tests to attempt to establish degrees of relationship between virus strains, it is necessary to be able to measure antibody content of absorbed and unabsorbed sera. There are other occasions when the measurement of antibody concentration is essential, for example, in the work establishing that the empty shell of TYMV is less immunogenic than the virus nucleoprotein (Markham *et al.*, 1948; Marbrook and Matthews, 1966).

A. Amounts of Specific Precipitate

A purified preparation of virus containing a known weight of nitrogen per milliliter is used. This is mixed with a known dilution of the antiserum to be measured, in ratios previously determined experimentally to be in the equivalence zone. It is assumed that in this zone all the virus and all the antibody protein is precipitated. The total nitrogen in the washed precipitates is determined. The amount of virus nitrogen is subtracted to give the amount of antibody nitrogen. Assuming antibody protein to contain 15% nitrogen, the weight of antibody per milliliter of undiluted serum can then be calculated.

B. Dilution Titer of Serum

This method is generally the simplest, most economical method in plant virus work to give an approximate estimate of antibody content. This measure is closely related to the weight of antibody protein present, at least in the same animal during the course of immunization (Matthews, 1957). In using tube precipitation tests, it is important to use the virus antigen at a concentration within one or two 2-fold steps of the virus end point. Lower dilutions of virus may give an antiserum titer that is too low owing to inhibition by excess virus (see Fig. 3).

The gel precipitation test can be usefully employed for measuring the antibody content of sera, especially when large numbers of sera are to be tested and when only small volumes of serum are available, as when mice are used.

C. Position of the α-Optimum

Using a constant antiserum dilution and a 2-fold dilution series of virus, the position of the α-optimum can be used to estimate relative antibody content, in a way similar to its use for estimating virus content (Section V,B). The method is more rapid than the end-point titer but uses more of the reagents. End-point and α-optimum methods give a similar estimate, within the limits of the 2-fold dilution steps employed, at least for TYMV (Matthews, 1957).

D. TIME TAKEN FOR PRECIPITATION

At or near the α-optimum the time for precipitation, under standard conditions, should follow much the same course with increasing dilution for any antiserum to the same virus. This fact can be used to give a method for estimating relative antibody concentration that is more accurate than the dilution titer or α-optimum methods (Matthews, 1957). It is, however, more time consuming.

E. LIGHT SCATTERING

The light-scattering method of Bradish and Crawford (1960) (Section V,E) would be useful under special circumstances for estimating antibody concentrations.

F. HEMAGGLUTINATION

The hemagglutination procedure of Saito and Iwata (1964) (Section V,F) should be well suited to estimating antibody content of sera where a supply of adequately purified virus is available.

VII. Methods for Determining Serological Relationships between Plant Viruses

For plant viruses to which serological tests can be applied, such tests provide a useful criterion for establishing relationships between viruses. Any of the serological tests described in Sections II–IV can be employed, but most commonly some modification of the precipitation reaction is used. Generally, all that is required in plant virus work is to know whether or not two viruses cross-react serologically. Unlike the situation with many human and animal viruses, it is not usually important to be able to identify serological types within a group of related virus strains.

There are a number of precautions that must be taken if the results of serological tests for relationships between viruses are to be interpreted correctly. Many of these precautions apply generally in the use of serological tests with plant viruses, but they are especially important in determining serological relationships, and for this reason will be summarized here.

A. Precautions Necessary in Using Serological Tests

1. Antibodies for Host Constituents

This is one of the most common causes of confusion, especially where crude or partially purified virus preparations are used for injection and where long courses of immunization are carried out. No systematic study has yet been made of the concentrations, stabilities, and immunogenicity of various host-plant antigens, but antigens occur in many extracts (e.g., S. T. C. Wright, 1960; Heitefuss et al., 1960). In healthy and in TYMV-infected Chinese cabbage plants, at least seven distinct host antigens can be distinguished in immunoelectrophoretic tests in agar gel (Reanney, 1965). Fraction I protein is immunogenic and is probably the most common contaminant of virus preparations, since (1) it occurs in relatively high concentration in the usual leaf extracts, and (2) it is a large protein ($\cong 18S$) that readily aggregates under appropriate conditions. Van Regenmortel (1964) has studied methods for freeing plant virus preparations from fraction I protein. Other common contaminants of plant virus preparations may be ribosomes, phytoferritin, and fragments of membrane structures.

Thus even when purified virus preparations are used to prepare antisera, it is essential to test for the presence of antibodies to host constituents. Such antibodies, if detected, can be removed by absorption of the serum with an appropriate amount of a preparation from healthy plants.

2. Nonspecific Precipitation of Host Constituents

Spontaneous nonspecific precipitation of host materials is always liable to occur, however carefully the crude sap has been clarified, by heat or otherwise. The time and extent of such precipitation will depend on such factors as (1) the method used to clarify the sap, (2) the temperature at which mixtures are incubated, (3) the time of incubation, (4) the concentration of normal serum constituents, which tend to inhibit nonspecific precipitation, and (5) the concentration of sap in the mixture. More concentrated sap tends to precipitate more rapidly. It is therefore necessary when using crude extracts to set up appropriate control mixtures containing normal serum and the extract containing the virus.

3. Nonspecific Precipitation of Viruses

Nonspecific precipitation of purified viruses is not usually a problem. However, with high concentrations of purified virus, especially when incubated at higher temperatures (e.g., 40°–50°C), such non-specific precipitation can sometimes give the appearanec of an optimum zone of precipitation.

4. Contamination with Other Viruses

Contamination with unrelated viruses is one of the most common causes of misleading results in serological tests. TMV is probably the most frequent cause of trouble. It is stable, highly immunogenic, occurs in high concentration in many hosts, has a wide host range, and is usually present in experimental glass houses. When viruses are grown in any plant that is a host for TMV (even a local lesion host such as *Nicotiana glutinosa*), antisera should be tested for the presence of antibodies to TMV before they are used. Tobacco necrosis viruses and some potato viruses are other likely contaminants. The possibility that the original natural host of a virus under study contained a second virus that is being carried along in the culture must also be considered.

5. Virus-Specific Noncoat Antigens

Although not yet demonstrated for any plant virus, it is very probable that virus infection leads to the production of other new proteins in the infected cells besides the virus coat protein. These might give anomalous results in serological tests where crude preparations from infected plants are used as antigens. However, a study of extracts from TYMV-infected Chinese cabbage leaves by immunodiffusion and immunoelectrophoresis failed to reveal any new antigens other than virus coat protein (Reanney, 1965). Any other virus-induced proteins were presumably in too low a concentration, too unstable, or too firmly bound to large cell structures to be detectable. If a similar situation exists with other plant viruses, this interesting source of confusion may remain a theoretical possibility.

6. Reciprocal Testing of Antisera

The first four precautions noted above apply generally to serological tests. There is an additional check needed when attempting to demonstrate that two viruses are serologically unrelated. Reactive antisera must be prepared against both viruses under test. It must be shown that while each reacts with its homologous antiserum, it gives no reaction with the heterologous serum. This reciprocal test is necessary, since the viruses might in fact be related, but one may occur in too low a concentration to give any serological test.

B. Methods for Determining Degrees of Relationship among a Group of Virus Strains

If two isolates of a virus are identical, they will react identically when cross-reacted with each other's antisera, whatever form of serological test is applied. If, however, they are related but distinct, some degree of cross-reaction will be observed, but the reactions will not be identical. Various types of serological test can be used to attempt to distinguish between virus strains. For example, Matthews (1949) prepared antisera against a selection of strains of potato virus X. Antisera were absorbed with heterologous strains and the strain-specific antibody remaining was then estimated by antiserum titer measurement using the homologous strain. Rappaport *et al.* (1957) in a careful study of a group of TMV strains used the quantitative measurements of the relative degree of inactivation by unabsorbed homologous and heterologous antisera to obtain estimates of the degree of relationship between the strains.

Immunodiffusion tests in agar can be applied to a group of virus strains and their antisera. The reactions of identity or partial identity when the various strains and their antisera are cross-reacted may give some indication of degree of relationship between strains. The use of immunodiffusion tests is illustrated by the work of Scott *et al.* (1961).

Wright (1963) used cross-absorption procedures and complement-fixation tests to measure antibody concentrations in a study of several groups of virus strains.

When a group of only two or three virus isolates is to be considered, it is a simple matter, relatively speaking, to determine whether the isolates are unrelated serologically, whether they are identical, or whether they show differing degrees of relationship. When large numbers of related strains are considered, the situation becomes quite complex and less and less meaningful. Matthews (1957) gives a detailed discussion of this situation.

Where small serological differences are being looked for, it is preferable to use fairly low-titer antisera (Matthews, 1957). A single injection of 0.1–1.0 mg of purified virus in rabbits usually gives a usable antiserum. On the other hand, when distant relationships are examined, high-titer antisera are preferable (Bercks, 1963).

The two major difficulties in interpreting the results of tests for degrees of serological relationship appear to be: (1) The population of antibody molecules produced by a given animal is not homogeneous, and different individual animals vary in the population of antibody molecules they produce in response to a given antigen. The difficulties involved owing to variation between animals and between antisera of low and high titer are well illustrated in the careful study by Bercks (1963). In any comparative study, groups of animals should be used for each virus antigen. (2) The chemical nature of antigenic sites is not at all well defined. It is not clear whether each virus strain is a mosaic having a number of distinct antigenic components, some of which may be shared by related strains, or whether each strain possesses one antigenic determinant that is more or less structurally similar in related strains. A combination of these possibilities might also occur. This problem is discussed by Rappaport (1961b) for TMV strains. An approach is being made toward a definition in chemical terms of an antigenic site in TMV from a study of tryptic peptides (Benjamin *et al.*, 1964). Serological tests for degrees of relationship will have much more value when the chemical basis of the reactions is more clearly understood.

VIII. Labeled-Antibody Methods

Viral antigens within cells will combine with specific antibody proteins, but with natural antibody this combination cannot be observed. Various procedures have been used to label antibody so that it can be used as a highly specific "stain" for locating virus antigen within cells and cell organelles. Three general types of label have been used: (1) fluorescent dyes, which give a characteristic color in ultraviolet light; (2) electron-dense materials, which enable antibody to be located by electron microscopy; and (3) radioactive materials, which allow antibody to be located by microautoradiography. There are two general types of difficulty with these methods—first, the problem of ensuring that the antibody conjugate can enter the cell and reach the virus antigen, and second, a variety of nonspecific effects, depending on the particular method. These methods have not yet been widely applied to plant viruses. Only a brief summary of these methods is given here; the reader is referred to the recent literature for details.

A. FLUORESCENT ANTIBODY

The fluorescent-antibody method of Coons *et al.* (1942) has been applied to the study of the intracellular location and distribution within tissues of plant viruses in insects (e.g., Day and Venables, 1961; Nagaraj and Black, 1961; Nagaraj, 1962; Sinha and Black, 1963; Sinha and Reddy, 1964) and in host plants (e.g., Worley and Schneider, 1963; Nagaraj, 1965).

1. *In Plants*

Nagaraj (1962, 1965) gives the detailed procedures that must be carried out in the preparation and storage of TMV antibody conjugated with fluorescein to avoid nonspecific staining. Appropriate controls to check for such staining should include: (1) infected material treated with a fluorescein-labeled heterologous antiserum; (2) infected material pretreated with an unconjugated specific antiserum before treatment with the conjugated specific serum; (3) comparable healthy tissue treated with the virus-specific fluorescent antibody.

Nagaraj used three methods for preparing tissue for staining with antibody: (1) the paraffin-embedding procedure of Saintemarie (1962). Ribbons prepared by this procedure could be stored for several months without affecting the capacity to stain with fluorescent antibody. (2) Frozen sections using a cryostat, as described by Coons *et al.* (1951). (3) Separation of mesophyll cells using pectinase (Zaitlin, 1959). Nagaraj found that the value of this procedure depends very much on the actual tissue used. It was not good for localizing antigen in stems, petioles, petals, and sepals, nor in local lesions. Epidermal and vascular tissues of leaves were lost during processing. The extent to which antibody penetrated mesophyll cells depended on the age of the leaf. Penetration occurred in cells from older leaves, but with younger leaves cells had to be fixed in alcohol, acetone, or Carnoy's fluid before penetration of antibody would take place.

2. *In Insects*

Sinha and Reddy (1964) described an improved fluorescent-smear technique for detecting virus antigens in an insect vector (wound tumor virus in the leafhopper *Agallia contricta*). They found that the dialysis technique of Clark and Shepard (1963) gave higher yields of fluorescent antibody, and that the specific staining was much brighter and the nonspecific staining much less bright than their previous method.

Smears of cells were prepared by squeezing insects directly onto marked areas of a microscope slide. The smears were then dried, fixed, stained, washed, and mounted in buffered glycerin–saline. Sinha *et al.* (1964) describe a modification of the procedure, in which small samples of the hemolymph of an insect can be taken for examination while allowing a high percentage of insects to survive.

B. Location of Antibody by Electron Microscopy

With animal viruses two electron-dense materials—ferritin and iodine—have been used to make antibody combined with intracellular virus visible by electron microscopy. Both these methods should, in principle, be applicable to plant viruses.

1. *Ferritin*

As an example with animal viruses, ferritin-labeled antibody was used by Morgan *et al.* (1961) to delineate vaccinia virus particles within infected HeLa cells. To allow penetration of the antibody, fixed cells were sectioned while frozen sections were then allowed to react with antibody at room temperature.

2. *Iodine*

Parfanovich *et al.* (1965) studied the distribution of measles virus antigen in chick embryo fibroblasts using antibody that had been coupled with icdine to increase electron density. Cells were frozen and thawed before treatment with antibody. This treatment caused some disorganization of internal cell structure but allowed the antibody to penetrate.

C. Radioactively Labeled Antibody

It is possible to label immune globulins with a radioactive tracer. For example, Rosen *et al.* (1963) showed that antibody globulin could be tritiated *in vitro* using ^{3}H-labeled methanesulfonic acid ethyl ester, without marked effect on immunologic activity. The usefulness of such methods for locating plant virus antigens within plant or animal cells by microradioautography remains to be assessed. The major difficulties would be (1) to get sufficient amounts of a low-energy emitter firmly bound to antibody without affecting antibody specificity and (b) to check carefully the specificity of the binding of antibody within cells, as with the fluorescent-labeled antibody methods.

References

Aach, H. G. (1959). *Biochim. Biophys. Acta* **32**, 140.

Allen, W. R., and Tremaine, J. H. (1965). *Virology* **25**, 122.

Ball, E. M. (1961). Serological Tests for the Identification of Plant Viruses. Am. Phytopathol. Soc., Ithaca, New York.

Bawden, F. C. (1964). "Plant Viruses and Virus Diseases," 361 pp. Ronald Press, New York.

Benjamini, E., Young, J. D., Shimizu, M., and Leung, C. (1964). *Biochemistry* **3**, 1115.

Bercks, R. (1963). *Phytopathol. Z.* **47**, 301.

Boyden, S. V. (1951). *J. Exptl. Med.* **93**, 107.

Bozicevich, J., Scott, H. A., and Vincent, M. M. (1963). *Proc. Soc. Exptl. Biol. Med.* **114**, 794.

Bradish, C. J., and Crawford, L. V. (1960). *Virology* **11**, 48.

Briody, B. A. (1959). *Bacteriol. Rev.* **23**, 61.

Chester, K. S. (1936). *Phytopathology* **26**, 715.

Clark, F. H., and Shepard, C. C. (1963). *Virology* **20**, 642.

Cleland, W. W. (1964). *Biochemistry* **3**, 480

Commoner, B., Yamada, N., Rodenberg, S., Wang, T., and Basler, E. (1953). *Science* **118**, 529.

Coons, A. N., Creech, H. J., Jones, R. N., and Berliner, E. (1942). *J. Immunol.* **45**, 159.

Coons, A. H., Leduc, H. C., and Kaplan, M. H. (1951). *J. Exptl. Med.* **93**, 173.

Crowle, A. J. (1961). "Immunodiffusion," 333 pp. Academic Press, New York.

Day, M. F., and Venables, D. G. (1961). *Australian J. Biol. Sci.* **14**, 187.

Gierer, A., and Schramm, G. (1956). *Nature* **177**, 702.

Grabar, P., and Williams, C. A. (1953). *Biochim. Biophys. Acta* **17**, 67.

Grabar, P., Nawinski, W. W., and Generaux, B. P. (1956). *Nature* **178**, 430.

Heitefuss, R., Buchanan-Davidson, D. J., Stahmann, M. A., and Walker, J. C. (1960). *Phytopathology* **50**, 198.

Jeener, R., Lemoine, P., and Lavand'homme, C. (1954). *Biochim. Biophys. Acta* **14**, 321.

Kabat, E. A., and Mayer, M. M. (1961). "Experimental Immunochemistry," 905 pp. Thomas, Springfield, Illinois.

Kleczkowski, A. (1957). *J. Gen. Microbiol.* **16**, 405.

Lyttleton, J. W., and Matthews, R. E. F. (1958). *Virology* **6**, 460.

Marbrook, J., and Matthews, R. E. F. (1966). *Virology* **28**, 219.

Markham, R. (1965). Personal communication.

Markham, R., and Smith, K. M. (1949). *Parasitology* **39**, 330.

Markham, R., Matthews, R. E. F., and Smith, K. M. (1948). *Nature* **162**, 88.

Matthews, R. E. F. (1949). *Ann. Appl. Biol.* **36**, 460.

Matthews, R. E. F. (1954). *J. Gen. Microbiol.* **10**, 521.

Matthews, R. E. F. (1957). "Plant Virus Serology," 127 pp. Cambridge Univ. Press, London and New York.

Matthews, R. E. F. (1960). *Virology* **12**, 521.

Moorhead, E. L. (1959). *Phytopathology* **49**, 151.

Moorhead, E. L. (1961). *Virology* **13**, 249.

Morgan, C., Rifkind, R. A., Hsu, K. C., Holden, M., Seegal, B. C., and Rose, H. M. (1961). *Virology* **14**, 292.

Munro, J. (1954). *Am. Potato J.* **31**, 73.

Nagaraj, A. N. (1962). *Virology* **18**, 329.

Nagaraj, A. N. (1965). *Virology* **25**, 133.

Nagaraj, A. N., and Black, L. M. (1961). *Virology* **15**, 289.

Newton, W., and Edwards, H. I. (1936). *Can. J. Res.* **14**, 412.

Ouchterlony, O. (1948). *Acta Pathol. Microbiol. Scand.* **25**, 186.

Ouchterlony, O. (1958). *Progr. Allergy* **5**, 1.

Ouchterlony, O. (1962). *Progr. Allergy* **6**, 30.

Oudin, J. (1946). *Compt. Rend. Acad. Sci.* **222,** 115.

Oudin, J. (1952). *Methods in Med. Res.* **5,** 353.

Parfanovich, M. I., Sokolov, N. N., Mekler, L. B., Fadeyeva, L. L., and Zhdanov, V. M. (1965). *Nature* **206,** 784.

Ragetli, H. W. J., and Weintraub, M. (1964). *Science* **144,** 1023.

Rappaport, I. (1961a). *Biochim. Biophys. Acta* **47,** 206.

Rappaport, I. (1961b). *Nature* **189,** 986.

Rappaport, I., and Siegel, A. (1955). *J. Immunol.* **74,** 106.

Rappaport, I., Siegel, A., Owen, R. D., and Wildman, S. G. (1957). *J. Immunol.* **78,** 259.

Rappaport, I., Wildman, S. G., and Furumoto, W. (1964). *Virology* **23,** 389.

Rappaport, I., Siegel, A., and Haselkorn, R. (1965). *Virology* **25,** 325.

Reanney, D. R. (1965). Personal communication.

Rosen, C. G., Ehrenberg, L., and Ahstrom, G. (1963). *Nature* **204,** 796.

Saintemarie, G. (1962). *J. Histochem. Cytochem.* **10,** 250.

Saito, Y., and Iwata, Y. (1964). *Virology* **22,** 426.

Scott, H. A., Vincent, M. M., and Zaumeyer, W. J. (1961). *Phytopathology* **51,** 755.

Scott, H. A., Khan, R. P., Bozicevich, J., and Vincent, M. M. (1964). *Phytopathology* **54,** 1292.

Singer, S. J., Eggman, L., Campbell, J. M., and Wildman, S. G. (1952). *J. Biol. Chem.* **197,** 233.

Sinha, R. C., and Black, L. M. (1963). *Virology* **21,** 183.

Sinha, R. C., and Reddy, D. V. R. (1964). *Virology* **24,** 626.

Sinha, R. C., Reddy, D. V. R., and Black, L. M. (1964). *Virology* **24,** 666.

Sobey, W. R. (1954). *Australian J. Biol. Sci.* **7,** 11.

Stapp, C., and Bercks, R. (1948). *Phytopathol. Z.* **15,** 47.

Thompson, A. D. (1964). *Nature* **201,** 422.

Tremaine, J. H., and Willison, R. S. (1961). *Can. J. Botany* **39,** 1843.

van der Veken, J. A., van Slogteren, D. H. M., and van der Want, J. P. H. (1962). *In* "Modern Methods of Plant Analysis" (H. F. Linskens and M. V. Tracey, eds.), Vol. 5, pp. 422–463. Springer, Berlin.

van Regenmortel, M. H. V. (1963). *Phytopathol. Z.* **48,** 197.

van Regenmortel, M. H. V. (1964). *Phytopathology* **54,** 282.

van Slogteren, D. H. M. (1955). *Proc. 2nd Conf. Potato Virus Diseases, Lisse-Wageningen* p. 51.

van Slogteren, D. H. M. (1958). *Proc. Intern. Sci. Tobacco Congr., Bruxelles.* p. 144.

van Slogteren, E., and van Slogteren, D. H. M. (1957). *Ann. Rev. Microbiol.* **11,** 149.

Whitcomb, R. F. (1964). *Virology* **24,** 488.

Whitcomb, R. F., and Black, L. M. (1961). *Virology* **15,** 507.

Worley, J. F., and Schneider, I. R. (1963). *Phytopathology* **53,** 1255.

Wright, N. S. (1963). *Virology* **20,** 131.

Wright, N. S., and Hardy, M. (1961). *Virology* **13,** 414.

Wright, S. T. C. (1960). *Nature* **185,** 82.

Zaitlin, M. (1959). *Nature* **184,** 1002.

6   *The Plaque Assay of Animal Viruses*

Peter D. Cooper

I. Introduction

In an earlier review of the methods involved in the plaque assay of animal viruses (Cooper, 1961a), it was mentioned that at that time there were over 200 reports on work relating to this subject. Since then this number has increased considerably. Many useful developments in technique have been made that have extended the method to new viruses or that have improved the convenience or efficiency of existing systems. A number of these developments will be discussed here. It is interesting to note that a large proportion of current work appears to involve plaque assay systems that have not changed significantly from those reviewed earlier. Whether this stems from a preference to make use of the techniques as they exist or whether further improvements are not feasible cannot be decided; perhaps both are contributing factors. Nevertheless, it may now be said that many of the techniques are to a considerable degree established.

The object of this article is to give in practical detail a number of representative methods that have proved to be reasonably reliable in several laboratories. One aim is therefore to present methods that are simple. Another aim is to select methods that, with minor modification, might be used with many cell–virus systems. To assist in this process, Table II lists references to methods or viruses not considered in detail.

It will be appreciated that no one method can be used for the plaque assay of all animal viruses, and that there are too many viruses under study to give a method for each here. Furthermore, in many cases several different methods have been reported for a given virus; these undoubtedly reflect the fact that there are many ways to kill a cat, but also that needs and facilities differ, and that local conditions, for example, of glassware preparation and of serum supply, or even of the virus and cell substrains that are in use, may also differ considerably throughout the world. Such sources of variation mean that any given method is not necessarily the most reliable and sensitive in all circumstances, and indeed it is to be expected that adaptations may have to be made to apply the methods to a particular locality, cell type, or virus. However, it is hoped that the earlier review (Cooper, 1961a) and the methods referred to in Table II will provide sufficiently useful guides to the type of changes that can be made in the various steps in the assay procedure. Some indication is also given here of the range of changes that give satisfactory results.

The methods cited here, therefore, are to be regarded only as practical examples that are simple and reliable, and often highly sensitive, for the systems that are described.

II. General Consideration of the Plaque Assay Method

A. THE PRINCIPLE OF THE METHOD

"Plaque assays" will be defined as methods enabling the counting of local lesions produced by an animal virus in cell culture.

In outline, the plaque assay consists of the inoculation of a statistically adequate yet easily countable number (say 30–100) of infective virus particles onto an immobilized layer of cells. Each particle is allowed to multiply under conditions in which the resulting lesion remains local, and the lesions are finally counted. It can be shown that each lesion is caused by a single particle, and this enables the calculation of the infective particle content of the original inoculum.

B. Differences between the Plaque Assay and Other Methods

The infectivity of virus preparations can be measured either in abstract units, which do not allow direct interpretation (e.g., in terms of "survival time") or in terms of real units, such as the individual infective particles. Real units are clearly preferable because of their ease of visualization. There exist two methods of counting them. One is the end-point method, giving an all-or-none response, in which virus is diluted until only a few inocula contain a single infective particle. The other is the lesion-counting method, in which inocula are all diluted to contain about 100 particles. On inoculation into a substrate containing living cells, one either scores for growth (positive or negative) or counts individual lesions, respectively.

The plaque assay method is distinguished in two ways from all other methods: (1) since it is a lesion-counting method, it produces many lesions in one container (a cell culture) rather than occupying a whole container with one lesion or wasting it by a total absence of lesion; (2) it uses a very reproducible substrate, namely, cells in culture. The increased accuracy of the plaque assay is achieved partly by its use of such cultures and partly by its economy, since equivalent accuracy could be obtained by the end-point method by use of a larger number of containers.

Provided that one is concerned simply with accurate comparisons of infectivity, there are several reasons for preferring cell cultures to *in vivo* or *in ovo* systems: (1) variations among individual cultures of a batch, and between batches made at different times, can be made quite small; (2) the number of cell types present can be reduced to one; (3) humoral reactions and other variable factors affecting sensitivity can be eliminated; (4) virus inactivation can be controlled; (5) it is easier to be sure of dealing with a single particle; and (6) in studies of virus neutralization, excess antiserum can be removed by washing after adsorption of surviving infectious units. These advantages apply equally to end-point titrations in cell culture. It is not the purpose here to discuss cell culture–virus systems in general; the essential difference between plaque assays and other cell-culture methods is the localization of virus infections by means other than confinement in individual containers, thus greatly increasing economy of time and materials.

In principle, this localization is identical with the localization of bacteriophage plaques or bacterial colonies, in which free diffusion of the infecting organism is slowed or prevented by a gelled substance (usually agar medium); spread by convection or mechanical currents is completely prevented. Some viruses are self-limiting in spread and require no artificial localization. In all cases the prime requirement is a discrete form of virus growth that can be distinguished macro- or microscopically from a background of uninfected cells. The function of the cells is, therefore, both to support growth of the virus and to provide a contrasting background against which virus growth can be recognized.

C. Mode of Development of a Local Lesion

Having achieved localized changes due to virus, there appear to be three ways in which such changes may spread and thus become recognizable. By far the commonest is by release of free virus into the medium, which then spreads by simple diffusion to reach and infect adjacent healthy cells. In this case, antiserum in the medium prevents development of a plaque. Dulbecco and Vogt (1954a) found viable poliovirus 3–4 mm beyond the visible limits of a plaque. While it seems that all viruses are able to spread by this means, in a few cases diffusion probably contributes little to plaque or focus develop- ment. Herpes B virus is of a size that diffuses poorly through agar (Polson, 1956), yet, even in the presence of antiserum, foci continue to enlarge by direct cell-to-cell interaction (Black and Melnick, 1955). Cells fuse and thereby become bigger and eventually disintegrate; the infection is transmitted by contact of cells. This mechanism is generally limited to the larger viruses. With Rous sarcoma virus (Temin and Rubin, 1958), on the other hand, cells are not destroyed, and only very small amounts of focus-forming virus are released; in this case the focus enlarges mainly by growth and division of the newly created Rous sarcoma cell.

D. Criteria and Requirements for a Reproducible Plaque Assay

Most of the factors affecting the assay will be discussed in detail below, but it may be useful at this point to list certain criteria for their adequate control.

In order to demonstrate the usefulness of a plaque assay, it is essen- tial to show the following points; the importance of some of these is self-evident.

1. There must be no "plaques" in absence of virus.

2. The characteristic virus must be regularly reisolated from a plaque in far higher concentration than from areas away from a plaque.

3. Plaques must follow a linear relationship with dose (and not with dilution), i.e., plaque count must be proportional to virus concentration, at least over a range within statistical practicability.

4. Plaques should be spread among cultures of one batch according to a Poisson distribution, and the coefficient of variation of duplicate assays should be near the value statistically expected from the total number of plaques counted.

5. Plaque initiation must be inhibited by low concentrations of heated specific antiserum that will not inhibit growth of another virus in the same cell system (to eliminate the possible presence of anticell antibodies), and not be inhibited by normal serum of the same source species.

6. Repeated assays of a preserved virus stock in cultures of different batches should give the same titer.

The most important criterion for assay purposes, number 3 in the above list, has been amply demonstrated for many systems, and the remainder have been shown for some others, but it is rare to find all criteria employed. Additionally, it is desirable to demonstrate that all cells have quantitatively equal sensitivity (cloning in the case of continuously cultured strains); the virus also should be cloned and be shown to be genetically stable, and stocks should be purified and subcultured by dilute passage, although these things have rarely been done.

E. Choice of Culture System

There are broadly two ways in which cells may be cultured while retaining a localization of virus growth, that is, either (1) as a confluent sheet on a surface (monolayer) or (2) suspended in a layer of gelled substrate, usually agar (agar cell-suspension). The general procedures involved can be outlined as follows.

1. *Monolayer Plaque Assay*

Cells are added in appropriate concentration, volume, and medium to a flat-bottomed container suitable for cell culture (e.g., plastic or neutral glass Petri dishes or capped bottles) and allowed to settle and attach (3–20 hours). Sometimes a period of growth of up to 14 days is then required, particularly for epithelial cells, to fill the surface completely with cells. The medium is then removed and, with or without washing, suitable virus dilutions containing 20–200 plaque-forming units (pfu) are added in small volume and a predetermined period allowed for virus to adsorb to the cells. After adsorption, liquid nutrient agar medium is added and allowed to set on a level surface, and the plates or bottles are incubated in a suitable temperature and atmosphere for a predetermined time (30 hours to 21 days, but usually 2–4 days). For some viruses the agar can be omitted from the nutrient medium. Usually plaques can be seen by indirect light against a dark background, and occasionally they are distinct enough to count in this way, but nearly always some stain, usually neutral red, is added to enhance the contrast. After a period during which the cells absorb the stain (usually 2–4 hours) plaques can be counted.

2. Agar Cell-Suspension Plaque Assay

This method is essentially similar to the monolayer method, except that the nutrient agar layer is added to the container before the cells and is allowed to set. These base layers can be stored for 1–2 weeks at 4°C. A small tube containing an appropriate number of cells in a small volume of medium receives a dilution of virus similar to that added to monolayers, followed by an equal volume of liquid agar medium; the whole is rapidly mixed and poured at once onto a base layer and allowed to set. No adsorption period is necessary. Subsequent treatment is then identical to that of the monolayer method.

3. Comparison of Monolayer and Cell-Suspension Methods

The relative merits and demerits of these two systems are compared in Table I.

The monolayer method was the original introduction by Dulbecco (1952), and has been employed the most extensively. It is particularly useful for rare or expensive primary cultures, such as monkey kidney, which it is desired to expand as much as possible by growth before use and then to use for plaque assays in the original growth containers. More attention is required, however, than if the cells are grown in bulk. If subcultured at any stage, then the particular convenience of the monolayer assay is lost. The monolayer method is also more suitable for very large viruses that diffuse slowly through agar (e.g., herpes simplex; Waterson, 1958b), for assays that take more than a week to develop (this may be a question of improving the medium to preserve cells in agar suspension), for microscopic determination of foci, for plaque-contrast enhancement by fixative stains, or for plaque development by hemadsorption, where cell-to-cell contact is required.

The agar cell-suspension method was developed by Cooper (1955)

TABLE I

A Comparison of the Monolayer and Agar Cell-Suspension Plaque Assay Methods

Monolayer method	Agar cell-suspension method
Introduced 1952 (Dulbecco)	Introduced 1955 (Cooper). Sensitivity higher (up to 7× for free virus and infected cells of fowl orphan,[a] vesicular stomatitis,[a] FMD,[a] poliovirus,[a] VEE[a]
	Probably cannot be used for viruses >120–150 mμ in diameter
Sensitivity higher for herpes virus[a] and probably for pox group[a]	
Infected cell assays usually require additional maneuvers	Particularly useful for infected cell assays[a]
Virus has long diffusion path in "spot tests"; stain diffuses slowly	Short diffusion path for "spot tests"; stain diffuses quickly[a]
Prediffusion of inhibitor less easy in plaque inhibition tests	Prediffusion gives high sensitivity in plaque inhibition tests[a]
Depth of agar often critical	Depth of agar not critical[a]
Most useful where cells are in short supply (e.g., primary cultures of small organs); cells can be multiplied and used in same container[a]	Requires more cells for primary cultures
	Requires same or less cells for continuous strains (KB, ERK)[a]
Cells grown in small monolayers require more attention than cells grown in bulk	Cells can be grown in bulk; less chance of contamination[a]
Cells can be "stored" as monolayers at 30°C	Cells can be "stored" in suspension at 30°C
Cultures have to be prepared in advance, usually 1–6 days	Cells can be used at any time at short notice, from monolayer or suspension cultures[a]

Cell concentration is rather critical (for confluency)	5–10 × range of cell concentration can be used[a]
Cells more anaerobic, make more acid	Cells more aerobic
Can only be used for cells forming monolayers	Can be used for all cells; essential method for ascites cells, which do not form monolayers[a]
Mixed cell populations may form localized colonies or overgrow	Mixed cell populations are fixed and cells generally do not grow in agar[a]
Nonviable cells can be removed by washing before plating[a]	Cell viability must remain high
State of culture-vessel surface fairly critical	Independent of culture-vessel surface; glass cleaning is easier, and method can be used with cheap plastic dishes that will not grow monolayers[a]
A 0.5–4-hour adsorption period required	No adsorption period necessary[a]
Cells can be examined microscopically for CPE[a]	CPE is generally not visible unless gross
If agar and killed cells are removed, fixative stain (e.g., crystal violet) can be used[a]	Specific cell stain must be used, e.g., neutral red, tetrazolium, or trypan blue
Plaques sharply defined but small	Plaques larger but less sharply defined, especially at low cell concentration. Method generally quicker[a]
Plaques can be developed by hemadsorption[a]	Presumably difficult to use with hemadsorption development

[a] Advantage lies with the system marked.

specifically to obtain a higher efficiency of plating of infected cell suspensions and to approach the versatility of bacteriophage assays. It
turned out to have a number of other advantages, mainly its higher
efficiency of plating for free virus of the small- and medium-sized
groups [7 ×, fowl orphan virus (Macpherson, 1960); 1.3–1.5 ×, vesicular stomatitis virus (Cooper, 1955); 1.6–2.8 ×, foot-and-mouth disease
virus, (Sellers and Stewart, 1959); 5 ×, Venezuelan equine encephalomyelitis (A. Brown and Officer, 1961)], and its generally greater convenience of handling (Cooper, 1961b). Since cells are always obtained
at harvest in suspension, it is convenient to keep them in this form;
plates can be poured at short notice, no adsorption period is necessary,
cell concentration, glassware and agar quantities are generally less
critical, "spot" and plaque-inhibition tests are higher in sensitivity, and
it is easier to use mixed cell populations. The amount of cells required
for some primary cultures appears to be higher than needed for monolayers, but the number of continuous-line cells required is if anything
slightly less than for monolayers; it is probable that the need for more
primary cells could be met by improving the medium. There is no
alternative to the agar cell-suspension method for ascites tumor cells
(Sanders, 1957), which do not form monolayers on glass. Cell suspensions can also be used to "develop" plaques in a cell sheet prevented
from absorbing stain by x-irradiation (Franklin, 1958a).

Thus it can be seen that both methods have individual merits,
depending mostly on the virus used and its growth characteristics,
but also on the cells available and the manipulations involved. The
choice depends on the sensitivity required and the particular convenience and applicability with regard to the selected cell–virus system
and information needed. Apart from the exceptions noted in favor of
the monolayer method, the weight of advantage would appear to be
with the cell-suspension method, particularly for laboratories that are
just beginning to set up plaque assay systems.

III. Preparation of Media

A. INTRODUCTION

Methods for plaque assay of animal viruses naturally rely on standard methods for culture of animal cells, and it will be taken for granted
that all materials and methods whose use is described in this article
(sterile technique, glassware, distilled water, and medium components)
are those suitable for general cell-culture work. For this purpose,
reference is made to a standard textbook of cell and tissue culture (Paul,

1965). In addition, many useful materials and methods relevant to the plaque assay are described by Schmidt (1964).

This section describes the preparation of those cell-culture media and medium components that are most frequently used for plaque assay purposes.

B. General Nature of Media Used for Plaque Assays

The literature contains reports of a large number of media that are suitable for cell culture. In spite of this variety, their composition is quite similar, in that their inorganic constituents are practically identical, and most contain a pH buffer, antibiotics, glucose and sources of vitamins, amino acids, peptides and protein, plus in some cases other substances. Their differences, therefore, reside mainly in the components of these main groups. Methods described for plaque assays tend to use those media that are simplest to prepare, and it would almost be true to say that all media used for the plaque assays of animal viruses consist of permutations of a few main sources of the groups of substances described above. These sources are virtually interchangeable in many cases, so that a few solutions can fulfill many needs. In case of difficulty, media can be supplemented with another source of the same group of substances.

The tabulation on page 254 gives some useful sources of the main groups of components. The concentrations given represent the range used of final concentrations of the dry substance or of the indicated solutions.

C. Phosphate-Buffered Saline and Other Media for Virus Dilution

A "balanced salt solution" (which contains solutes in addition to sodium chloride) is generally less harmful to cells in culture than is physiological saline alone, and a very widely used one for washing cells and for suspending virus is the "phosphate-buffered saline" (PBS) of Dulbecco and Vogt (1954a).

1. PBS Solution A

NaCl	8.0 gm	KH_2PO_4	0.2 gm
KCl	0.2 gm	Water	800 ml
Na_2HPO_4	1.15 gm		

2. PBS Solution B

$CaCl_2$	0.1 gm	Water	100 ml

3. PBS Solution C

MgCl₂·6H₂O   0.1 gm   Water   100 ml

Solutions A, B, and C are autoclaved separately, cooled, and mixed aseptically.

Other salines (Hanks', Gey's, Puck's) are perfectly satisfactory, and may be better for some cells. The PBS is an economical medium, but the safest procedure in case of difficulty may be to wash and handle cells and virus in a full-growth medium including serum, unless, of course, the object of the washing is to remove the serum. The suitability of any medium should naturally be checked separately beforehand for a particular cell–virus system (see Table II for some references).

Salt solutions	Earle's saline (bicarbonate omitted)	
	Eagle's basal salt solution (bicarbonate omitted)	
	Hanks' saline	80–95%, v/v
	Gey's saline	
	Puck's saline A	
Vitamins	Eagle's 1000-fold vitamin concentrate solution	0.1–0.5%, v/v
	Difco-Bacto yeast extract	1 mg/ml
Buffers	Bicarbonate	2–2.5 mg/ml
	Tris buffer (Sigma Chemical Co., St. Louis, Missouri)	3 mg/ml
Sugars	Glucose	1–2 mg/ml
	Galactose	1–6 mg/ml
Amino acids	Eagle's 10-fold amino acid concentrate solution	10–40%, v/v
	Lactalbumin hydrolyzate (Nutritional Biochemical Corp., Cleveland, Ohio)	0.5–5 mg/ml
	Difco-Bacto tryptose phosphate broth, reconstituted solution (isotonic)	10%, v/v
Proteins	Bovine plasma albumin, fraction V (Armour Laboratories, Chicago, Illinois)	1 mg/ml
	Serum (usually horse, ox, or calf)	1–20%, v/v
	Dried Skim Milk	0.1–1%

D. PREPARATION OF BUFFER STOCKS

1. Bicarbonate

It is convenient to omit bicarbonate from stocks of medium, and most of the media are described below in bicarbonate-free form. For these media, the bicarbonate is made up separately and can be added in different concentrations to suit different purposes. Sodium bicarbonate may be made up to 50 mg/ml in distilled water, or to 14 mg/ml; this last is isotonic, and may be added to a physiologically balanced medium in any concentration without making it hypertonic. Both solutions are autoclaved in screw-capped bottles and stored at room temperature.

2. Tris Buffer

Tris (Sigma 7–9, Sigma Chemical Co., St. Louis, Missouri) is conveniently made up in 1 M solution (121.1 gm/liter), adjusted to pH 7.4 with 6 N HCl, and autoclaved. It is used at a final concentration of 3 mg/ml (about 0.025 M). Alternatively, it can be made up to 0.05 M by dissolving 2.42 gm in about 100 ml of Earle's or Eagle's salt solutions (containing no bicarbonate; Section III,G,H), adding 76.8 ml of 0.2 M HCl, and making up to 400 ml (Porterfield, 1960). This solution is used at a dilution of 1 : 10 in medium.

3. Pardee's Buffer (Bellett, 1960)

This "buffer" is not added to the medium, but is placed in a separate container in a sealed incubation vessel. It provides a reservoir of CO_2 to give an atmosphere of known CO_2 concentration (see Section IX,B and Figs. 1 and 2), and the pH of the culture is then controlled in the usual way by inclusion of bicarbonate in the medium itself.

The substances in the following tabulation are added in the given order to a bottle that can be stirred magnetically while being tightly stoppered.

Diethanolamine (technical grade)	240 ml
Water	to 400 ml
Thiourea (20% suspension in water, warmed to dissolve)	3 ml
HCl (6 N)	200 ml
KHCO$_3$	120 gm

The solution is stirred in a tightly stoppered bottle at 37°C until dissolved, and stored at 37°C away from light. This solution equilibrates with 5% CO_2 in air at 37°C; about 100 ml is sufficient for a 10-liter vessel, in which it can be used for two equilibrations.

E. Antibiotics

Although there is a case for omitting antibiotics completely from normal cell cultures or from cultures used to prepare virus stocks, this case rarely applies to assays of virus. Concentrations of antibiotics that are harmful to the growth of cells often do not affect the efficiency of plaque assays, and it is usually worthwhile to include relatively large amounts of antimicrobial substances. The combination of antibiotics suggested below (i.e., 50 μg/ml each of penicillin, streptomycin, and neomycin) are sufficient to prevent the growth of most bacterial contaminants and are relatively harmless to cells. Others (tetracyclines, chloramphenicol, polymyxin) can also be used, but are more toxic for some cells, and the concentration to be employed needs to be determined for each system. With regard to antifungal agents, 4,4'-diamidinodiphenylamine dihydrochloride (May and Baker 938; Cooper, 1961b) and Fungizone (Squibb) are most useful, but their concentration also needs to be determined beforehand. Mycostatin is too insoluble to be effective when incorporated in agar.

Antibiotic Stock Solution (1000-fold)

Sodium penicillin G	5 gm
Streptomycin sulfate	5 gm
Neomycin sulfate	5 gm

The solution is dissolved aseptically in 100 ml of water or sterilized by filtration through sintered glass, dispensed in 1-ml amounts, and stored at —20°C.

F. Trypsin and EDTA (Versene)

Solid tissues are commonly disaggregated and cultured cells removed from the glass by the action of trypsin or of the chelating agent ethylenediaminetetraacetic acid (EDTA or Versene; Melnick, 1956). These agents are more effective if used in combination. The presence of Ca^{2+} or Mg^{2+} hinders their action.

1. *Trypsin*

Difco-Bacto trypsin (1/250)	0.25	gm
PBS solution A (Section III,C)	100	ml

The solution is stirred to dissolve, sterilized by filtration through sintered glass, and stored at 4°C for up to 2 weeks. If the trypsin is to be used on cultures in closed bottles, it is preferable to include sodium bicarbonate at 2 mg/ml. Wallis *et al.* (1961) recommended centrifuging the crude trypsin solution prepared at 4°C in order to remove bacteria, which may have toxic effects if they are permitted to be digested.

2. *Ethylenediaminetetraacetic Acid, Disodium Salt*

EDTA, disodium salt, $2H_2O$	0.02	gm
PBS solution A (Section III,C)	100	ml

The mixture is heated until dissolved, sterilized by autoclaving, and stored at 4°C.

3. *Trypsin Plus EDTA*

Solutions 1 and 2 may be mixed aseptically in equal volumes, or alternatively they may be dissolved together in the given quantities and sterilized by filtration through sintered glass.

G. EARLE'S SALINE WITH MINIMAL SUPPLEMENTS

This simple medium has many uses, some of which are described in Sections IV,B,C, VII,D, VIII,C, and VIII,D. It is conveniently prepared as a stock solution at double the normal strength.

Supplemented Earle's Saline Stock Solution (2-fold)

NaCl	6.8	gm
KCl	0.4	gm
$NaH_2PO_4 \cdot H_2O$	0.125	gm
Glucose	1.0	gm
Enzymatic lactalbumin hydrolyzate		
(Nutritional Biochemical Corp., Cleveland, Ohio)	5.0	gm
Difco-Bacto yeast extract	1.0	gm
Bovine plasma albumin (fraction V) (Armour)	1.0	gm
Phenol red	0.05	gm
$NaHCO_3$	2.2	gm
Antibiotic stock solution (Section III,E)	1	ml
Water	400	ml

The following solution is made separately and added to the above solution:

$CaCl_2$	0.2 gm	
$MgSO_4 \cdot 7H_2O$	0.1 gm	
Water	50	ml

The solution is now made up to 500 ml, adjusted to about pH 7 with CO_2 gas, and sterilized by Seitz or Selas filtration; it can be stored at 4°C for up to 2 weeks or at −20°C indefinitely. This medium will be used diluted 2-fold with agar or distilled water, and so it is convenient to dispense it in volumes (e.g., 50 ml) equal to those in which agar and distilled water are dispensed. Since it contains bicarbonate, it must be used for incubation in an atmosphere of 5% CO_2 in air, but the bicarbonate–CO_2 system can be omitted and a buffer provided by Tris (Section III,D) for some purposes. Other supplements, including serum, can be added to the completed 2-fold stock. The lactalbumin hydrolyzate, yeast extract, and bovine albumin can be made up in separate solutions (5, 1, and 5%, respectively, in a balanced salt solution), filtered through sintered glass, stored at −20°C, and added separately.

H. EAGLE'S MEDIUM (Eagle, 1959)

This medium is the most widely used of the defined media, and is conveniently prepared as a series of concentrated stock solutions.

1. Salt Solution (10-fold)

NaCl	80.0 gm
KCl	4.0 gm
$MgCl_2 \cdot 6H_2O$	2.0 gm
$Na_2HPO_4 \cdot 2H_2O$	1.5 gm
Glucose	10.0 gm
Water	1000 ml

The solution is heated until dissolved, sterilized by Seitz filtration, dispensed in 100-ml volumes in screw-capped bottles, and stored at 4°C.

Calcium can often be omitted, but if it is needed a separate solution can be made at 100-fold strength (1.4 gm $CaCl_2$ in 100 ml water), sterilized by autoclaving, and stored at room temperature. This solution is added to the final medium to 1%, if required.

2. Amino Acid Concentrate (10-fold)

L-Arginine	1.05 gm
L-Histidine	0.31 gm
L-Lysine	0.58 gm
L-Leucine	0.52 gm
L-Isoleucine	0.52 gm
L-Methionine	0.15 gm
L-Phenylalanine	0.32 gm
L-Threonine	0.48 gm
L-Tryptophan	0.10 gm
L-Valine	0.46 gm
Water	800 ml

The following amino acids are dissolved in a little 0.1 N HCl with heating and added to the above solution:

L-Tyrosine	0.36 gm
L-Cystine	0.24 gm

The whole solution is now made up to 1000 ml, sterilized by filtration through sintered glass, dispensed in 100-ml volumes, and stored at −20°C.

3. Vitamin Concentrate A (1000-fold)

Choline	0.1 gm
Nicotinic acid	0.1 gm
Pantothenic acid	0.1 gm
Pyridoxal	0.1 gm
Riboflavin	0.01 gm
Thiamine	0.1 gm
Inositol	0.1 gm
Water	100 ml

The vitamins are dissolved and the solution sterilized by filtration through sintered glass, dispensed in 1-ml amounts, and stored at −20°C.

4. Vitamin Concentrate B (100-fold)

Biotin	0.01 gm
Folic acid	0.01 gm
Water	100 ml

These vitamins are dissolved by adding a few drops of 0.5 N NaOH (final pH being about 7.0), the solution sterilized by filtration through sintered glass, dispensed in 10-ml amounts, and stored at −20°C.

5. Phenol Red (100-fold)

Phenol red	1 gm
0.1 N NaOH	28 ml
Water	to 500 ml

The solution is dissolved, dispensed in 10-ml amounts, autoclaved, and stored at room temperature.

6. Glutamine (10-fold)

L-Glutamine	2.92 gm
Water	100 ml

The solution is dissolved, sterilized by filtration through sintered glass, dispensed in 10-ml amounts, and stored at −20°C.

7. Eagle's Working Stock Solution (2-fold)

Stock solution 1 (salts)	100 ml
Calcium chloride solution	10 ml
Stock solution 2 (amino acids)	100 ml
Stock solution 3 (vitamins)	1 ml
Stock solution 4 (vitamins)	10 ml
Stock solution 5 (phenol red)	10 ml
Stock solution 6 (glutamine)	10 ml
Antibiotics (Section III,E)	1 ml
Sterile water	to 500 ml

This solution is adjusted to pH 7.4 with N NaOH and can be dispensed in 50-ml volumes for dilution with an equal volume of agar solution for plaque assays, or of distilled water for preliminary cell-culture work or dilution of virus. Various supplements, and either Tris or bicarbonate buffers (Section III,D), may be added. Bicarbonate is commonly used at 0.35 mg/ml (equivalent to Hanks' saline, needing no CO_2 in the atmosphere) or at 2.2 mg/ml (equivalent to Earle's saline, needing CO_2 in the atmosphere, Section IX,B). The methods described in Sections VII and VIII give individual recommendations for such additions.

I. REPLACEMENT OF GLUCOSE BY GALACTOSE

The media described in Sections III,G and III,H can be used with bicarbonate–CO_2 buffers for a very large number of cell systems, or with Tris or phosphate buffers (Section III,D) for certain of these systems. However, Tris and phosphate buffers are toxic for some cells and are not adequate for many continuous line cells (e.g., HeLa) that produce large quantities of nonvolatile acids. It is, nevertheless, useful to have a buffering system that is independent of an atmosphere containing CO_2. The following medium (Cooper, 1961b) provides such a system by taking advantage of the finding (Darnell and Eagle, 1958) that galactose can be metabolized in place of glucose by HeLa cells, with the formation of very little lactic acid. This medium has been found satisfactory for several strains of human cells, including HeLa cells, and for monkey kidney and chick embryo primary cultures. The galactose must be free of glucose ($<0.3\%$ by weight). For some virus–cell systems the $CaCl_2$ content may well be reduced and the NH_4Cl and some other supplements omitted, but the extra nutritives have been found by this writer to increase its reliability for the poliovirus system. It is necessary to add glucose (to 10–20 mg/ml) to neutral red or tetrazolium stains (Section IX,C) when they are used with glucose-free media.

Galactose Medium Stock Solution (2-fold)

Solution A

NaCl	16.0	gm
KCl	1.0	gm
NH$_4$Cl	0.1	gm
NaH$_2$PO$_4$.2H$_2$O	1.0	gm
Galactose	12.0	gm
Water	400	ml

Solution B

CaCl₂	2.0 gm
MgCl₂.6H₂O	0.4 gm
Water	100 ml

Solution C	
Difco-Bacto yeast extract	2.0 gm
Lactalbumin hydrolyzate	10.0 gm
4,4-Diamidino diphenylamine dihydrochloride	0.05 gm
L-Glutamine	0.2 gm
L-Glutamic acid	0.6 gm
L- or DL-Methionine	0.5 gm
Water	200 ml

The final stock is made with the following solutions:

Solution A	400 ml
Solution B	100 ml
Solution C	200 ml
Eagle's vitamin concentrate A (Section III,H)	2 ml
Eagle's vitamin concentrate B (Section III,H)	20 ml
Phenol red solution (Section III,H)	20 ml
Water	to 1000 ml

The pH is adjusted to 7.4, the serum is added as required (e.g., 200 ml), and the solution is sterilized by Seitz filtration, dispensed in 60-ml amounts (for mixing with 50 ml of agar solution), and stored for up to 3 weeks at 4°C. This medium may also be used with a glucose carbohydrate supply (4 gm/liter in 2-fold strength medium), in which case NaHCO₃ (5.4 gm/liter) is added and the NaCl decreased to 12.0 gm/liter. The bicarbonate-containing medium must be used either in sealed bottles or with an atmosphere of CO_2 (Section IX,B).

J. Preparation of Solid-Gel Media

Although the lesions in a plaque assay can be localized in a variety of ways (Cooper, 1961a), by far the most generally applicable method is to solidify the medium with an agar gel. Because of its reliability and range of usefulness, all the solid media whose use is described in Sections VII and VIII are those made with agar. The preparation of the agar is described in this section, together with some alternatives that are useful when agar cannot be employed, for example, because it is toxic for the cells, inhibits plaque formation, or interferes with fluorescent-antibody staining. It might be mentioned here that silica can be induced to form good gels (Funk and Krulwich, 1964), but its use does not yet appear to be reported for cell-culture work.

1. *Agar*

The source of agar almost universally used is Difco-Bacto agar. This is a purified agar, and its washing is not necessary for the methods described in Sections VII and VIII. However, agar is a complex substance [its composition has recently been discussed by Campbell and Colter (1965)], and if washing is desired, a convenient method is to place a suitable amount (say 1 lb) in a clean cloth and leave it in running water for 3–4 hours. It is then allowed to soak overnight, transferred to a Buchner funnel, and washed with three changes of distilled water followed by three changes of reagent-grade acetone. The powder is spread on aluminum foil and left in a ventilated place to dry (Dulbecco and Vogt, 1954a). Specially purified agars or agar derivatives are available commercially, and are useful for certain purposes.

The final concentrations of agar recommended often differ for different methods (see Sections VII and VIII). The following method gives a 3% agar solution, which can be diluted further if need be. To 30 gm of the dry powder (washed, or untreated Difco-Bacto agar) in a 2-liter conical flask is added 1 liter of distilled water. This is steamed or boiled for 2 hours with occasional shaking, and when completely dissolved is dispensed into convenient amounts (say 50 ml in screw-capped bottles) and autoclaved for 1 hour at 15 psi. This solution can be used at once or can be allowed to cool and then stored at room temperature for long periods. When needed, it is melted by immersion in a boiling water bath for about 20–30 minutes and is allowed to cool to 44°–50°C in a water bath set at that temperature. The appropriate nutrient medium (prepared in 2-fold strength and dispensed in bottles in a volume that can be mixed with one agar bottle to give the correct final strength) is allowed to warm in the bath at 44°–50°C, and when both medium and agar have reached approximately the same temperature, the entire contents of the medium bottle are poured into the agar bottle. This nutrient agar mixture is now left in the water bath until it is dispensed into the assay container. This should be done within 1–2 hours, using a prewarmed pipet with a wide tip or a Cornwall-type automatic syringe. After cooling, the agar mixture should not be remelted and used again.

2. *Methyl Cellulose*

The method of using this solidifying agent has been described by Hotchin (1955), by Rapp *et al.* (1959), and by Schulze and Schlesinger (1963). Methyl cellulose (Methocel, Dow Chemical Company, 4000 centipoise) is washed several times with absolute ethyl alcohol and ether and dried in air. Two grams of the powder is resuspended with vigorous mixing in 50 ml of boiling distilled water, the suspension autoclaved (121°C for 20 minutes), and then cooled to 45°C. To the suspension is added an equal volume of double-strength medium at 4°C. The whole mixture is then cooled to 4°C, when the last of the Methocel dissolves. This medium can be prepared in large batches and stored for a long period at −20° to −40°C if need be, thus providing a supply of medium of constant composition.

At the time of use, the medium is brought to 4°C and poured onto the assay monolayers (so far its use has not been reported for the cell-suspension method). The medium gels when incubated at 37°C and reliquifies (and can then be poured off) if returned to 4°C. A second overlay of agar medium can be added to stabilize the Methocel gel for inversion of the plates, if this is necessary.

3. *Starch*

Commercially available hydrolyzed potato starch (Mann Laboratories, New York; De Maeyer and Schonne, 1964) is used. To obtain 100 ml of starch overlay, 10 gm of the dry starch is suspended in 20 ml of cold sterile distilled water. This suspension is added with continuous stirring to 54 ml of boiling distilled water on a hot plate with an incorporated magnetic stirrer. It is allowed to boil for a few minutes until it is fluid and nearly transparent, cooled to 50°C, and 18.5 ml of 5 times concentrated nutrient medium are added, followed by serum and isotonic bicarbonate solution as needed (Section III,D). The solution is cooled to 39°C, and aliquots are added to the assay container and allowed to set.

This procedure is described as providing a firm gel at 37°C, but as being more cumbersome than that involving agar, and so its use will probably be restricted to cases for which agar is unsatisfactory.

K. PREPARATION OF SERUM

Serum is often included in plaque assay media, but its preparation for this purpose is the same as that for normal cell culture. Horse or ox serum can frequently be used, but calf serum is probably suitable for the largest number of systems. The best procedure is to obtain blood sterilely by venipuncture from a calf or other young animal and allow this to clot in small batches for an hour or so at 37°C and the clot to retract overnight at 4°C. The supernatant serum is then centrifuged (60 minutes at 1000 rpm) to sediment remaining red cells,

Seitz-filtered, and stored at —20°C. Some workers heat the serum for 30–60 minutes at 56°C before filtration.

It is essential to test sera before use, for toxicity to cells and for virus-neutralizing substances. This is done by adding the serum to a small amount of a serum-free plaque assay medium and using this for a trial assay with virus of known titer. It will be necessary to include control assays with a serum that is known to be satisfactory. If this is not available, then serum-free controls must be used in which other protein is included [0.5–1% boiled, centrifuged, skimmed milk (Wallis et al., 1962); 0.5% gelatin (Simpson and Hirst, 1961); 0.1% bovine plasma albumin (Cooper, 1955)], preferably together with 10% of tryptose phosphate broth. Some extrapolation to a serum-free condition can be obtained by using decreasing concentrations of the unknown serum. If the plaque count is unchanged over a wide range of concentration of this serum, then the serum may be satisfactory.

It should be noted that serum is approximately isotonic. Hence when using medium concentrates, the serum should not be added until the concentrate has been diluted to normal physiological levels by the addition of distilled water or agar dissolved in distilled water. Addition of serum or other isotonic solutions before "making up to volume" will result in a hypertonic medium, a condition to be avoided, since loss of some water during incubation will invariably increase the osmolarity still further.

L. COMMERCIAL SOURCES OF MEDIUM

Many cell-culture media that can be adapted for plaque assays can be obtained from commercial sources (Paul, 1965). These are supplied as liquid media at normal strength or in concentrated form, or as dry powders (General Biochemicals, Inc., Laboratory Park, Chagrin Falls, Ohio; Hayflick et al., 1964). The latter source is the most economical and can provide a stock of medium of constant potency that can be kept for a long period.

IV. Preparation of Cell Suspensions

A. INTRODUCTION

All plaque assays involve a suspension of cells at some stage. This section describes the preparation of suitable cell suspensions from sources of a variety sufficient to serve as examples, since most cells used for plaque assays can be handled by one or more of the methods given below. The further treatment of these cell suspensions is described in Sections VII and VIII. Once again attention is drawn to standard methods for handling cells in culture (Paul, 1965).

B. SUSPENSIONS OF PRIMARY CHICK EMBRYO CELLS

This cell source has been used for plaque assays of many viruses. It is the most useful and inexpensive cell source for those viruses (e.g., poxviruses, certain herpesviruses, myxoviruses, and arboviruses) that are not very restricted in the variety of animal species that they infect. It is, of course, also the best source for those viruses that predominantly infect chicken or avian species (e.g., Rous sarcoma virus). The procedure described below is also suitable for the more robust types of tissue from other sources.

The embryos are removed aseptically from twelve 9–13-day-old hens' eggs and are decapitated and eviscerated. The wings and feet may be removed, and the remaining tissue is finely chopped in physiological saline or squeezed through the nozzle of a large syringe. This tissue is washed several times with saline to remove red cells, digested repeatedly by stirring strongly with 100 ml of 0.25% trypsin (Section III,F) prewarmed to 37°C. The time of each digestion is adjusted so that predominantly single cells or clumps of two to three cells are produced (about 20 minutes), and the successive harvests are removed and chilled. When only fibrous tissue and bone remain, the digestion is stopped and the pooled harvests centrifuged at 1000 rpm and washed twice with growth medium. The growth medium consists either of supplemented Earle's saline (Section III,G) containing 5% horse or bovine serum (see Section VII,D) or of Eagle's medium containing double strengths of amino acids and vitamins (8 parts) plus Difco-Bacto tryptose broth (1 part) plus a calf–chicken serum mixture (1 part) (see Section VII,E). The cells are resuspended in growth medium (2 ml/embryo) and kept at 4°C for 15 minutes to allow coarse debris to settle. The supernatant is decanted and the cells are counted in a hemocytometer. The suspension is adjusted to 1–1.5 $\times 10^8$ cells/ml if necessary, and is used undiluted (Section VIII,C) or diluted as described in Sections VII,D and VII,E.

Several versions of this procedure have been described (Dulbecco, 1952; Rubin, 1957; Porterfield, 1960).

C. SUSPENSIONS OF PRIMARY MONKEY KIDNEY CELLS

The method given below is similar to that described by Dulbecco and Vogt (1954a) and Youngner (1954). It is suitable for many of the more delicate kinds of tissue.

The kidneys from rhesus monkeys are taken out aseptically and the capsule and pelvis removed. The tissue is then coarsely chopped in a physiological saline or in Eagle's medium with scalpels or scissors until the pieces are 2–5 mm in size. The pieces are washed twice with medium. About 100 ml of 0.25% trypsin solution (Section III,F) at 37°C is added and the suspension agitated gently for 20 minutes with a magnetic stirrer. The pieces are allowed to settle and the supernatant is discarded. More trypsin is added as before, and the supernatant is decanted and chilled after a period of trypsinization that is adjusted so that aggregates of 10–50 cells, rather than single cells, are produced. Such a period, which may occupy about 20 minutes, is found to produce the least cell damage. This procedure is repeated three or four times, and the pooled harvest is centrifuged and resuspended in growth medium (Eagle's medium, Section III,H) plus 10% calf serum, or supplemented Earle's saline (Section III,G) to give $3-6 \times 10^5$ cells/ml by a hemocytometer count. Bishop et $al.$ (1960) recommended the standardization of the cell suspension in terms of the number of aggregates rather than of the cells themselves, in which case the cell suspension is adjusted to 75,000 aggregates/ml, and the seeding rate is 5000 aggregates/cm^2 of culture surface. The further handling of this suspension is described in Section VII,B).

Several modifications of this method have been described (Melnick et $al.$, 1955; Rappaport, 1956a,b; Bodian, 1956; Bishop et $al.$, 1960).

D. Suspensions of Continuous-Line Cells—HeLa

A small seed stock of HeLa cells, preferably tested to be free of mycoplasma, is obtained from another laboratory. Cell strains treated with antibiotics and thoroughly tested for mycoplasma have been reported (Gori and Lee, 1964; Hayflick, 1965). The medium is decanted and the cells removed from the glass by gentle treatment with 0.25% trypsin or trypsin plus EDTA (Section III,F), after which serum is added to 5% to stop the action of the suspending agents. The cells are centrifuged and resuspended in growth medium (Eagle's medium, Section III,H) containing 2 mg/ml of NaHCO$_3$, 4 times the given strength of amino acids and vitamins, and 10% calf serum). The cells are counted, adjusted to 5×10^4 cells/ml with growth medium and reinoculated into larger bottles (1–2 ml/10 cm^2 of culture surface). This process is repeated when the layer just becomes confluent or when the pH falls below 7.1 (4–5 days). When a sufficient stock of cells has been built up by several subcultures in this manner, a large proportion of the harvest can be used for plaque assays or for other purposes. [It is wise to maintain a reserve of cells in a frozen state, preferably in liquid nitrogen (Paul, 1965).] This procedure is suitable, with minor modification, for most continuous cell lines.

For plaque assays, cells are harvested as described above, centrifuged, and resuspended in PBS plus 10% serum to 6×10^6 cells/ml. The further handling of this suspension is described in Sections VII,C and VIII,B.

E. Suspensions of Continuous-Line Cells—Krebs-2 Ascites Tumor Cells

These cell strains are relatively easy to maintain and provide a bountiful source of cells. Mice containing a mature ascites tumor (cells in suspension in peritoneal fluid) are obtained from another laboratory or the cells are shipped in a frozen state; it is also possible to adapt solid tumors to growth in ascitic form in the homologous species. The mice are killed and the cells extracted aseptically from the peritoneum with a syringe (18-gage needle) or, after opening the peritoneum, with a Pasteur pipet. Up to 10 ml of fluid, containing 1–2×10^8 cells/ml, is obtained. Fresh mice are inoculated intraperitoneally with 0.1 ml of this suspension, and the tumors are ready to be harvested after a further week to 10 days. Some ascites tumors (e.g., Krebs, Ehrlich) grow in all strains of mice, but other tumors require particular strains. It is wise to maintain a reserve of cells in a frozen state (Martin *et al.*, 1961).

The virus susceptibility of these cells is limited to those viruses that will grow in rodent cells. For plaque assays, the cells are washed and resuspended to 10^8 cells/ml in Earle's saline (Section III, G) from which the lactalbumin hydrolyzate, yeast extract, and bovine albumin have been omitted. Their further handling is described in Section VIII,D.

F. Development of Continuous-Line Cells

If a particular type of cell is not available in a form that can be subcultured indefinitely in the laboratory, it is often possible to adapt ("transform") primary cultures from normal tissue to this form of growth or to grow these cells in special media for extended periods (Paul, 1965). However, these procedures are slow and require considerable experience. A promising source of continuous-line cells (for growth *in vitro* or in ascitic form) is a solid tumor that has been induced or that has occurred spontaneously.

V. Virus-Dilution Media and Procedures

Many viruses can be diluted without loss of infectivity in a simple saline (e.g., PBS), but others may need more complex media (for particular viruses, see references in Table II). The best dilution medium for any given virus must be determined beforehand; this medium must not permit inactivation of virus, must discourage adsorption of virus to glassware yet must not hinder adsorption to cells, and must not damage the cells themselves. A good general purpose medium is PBS containing 0.5% gelatin or 5% tryptose phosphate broth.

The most reliable if expensive procedure may be to use for diluting fluid the medium in which virus stocks are produced. Virus is rapidly diluted with thorough mixing in 10- or 100-fold steps, using a fresh pipet for each dilution, a large volume of diluting fluid (2–10 ml), and as low a temperature as possible. Each sample is added to the assay cells as soon as it is diluted. Near the dilution end point, approximately 3-fold dilution steps (e.g., 1 : 3, 1 : 10, 1 : 30, 1 : 100) can be used. The diluted samples that are estimated to contain between 10 and 300 plaque-forming units are added to the cells, in as small a volume as possible (e.g., 0.1–0.5 ml) to encourage rapid adsorption. Three replicates for each dilution are plated. This should provide an assay with a standard deviation of less than 17%. If greater accuracy is needed, it is better to repeat the plating procedure with a fresh⁻ series of dilutions.

VI. Culture Containers

In practice only two types of containers are generally used; (1) open Petri plates (Dulbecco and Vogt, 1954a), either of glass or of disposable plastic, and (2) sealed bottles, particularly prescription bottles (Hsiung and Melnick, 1955). Some relative advantages and disadvantages are discussed elsewhere (Cooper, 1961a). Two advantages of the sealed bottle are that precise temperature control is possible by immersion of the bottles in a water bath and that the bottles do not need an incubator that is gassed or humidified. Most of the methods that are described in Sections VII and VIII in terms of their use with Petri plates are easily adaptable to sealed bottles, but in this case all media have to contain some bicarbonate. Which container is the simpler to use will depend on the particular needs of the user. It should be stressed that containers to be used for monolayer cultures, whether made of glass or of plastic, must have a culture surface of a quality that permits the attachment and if necessary growth of cells.

VII. Monolayer Assay Methods

A. INTRODUCTION

All these methods have the following procedures in common.

1. A suspension of cells is added to a culture container (usually a Petri plate with a perfectly flat base) and suitably diluted in a medium that permits the cells to attach to and spread on the glass surface, and usually to multiply. The Petri plate must naturally have a surface that permits attachment and growth of the cells. Containers other than Petri plates are discussed briefly in Section VI.

2. The cell cultures are incubated at 37°C in a suitable atmosphere (humidified and containing CO_2 if bicarbonate buffers are used) until the cells have attached to the glass and have spread or multiplied to a predetermined extent. One usually aims for a monolayer that has just reached confluency. It is important to examine each culture before use, preferably by means of an inverted microscope, to ensure that it has developed properly.

3. The growth medium is removed, and the cells are washed with the medium in which virus will be allowed to adsorb to the cells. This medium is then drained off thoroughly, and samples of virus dilutions containing 10–300 plaque-forming units are gently added in a small volume to the center of the plate. The inoculum spreads spontaneously over the surface of the cells, and the cultures are kept on a level surface for a time and at a temperature that have been previously found to permit adsorption of as much as possible of the added virus. Care is taken to prevent the cells from becoming dry during this adsorption period. The inoculum may be respread at intervals, as a proportion of the virus becomes trapped under the meniscus.

4. Meanwhile a nutrient agar medium has been prepared by mixing equal volumes of a nutrient medium made up in double strength and warmed to 42°–44°C and a molten agar solution cooled to the same temperature. After adsorption is completed, a measured volume of this liquid-nutrient agar medium, at a temperature below 45°C, is gently added, taking care not to damage the cells or to remove them from the glass. Bubbles are removed by stroking the agar surface with a Bunsen flame before the agar has set. The agar medium is then allowed to cool and set while the plates are standing on a level surface.

5. The plates are finally incubated at 37°C, preferably inverted, for a predetermined time in a thoroughly humidified atmosphere (containing CO_2 if necessary). The cells are stained, or plaque contrast is enhanced in some other way, and the plaques are counted.

The viruses for which methods are given below (poliovirus, Sabin vaccine strain LSc; Semliki Forest virus; Rous sarcoma virus; polyomavirus) are purely exemplary, but are sufficiently nonpathogenic to humans to be suitable for use in a student laboratory. Methods for some other viruses, which generally differ only in particular details, are referred to in Table II. The volumes given below are generally those suitable for use with Petri plates of 4-inch (100-mm) external diameter; smaller volumes may be used for smaller containers, in proportion to the relative areas of the culture surfaces.

B. Assay of Poliovirus Using Monolayers of Monkey Kidney Cells

Ten milliliters of the suspension of monkey kidney cells in growth medium whose preparation is described in Section IV,C are added to each of a series of Petri plates (100-mm diameter). The plates are incubated at 37°C in a humidified atmosphere containing CO_2 (Section IX,B) until the monolayers become confluent (3–6 days). If it is desired to increase the number of plates that are available for assay, the cells can be removed from the glass at this stage with trypsin (Section IV,D), washed, and subcultured with fresh medium into 3–6 times as many Petri plates. These are reincubated and again used when confluent.

A nutrient agar medium is now prepared by mixing equal volumes of molten 1.8% agar solution (Section III,J) at 43°C with the 2-fold-strength solutions either of the supplemented Earle's saline (Section III,G) or of the Eagle's medium (Section III,H), equilibrated to the same temperature. In the case of the Eagle's medium, $NaHCO_3$ is added to give a final concentration of 1.5–2 mg/ml. To either nutrient agar medium 5 ml of serum (horse or bovine) is added per 100 ml of normal-strength agar medium.

The medium is removed from the confluent monolayers and the cells washed twice with 5 ml of PBS. A stock of poliovirus (type 1 Sabin vaccine strain LSc) appropriately diluted (Section V) in PBS is added in 0.5-ml volumes to the plates, which are then kept at 37°C or room temperature on a level surface for 30 minutes.

When adsorption is completed, 10 ml of the nutrient agar medium is added to each Petri plate and the plates allowed to set in a level position. The plates are then incubated for 3–4 days at 37°C in a humidified atmosphere containing CO_2; 3 ml of neutral red solution

(5–30 μg/ml in normal saline or PBS) is added, the plates reincubated for 1–5 hours, and the plaques counted.

This method is a modification of the procedures described by Dulbecco and Vogt (1954a), Youngner (1956a), and Vogt et al. (1957).

C. Assay of Poliovirus Using Monolayers of HeLa Cells

The suspension of HeLa cells whose preparation is described in Section IV,D is diluted to 5×10^5 cells/ml in normal-strength Eagle's medium (Section III,H) containing 5% calf serum. The Eagle's medium may contain 2–2.5 mg $NaHCO_3$/ml, in which case the plates are incubated in an atmosphere of CO_2 (Section IX,B) or may contain 0.3–0.5 mg $NaHCO_3$/ml, in which case the plates can be incubated for 2–3 days in the absence of added CO_2 without becoming too acid. Tris buffers are not usually satisfactory for these cells. The glucose can also be replaced by galactose (Section III,I) in this step.

Ten milliliters of this cell suspension are added to each of a series of Petri plates (100-mm diameter). The plates are incubated at 37°C in a humid atmosphere, containing CO_2 (Section IX,B) if bicarbonate has been used, until the monolayers become confluent (1–2 days).

A nutrient agar medium is now prepared by mixing equal volumes of molten 1.8% agar solution (Section III,J) at 43°C with the 2-fold-strength solutions either of Eagle's medium (Section III,G) supplemented to give a final concentration of 5% calf serum and 2–2.5 mg $NaHCO_3$/ml, or of the galactose medium described in Section III,I.

The medium is removed from the confluent monolayers and the cells washed twice with 5 ml of PBS. A stock of poliovirus (type 1 Sabin strain LSc) appropriately diluted (Section V) in PBS is added in 0.5-ml volumes to the plates, which are then kept at 37°C or room temperature on a level surface for 30 minutes.

When adsorption is completed, 10 ml of the nutrient agar medium is added to each Petri plate and the plates allowed to set in a level position. The plates are then incubated for 3–4 days at 37°C in a humidified atmosphere (containing CO_2, if necessary); 3 ml of neutral red solution (5–30 μg/ml in normal saline or PBS) are added, the plates reincubated for 1–5 hours, and the plaques counted.

This method is a modification of the procedure described by Mandel (1958).

Some laboratories have difficulties in the use of neutral red with these cells; if so, it is satisfactory to add 3 ml/plate of the tetrazolium stain described in Section IX,C.

D. Assay of Semliki Forest Virus Using Monolayers of Chick Embryo Cells

The suspension of chick embryo cells whose preparation is described in Section IV,B is diluted to 2.75×10^6 cells/ml in normal-strength supplemented Earle's saline (Section III,G) or in Eagle's medium (Section III,H) containing 2–2.5 mg $NaHCO_3$/ml. Alternatively, the bicarbonate–CO_2 system may be replaced by Tris buffer (Section III,D), or the galactose medium (Section III,I) can be used. All media also contain 5% serum (horse or bovine).

Ten milliliters of this cell suspension are added to each of a series of Petri plates (100 mm in diameter). The plates are incubated at 37°C in a humidified atmosphere, containing CO_2 (Section IX,B) if necessary, until the monolayers become confluent (1–2 days). The medium is removed from the confluent monolayers, and the cells are washed twice with 5 ml of PBS. A stock of Semliki Forest virus appropriately diluted (Section V) in PBS is added in 0.5-ml volumes to the plates, which are then kept at 37°C or room temperature on a level surface for 30 minutes.

A nutrient agar medium has meanwhile been prepared by mixing equal volumes of molten 1.8% agar solution (Section III,J) at 43°C with the 2-fold-strength solutions either of the supplemented Earle's saline (Section III,G) or of the Eagle's medium (Section III,H) equilibrated to the same temperature. To the Eagle's nutrient agar is added $NaHCO_3$ to 2–2.5 mg/ml, or the Tris buffer (Section III,D); to either medium 5 ml of serum (horse or bovine), or a solution containing 100 mg of bovine plasma albumin, are added per 100 ml of normal-strength agar medium.

When adsorption is completed, 10 ml of this nutrient agar are added to each Petri plate and the plates allowed to set in a level position. The plates are then incubated for 1–2 days at 37°C in a humidified atmosphere (containing CO_2, if necessary); 3 ml of neutral red solution (5–20 μg/ml in normal saline or PBS) are added, the plates reincubated for 1–5 hours, and the plaques counted.

This method is a modification of the procedure originally described by Dulbecco and Vogt (1954b).

E. Assay of Rous Sarcoma Virus Using Monolayers of Chick Embryo Cells

The suspension of chick embryo cells whose preparation is described in Section IV,B is diluted to 4×10^5 cells/ml in a medium consisting of 8 parts of normal-strength Eagle's medium (Section III,H, but containing double concentrations of amino acids and vitamins and 4.2 gm of NaHCO$_3$ per liter), 1 part of Difco-Bacto tryptose phosphate broth, and 1 part serum (0.8 parts calf serum and 0.2 parts chicken serum).

Ten milliliters of this cell suspension are added to each of a series of Petri plates (100 mm in diameter). The plates are incubated at 37°C in a humidified atmosphere containing CO$_2$ (Section IX,B). After 3–5 days' incubation, the cells are washed twice with Eagle's medium made up without calcium and magnesium. They are then subcultured by incubating them with 2 ml of this medium containing 0.05% trypsin (Section III,F). Two milliliters of the Eagle's tryptose-serum medium described above are added after 15 minutes to stop the trypsinization, and the cells are gently resuspended and centrifuged at 1500 rpm for 1 minute. The pellet is resuspended and diluted to about 10^5 cells/ml in the Eagle's tryptose-serum medium, and 3–5 ml of the diluted cell suspension are added to Petri plates of 50 mm in diameter. These plates are then incubated for 16–20 hours.

The medium is removed from the cells, which only cover a small proportion of the glass surface, and the cultures are washed once with 3 ml of Eagle's medium. A stock of Rous sarcoma virus appropriately diluted (Section V) in Eagle's medium is added in 0.2-ml volumes to the plates, which are then kept at 37°C for 40 minutes.

A nutrient agar medium has meanwhile been prepared by mixing 4 parts of 2-fold-strength Eagle's medium (containing 8.4 gm of NaHCO$_3$ per liter and 4-fold concentrations of amino acids and vitamins) with 4 parts of 1.8% agar at 44°C, then adding 1 part of tryptose broth and 1 part of serum (calf plus chicken).

When adsorption is completed, 5 ml of the nutrient agar medium is added to each Petri plate and allowed to set in a level position. The plates are then incubated for 3 days at 37°C in a humidified atmosphere containing CO$_2$, when the cultures are fed by adding a second layer of 2 ml of the nutrient agar medium. Five to 7 days after infection, 3 ml of neutral red solution (5 μg/ml in Eagle's medium) are added, the plates reincubated for a further 2 hours, and the stain removed. The Rous sarcoma foci are finally counted under 25-fold magnification using an inverted microscope; the plates are placed for observation on a piece of glass ruled with a grid of 2-mm squares.

This method is that described by Temin and Rubin (1958). Rubin (1960a,b) has described modifications in which medium 199 (Morgan et al., 1950), made up without the purines, pyrimidines, and nucleotides, is substituted throughout for the Eagle's medium. The agar overlay is added in a volume of 6.5 ml, and the cultures are fed on the sixth day by adding liquid medium 199; foci are counted on the seventh day. An additional improvement is to seed the secondary cultures with 10^6 cells/plate and to add the dilutions of virus to this suspension. Thus adsorption proceeds while the monolayer is being formed. It is desirable to use a source of eggs from flocks that are free of the related viruses that may interfere with growth of Rous sarcoma virus (Rubin, 1960a,b).

F. Assay of Transforming Capacity of Polyomavirus Using BHK Cells and Monolayers of Mouse Embryo Cells

A series of mouse embryo "feeder" cultures is first prepared [the following method for their preparation is that described by Stoker and Macpherson (1961)]. Whole mouse embryos or 1–2-day-old mice are left overnight in trypsin (0.5 mg/ml) plus EDTA (2 μg/ml) solution in PBS (Section III,F). The next day the solution is replaced by fresh trypsin–EDTA mixture, the suspension incubated for 15 minutes, and then gently pipeted to produce a nearly monodisperse suspension. The cells are centrifuged (250 g for 5 minutes) and resuspended to about 5×10^5 cells/ml in growth medium consisting of 8 parts of Eagle's medium (Section III,H) with amino acids and vitamins in double strength, 1 part of calf serum, and 1 part of Difco-Bacto tryptose phosphate broth. Ten milliliter volumes of this suspension are incubated in 250-ml culture bottles for 4–6 days. The cells are removed with trypsin solution (2.5 mg/ml in PBS), centrifuged, resuspended in the Eagle's tryptose–calf serum growth medium to about 5×10^6 cells/ml and x-irradiated in 5-ml amounts in Petri plates of 60 mm in diameter. The dose is 1500 roentgens, delivered by a Watson type C Mobilix. The cells are recentrifuged, suspended in fresh growth medium, and dispensed in 60-mm Petri plates in growth medium to give 2×10^5 cells per plate. These cultures are incubated and used after 1–7 days.

A stock of BHK 21 cells (clone Cl3N), a continuous line of "nontransformed" cells derived from baby hamster kidney fibroblasts (Macpherson and Stoker, 1962), has previously been developed in a fashion similar to that described for HeLa cells (Section IV,D). The medium is the same as that used for the mouse embryo cells (see above).

A stock of polyomavirus is diluted in Tris-buffered saline serum (NaCl, 0.8 gm; KCl, 0.038 gm; Na$_2$HPO$_4$, 0.01 gm; glucose, 0.1 gm; Tris, 0.3 gm; water to 100 ml; adjust pH to 7.4 with 1 N HCl, filter to sterilize and add 2.5 ml calf serum) to give 10^7–10^8 pfu/ml. Some BHK 21/Cl3N cells in Tris–saline serum are added to give 1–2×10^6 cells in a final volume of 1 ml, and the suspension is stirred magnetically for 1 hour at 37°C. The cells are then counted, and a number of cells sufficient to give 100–600 transformed colonies are added to each of eight 50-mm Petri plates containing the mouse embryo "feeder" cells, which have preferably been set up 1–2 days previously (see above).

These mixed cultures are now incubated for a further 7 days at 37°C, when the cultures are fixed in 10% Formol saline and stained (Jenner-Giemsa stain) in order to count the "transformed" colonies. The colonies are recognized by their distinct morphology (Stoker and Abel, 1962); they are round in shape and consist of cells oriented randomly. It may be noted that it is not necessary to localize the lesions with agar in this case.

This method is that described by Stoker and Abel (1962), who report a number of factors affecting the assay. The lytic ability of polyomavirus is determined in the normal way using primary mouse-embryo cell monolayers (for some references see Table II), the main differences from other methods being the very long incubation times (1–4 weeks) and the consequent need for repeated feeding of the cultures.

VIII. Agar Cell-Suspension Methods

A. Introduction

All of these methods have the following procedures in common.

1. A nutrient agar medium is prepared by mixing equal volumes of a nutrient medium made up in double strength and warmed to 45°–50°C with a molten agar solution cooled to the same temperature. Agar base layers are formed by dispensing a measured volume of this agar medium into a culture container (usually a Petri plate with a flat base). The agar is allowed to cool and set while the plates are standing on a level surface. A portion of the agar medium is kept in the molten state for making the cell–virus overlay later (see below). Containers other than Petri plates are discussed briefly in Section VI.

2. Small volumes of a standardized and fairly concentrated cell suspension are dispensed into small test tubes (75 × 10 mm). Before use this suspension is kept cold, and preferably stirred or rocked. Care must be taken to prevent the cells from becoming anoxic; consequently it is best to dispense the cell suspension into a small number of tubes at a time, so that the cells will not have the opportunity to settle. Samples of virus dilutions containing 10–300 pfu are added in a small volume to these cells. The cell suspensions may be maintained beforehand at 0°–4°C, but at the time of use they should be at room temperature. They are *not* prewarmed to 44°C.

3. The cell–virus mixture is thoroughly resuspended, and, without

allowing time for virus adsorption to occur, an equal volume of the molten agar medium mentioned above is added. The contents of the tube are very rapidly mixed again and poured at once on top of the agar base layer.

4. After draining in an inverted position for a few seconds, the tube is touched on the second agar layer, which is again allowed to set in a level position.

5. The plates are finally incubated at 37°C, preferably inverted, for a predetermined time in a thoroughly humidified atmosphere (containing CO_2, if necessary). The cells are stained and the plaques counted.

The viruses for which methods are given below (poliovirus, Sabin vaccine strain LSc; Semliki Forest virus; encephalomyocarditis virus; polyomavirus) are purely exemplary, but are sufficiently nonpathogenic to humans to be suitable for use in a student laboratory. Methods for some other viruses, which generally differ only in particular details, are referred to in Table II. The volumes given below are generally those suitable for use with Petri plates of 4-inch (100-mm) external diameter; smaller volumes may be used for smaller containers, in proportion to the relative area of the culture surfaces.

B. Assay of Poliovirus Using Agar Suspensions of HeLa Cells

A nutrient agar medium is made by mixing equal volumes of molten 3% agar solution (Section III,J) at 50°C with the 2-fold-strength solutions either of Eagle's medium (Section III,H) supplemented to give a final concentration of 5% calf serum and 2–2.5 mg of $NaHCO_3$ per ml or of the galactose medium described in Section III,I. Ten milliliters of this nutrient agar are added to each of a series of Petri plates 100 mm in diameter and allowed to set in a level position to form base layers (Section VIII,A).

A HeLa cell suspension, prepared as described in Section IV,D, is diluted with growth medium to contain about 6×10^6 cells/ml, and 1.5–2-ml volumes of the diluted suspension are dispensed in small test tubes. A sample (0.1 ml) of an appropriate dilution (Section V) in PBS of poliovirus (type 1 Sabin vaccine strain LSc) is added to each tube, followed by 2 ml of the nutrient agar used for the base layers and described above; the contents are very rapidly mixed, poured at once on the base layers as described in Section VIII,A, and allowed to set in a level position. The plates are then incubated for 3–4 days at 37°C in a humidified atmosphere (containing CO_2, if necessary: Section IX,B), when 5 ml of neutral red solution (5–20 μg/ml) in PBS or 2 ml of

INT stain (Section IX,C) are added. The plates are reincubated for a further 1–5 hours, the neutral red dye solution removed, and the plaques counted.

This method is essentially that reported by Cooper (1961b).

C. Assay of Semliki Forest Virus Using Agar Suspensions of Chick Embryo Cells

A nutrient agar medium is made by mixing equal volumes of molten 3% agar solution (Section III,J) at 50°C and a 2-fold-strength medium (either the Eagle's medium (Section III,H) or the supplemented Earle's saline (Section III,G). To the Eagle's medium may be added NaHCO$_3$ (2–2.5 mg/ml) or the Tris buffer (Section III,D); bicarbonate may also be omitted from the Earle's saline and replaced by Tris buffer. Serum (horse or bovine) is added to all of these media, in 5-ml amounts per 100 ml of final-strength nutrient agar medium. Ten milliliters of this nutrient agar are added to each of a series of Petri plates 100 mm in diameter and allowed to set in a level position to form base layers (Section VIII,A).

A chick embryo cell suspension, prepared as described in Section IV, B and containing 1–1.5 × 10^8 cells/ml, is dispensed in 0.5-ml volumes in small test tubes. A sample (0.1 ml) of an appropriate dilution (Section V) of Semliki Forest virus in PBS is added to each tube, followed by 2 ml of the nutrient agar used for the base layers and described above; the contents are very rapidly mixed, poured at once onto the base layers as described in Section VIII,A, and allowed to set in a level position. The plates are then incubated for 1–2 days at 37°C in a humidified atmosphere, containing CO$_2$ (Section IX,B) if necessary, when 5 ml of neutral red solution (5–20 μg/ml) in PBS are added. The plates are reincubated for 1–5 hours, the stain decanted, and the plaques counted.

This method is that reported by Cooper (1955).

D. Assay of Encephalomyocarditis Virus Using Agar Suspensions of Krebs-2 Ascites Tumor Cells

A nutrient agar medium is made by mixing equal volumes of molten 3% agar solution (Section III,J) at 50°C and a 2-fold-strength of Earle's saline (as described in Section III,G but without the lactalbumin hydrolyzate, yeast extract, and bovine albumin). Twelve milliliters of this nutrient agar are added to each of a series of Petri plates

100 mm in diameter and allowed to set in a level position to form base layers (Section VIII,A).

A Krebs-2 ascites tumor cell suspension, prepared as described in Section IV,E and containing 10^8 cells/ml, is dispensed in 1.2-ml volumes in small test tubes. A sample (0.1 ml) of an appropriate dilution (Section V) of encephalomyocarditis virus in PBS is added to each tube, followed by 1.8 ml of the nutrient agar medium described above; the contents are very rapidly mixed, poured at once onto the base layers as described in Section VIII,A, and allowed to set in a level position. The plates are then incubated for 3 days at 37°C in a humidified atmosphere containing CO_2 (Section IX,B), when 5 ml of neutral red solution (1 μg/ml) in PBS are added. The plates are reincubated for a further hour at 37°C, the dye solution decanted, and the plaques counted.

This method is that developed by Sanders (1957) and described in detail by Martin *et al.* (1961). Monolayer plaque assay methods that involve ascites tumor cells do not yet appear to be available.

E. Assay of the Transforming Capacity of Polyoma Virus Using Agar Suspensions of BHK Cells

A nutrient agar medium is made by mixing 4 parts of 2-fold strength Eagle's medium (Section III,H, but containing the vitamins and amino acids in 4-fold strength and 0.70 mg of $NaHCO_3$ per ml), 4 parts of molten 1.25% agar solution (Section III,J) at 45°C, 1 part of calf serum and 1 part of Difco-Bacto tryptose phosphate broth. Seven milliliters of this nutrient agar are added to each of a series of Petri plates 60 mm in diameter and allowed to set in a level position to form base layers (Section VIII,A).

An appropriate number of BHK/Cl3N cells (10^3 to 5×10^5) are infected with polyoma virus as described in Section VII,F. These cells are dispensed in 0.6-ml volumes containing 100–600 transformed cells in small test tubes. A volume of 0.9 ml of the nutrient agar medium described above is added to the cells, and the contents rapidly mixed, poured on the base layers as described in Section VIII,A, and allowed to set in a level position. The plates are then incubated for 7–10 days in a thoroughly humidified atmosphere containing CO_2 (Section IX,B). Colony counts are made on unstained cultures with the aid of a low-powered microscope. Untransformed cells do not form colonies with the concentration of cells given above.

This method is that described by Macpherson and Montagnier (1964).

IX. Incubation and Staining of Plates and Counting of Plaques

A. INTRODUCTION

Sections VII and VIII give in detail the procedures for the setting up of the assay plates during plaque assays. This section discusses some practical factors that are involved after the assay plates are ready for their final incubation.

B. INCUBATION AND pH CONTROL

For most plaque assay purposes a standard laboratory incubator is satisfactory, both for culturing cells before assay and for final incubation of the assay plates. If Petri plates are used, the incubator must be thoroughly humidified by including a tray of water and by sealing all openings and spaces around the door almost completely. The gas that is pumped in can be humidified by passing it through a diffuser immersed in the tray of water. Alternatively, plates may be incubated in a sealed vessel containing a water dish and a dish of Pardee's buffer (Section III,D). A useful modification of this system is to support the plates and the dish of buffer on a stand, which is placed in a tray containing 2–3 inches of water. The atmosphere is retained by placing over the stand of plates a large Perspex box, which also stands in the tray of water. The atmosphere is thus fully humidified, yet a slow gas exchange with the ambient atmosphere is possible through the water seal.

The incubation temperature prescribed for the methods given in Sections VII and VIII is 37°C. Fluctuations within the range 36°–37.5°C are generally not critical. For some purposes, however, the temperature needs to be lower than this (e.g., 33°C for the rhinoviruses, see Table II). On the other hand, work with temperature-sensitive (heat-defective) conditional lethal mutants may necessitate a very accurately controlled high incubation temperature (e.g., $39.5 \pm 0.1°C$; Cooper, 1965), and for this purpose incubation in bottles immersed in a water bath is preferable.

The control of pH with a combination of standard incubators, Petri plates, and bicarbonate-containing media is usually effected by passing into the incubator a humidified mixture of air from a pump or compressed air supply and carbon dioxide from a cylinder. Gases from a cylinder can be controlled sensitively with a regulating valve (No. BOR 12, British Oxygen Gases, Greenwich, England). The proportion of these gases is metered in a simple fashion by passing them through a fine capillary; the pressure difference across the ends of the capillary is measured by connecting each end to an arm of a mercury U-tube manometer, and the manometer is calibrated by collecting the gas passed in a measured time in an inverted measuring cylinder filled with acidified water. The flow rates are then adjusted to known values by measuring the manometer levels. Alternatively, gas flow meters (e.g., "rotameters") are available commercially; an automatic pH control device has been described (Perkins and Hotchin, 1955).

A pure aqueous solution containing 2.27 gm of $NaHCO_3$ per liter equilibrates with a concentration of 5% CO_2 in air at 37°C to give a pH of 7.6 (Fig. 1). Figure 2 gives some values for Pardee's buffer suitable for low CO_2 concentrations. However, it is rare in practice with complete medium to achieve the pH value that is theoretically derived from the applied concentrations of CO_2 and $NaHCO_3$. The

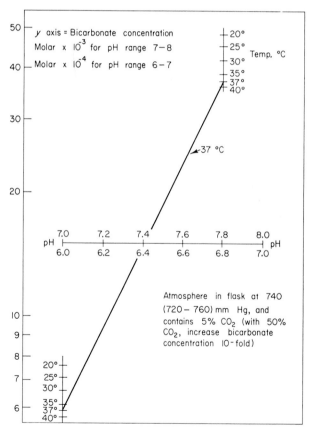

FIG. 1. Chart for determining the proper bicarbonate concentration to use at a given pH, pCO_2, and temperature (Umbreit *et al.*, 1964).

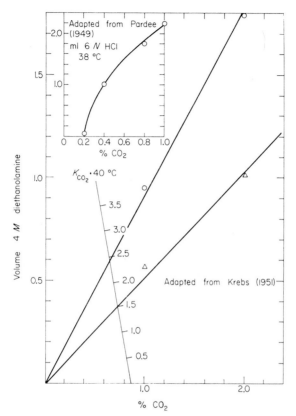

FIG. 2. Graphs supplying information needed for the preparation of mixtures of diethanolamine designed to maintain a constant pressure of CO_2 (Umbreit *et al.*, 1964).

bicarbonate concentration actually available may be changed by reaction with acidic or basic medium components, the cells themselves contribute CO_2 and other acidic substances, and some leakage from the incubator decreases the effective CO_2 concentration. The best CO_2–$NaHCO_3$ concentration must, therefore, be determined for each system comprising incubator, cells, and medium. The most useful pH value for most cell culture work is about 7.3, and it may be simplest to rely on the color of the pH indicator included in the medium (phenol red) that has been found to give the best results.

It can be seen that there are considerable incentives to the complete avoidance of a separate gassing system, either by the use of sealed incubation vessels or culture containers or by the omission of bicarbonate. Although bicarbonate *per se* may be needed for growth of cells (Paul, 1965), the relatively high density of cells often used for plaque assays means that such cultures can provide their own CO_2 requirements.

C. Staining

In most of the methods described in Sections VII and VIII the surviving cells are stained with a vital dye (neutral red) after plaque development. The plaques are revealed as round areas in which cells have not taken up the stain. Neutral red solutions may be made up as a stock of 1 mg/ml in distilled water and sterilized by filtration; Wallis *et al.* (1962) advise against heat sterilization. This stock is diluted to an appropriate concentration (1–50 µg/ml) in PBS before use. Cells retain their viability (and hence the neutral red stain) for longer if they are incubated after staining in darkness, as neutral red has a pronounced photodynamic effect. Neutral red may also be incorporated in the nutrient agar medium; low concentrations are used (<20 µg/ml), and plates are kept in darkness during incubation.

Some other stains, and other ways of enhancing the appearance of localized lesions for counting purposes, are discussed by Cooper (1961a). For this writer a useful alternative to neutral red is 2-(*p*-iodophenyl)-3-(*p*-nitrophenyl)-5-phenyltetrazolium chloride (Lights, Colnbrook, England; Cooper, 1959). This substance is autoclaved in 1.5 mg/ml solution in 0.9% NaCl; its stain does not fade. A. Brown and Officer (1961) report that the neutral red stain can be prevented from fading by the action of mercuric chloride.

D. Plaque Counting and Calculation of Titer

The localized lesions, nearly always enhanced in contrast with a suitable stain (Section IX,C), are usually counted with the unaided eye. Some lesions may have to be counted microscopically. To count macroscopically visible plaques, the writer draws a line radially with a glass-marking pen on the base of the Petri plates (holding the plates in a normal position, i.e., not inverted) and marks each plaque while working round the plate sectorially. Areas of dead cells (presumably plaques) can be distinguished from gaps in the cell sheet by their gray appearance when held against a black background; most virus strains produce round and symmetrical plaques, and in this case areas of dead cells with irregular outlines indicate a nonspecific cause of cell death. An automatic recording pen is available commercially (Scientifica, London) which does not depend on electrodes immersed in the medium.

Plaque counts are recorded only for those plates in which losses by overlapping of plaques are statistically negligible (Cooper, 1961a). An adequate guide is that 100 plaques per plate will give no significant loss by overlapping if the internal diameter of the Petri plate is at least 25 times the average plaque diameter.

The virus titer is obtained by multiplying the average plaque count per plate by the total dilution factor. Thus an average of 66 plaques per plate obtained from plating 0.2 ml of a 3×10^{-4} dilution represents a titer in the original preparation of $66/0.2 \times 1/3 \times 10^4 = 1.1 \times 10^6$ plaque-forming units per milliliter. One hundred plaques per plate obtained from plating 0.1 ml of a 10^{-4} dilution represent 10^7 pfu/ml in the original. In the case of animal viruses, the somewhat conservative term "plaque-forming unit" (pfu) represents the entity actually measured more correctly than does, say, "infective unit" or "virus particle."

X. Special Uses of the Plaque Assay Method

A. ASSAY OF INFECTIOUS NUCLEIC ACID

Following the phenolic extraction of infectious RNA from tobacco mosaic virus, a considerable effort has been devoted to obtaining similar preparations from animal viruses, with success in many cases (mostly yielding infective RNA but in some cases DNA). An obvious need was to apply the plaque assay to this material. Unfortunately, this proved difficult initially; although nonsedimentable infectivity sensitive to nucleases (the distinctions from intact virus on which the designation "free nucleic acid" rests in most cases) was clearly shown in animals, its plaque-forming activity was sporadic and not proportional to dose [Western equine encephalomyelitis virus (Wecker and Schäfer, 1957); mouse encephalitis virus (Franklin et al., 1959)].

Fortunately, Alexander et al. (1958a,b), starting from concentrated and partly purified poliovirus preparations that contained a high concentration of NaCl, were able to obtain plaques reproducibly from preparations of free RNA, and many other authors have since been successful.

The main differences from assays of free virus lie in the plating properties of infectious nucleic acid and in its relative instability. Since infectious RNA is sensitive to RNase, cells must be washed well to free them from serum; it is likely that trace contamination with this enzyme is the main cause of the instability of infectious RNA. The efficiency of plating can be greatly increased by a variety of treatments, in particular by the use of a high ionic strength in the medium used for adsorption. More recently, other procedures involving basic polymers (in particular DEAE-dextran, see below) have replaced the use of high ionic strength media.

The following is a typical method, modified from that described for assay of poliovirus infectious RNA by G. Koch *et al.* (1960). A series of monolayers of HeLa cells in Petri plates (100 mm in diameter) is set up and incubated as described in Section IV,D, except that the medium contains 20% of calf serum, or 10% of fetal calf serum, to cause the cells to attach strongly to the glass. Twelve plates are made for each sample to be assayed.

The following reagents are now assembled.

1. *Aqueous Phenol Solution*

About 20 ml of phenol are distilled not sooner than 1 day before use and collected in a flask containing 5 ml of distilled water. This flask is stoppered and kept at 4°C in darkness until needed.

2. *0.1 M EDTA (See Section III,F)*

Ethylenediaminetetraacetic acid, disodium salt (2H₂O)	3.72 gm
Water	to 100 ml

The solution is dissolved and autoclaved.

3. *Bentonite Suspension (Fraenkel-Conrat et al., 1961)*

Two grams of bentonite (Clayspur, Wyoming; Braun-Knecht-Heimann Co., San Francisco, California) are suspended in 40 ml of water and centrifuged at 2500 rpm for 15 minutes. The supernatant is recentrifuged at 8500 rpm for 20 minutes. The sediment is resuspended and kept in 0.1 M EDTA (pH 7) for 48 hours at 25°C, then again centrifuged differentially. The 8500 rpm sediment is resuspended in 0.01 M acetate (pH 6), again centrifuged at 8500 rpm, and the sediment resuspended in fresh acetate solution to 1.5–6% by dry weight.

4. *1 M NaCl*

NaCl	58.45 gm
Water	to 1 liter

The solution is dissolved and autoclaved.

5. *1 M Tris Buffer (Section III,D)*

Tris	12.1 gm
Water	to 80 ml

The pH is adjusted to 8 with 6 N HCl. Water is added to 100 ml and the solution is autoclaved.

6. Anesthetic Ether (Unopened)

7. Nutrient Agar Medium (Molten and at 45°C; see Section VII,C)

When the monolayers are confluent (1–2 days), a preparation of infectious RNA is made as follows from a stock of poliovirus (type 1, Sabin vaccine strain LSc). The stock should be free of serum, if possible, and its titer should be greater than 10^6 plaque-forming units/ml. A volume of 2 ml of the aqueous phenol solution is dispensed in each of three 6-ml screw-capped bottles immersed in ice, together with 0.1 ml of the EDTA solution and 0.1 ml of the bentonite suspension. A volume of 2 ml of the chilled virus stock is added to one bottle containing the phenol mixture, which is then vigorously shaken mechanically for 3 minutes at 4°C and centrifuged for 5 minutes at 1500 rpm. The aqueous supernatant is transferred to a second bottle containing the phenol mixture, which is shaken and centrifuged as before. This extraction procedure is repeated once more with the third bottle, and the final aqueous supernatant transferred to a bottle containing 30 ml of anesthetic ether at 0°C. This is vigorously shaken and the contents allowed to settle; the small aqueous layer is then transferred to a fresh container at 0°C. It is not necessary to remove traces of ether if dilutions greater than 10^{-2} are used for plating, but otherwise the ether can be removed by passing a stream of N_2.

The medium is now removed from 12 confluent HeLa monolayers, which are washed three times each with 5 ml of PBS. Between washes the plates are allowed to drain thoroughly in a tilted position and the drainings are removed. Ten milliliters of the 1 M Tris buffer (pH 8) are mixed with 100 ml of M NaCl, and the plates are washed once with this mixture and drained thoroughly, as before. An interval timer is set for 15 minutes at the time of addition of the 1 M NaCl–Tris solution. The RNA preparation is diluted rapidly in 10-fold steps with 1 M NaCl–Tris to 10^{-1}, 10^{-2}, and 10^{-3}, changing the pipet with each dilution, and 0.2 ml volumes of each dilution are added to the center of each of four plates. The plates are incubated at 37°C in a level position for the remainder of the 15 minutes, at which time 10 ml of cold PBS are added quickly to each plate, taking care, however, not to dislodge the cells. Finally, this PBS is removed, 10 ml of the nutrient agar medium are added and allowed to set in a level position, and the plates are incubated and stained and the plaques counted as described in Section VII,A and VII,C. Alternatively, the extensive washing and treatment with 1 M NaCl can be replaced by one wash in saline and simple dilution of the RNA extract in 1 mg/ml of DEAE-dextran (Pagano and Vaheri, 1965). After 10 minutes at 37°C, the plates are overlaid with agar without washing and incubated.

The method cited gives an extraction efficiency (ratio of total plaque-forming units of RNA recovered to total plaque-forming units of virus from which it was extracted) of about 10^{-4}. Many methods have been described for the assay of infectious nucleic acid. They are basically similar to the above, the differences residing mainly in the variety of treatments given to the cells in order to increase the plating efficiency. The following reports are among those that consider these technical factors: G. Koch (1960), Sprunt et al. (1961), Weil (1961), Dubes and Klingler (1961), Smull et al. (1961), Amos (1961), Dubes et al. (1964), and Colón and Idoine (1964).

B. ASSAY OF INFECTED CELLS

It is frequently necessary to determine the content of cells in a suspension able to liberate virus (infective centers), and this can be done by methods similar to those used for free virus. Some minor differences need to be borne in mind, however. Infected cells are more delicate than free virus, and their ability to adsorb and produce virus is easily damaged by trypsin, EDTA, and strong pipeting through narrow pipets; they should be gently diluted in serum-containing medium using wide-bore pipets with avoidance of frothing. Dilutions should be made rapidly in order to avoid sedimentation of the cells and should be kept at ice temperature to minimize firm attachment to glass and development of virus growth; the use of silicone- or paraffin wax-treated glassware is also desirable. The control should be performed of centrifuging the infective center suspension for 5 minutes at 1000 g after final plating of the cells and assaying the supernatant to ensure that free virus is negligible; a most essential point is to add the agar *before* any cells have been allowed to release new virus (i.e., at least a half hour before the end of the latent period). This point, of course, applies to all plaque assays in which the lesions are artificially localized.

Having obtained the final dilution, infected cells can be plated like free virus onto monolayers (30 minutes' adsorption in PBS at 37°C). This is satisfactory for small stable viruses such as poliovirus, but it gives low plating efficiencies (20–30%) with larger and less stable viruses, as the cells are resuspended on adding the agar and become fixed at points distant from the monolayer, with the result that their yield of virus may die before reaching the monolayer. The simplest way of overcoming this difficulty is to use the agar cell-suspension method (Cooper, 1955), which may improve the efficiency of plating of infected cells 3- to 4-fold by achieving very short diffusion paths. A variety of other devices have been employed to gain the same effect. One can incubate the cells for an extended time (4–16 hours) at 24°–37°C in nutrient medium to allow the cells to attach more firmly to a monolayer [e.g., vaccinia virus (Furness and Youngner, 1959); Rous sarcoma virus (Temin and Rubin, 1958); polyomavirus (Winocour and Sachs, 1960)], but this is only suitable for those viruses with a long latent period; in this case one can also add the infected cells with the cell suspension used to make the monolayer (Rubin, 1960a). Alternatively, one can set the infected cells in a small volume of agar (about 1 ml) over a monolayer to obtain a shorter diffusion path before adding the larger volume of nutrient agar necessary to keep the cells alive [poliovirus (Drake, 1958); polyomavirus (Winocour and Sachs, 1960); herpesvirus (Kaplan, 1957)]. Cells are not harmed as infective centers by a short sojourn at 43°–44°C. Infective centers forming part of monolayers that will not support plaque formation can be "developed" by overlaying with an agar cell suspension (Franklin, 1958a). Infective centers should be proportional to the virus dose used to produce them, but may not always be so (Rous sarcoma virus; Temin and Rubin, 1958); Drake (1958) found that the number of infective centers of poliovirus does not quite follow the Poisson distribution.

C. PLAQUE-INHIBITION TESTS

Substances inhibiting virus growth (e.g., antisera or interferon) can be estimated rather accurately by using a method analogous to the cup-plate assay for antibiotics, although its sensitivity is lower than end-point methods. In this method, a virus inhibitor is placed in a container on an agar substrate and allowed to diffuse during plaque development. If the agar substrate contains a cell culture through which virus growth is spreading at the correct rate, then each cup will produce a circular zone of protected cells, the diameter of which will increase with inhibitor concentration. The plates are stained in a fashion similar to plaque assays after an appropriate incubation.

A simple method for the assay of poliovirus antibody is as follows. Several nutrient agar base layers are prepared as described in Section VIII,B, except that 7.5-ml volumes of nutrient agar medium are used. A series of 2-fold dilutions of the unknown antibody solution, together with similar dilutions of a standard antibody preparation, are made in

PBS. Either 1-cm discs cut from thick filter paper, or "fish-spine insulator beads" (Size 3, Taylor, Tunnicliffe and Co., Stoke-on-Trent, England) are touched on the surface of a dilution of antibody so that the discs or beads are saturated with fluid. Several of the wet discs or beads are then placed on each base layer so that each layer contains several dilutions of both the unknown and the standard preparations. Their contents are allowed to diffuse into the agar for 24–72 hours at 4°C in a humidified vessel, containing CO_2 if necessary. The discs or beads are then removed, the surface of the layer is dried for 1 hour at 37°C with the lid of the Petri plate open, and a cell–virus–agar mixture is poured on and allowed to set. This mixture is as described in Section VIII,B, except that its virus content is 10^5 plaque-forming units. The plates are then incubated for 2–3 days and stained as described in Section VIII,B. The average diameter of the zones in millimeters is recorded. The zone diameters of the standards are plotted against the logarithm of the relative serum concentration (expressed as a percentage of the undiluted value) to obtain a straight line. The values of the unknown sera are obtained by interpolation.

This method is that of Burt and Cooper (1961). Similar methods have been described by De Somer and Prinzie (1957), Farrell and Reid (1959), and Porterfield (1959b).

D. GENETIC TECHNIQUES

1. *Isolation of Clones*

The concept that each plaque arises from a single particle (Dulbecco and Vogt, 1954a) means that virus isolated from a single plaque should comprise a pure clone derived from a single particle. Two factors may render this conclusion invalid in practice: (1) mutants may have arisen spontaneously during the growth of the plaque or of the clone; and (2) the plaque may have multiple origins.

The second possibility can be eliminated by appropriate technical safeguards. Plaque assays are made in which each Petri plate contains only 1–5 plaques. The plates have been incubated inverted, and no moisture is present on the surface of the agar. These plaques may be picked without staining, but it is better to employ a stain in order to ensure that no small plaque is adjacent to the plaque that is picked. For this purpose, neutral red must be incorporated in the agar medium (Section IX,C). Alternatively, the tetrazolium stain (INT, Section IX,C) may be sprayed onto plates (Cooper, 1964) as follows: 15 mg of

INT and 40 mg of glucose are dissolved with warming in 100 ml of 80% ethanol and the solution lightly and evenly applied to the plates with a hand chromatogram spray. It is important not to make the surface appear wet, since if this happens virus from one plaque may run into another.

A 1-mm cylinder of agar is removed from the center of the plaque with a Pasteur pipet, or the entire plaque may be cut out with a small sterile spatula; these pieces of agar are transferred to a culture tube, and a stock is grown up. For this purpose it is best to adsorb virus in the cold, to allow virus to grow for one cycle, and then to release virus from the cells artificially, if necessary, in order to start further cycles. This procedure minimizes thermal inactivation and the number of viral replications needed to produce a given titer, and hence decreases the number of mutational errors.

This cloning procedure is repeated at least once.

2. Plaque Character as a Genetic Marker

Several types of plaque character are now available for genetic work. The most useful character is one that can be altered by a relatively few mutations (so that an appropriate "label" can easily be built into a virus strain) yet that is sufficiently stable to make back-mutations rare.

a. Plaque Morphology. Strains of virus may have the following inheritable plaque characteristics: large, medium, small, or minute in size; round or irregular in outline; sharp or diffuse in boundary; clear, hazy, turbid, or opaque in center; red or white when cells are stained with neutral red. These characteristics often serve to distinguish virus strains in mixed plating, but unless the differences are very marked they may be difficult to use because subjective judgments are involved.

b. Rate of Development. Although the final size may be similar, plaques of some viruses may develop much more rapidly than others (Henderson and Taylor, 1959, 1960). They are thus distinguished in mixture by counting the plaques after different times of incubation.

c. Temperature Sensitivity. Mutant strains of virus can be isolated (Cooper, 1964) that are strongly inhibited in plaque formation by small increases in temperature in the upper range of temperature at which virus growth occurs (usually 39°–40°C). It is possible to separate normal (wild type) virus from such mutants with an efficiency of 10^{-3} to 10^{-5} residual contamination by incubating assay plates of the mixture at 39°–40°C. (Cooper, 1965; Burge and Pfefferkorn, 1964; Sambrook *et al.*, 1966). This type of conditional lethal mutant, and the host-dependent type described in the next paragraph, are potentially extremely useful for genetic and biochemical studies. Plating efficiency in the low-temperature range can also be affected by temperature (Cooper, 1964).

d. *Host Dependence.* Mutant strains of certain viruses [rabbitpox (Fenner and Sambrook, 1966); herpesvirus (Roizman and Aurelian, 1965)] are unable to grow in certain cell types, although the parental virus strains grow normally. Stocks of these mutants are prepared in cells in which they grow well; they are distinguished by assay in parallel cultures of the two cell types. The efficiency of separation in plaque assays is rather better than that of the heat-defective type of temperature-sensitive mutant mentioned in the previous paragraph.

e. *Drug Resistance and Dependence.* Several substances are known that selectively inhibit the growth of certain animal viruses (e.g., guanidine, hydroxybenzylbenzimidazole, isatin thiosemicarbazone). Virus mutants can readily be isolated that are resistant to inhibition or even dependent for growth on the presence of the drug (Tamm and Eggers, 1963). Such mutants can be distinguished in a mixture by performing parallel assays in which the drug is either incorporated in the agar or omitted.

f. *Serum Inhibitors.* Certain viruses, for example, type 1 and type 2 poliovirus, can be separated in plaque assays by including the appropriate antiserum in the agar overlay or base layer. Care has to be taken to avoid difficulties raised by phenotypic mixing (Ledinko and Hirst, 1961). Polioviruses may also be sensitive to other inhibitors present in normal horse and bovine sera, and resistant mutants can be obtained (Hirst, 1962).

g. *Agar Inhibitors.* Certain virus mutants turn out to be relatively sensitive to inhibitors (sulfated polysaccharides) present in the agar (Takemoto and Liebhaber, 1962). Sensitive and resistant strains can be distinguished by the use of washed agar, and by making parallel assays in which one series contains dextran sulfate in the agar medium. Other mutant strains of poliovirus (*d* mutants; Vogt *et al.*, 1957) are inhibited by certain agar components when the pH is low. Sensitive and resistant strains may be distinguished by performing parallel assays in the same atmosphere containing CO_2, but with one series containing a normal and the other a low bicarbonate concentration in the agar medium.

h. *Difference in Transforming Ability.* Certain strains of Rous sarcoma virus can be distinguished by the morphology of cells in foci induced by the virus (Temin, 1961).

XI. Some Recent Developments

Many reports that describe new developments in plaque assay methods have appeared since the earlier review (Cooper, 1961a) was completed. Most of these are listed in Table II, since their findings relate to specific viruses. However, some are of more general relevance, and these will be summarized briefly in this section.

A. TECHNICAL IMPROVEMENTS

Perhaps the most helpful advance made in the last 5 years has been the use of DEAE-dextran or protamine. These substances, when added to the overlay medium, have overcome the inhibitory effect of agar components and have enabled the production of plaques by many viruses that otherwise could not be assayed by this means. Individual references are too numerous to give here, but many of the methods referred to in Table II depend on this use of cationic polymers. A high magnesium concentration has given similarly beneficial results for certain enteroviruses (Wallis *et al.*, 1962).

Several devices have been employed that enhance the contrast of plaques and facilitate their counting. For improving the contrast of lesions that are already visible, Frothingham (1963) found that Sindbis virus plaques could be made larger by the presence of mumps virus. Moore and Walker (1962) showed that the incorporation of specific antiserum into the medium did not affect the development of myxoma or fibroma foci in secondary rabbit kidney cultures, but rendered them more easily detectable by the precipitation of antibody around the focus. Specific antiserum could be used to reveal one or another of the viruses in a mixture.

Certain mutants of vaccinia virus could also be differentiated in a mixture by their production of hemagglutinin (Oda, 1964). Those strains that produced hemagglutinin formed plaques around which red cells were adsorbed; virus mutants lacking the hemagglutinin were revealed by plaques that did not show hemadsorption. Some mutants of Newcastle disease virus (Thiry, 1963) and of SV40 (Riggs and Lennett, 1965) produced plaques with a red center when the cells were stained with neutral red.

Some procedures for staining and thus making visible certain plaques that were normally invisible (e.g., fluorescent-antibody staining, hemadsorption) were mentioned earlier (Cooper, 1961a). Agar normally interferes with the use of fluorescent antibody for this purpose because it produces a nonspecific fluorescence, but Spendlove and Lennette

(1962) grew virus under agar in cells attached to cover slips, then heated the agar to melt it and removed the cover slips for reaction with the fluorescent antibody. As a development of the hemadsorption test, Marcus and Carver (1965) allowed plaques of rubella virus to develop in monkey kidney cell monolayers, which were then challenged with Newcastle disease virus. The rubella virus interfered with growth of the challenge virus, and plaques were revealed as areas of negative hemadsorption.

A. Brown and Officer (1961) found that mercuric chloride could be used to precipitate neutral red in stained cells, thus permanently "fixing" plaques in cell sheets stained with this dye. Rather than incorporate stain in the medium, Cooper (1964) applied an alcoholic solution of a tetrazolium salt as a spray in order to detect plaques suitable for isolating virus clones (the use of a spray of highly colored substances such as neutral red is extremely inconvenient).

A. Brown and Officer (1961) also developed a replica-plating method for the analysis of plaques formed by Eastern and Venezuelan equine encephalomyelitis viruses. Bachrach et al. (1962) and Spendlove and Taylor (1963) described racks for holding plaque assay bottles. Zebovitz (1965) gave a defined maintenance medium suitable for supporting chick embryo monolayers and for production of plaques by two group A arboviruses. Lindenmann and Gifford (1963b) reported a simplified plaque inhibition test for interferon.

B. ANALYSIS OF FACTORS INVOLVED IN PLAQUE ASSAYS

The kinetics of the enlargement of bacteriophage plaques have been discussed by A. L. Koch (1964); he expects that his findings will also apply to the enlargement of animal virus plaques. Hellwig and Thomssen (1962) have considered the relation of the diffusion constants of poliovirus and Western equine encephalomyelitis virus to plaque development, and Lindenmann and Gifford (1963a) have studied the appearance of vaccinia virus plaques with time of development. Pipeting errors have been discussed by Lorenz (1961), and statistical factors by Lorenz (1962) and by Mai and Bonitz (1963). Berg et al. (1963) have reported on the effects on accurate counting of the overcrowding of enterovirus plaques. Other specific technical factors considered are the effects of anticellular serum (Timbury, 1962), the aggregation of vaccinia particles (Galasso and Sharp, 1962), the presence of nonplaque-forming particles (Taylor and Graham, 1961), oxygenation (Baron et al., 1961), interferon (Gifford et al., 1963), temperature (A. Brown, 1963), mycoplasma (Rouse et al., 1963), interfering viruses (Rubin,

1960b), agar inhibitors (Liebhaber and Takemoto, 1963; L. N. Brown and Packer, 1964; and others), and the distribution of poliovirus in the assay bottle and its relevance to the purity of clones isolated from plaques (Mosley and Enders, 1961).

Several virus–cell systems have been analyzed with respect to a number of variables: herpes simplex virus (Rapp, 1963; Taniguchi and Yoshino, 1964); entero- and reoviruses (Wallis *et al.*, 1962); porcine enteroviruses (Singh and Bohl, 1960); foot-and-mouth disease virus (Bengelsdorff, 1963); vaccinia virus (Kirn and Braunwald, 1963), and poliovirus (Grachev, 1963).

XII. Methods for Individual Viruses

References to some methods for individual viruses are given in Table II.

XIII. Some Common Sources of Difficulty

Table III lists some simple technical difficulties that may arise in the use of an established plaque assay method and gives some suggestions for overcoming them.

TABLE II

METHODS AVAILABLE FOR PLAQUE ASSAY OF ANIMAL VIRUSES[a]

POXVIRUSES		
Vaccinia Subgroup		
Vaccinia	P—CE	Noyes (1953), Postlethwaite (1960), Porterfield and Allison (1960)
	P—MK	Youngner (1956b), Furness and Youngner (1959)
	P—CEK	Wright and Sagik (1958)
	C—mouse	Hanafusa et al. (1959)
	C—hu	Nishmi and Keller (1961), Oda (1964)
Cowpox	P—CE	Porterfield and Allison (1960)
	P—MK, P—RK	McConnell et al. (1964)
Ectromelia	C—mouse	Hanafusa et al. (1959)
	P—CE	Porterfield and Allison (1960)
Rabbitpox	P—CE	Mika and Pirsch (1960)
	P—MK, P—RK	McConnell et al. (1964)
	C—mammalian cells	McClain (1965)
Monkey pox	P—CE	Mika and Pirsch (1960)
	P—MK, P—RK	McConnell et al. (1964)
Variola	P—CE	Bedson and Dumbell (1964b)
Alastrim	P—CE	Bedson and Dumbell (1964a)
Myxoma Subgroup		
Myxoma	P—, C—RK	Schwerdt and Schwerdt (1962)
	P—, C—R cells	Padgett et al. (1962)
	P—CE,P—, C—R cells	Woodroofe and Fenner (1965)
Fibroma	P—RK	Padgett et al. (1962)
	P—, C—R cells	Verna and Eylar (1962)
	P—RE	Woodroofe and Fenner (1965)
Orf Subgroup		
Contagious pustular dermatitis (orf)	P—hu amnion	Nagington and Whittle (1961)
Pseudocowpox	P—bovine E testis	Moscovici et al. (1963)

	Cells	Reference
Unclassified Mammalian		
Swinepox	P—pig cells	Kasza et al. (1960)
Avian Pox Subgroup		
Fowlpox, canary pox, pigeon pox	P—CE	Mayr and Kalcher (1961)
PAPOVAVIRUSES		
Polyoma	P—, S—mouse E	Dulbecco and Freeman (1959), Winocour and Sachs (1959, 1960), Sheinin (1961), Macpherson and Montagnier (1964), Diamond (1964)
	S—mouse E	Stinebaugh and Melnick (1962)
	C—baby hamster K	
SV40	P—MK	Riggs and Lennette (1965)
	C—MK	
ADENOVIRUSES		
Adenovirus		
Type 2	C—hu	V. Bonifas and Schlesinger (1959)
	C—hu	F. H. Bonifas and Mullally (1960)
Types 4, 5	C—hu	Rouse et al. (1963)
Types 1, 4, 5, 6, 19A, 20, 24	C—hu	Kjellén (1961)
Types 1–7	C—hu	Wassermann (1962)
Infectious canine hepatitis	P—MK	Tytell et al. (1962)
	P—dog K	Levine et al. (1959)
	P—pig K	Singh et al. (1959)
Fowl orphan (GAL, originally described as avian lymphoma)	P—CE liver, P—CE	Stoker (1959)
	P—CE liver	Levine and Sharpless (1959)
	P—CEK, P—CE liver	Macpherson (1960)
	P—CEK	Buthala (1960)
HERPESVIRUSES		
Herpes simplex	P—RK	Kaplan (1957), Kaplan and Vatter (1959)
	P—CE	Waterson (1958b), Porterfield and Allison (1960), Taniguchi and Yoshino (1964)
	P—CEK	Wright and Sagik (1958)
	C—hu	Farnham (1958)
	P—hu amnion	Osterhout and Tamm (1959)

TABLE II (*Continued*)

	C—hu conjunctiva	Hinze and Walker (1961)
	C—hu, C—BHK 21, P—CE, P—mouse E	Russell (1962)
	P—MK, P—RK, C—MK	Tytell and Neuman (1963)
	P—RK, P—mouse E, P—hu lung	Rapp (1963)
Herpes B	P—MK	Black and Melnick (1954, 1955) Youngner (1956b)
Pseudorabies	P—CE	Cooper (1954)
	P—RK	Kaplan and Vatter (1959)
	P—pig K	Singh et al. (1959), Singh (1962)
Equine abortion (rhinopneumonitis)	P—horse K	Shimizu et al. (1960, 1963)
	C—mouse	Randall and Lawson (1962)
Infectious bovine rhinotracheitis	P—horse, pig, sheep K	McCollum et al. (1962)
	P—pig, M, bovine EK	Rouhandeh and Werder (1961, 1963)
	C—bovine K	Stevens and Groman (1963)
Feline rhinotracheitis	P—cat K	Crandell et al. (1960)
Murine salivary gland	P—mouse E	Henson and Pinkerton (1963)
	C—mouse E	Field and Fong (1964)
Zoster	P—hu E lung	Rapp and Benyesh-Melnick (1963), Rapp and Vanderslice (1964), Rapp (1964b)
Human cytomegalo	P—hu E lung	Plummer and Benyesh-Melnick (1964)
MYXOVIRUSES		
Influenza, various strains	P—CE lung, liver	Ledinko (1955)
	P—CE, P—CE lung	Granoff (1955)
	P—CEK	Wright and Sagik (1958)
	P—CE	Hirst (1959), Hotchin et al. (1960), Simpson and Hirst (1961)
	P—MK	Choppin (1962)
	P—calf K	Lehmann-Grube (1963)
	P—MK	Takemoto and Fabisch (1963)
	P—hamster K	Grossberg (1964)
	C—hu	Sugiura and Kilbourne (1965)

Swine influenza	P—calf K	Zimmermann and Schäfer (1959)
Fowl plague	P—CE	Hotchin (1955), Breitenfeld and Schäfer (1957), Franklin (1958b), Waterson (1958a)
Unidentified myxovirus	P—hu K	Hsiung (1959b)
PARAMYXOVIRUSES		
NDV	P—CE	Dulbecco (1952), Levine and Sagik (1956), Franklin et al. (1957)
	P—CEK	Wright and Sagik (1958)
	P—, S—CE	Marcus (1959)
	C—hu cells	Závada (1963)
Mumps	P—CE	Hotchin et al. (1960)
	P—CE, C—hu	Frothingham and Granoff (1961)
Parainfluenza 1 (Sendai)	P—CE	Hotchin et al. (1960)
	P—CEK	Shigita (1964)
Parainfluenza 2	P—MK	Tytell et al. (1961)
Parainfluenza 3 (HA 1)	C—hu	Deibel (1959)
	C—hu, others	Marston and Vaughan (1960)
Measles	P—MK	Hsiung et al. (1958)
	C—hu	Rapp et al. (1959)
	C—hu	Underwood (1959)
	P—CE, P—hu amnion	De Maeyer (1960)
	C—hu	Yarosh and Armstrong (1963)
	C—M	Rapp (1964)
Canine distemper	P—CE	Karzon and Bussell (1959), Bussell and Karzon (1962)
Rinderpest	P—calf K	McKercher (1963)
Respiratory syncytial	C—hu	Kisch and Johnson (1963)
RHABDOVIRUSES		
Vesicular stomatitis, Indiana and New Jersey serotypes	P—CE, P—ox EK, P—calf K	Sellers (1955)

TABLE II (Continued)

	Culture	Reference
	P—CE	Cooper (1955, 1957)
	P—CE, P—MK, P—pig K	McClain and Hackett (1958)
	C—hu, C—L, P—CE	Franklin (1958a)
ARBOVIRUSES		
A Subgroup		
Eastern equine encephalomyelitis	Rat sarcoma	Gey and Bang (1951)
Western equine encephalomyelitis	P—CE	A. Brown and Officer (1961), Zebovitz (1965)
	P—CE	Dulbecco (1952), Dulbecco and Vogt (1953a,b, 1954b)
Venezuelan equine encephalo-myelitis	P—CEK	Wright and Sagik (1958)
	P—CE, C—mouse	Hardy and Hearn (1961)
	P—CE	A. Brown and Officer (1961), Zebovitz (1965)
Some group A	Several primary tissues	Henderson and Taylor (1959, 1960), Henderson (1961)
O'Nyong nyong fever	P—CE	Porterfield et al. (1960)
Semliki Forest	P—CE	Porterfield (1960), Cheng (1961)
Semliki Forest, AMM 2354	P—CE, P—duck E	Miles and Austin (1963)
Sindbis	P—CE	Frothingham (1959), Pfefferkorn and Hunter (1963), Burge and Pfefferkorn (1964)
Mayaro, Chikungunya	P—CE	Porterfield (1960)
B Subgroup		
West Nile	P—MK	Bhatt and Work (1957)
Yellow fever, West Nile, Jap. B Wesselbron, Zika, Uganda	P—CE	Porterfield (1959a,c, 1960)
Some group B	Several primary tissues	Henderson and Taylor (1959, 1960), Henderson (1961)
Yellow fever	P—duck, P—CE	Hannoun and Panthier (1960)
St. Louis encephalitis	P—CE	Miles and Austin (1963)
	P—CE	Nagai et al. (1965)
Murray Valley encephalitis	P—CE	Austin (1963)
Dengue—1, —2, yellow fever, Jap. B, St. Louis, Murray Valley encephalitis	C—hu	Schulze and Schlesinger (1963)

Dengue (all 6 types)	P—MK	Georgiades et al. (1965)
Tick-borne encephalitis	P—CE	Mayer (1961, 1962)
Louping ill	P—CE	Porterfield (1960)
Jap. B	P—CE	Inoue et al. (1961), Nagai and Hammon (1964)
	P—hamster K	Rhim (1962), Nagai and Hammon (1964)
	C—pig K	Kato and Inoue (1962)
C Subgroup and Others	Several primary tissues	Henderson and Taylor (1959, 1960), Henderson (1961)
Various	Rat sarcoma	Takemori et al. (1955)
Rift Valley fever	P—CE	Porterfield et al. (1960)
	C—hamster K, C—mouse	Runnels and Brown (1962)
	C—hamster E	Deig and Watkins (1964)
Colorado tick fever	P—CE	Porterfield (1960)
Bunyamwera group	P—duck E, P—CE	Miles and Austin (1963)
PICORNAVIRUSES		
Polio	P—MK	Dulbecco and Vogt (1953a,b, 1954a), Hsiung and Melnick (1955, 1957b), Youngner (1956a), Vogt et al. (1957)
		McClain and Schwerdt (1954), Gifford and Syverton (1957), Mandel (1958)
	C—hu	Fogh and Lund (1955)
	P—hu amnion	Ginsburg and Kazymov (1959)
	P—hu E	Lwoff and Lwoff (1960)
	C—hu	Cooper (1961b)
Coxsackie, Echo (many types)	C—hu	Hsiung and Melnick (1955, 1957a,b), Sommerville (1959, 1960), Heberling and Cheever (1961), Wallis et al. (1962), Choppin and Eggers (1962), Hsiung (1959a,b)
	P—MK	Hsiung and Melnick (1957a,b)
	P—MK, P—huK	McLaren et al. (1960)
	P—MK, P—hu amnion	

TABLE II (*Continued*)

Coe	C—HeLa	Pereira and Periera (1959)
Porcine entero	P—pig K	Singh et al. (1959), Singh and Bohl (1960)
Talfan and Teschen diseases	P—pig K	F. Brown and Stewart (1960)
Bovine entero	P—MK, P—bovine K	Moscovici et al. (1961)
Rhino (2 strains)	P—hu EK	Parsons and Tyrrell (1961)
(3 strains)	P—MK, P—hu E lung	Porterfield (1962)
(several)	C—hu diploid	Kisch et al. (1964), Behbehani and Lee (1964)
ME	C—mouse	Franklin et al. (1959)
Encephalomyocarditis	C—mouse ascites tumors	Sanders (1957), Martin et al. (1961)
Mengo	C—mouse	Ellem and Colter (1960)
Foot and mouth disease group	P—, S—pig K	Sellers (1955, 1957), Sellers and Stewart (1959), Sellers et al. (1959)
		Bachrach et al. (1957)
	P—calf K	Khera and Maurin (1958)
	P—pig K	Saito, quoted by Sellers et al. (1959)
	P—mouse E	Sellers (1955)
Vesicular exanthema of swine	P—pig K	McClain et al. (1958)
	C—pig K	
REOVIRUSES		
Reovirus 1 (ECHO 10)	P—MK	Rhim and Melnick (1961), Wallis et al. (1962)
Reovirus 3	C—mouse	Franklin (1961), Gomatos et al. (1962)
UNCLASSIFIED VIRUSES		
African horse sickness	C—baby hamster K	Mirchamsy and Taslimi (1963, 1966)
	C—MK	Ozawa and Hazrati (1964)
Avian leucosis, particularly	P—CE	Manaker and Groupé (1956)
Rous sarcoma	S—CE	Temin and Rubin (1958), Rubin (1960a,b) Dougherty and Simons (1962), Adams and Groupé (1963), Siminoff and Reed (1963),
Infectious bronchitis of fowls	P—CEK	Wright and Sagik (1958)
Lymphocytic choriomeningitis	P—CE	Benson and Hotchin (1960)

Mouse hepatitis—3	P—mouse E	Haff (1962)
	P—mouse macrophage	Mallucci (1965)
Mouse hepatitis (four strains)	C—mouse liver (NCTC 1469)	Hartley and Rowe (1963)
Rubella	P—MK	Rozee et al. (1963), Marcus and Carver (1965)
	C—RK	Taylor-Robinson et al. (1964)

[a] P—, S—: primary, secondary; C—: continuous cell lines; M, R, C, hu: monkey, rabbit, chick, human; K: kidney; E: embryo.

TABLE III

SOME SOURCES OF DIFFICULTY

Symptom	Possible cause	Suggested test or remedy
(1) Plaques very small or absent; cells stained poorly or not at all	Toxic glassware	Change detergent or clean glassware with chromic acid; compare with unused batch of glassware; if using monolayer method, compare with cell-suspension method. Compare with plastic container
	Confluent lysis	Check that water is not condensing on agar surface; check that virus is sufficiently diluted and pipet changed between dilutions
	Microbial contamination	Toxic contamination by bacteria or fungi is generally macroscopically visible after staining with vital dyes. Check for mycoplasma (Gori and Lee, 1964; Hayflick, 1965); compare with reserve cell stock held in liquid nitrogen
	Incubator overheating (a common fault if a large load of cold plates is added)	Keep a clinical thermometer in the incubator
	Poor pH control	Check color of indicator and CO_2 flow during incubation
	Neutral red toxic	Keep plates in darkness; compare with another stain (e.g., tetrazolium, trypan blue)
	Medium faulty or serum contains anticellular substances	Dilute the 2-fold medium stock to normal strength with distilled water, add serum and test it for toxicity on an established cell monolayer; compare with other batches of medium or serum
	Agar toxic	Freeze and thaw a batch of gelled nutrient agar and test the exuded fluid for toxicity on an established monolayer
	Cells in poor condition at time of use; initial cell concentration miscounted	Check prior handling of cells

(2) As (1), but surface of agar "crinkly"	Plates drying out in incubator	Check water tray; check incubator for gross air leaks
(3) Plaques absent, or if present very small and plating efficiency low, but cells stained well	Incubation period too short, or random delay too large	Compare with another cell source; increase incubation period and add nutrient agar feeder layer; check prior handling of cells
	Genetic character of virus altered	Compare with a reserve stock of virus
	Mycoplasma contamination	See above
	Virus-neutralizing substances in serum, agar, or medium	Compare with other batches of serum or medium; add DEAE-dextran
	Genetic character of cell source altered	Compare with a cell stock kept in reserve in liquid nitrogen (continuous line), or with a primary tissue from another source; check for overgrowth of a resistant cell type (possible in primary as well as continuous cell cultures)
	Cell concentration too high initially	Check prior handling of cells
(4) Cells well stained, no plaques at high dilution but confluent lysis at lower dilutions	Virus cytopathic in first cycle, but insufficient progeny available to make a plaque	Compare higher and lower incubation temperatures; check for viral inhibitors in medium, serum, or agar; check pH control
(5) Plaques large but faint or only visible under oblique light; cell staining poor or absent	Initial cell concentration too low to maintain viability; microbial contamination; plates drying out; incubator overheating; poor pH control; medium, agar, or stain faulty; cell state poor	See above; apply procedures to extend viability of cells.
(3) Plaques large and cells well stained, but statistical variation high, plaque distribution non-Poissonian	Monolayers formed, virus adsorbed or agar poured in a nonlevel position; Petri plate not planar	Use a leveled glass plate on bench and in incubator; check quality of Petri plates.
	Mycoplasma contamination	See above

TABLE III (*Continued*)

Symptom	Possible cause	Suggested test or remedy
	If using monolayers, trouble may lie in adsorption: insufficient or variable time for adsorption, virus trapped in meniscus, pH variation on plate, plates drying out, aggregation or elution of virus	Check adsorption technique; compare with agar cell-suspension method
	Loss of virus during dilution due to heat inactivation, adsorption on glassware, or trapping in froth	Check dilution technique
	Plates warming unevenly in incubator	Incubate plates as a single layer on trays
	If inverted, some plates are sealed with condensed moisture, giving a low pH; if in bottles, some stoppers are leaking, giving a high pH	Cut a notch in rim of plates or reduce humidity in incubator; check stoppers
(7) Plaque count not proportional to dose	Pipets not changed between dilutions	Check dilution technique
	Plaques have multiple origins at high doses	Reduce plaque size by shorter incubation; use larger plates
	Secondary plaques are formed	Check immobilization method
	Causes of nonlinearity at low doses are not known; interfering viruses or substances, or minimal cellular damage, are possibilities	Compare with another cell source
(8) Lack of reproducibility from day to day	Variations in cell state; variations in batches of serum; errors in dilution technique; inactivation of medium on storage	See above

REFERENCES

Adams, E. V., and Groupé, V. (1963). *Virology* **21,** 271.

Alexander, H. E., Koch, G., Mountain, I. M., Sprunt, K., and Van Damme, O. (1958a). *Virology* **5,** 172.

Alexander, H. E., Koch, G., Mountain, I. M., and Van Damme, O. (1958b). *J. Exptl. Med.* **108,** 493.

Amos, H. (1961). *Biochem. Biophys. Res. Commun.* **5,** 1.

Austin, F. J. (1963). *Australian J. Exptl. Biol. Med. Sci.* **41,** 205.

Bachrach, H. L., Callis, J. J., Hess, W. R., and Patty, R. E. (1957). *Virology* **4,** 224.

Bachrach, H. L., Callis, J. J., Hess, W. R., Patty, R. E., De Boer, C. J., and Hamblet, F. E. (1962). *Am. J. Vet. Res.* **94,** 608.

Baron, S., Porterfield, J. S., and Isaacs, A. (1961). *Virology* **14,** 444.

Bedson, H. S., and Dumbell, K. R. (1964a). *J. Hyg.* **62,** 141.

Bedson, H. S., and Dumbell, K. R. (1964b). *J. Hyg.* **62,** 147.

Behbehani, A. M., and Lee, L. H. (1964). *J. Bacteriol.* **88,** 1608.

Bellett, A. J. D. (1960). *Virology* **10,** 285.

Bengelsdorff, H. J. (1963). *Zentr. Bakteriol., Parasitenk., Abt. I. Orig.* **190,** 139.

Benson, L. M., and Hotchin, J. E. (1960). *Proc. Soc. Exptl. Biol. Med.* **103,** 623.

Berg, G., Harris, E. K., Chang, S. L., and Busch, K. A. (1963). *J. Bacteriol.* **85,** 691.

Bhatt, P. N., and Work, T. H. (1957). *Proc. Soc. Exptl. Biol. Med.* **96,** 213.

Bishop, L. W. J., Smith, M. K., and Beale, A. J. (1960). *Virology* **10,** 280.

Black, F. L., and Melnick, J. L. (1954). *Federation Proc.* **13,** 487.

Black, F. L., and Melnick, J. L. (1955). *J. Immunol.* **74,** 236.

Bodian, D. (1956). *Virology* **2,** 575.

Bonifas, F. H., and Mullally, D. I. (1960). *Bacteriol. Proc.* (*Soc. Am. Bacteriologists*) p. 93.

Bonifas, V., and Schlesinger, R. W. (1959). *Federation Proc.* **18,** 560.

Breitenfeld, P. M., and Schäfer, W. (1957). *Virology* **4,** 328.

Brown, A. (1963). *Virology* **21,** 362.

Brown, A., and Officer, J. E. (1961). *Proc. Soc. Exptl. Biol. Med.* **107,** 790.

Brown, F., and Stewart, D. L. (1960). *Nature* **187,** 714.

Brown, L. N., and Packer, R. A. (1964). *Am. J. Vet. Res.* **25,** 487.

Burge, B. W., and Pfefferkorn, E. R. (1964). *Virology* **24,** 126.

Burt, A. M., and Cooper, P. D. (1961). *J. Immunol.* **86,** 646.

Bussell, R. H., and Karzon, D. T. (1962). *Virology* **18,** 589.

Buthala, D. A. (1960). *Virology* **10,** 382.

Campbell, J. B., and Colter, J. S. (1965). *Virology* **25,** 608.

Cheng, P. Y. (1961). *Virology* **14,** 124.

Choppin, P. W. (1962). *Virology* **18,** 332.

Choppin, P. W., and Eggers, H. J. (1962). *Virology* **18,** 470.

Colón, J. I., and Idoine, J. B. (1964). *J. Infect. Diseases* **114,** 61.

Cooper, P. D. (1954). Unpublished data.

Cooper, P. D. (1955). *Virology* **1,** 397.

Cooper, P. D. (1957). *J. Gen. Microbiol.* **17,** 327.

Cooper, P. D. (1959). *Virology* **7,** 469.

Cooper, P. D. (1961a). *Advan. Virus Res.* **8,** 319.

Cooper, P. D. (1961b). *Virology* **13,** 153.

Cooper, P. D. (1964). *Virology* **22,** 186.

Cooper, P. D. (1965). *Virology* **25,** 431.

Crandell, R. A., Ganaway, J. R., Niemann, W. H., and Maurer, F. D. (1960). *Am. J. Vet. Res.* **21,** 504.

Darnell, J. E., Jr., and Eagle, H. (1958). *Virology* **6,** 556.

Deibel, R. (1959). *Virology* **8,** 262.

Deig, E. F., and Watkins, H. M. S. (1964). *J. Bacteriol.* **88,** 42.

De Maeyer, E. (1960). *Virology* **11,** 634.

De Maeyer, E., and Schonne, E. (1964). *Virology* **24,** 13.

De Somer, P., and Prinzie, A. (1957). *Virology* **4,** 387.

Diamond, L. (1964). *Virology* **23,** 73.

Dougherty, R. M., and Simons, P. J. (1962). *Virology* **18,** 559.

Drake, J. W. (1958). *Virology* **6,** 244.

Dubes, G. R., and Klingler, E. A., Jr. (1961). *Science* **133,** 99.

Dubes, G. R., Faas, F. H., Kelly, D. G., Chapin, M., Lamb, R. D., and Lucas, T. A. (1964). *J. Infect. Diseases* **114,** 346.

Dulbecco, R. (1952). *Proc. Natl. Acad. Sci. U.S.* **38,** 747.

Dulbecco, R., and Freeman, G. (1959). *Virology* **8,** 396.

Dulbecco, R., and Vogt, M. (1953a). "Symposium on Interactions of Cells and Viruses." Ist. Super. di Sanita, Rome.

Dulbecco, R., and Vogt, M. (1953b). *Cold Spring Harbor Symp. Quant. Biol.* **18,** 273.

Dulbecco, R., and Vogt, M. (1954a). *J. Exptl. Med.* **99,** 167.

Dulbecco, R., and Vogt, M. (1954b). *J. Exptl. Med.* **99,** 183.

Eagle, H. (1959). *Science* **130,** 432.

Ellem, K. A. O., and Colter, J. S. (1960). *Virology* **11,** 434.

Farnham, A. E. (1958). *Virology* **6,** 317.

Farrell, L. N., and Reid, D. B. W. (1959). *Can. J. Public Health* **50,** 20.

Fenner, F., and Sambrook, J. F. (1966). *Virology* **28,** 600.

Field, A. K., and Fong, J. (1964). *J. Bacteriol.* **87,** 1238.

Fogh, J., and Lund, R. O. (1955). *Proc. Soc. Exptl. Biol. Med.* **90,** 80.

Fraenkel-Conrat, H., Singer, B., and Tsugita, A. (1961) *Virology* **14,** 54.

Franklin, R. M. (1958a). *Virology* **5,** 408.

Franklin, R. M. (1958b). *Virology* **6,** 81.

Franklin, R. M. (1961). *Proc. Soc. Exptl. Biol. Med.* **107,** 651.

Franklin, R. M., Rubin, H., and Davis, C. A. (1957). *Virology* **3,** 96.

Franklin, R. M., Wecker, E., and Henry, C. (1959). *Virology* **7,** 220.

Frothingham, T. E. (1959). *Proc. Soc. Exptl. Biol. Med.* **100,** 505.

Frothingham, T. E. (1963). *Virology* **19,** 583.

Frothingham, T. E., and Granoff, A. (1961). *Virology* **15,** 213.

Funk, H. B., and Krulwich, T. A. (1964). *J. Bacteriol.* **88,** 1200.

Furness, G., and Youngner, J. S. (1959). *Virology* **9,** 386.

Galasso, G. J., and Sharp, D. G. (1962). *J. Immunol.* **88,** 339.

Georgiades, J., Stim, T. B., McCollum, R. W., and Henderson, J. R. (1965). *Proc. Soc. Exptl. Biol. Med.* **118,** 385.

Gey, G. O., and Bang, F. B. (1951). *Trans. N.Y. Acad. Sci.* [2] **14,** 15.

Gifford, G. E., and Syverton, J. T. (1957). *Virology* **4,** 216.

Gifford, G. E., Toy, S. T., and Lindenmann, J. (1963). *Virology* **19,** 294.

Ginsburg, N. N., and Kazymov, K. T. (1959). *Probl. Virol.* (USSR) (*English Transl.*) **4,** No. 6, 115.

Gomatos, P. J., Tamm, I., Dales, S., and Franklin, R. M. (1962). *Virology* **17,** 441.

Gori, G. B., and Lee, D. Y. (1964). *Proc. Soc. Exptl. Biol. Med.* **117,** 918.

Grachev, V. P. (1963). *Acta Virol.* (*Prague*) **7,** 447.

Granoff, A. (1955). *Virology* **1**, 252.
Grossberg, S. E. (1964). *Science* **144**, 1246.
Haff, R. F. (1962). *Virology* **18**, 507.
Hanafusa, T., Hanafusa, H., and Kamahora, J. (1959). *Biken's J.* **2**, 77.
Hannoun, C., and Panthier, R. (1960). *Bull. Soc. Pathol. Exotique* **53**, 424.
Hardy, F. M., and Hearn, H. J. (1961). *Am. J. Hyg.* **73**, 258.
Hartley, J. W., and Rowe, W. P. (1963). *Proc. Soc. Exptl. Biol. Med.* **113**, 403.
Hayflick, L. (1965). *Texas Rept. Biol. Med.* **23**, Suppl. 1, 285.
Hayflick, L., Jacobs, P., and Perkins, F. (1964). *Nature* **204**, 146.
Heberling, R. L., and Cheever, F. S. (1961). *Bacteriol. Proc.*, p. 156.
Hellwig, G., and Thomssen, R. (1962). *Z. Naturforsch.* **17b**, 29.
Henderson, J. R. (1961). *Yale J. Biol. Med.* **33**, 350.
Henderson, J. R., and Taylor, R. M. (1959). *Proc. Soc. Exptl. Biol. Med.* **101**, 257.
Henderson, J. R., and Taylor, R. M. (1960). *J. Immunol.* **84**, 590.
Henson, D., and Pinkerton, H. (1963). *Proc. Soc. Exptl. Biol. Med.* **114**, 130.
Hinze, H. C., and Walker, D. L. (1961). *J. Bacteriol.* **82**, 498.
Hirst, G. K. (1959). *Symp. Soc. Gen. Microbiol.* **9**, 82.
Hirst, G. K. (1962). *Cold Spring Harbor Symp. Quant. Biol.* **27**, 303.
Hotchin, J. E. (1955). *Nature* **175**, 352.
Hotchin, J. E., Deibel, R., and Benson, L. M. (1960). *Virology* **10**, 275.
Hsiung, G. D. (1959a). *Proc. Soc. Exptl. Biol. Med.* **102**, 612.
Hsiung, G. D. (1959b). *Virology* **9**, 717.
Hsiung, G. D., and Melnick, J. L. (1955). *Virology* **1**, 533.
Hsiung, G. D., and Melnick, J. L. (1957a). *J. Immunol.* **78**, 128.
Hsiung, G. D., and Melnick, J. L. (1957b). *J. Immunol.* **78**, 137.
Hsiung, G. D., Mannini, A., and Melnick, J. L. (1958). *Proc. Soc. Exptl. Biol. Med.* **98**, 68.
Inoue, Y. K., Iwasaki, T., and Kato, H. (1961). *J. Immunol.* **87**, 337.
Kaplan, A. S. (1957). *Virology* **4**, 435.
Kaplan, A. S., and Vatter, A. E. (1959). *Virology* **7**, 394.
Karzon, D. T., and Bussell, R. H. (1959). *Science* **130**, 1708.
Kasza, L., Bohl, E. H., and Jones, D. O. (1960). *Am. J. Vet. Res.* **21**, 269.
Kato, H., and Inoue, Y. K. (1962). *Virology* **18**, 500.
Khera, K. S., and Maurin, J. (1958). *Ann. Inst. Pasteur* **95**, 557.
Kirn, A., and Braunwald, J. (1963). *Ann. Inst. Pasteur* **104**, 49.
Kisch, A. L., and Johnson, K. M. (1963). *Proc. Soc. Exptl. Biol. Med.* **112**, 583.
Kisch, A. L., Webb, P. A., and Johnson, K. M. (1964). *Am. J. Hyg.* **79**, 125.
Kjellén, L. (1961). *Virology* **14**, 234.
Koch, A. L. (1964). *J. Theoret. Biol.* **6**, 413.
Koch, G. (1960). *Virology* **12**, 601.
Koch, G., Koenig, S., and Alexander, H. E. (1960). *Virology* **10**, 329.
Ledinko, N. (1955). *Nature* **175**, 999.
Ledinko, N., and Hirst, G. K. (1961). *Virology* **14**, 207.
Lehmann-Grube, F. (1963). *Virology* **21**, 520.
Levine, S., and Sagik, B. P. (1956). *Virology* **2**, 57.
Levine, S., and Sharpless, G. R. (1959). *Virology* **8**, 265.
Levine, S., Cabasso, V. J., Avampato, J. M., and Stebbins, M. R. (1959). *Proc. Soc. Exptl. Biol. Med.* **100**, 600.
Liebhaber, H., and Takemoto, K. K. (1963). *Virology* **20**, 559.
Lindenmann, J., and Gifford, G. E. (1963a). *Virology* **19**, 283.
Lindenmann, J., and Gifford, G. E. (1963b). *Virology* **19**, 302.

Lorenz, R. J. (1961). *Arch. Ges. Virusforsch.* **10**, 551.

Lorenz, R. J. (1962). *Arch. Ges. Virusforsch.* **12**, 108.

Lwoff, A., and Lwoff, M. (1960). *Ann. Inst. Pasteur* **98**, 173.

McClain, M. E. (1965). *Australian J. Exptl. Biol. Med. Sci.* **43**, 31.

McClain, M. E., and Hackett, A. J. (1958). *J. Immunol.* **80**, 356.

McClain, M. E., and Schwerdt, C. E. (1954). *Federation Proc.* **13**, 505.

McClain, M. E., Hackett, A. J., and Madin, S. H. (1958). *Science* **127**, 1391.

McCollum, W. H., Doll, E. R., Wilson, J. C., and Johnson, C. B. (1962). *Cornell Vet.* **52**, 534.

McConnell, S. J., Spertzel, R. O., Huxsoll, D. L., Elliott, L. H., and Yager, R. H. (1964). *J. Bacteriol.* **87**, 238.

McKercher, P. D. (1963). *Can. J. Comp. Med. Vet. Sci.* **23**, 71.

McLaren, L. C., Holland, J. J., and Syverton, J. T. (1960). *J. Exptl. Med.* **112**, 581.

Macpherson, I. A. (1960). *Nature* **188**, 1213.

Macpherson, I., and Montagnier, L. (1964). *Virology* **23**, 291.

Macpherson, I., and Stoker, M. (1962). *Virology* **16**, 147.

Mai, K., and Bonitz, (1963). *Nature* **197**, 166.

Mallucci, L. (1965). *Virology* **25**, 30.

Manaker, R. A., and Groupé, V. (1956). *Virology* **2**, 838.

Mandel, B. (1958). *Virology* **6**, 424.

Marcus, P. I. (1959). *Virology* **9**, 546.

Marcus, P. I., and Carver, D. H. (1965). *Science* **149**, 983.

Marston, R. Q., and Vaughan, E. R. (1960). *Proc. Soc. Exptl. Biol. Med.* **104**, 56.

Martin, E. M., Malec, J., Sved, S., and Work, T. S. (1961). *Biochem. J.* **80**, 585.

Mayer, V. (1961). *Acta Virol. (Prague)* **5**, 131.

Mayer, V. (1962). *Acta Virol. (Prague)* **6**, 309.

Mayr, A., and Kalcher, K. (1961). *Arch. Ges. Virusforsch.* **11**, 307.

Melnick, J. L. (1956). *In* "Diagnostic Procedures for Virus and Rickettsial Disease," p. 143. Am. Public Health Assoc., New York. 2nd Ed.

Melnick, J. L., Rappaport, C., Banker, D. D., and Bhatt, P. N. (1955). *Proc. Soc. Exptl. Biol. Med.* **88**, 676.

Mika, L. A., and Pirsch, J. B. (1960). *J. Bacteriol.* **80**, 861.

Miles, J. A. R., and Austin, F. J. (1963). *Australian J. Exptl. Biol. Med. Sci.* **41**, 199.

Mirchamsy, H., and Taslimi, H. (1963). *Nature* **198**, 704.

Mirchamsy, H., and Taslimi, H. (1966). *Can. J. Comp. Med.* **30**, 47.

Moore, M. S., and Walker, D. L. (1962). *Proc. Soc. Exptl. Biol. Med.* **111**, 493.

Morgan, J. F., Morton, H. J., and Parker, R. C. (1950). *Proc. Soc. Exptl. Biol. Med* **73**, 1.

Moscovici, C., La Placa, M., Maisel, J., and Kempe, C. H. (1961). *Am. J. Vet. Res.* **22**, 852.

Moscovici, C., Cohen, E. P., Sanders, J., and De Long, S. S. (1963). *Science* **141**, 915.

Mosley, J. W., and Enders, J. F. (1961). *Proc. Soc. Exptl. Biol. Med.* **108**, 406.

Nagai, K., and Hammon, W. McD. (1964). *Proc. Soc. Exptl. Biol. Med.* **117**, 154.

Nagai, K., Sather, G., and Hammon, W. McD. (1965). *Proc. Soc. Exptl. Biol. Med.* **118**, 1065.

Nagington, J., and Whittle, C. H. (1961). *Brit. Med. J.* **II**, 1324.

Nishmi, M., and Keller, R. (1961). *Bacteriol. Proc.*, p. 152.

Noyes, W. F. (1953). *Proc. Soc. Exptl. Biol. Med.* **83**, 426.

Oda, M. (1964). *Virology* **23**, 432.

Osterhout, S., and Tamm, I. (1959). *J. Immunol.* **83**, 442.

Ozawa, Y., and Hazrati, A. (1964). *Am. J. Vet. Res.* **25**, 505.
Padgett, B. L., Moore, M. S., and Walker, D. L. (1962). *Virology* **17**, 462.
Pagano, J. S., and Vaheri, A. (1965). *Arch. Ges. Virusforsch.* **17**, 456.
Parsons, R., and Tyrrell, D. A. J. (1961). *Nature* **189**, 640.
Paul, J. (1965). "Cell and Tissue Culture," 3rd ed. Livingstone, Edinburgh and London.
Pereira, M. S., and Pereira, H. G. (1959). *Lancet* **II**, 539.
Perkins, W. J., and Hotchin, J. E. (1955). *Lab. Practice* **4**, 297.
Pfefferkorn, E. R., and Hunter, H. S. (1963). *Virology* **20**, 433.
Plummer, G., and Benyesh-Melnick, M. (1964). *Proc. Soc. Exptl. Biol. Med.* **117**, 145.
Polson, A. (1956). *Biochim. Biophys. Acta* **19**, 53.
Porterfield, J. S. (1959a). *Trans. Roy. Soc. Trop. Med. Hyg.* **53**, 458.
Porterfield, J. S. (1959b). *Lancet* **II**, 326.
Porterfield, J. S. (1959c). *Nature* **183**, 1069.
Porterfield, J. S. (1960). *Bull. World Health Organ.* **22**, 373.
Porterfield, J. S. (1962). *Nature* **194**, 1044.
Porterfield, J. S., and Allison, A. C.'(1960). *Virology* **10**, 233.
Porterfield, J. S., Williams, M. C., and Woodall, J. P. (1960). *Nature* **188**, 252.
Postlethwaite, R. (1960). *Virology* **10**, 466.
Randall, C. C., and Lawson, L. A. (1962). *Proc. Soc. Exptl. Biol. Med.* **110**, 487.
Rapp, F. (1963). *J. Bacteriol.* **86**, 985.
Rapp, F. (1964a). *J. Bacteriol.* **88**, 1448.
Rapp, F. (1964b). *J. Immunol.* **93**, 643.
Rapp, F., and Benyesh-Melnick, M. (1963). *Science* **141**, 433.
Rapp, F., and Vanderslice, D. (1964). *Virology* **22**, 321.
Rapp, F., Seligman, S. J., Jaross, L. B., and Gordon, I. (1959). *Proc. Soc. Exptl. Biol. Med.* **101**, 289.
Rappaport, C. (1956a). *Proc. Soc. Exptl. Biol. Med.* **91**, 464.
Rappaport, C. (1956b). *Bull. World Health Organ.* **14**, 147.
Rhim, J. S. (1962). *Proc. Soc. Exptl. Biol. Med.* **109**, 887.
Rhim, J. S., and Melnick, J. L. (1961). *Virology* **15**, 80.
Riggs, J. L., and Lennett, E. H. (1965). *Science* **147**, 408.
Roizman, B., and Aurelian, L. (1965). *J. Mol. Biol.* **11**, 528.
Rouhandeh, H., and Werder, A. A. (1961). *Bacteriol. Proc.*, p. 149.
Rouhandeh, H., and Werder, A. A. (1963). *Proc. Soc. Exptl. Biol. Med.* **112**, 1030.
Rouse, H. C., Bonifas, V. H., and Schlesinger, R. W. (1963). *Virology* **20**, 357.
Rozee, K. R., Grivan, K. F., Doane, F. W., and Rhodes, A. J. (1963). *Can. Med. Assoc. J.* **89**, 314.
Rubin, H. (1957). *Virology* **4**, 533.
Rubin, H. (1960a). *Virology* **10**, 29.
Rubin, H. (1960b). *Proc. Natl. Acad. Sci. U.S.* **46**, 1105.
Runnels, J. L., and Brown, A. (1962). *Bacteriol. Proc.*, p. 159.
Russell, W. C. (1962). *Nature* **195**, 1028.
Sambrook, J. F., Padgett, B. L., and Tomkins, J. K. N. (1966). *Virology* **28**, 592.
Sanders, F. K. (1957). *Proc. Roy. Soc. Med.* **50**, 911.
Schmidt, N. J. (1964). In "Diagnostic Procedures for Viral and Rickettsial Diseases," p. 78, 3rd ed. (E. D. Lennette and N. J. Schmidt, eds.). Am. Public Health Assoc., New York.
Schulze, I. T., and Schlesinger, R. W. (1963). *Virology* **19**, 40.
Schwerdt, P. R., and Schwerdt, C. E. (1962). *Proc. Soc. Exptl. Biol. Med.* **109**, 717.

Sellers, R. F. (1955). *Nature* **176**, 547.

Sellers, R. F. (1957). *Proc. Roy. Soc. Med.* **50**, 915.

Sellers, R. F., and Stewart, D. L. (1959). *Arch. Ges. Virusforsch.* **9**, 594.

Sellers, R. F., Burt, L. M., Cumming, A., and Stewart, D. L. (1959). *Arch. Ges. Virusforsch.* **9**, 637.

Sheinin, R. (1961). *Virology* **15**, 85.

Shigita, S. (1964). *Tohoku J. Exptl. Med.* **83**, 114.

Shimizu, T., Ishizaki, R., and Matumoto, M. (1960). *Japan. J. Vet. Sci.* **22**, 538.

Shimizu, T., Ishizaki, R., and Matumoto, M. (1963). *Japan. J. Exptl. Med.* **33**, 85.

Siminoff, P., and Reed, F. C. (1963). *Virology* **21**, 284.

Simpson, R. W., and Hirst, G. K. (1961). *Virology* **15**, 436.

Singh, K. V. (1962). *Cornell Vet.* **52**, 237.

Singh, K. V., and Bohl, E. H. (1960). *Am. J. Vet. Res.* **21**, 1114.

Singh, K. V., Bohl, E. H., and Birkeland, J. M. (1959). *Am. J. Vet. Res.* **20**, 568.

Smull, C. E., Mallette, M. F., and Ludwig, E. H. (1961). *Biochem. Biophys. Res. Commun.* **5**, 247.

Sommerville, R. G. (1959). *Virology* **9**, 701.

Sommerville, R. G. (1960). *Brit. J. Exptl. Pathol.* **41**, 229.

Spendlove, R. S., and Lennette, E. H. (1962). *J. Immunol.* **89**, 106.

Spendlove, R. S., and Taylor, F. L. (1963). *Am. J. Clin. Pathol.* **40**, 34.

Sprunt, K., Koenig, S., and Alexander, H. E. (1961). *Virology* **13**, 135.

Stevens, J. G., and Groman, N. B. (1963). *Am. J. Vet. Res.* **24**, 1158.

Stinebaugh, S., and Melnick, J. L. (1962). *Virology* **16**, 348.

Stoker, M. G. P. (1959). *Virology* **8**, 250.

Stoker, M. G. P., and Abel, P. (1962). *Cold Spring Harbor Symp. Quant. Biol.* **27**, 375.

Stoker, M. G. P., and Macpherson, I. A. (1961). *Virology* **14**, 359.

Sugiura, A., and Kilbourne, E. D. (1965). *Virology* **26**, 478.

Takemori, N., Nakano, M., and Hemmi, M. (1955). *Virology* **1**, 250.

Takemoto, K. K., and Fabisch, P. (1963). *Proc. Soc. Exptl. Biol. Med.* **114**, 811.

Takemoto, K. K., and Liebhaber, H. (1962). *Virology* **17**, 499.

Tamm, I., and Eggers, H. J. (1963). *Science* **142**, 24.

Taniguchi, S., and Yoshino, K. (1964). *Arch. Ges. Virusforsch.* **14**, 537.

Taylor, J., and Graham, A. F. (1961). *Virology* **13**, 427.

Taylor-Robinson, C. H., McCarthy, K., Grylls, S. G., and O'Ryan, E. M. (1964). *Lancet* **I**, 1364.

Temin, H. M. (1961). *Virology* **13**, 158.

Temin, H. M., and Rubin, H. (1958). *Virology* **6**, 669.

Thiry, L. (1963). *Virology* **19**, 225.

Timbury, M. C. (1962). *Brit. J. Exptl. Pathol.* **43**, 506.

Tytell, A. A., and Neuman, R. E. (1963). *Proc. Soc. Exptl. Biol. Med.* **113**, 343.

Tytell, A. A., Torop, H. A., and McCarthy, F. J. (1961). *Proc. Soc. Exptl. Biol. Med.* **108**, 723.

Tytell, A. A. Torop, H. A., and McCarthy, F. J. (1962). *Proc. Soc. Exptl. Biol. Med.* **109**, 916.

Umbreit, W. W., Burris, R. H., and Stauffer, J. F. (1964). "Manometric Techniques," 4th ed. Burgess, Minneapolis, Minnesota.

Underwood, G. E. (1959). *J. Immunol.* **83**, 198.

Verna, J. E., and Eylar, O. R. (1962). *Virology* **18**, 266.

Vogt, M., Dulbecco, R., and Wenner, H. A. (1957). *Virology* **4**, 141.

Wallis, C., Lewis, R. T., and Melnick, J. L. (1961). *Texas Rep. Biol. Med.* **19**, 194.

Wallis, C., Melnick, J. L., and Bianchi, M. (1962). *Texas Rept. Biol. Med.* **20,** 693.

Wassermann, F. E. (1962). *Virology* **17,** 335.

Waterson, A. P. (1958a). *Arch. Ges. Virusforsch.* **8,** 113.

Waterson, A. P. (1958b). *Arch Ges. Virusforsch.* **8,** 592.

Wecker, E., and Schäfer, W. (1957). *Z. Naturforsch.* **12b,** 415.

Weil, R. (1961). *Virology* **14,** 46.

Winocour, E., and Sachs, L. (1959). *Virology* **8,** 397.

Winocour, E., and Sachs, L. (1960). *Virology* **11,** 699.

Woodroofe, G. M., and Fenner, F. (1965). *Australian J. Exptl. Biol. Med. Sci.* **43,** 123.

Wright, B. S., and Sagik, P. S. (1958). *Virology* **5,** 573.

Yarosh, W., and Armstrong, R. E. (1963). *Can J. Microbiol.* **9,** 417.

Youngner, J. S. (1954). *Proc. Soc. Exptl. Biol. Med.* **85,** 202.

Youngner, J. S. (1956a). *J. Immunol.* **76,** 50.

Youngner, J. S. (1956b). *J. Immunol.* **76,** 288.

Závada, J. (1963). *Acta Virol. (Prague)* **7,** 279.

Zebovitz, E. (1965). *J. Infect. Diseases* **115,** 77.

Zimmermann, T., and Schäfer, W. (1959). *Z. Naturforsch.* **14b,** 213.

7 Transformation Assays

M. G. P. Stoker and I. A. Macpherson

I. Introduction

The biological assays for many viruses are based on their ability to cause cell death with subsequent degeneration and a visible cytopathic effect in tissue culture. The principal and important feature of tumor viruses, however, is to infect cells nonlethally, with consequent hereditary changes in some normal processes of cell regulation. All tumor viruses do this in susceptible hosts, but a number will also induce a permanent hereditary change or transformation in cultured cells, and this transformation is thought to be the same as the primary change caused by the virus *in vivo*. The word transformation is also used in a much wider sense by cell biologists to cover any permanent hereditary change in a cell (see below). In this chapter, however, we shall generally restrict it to viral-induced neoplastic change occurring either *in vivo* or *in vitro*. Up to the present such viral-induced changes observed in animal cells have all been caused by tumor viruses, but it is now known that several viruses, mostly myxoviruses not known to induce tumors, are capable of causing continued nonlethal infection of cells in culture. Such cells may well be found to show hereditary

313

changes in behavior which should be included in the term "transformation," although not necessarily of the type associated with neoplasia.

Transformation by tumor viruses generally results in loss of the normal processes of contact inhibition of growth and movement, so that transformed cells grow into multilayers of irregularly arranged overlapping cells. Another characteristic is loss of dependence on solid surfaces for growth, so that transformed cells grow in suspension in fluids or in gels. They also acquire the ability to grow and form progressive tumors upon transplantation into suitable animals.

In systems where detailed analysis has been possible it has been shown that the change is due to direct interaction of viral nucleic acid with the cell, and the specificity of the effect is demonstrated by the fact that transformed cells permanently acquire virus-specific antigens. Cells transformed by many tumor viruses containing ribonucleic acid (RNA) also continue to release infectious virus, but infectious virus is not generally produced by cells transformed by deoxyribonucleic acid (DNA) viruses.

There seems little doubt that transformation observed *in vitro* represents a critical step in oncogenesis by the virus in animals. Assay of the transforming activity of a tumor virus in tissue culture is, therefore, a valid measurement of an important biological action of the virus. It removes many of the variables affecting the development of tumors in an animal and gives greater precision, while it considerably shortens the time needed for assay. At the same time it should be remembered that the *in vitro* transforming activity of a virus does not measure all aspects of the tumor-producing activity of the virus. For example, antigenic changes in a cell may considerably affect its fate in animals but not in tissue culture. It should also be remembered that suitable conditions for *in vitro* transformation have not yet been found for many tumor viruses, and these must still be assayed by tumor production.

Measurement of transforming or tumor-inducing activity is not the only way of assaying tumor viruses. Several of the DNA-containing tumor viruses, such as polyoma, SV40, and adenoviruses, will grow vegetatively in suitable cells with consequent cytopathic effect, suitable for assay by plaque formation, or end-point titration. An important group of chicken tumor viruses causes no obvious change in cell morphology but instead are assayed *in vitro* for their ability to induce interference with transformation by Rous sarcoma virus or their ability to induce viral group-specific antigen production. Many tumor viruses cause hemagglutination, and this is a convenient method for assay of physical as opposed to infectious particles. Clearly, however, assay of transforming activity is an important technique for the investigation of any virus with tumor-producing potentialities.

Studies on virus transformation may be complicated by "spontaneous" transformation. It is now well established that mammalian cells in culture eventually enter a critical phase of growth after a period of serial subcultivation. This critical phase is characterized by the appearance of large degenerate cells with long generation times. Such cultures eventually degenerate completely or else give rise to foci of rapidly growing cells. These repopulate the culture and are apparently capable of being passed indefinitely. The cells are almost invariably aneuploid and acquire certain distinctive characteristics including morphological changes and the ability to induce tumors in the homologous animal.

The frequency with which cells in culture give rise to spontaneously transformed lines seems to be a function of their species. Human fibroblasts may be cultured in the diploid condition for a comparatively long time but rarely, if ever, give rise to continuous cell lines and thus eventually die (Hayflick and Moorhead, 1961). Rat cells may behave similarly. Mouse cells rapidly decline in growth rate and frequently give rise to aneuploid variants. The cause of "spontaneous" transformation is not known but it is clear that, in cell systems being studied over an extended period for the appearance of virus transformation, it is necessary to have adequate controls to account for the possibility of spontaneous transformation.

Some cell lines have proved to be very useful for the study of viral transformation since they grow rapidly and have a high cloning efficiency. Further hereditary changes may also occur spontaneously in these cell lines, leading to altered morphology, transplantability, etc., which may mimic a viral transformation under study.

This chapter will be concerned with techniques for measuring transforming activity by tumor viruses *in vitro*, and the greatest detail will be reserved for model systems such as Rous sarcoma virus and polyomavirus, which have been most fully investigated. Several tumor viruses will be briefly mentioned which have been found to induce transformation in mass cultures but which have not yet been subjected to quantitative analysis. Assay for oncogenic activity by tumor induction in animals or birds will only be mentioned in general terms.

II. Principles of Assays for Transforming Activity

In theory, any tumor virus can be assayed by its tumor-producing ability in susceptible hosts. For example, the quantal response method may be used whereby groups of animals are inoculated with diminishing doses of virus, and the 50% dose calculated from the proportion developing tumors in each group. With rapidly growing cutaneous or subcutaneous tumors one animal may be used for several virus doses, as with rabbit papilloma virus in the rabbit skin and Rous sarcoma virus in the chick wing web.

Difficulties arise with *in vivo* assays when the interval between inoculation and tumor detection is very long and varies with the virus dose used. It is usually necessary to adopt some arbitrary time limit for scoring results even though this may mean missing late tumors, thus reducing the sensitivity of the method. The relationship between time of appearance of tumors and virus dose can, however, be used as a satisfactory alternative to end-point titrations, by measuring the average length of latent period.

Even in the highest concentration available, however, many viruses fail to produce tumors in every inoculated animal, and activity is rapidly lost upon dilution. Nevertheless, titration in animals is still the only method available to date for assay of mouse leukemia, mouse mammary cancer, and several other tumor viruses.

A focus assay, as opposed to a quantal, end-point-type assay has considerable advantages in accuracy, since it measures actual rather than "statistical" particles. The chick chorioallantoic membrane may be used for focus assay by Rous sarcoma virus since individual virus particles will initiate a cell transformation which eventually results in a small visible tumor. Although largely replaced by focus formation in cultured cells (see below), the chorioallantoic membrane technique remains a simple and sensitive method which does not require facilities for tissue culture.

Certain members of the poxvirus group also cause proliferative foci in the chick chorioallantoic membrane. Although this is extensively used for assay purposes, the change may not be a true neoplastic transformation.

Recognition of viral-induced transformation *in vitro* depends on altered characteristics of the cells which can be recognized in culture. The first observation of this type of change was made by Manaker and Groupé (1956) who reported focal areas of cell proliferation in chick fibroblast cultures inoculated with Rous sarcoma virus. Subsequently other viruses have been shown to cause proliferative foci *in vitro* where growth of untransformed cells is otherwise slow or has ceased. Additional changes are known to accompany transformation, and the more important are shown in Table I.

Transformation does not necessarily involve all the changes enumer-

TABLE I

SOME CHANGES CHARACTERISTIC OF TRANSFORMED CULTURES

1. Cell growth in otherwise stationary cultures
2. Piling up or multilayering of cells
3. Altered cell morphology
4. Altered intercellular arrangement—randomness and overlapping
5. Growth when suspended in fluid or gel
6. Increased glycolysis
7. High cloning efficiency
8. Immortality

ated, but depends on the virus and cell type involved. For example, random growth may not be a feature of polyoma-transformed mouse fibroblasts, and chick fibroblasts transformed by Rous sarcoma virus do not have a particularly high cloning efficiency, nor do they achieve immortality. As long as the alteration is hereditary and is due specifically to the virus, however, it may be used for assay of transformation.

Transformation assays may be made by end-point titrations or by focus counts. The latter is based on counts of transformed clones arising from individual cells immediately after exposure to virus. Since the number of transformed clones is proportional to virus dose, it may be assumed that each clone arises from the action of a single virus particle and, therefore, the number of transformed clones is a measure of the effective number of active virus particles.

Clonal assays of this type, although quantitatively preferable, depend upon the rapid transforming action of the input virus without any intervening period during which secondary virus multiplication may occur. Several tumor viruses (SV40 in human cells, for example) cause transformation which is not detectable until many weeks after infection and often follows partial cytopathic changes and virus growth. In such systems counts of transformed cells would not be meaningful in terms of original virus inoculation, so cultures must be scored on an all-or-none basis in an end-point titration giving a measurement of 50% transforming dose of input virus. This type of assay has some of the same objections as measurement of tumor production in animals.

The choice of cells for transformation assays depends on the virus. Freshly isolated cells may be susceptible, but Jensen et al. (1963) and Todaro et al. (1963) have shown that human embryo fibroblasts at least may be more sensitive to transformation when near the end of their normal life in culture. Two stable lines of cells, BHK21 hamster fibroblasts and 3T3 mouse cells, which differ markedly, are sensitive to transformation by some viruses.

III. Assay Methods for Particular Viruses

A. ROUS SARCOMA VIRUS AND RELATED VIRUSES

Manaker and Groupé (1956) found that Rous sarcoma virus induces discrete foci of altered cells in cultures of chick embryo cells. Each focus results from the proliferation of a single cell transformed by Rous sarcoma virus and also from the recruitment of neighboring cells transformed by new virus produced in the focus. A number of factors contribute to variation in assays based on focus formation, but many are now well understood, and appropriate steps can be taken to minimize their effects. A summary of these factors follows.

1. Factors Affecting Focus Formation

a. Virus-Induced Resistance in Chick Embryo Cells. A proportion of birds in some flocks harbor the virus of avian visceral lymphomatosis and pass it cytoplasmically to their eggs. Persistent infection of chick embryo cells with this virus renders them resistant to transformation by some strains of Rous sarcoma virus *in vitro.* Viruses that exert this effect were first described as resistance-inducing factors (RIF) (Rubin, 1960a; Vogt and Rubin, 1963).

b. Genetic Resistance to Rous Sarcoma Virus in Chicken Cells. The susceptibility of chicken cells to Rous sarcoma virus with an outer coat derived from certain "helper" virus or "Rous associated virus" (RAV2) is determined by a single pair of autosomal genes. Susceptibility of chicken cells to Rous sarcoma virus with this coat specificity is dominant over resistance. Cells that are homozygously recessive for this determinant will not be transformed by Rous sarcoma virus with RAV2 specificity, although they may be susceptible to Rous sarcoma virus with another helper, such as RAV1 (Vogt, 1965).

c. Interference by Mycoplasmas. Marked inhibition of focus formation by some Rous sarcoma virus strains occurs in chick embryo cells infected with certain mycoplasmas (Somerson and Cook, 1965; Pontén and Macpherson, 1966). Mycoplasmas have been isolated from eggs, and it is conceivable that they may proliferate sufficiently in chick embryo cultures to inhibit focus formation. They may also contaminate the material being assayed or they may be introduced from the upper respiratory tract of those preparing the cultures.

d. The Strains of Rous Sarcoma Virus. The response of susceptible chick embryo cells depends on the strain of Rous sarcoma virus. Some strains form foci that are difficult to count because they are small or only slightly different from the background of untransformed cells. The types of foci formed by different strains of Rous sarcoma virus are described in Table II. One example, morph^r, is shown in Fig. 1.

TABLE II

CHANGES IN CHICK EMBRYO CELLS INFECTED WITH
VARIOUS STRAINS OF ROUS SARCOMA VIRUS *in Vitro*[a]

| Strains of Rous sarcoma virus | Cells infected *in vitro* | | Reference |
	Morphology	Growth pattern	
Bryan			
morph[r]	Round refractile, basophilic	Foci	Temin (1960)
morph[f]	Long, fusiform cells	Foci	Temin (1960)
polykaryocytes	Polykaryocytes	Diffuse	Moses and Kolin (1963)
Harris	Elongated, slightly basophilic	Diffuse	Dougherty *et al.* (1963)
No. 29	Round, basophilic	Foci	Dougherty *et al.* (1963)
Schmidt-Ruppin	Round cells	Large foci	Sarma *et al.* (1964a)
Zil'ber	Round cells	Diffuse	Traub and Morgan (unpublished)

[a] From Morgan (1964).

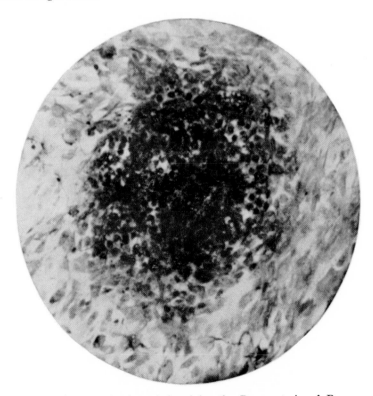

FIG. 1. A typical morph[r] form induced by the Bryan strain of Rous sarcoma virus in a chick embryo fibroblast monolayer. May-Grünwald and Giemsa stain. × 90. (From Dougherty *et al.*, 1963.)

e. Physiological Conditions of Cells in Culture. Rous sarcoma virus focus formation is inhibited in overcrowded cultures of chick embryo cells. Cultures must be infected in a condition that permits further cell proliferation.

f. Composition of the Medium. Some batches of bovine serum contain inhibitors of focus formation. This is especially true for fetal calf serum in which one of the inhibitory factors is fetuin (Rubin, 1960b). There are conflicting reports about the proportion of individual serum batches that are inhibitory. Even satisfactory batches may show inhibition if the concentration in the medium is 10% or higher. It is advisable to test batches of serum before use. Heating at 56°C for 30 minutes may improve some calf sera, as may the addition of 1–2% of beef embryo extract (Adams and Groupé, 1963). The addition of Difco tryptose phosphate broth may also increase the number of foci. It is difficult to assess the importance of individual medium components since their action may be dependent on the presence or absence of other components.

g. The Temperature of Incubation. Focus formation by Rous sarcoma virus may be accelerated and the focus size increased by incubating infected chick embryo cultures at 40°–41°C (Adams and Groupé, 1963; Dougherty and Rasmussen, 1964).

2. *Assay Method in Chick Cell Cultures* (after Temin and Rubin, 1958)

Because of the variable sensitivity of chick embryos due to genetic resistance or interfering viruses, it is first necessary to test for nonreacting embryos. Flocks of inbred chickens that are genetically susceptible to Rous sarcoma virus and free from RIF are available in some countries, e.g., Carr's Edinburgh strain of brown Leghorn chickens. The embryos from such flocks are uniformly susceptible (Dougherty and Simons, 1962), and pretesting for resistance is unnecessary. If such stocks are not available, then the cells from an individual embryo must be tested for sensitivity before their use in an assay. This is carried out in the following way. Individual 9- to 10-day-old chick embryos are decapitated, minced, and trypsinized by standard methods. Care should be taken to insure that the cells are well dispersed by pipetting or by filtering the cell suspension in medium through several layers of gauze. Primary cultures are prepared in large Petri dishes or bottles in growth medium i.e., synthetic medium (Eagle's, 199, or Scherer's), 80%; Difco tryptose phosphate broth, 10%; calf serum, 10%. The cell concentration should be about 10^5 cells per square centimeter of the culture vessel's growth surface. Other primary cultures for sensitivity testing are prepared in plastic Petri dishes 50 mm in diameter and seeded with 2×10^6 cells in 4 ml of assay medium, i.e., synthetic medium, 83%; tryptose phosphate broth, 10%; calf serum, 5%; beef embryo extract, 2%. Dilutions of stock Rous sarcoma virus containing 100–1000 focus-forming units (ffu) are added, and the cultures are incubated overnight in a humidified carbon dioxide incubator. The medium is then removed and replaced with 7 ml of agar medium, i.e., assay medium plus 0.8% agar. Incubation is continued for a further 5 days when a second overlay of 2.5 ml of agar medium is added. On the seventh day the agar is carefully removed and the cell sheet fixed with methanol and stained by the May-Grünwald and Giemsa method. Foci can then be counted by low-power microscopy. If the number of foci correspond to that previously found in susceptible cells, the embryo cells may be used in the assay. During the period of the screening test, the stock of primary cultures should be subcultured on the third to fifth day, each culture being split into four secondary cultures. When the result of the screening test is available these cultures will be ready to be harvested to provide cells for the assay. The cells are resuspended with trypsin and then infected, plated, incubated, and stained in the same way as described for the cells in the screening test. The only differences are that a smaller cell inoculum of 8×10^5 cells/50-mm plastic Petri dish is used and that the cultures may be incubated for up to 10 days to obtain the maximum number of foci.

Dougherty and Rasmussen (1964) have shown that it is possible to prepare large stocks of susceptible cells from individual chick embryos and preserve these in aliquots in the deep freezer for subsequent recovery and use in assays as required. The paper by these authors should be consulted for details of the storing technique.

Cells cultured from individual embryos may also be tested for their content of RIF by determining their ability to fix complement with serum from hamsters bearing tumors induced by the Schmidt-Ruppin strain of Rous sarcoma virus. The complement-fixing antigen is possessed by all cells infected by viruses of the avian leukosis complex. This is the COFAL test. Sarma et al. (1964b) have found that the antigens were present in culture fluids of 3- to 4-day-old primary cultures of chick embryo cells.

3. Transformation of Mammalian Cells in vitro by Rous Sarcoma Virus

There have been many reports of in vitro transformation of mammalian cells with Rous sarcoma virus strains; in general the changes induced resemble those seen in chick embryo cells (see National Cancer

Institute Monograph No. 17, 1964). Cells of the BHK21 line of hamster fibroblasts are transformed by both the Schmidt-Ruppin (Macpherson, 1965) and Bryan (Macpherson, 1966) strains of Rous sarcoma virus, and the transformed cells may be assayed by the agar suspension culture technique as for polyomavirus (see Section III,C,4).

4. *Pock Assay for Rous Sarcoma Virus on the Chorioallantoic Membrane of the Chick Embryo*

Embryos of 11-day gestation periods are prepared for chorioallantoic inoculation by standard methods (see elsewhere in this treatise). The virus is diluted in assay medium, and 0.1 ml of each dilution is inoculated into at least ten eggs. The eggs are sealed and incubated for 7 days in a humidified incubator at 39°C. The chorioallantoic membranes are then removed and the pocks counted with the aid of a low-power microscope. The chorioallantoic membranes from nonreacting eggs are discarded and not taken into consideration in estimating the pock-forming units (pfu) in a given sample. The causes of insusceptibility are probably the same as those demonstrated in focus assays *in vitro*, i.e., genetic, and the presence of RIF.

B. AVIAN MYELOBLASTOSIS VIRUS

Avian myeloblastosis virus like other members of the fowl leukosis complex can be assayed by its ability to interfere with Rous sarcoma virus focus formation. In addition, Baluda and Goetz (1961) have demonstrated that avian myeloblastosis virus induces the growth and differentiation of some cells in cultures of chick embryo hematopoietic tissues. These cells are probably the precursors of myeloid and lymphoid series.

This *in vitro* end-point assay for avian myeloblastosis virus is carried out as follows: The yolk sacs from 15-day-old chick embryos are trypsinized. Approximately 2×10^7 cells are plated in 100-mm plastic Petri dishes in a medium consisting of enriched Eagle's medium,* 80%; Difco tryptose phosphate broth, 10%; calf serum (heated at 56°C for 30 minutes), 5%, and chick serum, 5%. One yolk sac yields three such cultures. The cultures are fed with fresh medium 3–4 days later; sec-

* Eagle's basal medium was modified by having 4 times the concentration of amino acids and vitamins and a double concentration of glucose; 2.2 gm of $NaHCO_3$ per liter; and the following additional ingredients (in milligrams per liter)—aspartic acid, 30; glutamic acid, 60; glutamine, 584; glycine, 50; hydroxyproline, 10; proline, 40; serine, 30; adenosine, 20; phenol red, 16; streptomycin, 100; penicillin, 50,000 units; antimycotic (*n*-butyl *p*-hydroxybenzoate), 0.2. The pH is adjusted to 7.4 with NaOH. Sterilization by filtration.

ondary cultures are made after a further 3–4 days of incubation. Secondary cultures are prepared in 60-mm glass Petri dishes, each being seeded with 5×10^6 cells. Within 48 hours of preparation, ten secondary cultures are each infected with 0.1 ml of each avian myeloblastosis virus dilution for 2–4 hours at 37°C. Medium is then added, and the cultures are fed every 3–4 days until the end of the experiment. The cultures do not require transferring and usually show transformation within 3 weeks of infection with at least one transforming dose of avian myeloblastosis virus (one transforming dose is equivalent to 10 –100 infectious units for chick embryos). If 100 or more transforming doses of avian myeloblastosis virus are added to the culture, then transformation appears within 10 days. Transformation is characterized in cultures that have been fixed and stained (Giemsa) by the accumulation of intensely stained myeloblasts. Cultures are held for a total of 5 weeks before being recorded as negative.

C. POLYOMAVIRUS

Like several other DNA-containing tumor viruses, polyomavirus can be assayed for its ability to grow vegetatively and to form plaques in mouse embryo fibroblast cultures. In such cultures, transformed cells eventually appear, after a long delay, among the survivors, but the system is not suitable for assay of transforming particles in the original virus inoculum. Transformation assays are performed in fresh hamster or rat cells, or certain stable lines of hamster or mouse cells, where cytopathic changes are minimal or absent.

The assay in each cell type and the factors affecting sensitivity will be described separately. In general it should be stressed that transformation by polyoma and other DNA-containing viruses is an inefficient process in terms of virus particles, and even in the most sensitive assay system each transformation requires the presence of at least 10^3 pfu (10^5 physical particles). Highly concentrated virus stocks containing at least 10^8 pfu per milliliter are, therefore, needed for most transformation assays. (See Fig. 4 in Section III,C,4.)

1. *Hamster Fibroblasts*

Cultures of freshly isolated hamster fibroblasts obtained from embryos or newborn animals are susceptible to polyoma transformation (Vogt and Dulbecco, 1960; Sachs and Medina, 1961). In monolayer cultures, a variable amount of virus growth may be detected without obvious cytopathic effect. Foci of piled-up cells are seen after 7 days, and those continue to grow in the static conditions of a confluent monolayer. According to Vogt and Dulbecco (1962) such foci are not composed of fully transformed cells, but on propagation show progressive change with acquisition of high transplantability and plating efficiency. The first assay system for transformation by polyomavirus was based on the use of such cells (Stoker and Macpherson, 1961).

Method. Fibroblasts from hamster embryos are obtained by conventional methods of trypsinization and cultured in suitable growth medium with calf serum, e.g., 10% calf serum and 10% tryptose phosphate broth in Eagle's medium. Kidneys from newborn hamsters (but not weaned animals) also provide a suitable source of fibroblasts. Cells from primary or secondary cultures are generally used.

Confluent monolayer cultures may be exposed to small volumes of inocula of virus (0.2 ml/60-mm Petri dish) in buffered saline with 2% calf serum or in medium for 1 hour at 37°C, or, alternatively, stirred suspended cells can be exposed to virus for 1 hour at 37°C (e.g., about 10^6 cells in 1 ml of virus dilution in buffered saline with 2% calf serum or medium). After adsorption using either method the cells are suspended, diluted, and plated to give a known number (usually about 10^4 cells/60-mm Petri dish), preferably using preexisting feeder layers, for example, of irradiated hamster, rat, or mouse embryo fibroblasts. The use of cells sensitive to vegetative infection such as mouse cells as feeders does not seriously affect the assay since any new virus growth in feeder cells makes a negligible contribution to the number of hamster cells transformed.

The cultures are incubated for about 10 days. Usually about 1% of untransformed cells form colonies of various types, and transformed colonies can often be seen with the naked eye as comparatively large, round, opaque foci, but for identification of smaller colonies as well it is best to fix (10% Formol–saline) and stain the cultures (Giemsa or Jenner Giemsa) and to use low-power magnification (about $\times$ 10) with a dissecting microscope. This reveals the random arrangement of cells in the transformed clones, in contrast to the orderly array of the normal clones of various types. At suitable densities both normal and transformed colonies may be counted and the transformation frequency expressed either as transformed colonies per total cells plated (T/cell) or as transformed colonies per total colonies formed (T/col.).

This assay method has the advantage that it uses freshly isolated cells from animals known to be highly sensitive to the oncogenic properties of the virus. The disadvantage lies in the low efficiency of transformation and the fact that growth or expression of transformed clones is suppressed at high cell densities. This means that it is not possible to increase the number of countable transformed colonies per culture by increasing the total cells plated. There is also a considerable variability in sensitivity between different batches of embryo fibroblasts (Stoker, 1962). This may be due to the presence or absence of interfering viruses (see Section III,C,2).

2. Rat Embryo Fibroblasts

Freshly isolated rat embryo fibroblasts provide a satisfactory and reliable alternative, and a method similar to that used for hamster fibroblasts is described by Williams and Till (1964). Little variability was found in repeated assays of the same virus stock using different rat cell batches. According to Bayreuther (personal communication, 1965), however, rat embryo heart cell cultures provide the most reliable assay system with freedom from contaminating viruses.

Either rat or hamster fibroblast cultures may be tested for preexisting interfering viruses by measuring the sensitivity of sample monolayer cultures of a cell batch to a known number of plaque-forming units of herpesvirus.

3. Stable Cell Lines

Since stable cell lines can easily be cloned and stored, they should provide homogeneous populations for reproducible assays. The majority of stable cell lines, such as L cells and HeLa cells, already have many properties of neoplastic cells and are unsuitable (or insusceptible) to transformation by polyoma or other tumor viruses. Two cell lines, however, retain some of the properties of freshly isolated cells, and are also susceptible to neoplastic transformation and are commonly used for assay.

a. BHK21 Cells. These cells are fibroblasts originally isolated from baby hamster kidney cultures (Macpherson and Stoker, 1962). They grow rapidly and have a high efficiency of colony formation. Unlike most stable cell lines, these cells are diploid or, more probably, pseudodiploid (Macpherson, 1963). They exhibit the parallel orientation of normal fibroblasts but grow to high cell density in monolayer cultures.

The BHK21 cells can be transformed by polyomavirus, with consequent loss of parallel orientation leading to randomly arranged multilayered cells which can easily be distinguished and which are similar to transformed hamster embryo cells. The virus causes no recognizable cytopathic effect, but there is evidence that vegetative growth does occur in a small proportion of cells (Fraser and Gharpure, 1962; Bourgaux, 1964).

For assay of transforming activity, Clone 13 (C13) of BHK21 cells is commonly used (Stoker and Abel, 1962), but variants from this clone have been isolated with increased sensitivity to transformation (Stoker and Smith, 1964). Cells may be exposed to virus for 1 hour either stirred in suspension or as confluent monolayer cultures as for freshly isolated fibroblasts. In suspension cultures exposed to high virus concentrations (10^3 pfu/cell or more), cell clumps may form but tend to disperse upon dilution of the virus after absorption. The degree of clumping varies with the virus stock rather than the cells. No clumping occurs after virus adsorption to monolayers if subsequent suspension of the cells is delayed for 2 hours after stopping absorption by addition of medium. In monolayer cultures adsorption may be uneven unless the plates are rocked, or unless the virus is in a volume of more than 0.2 ml/60-mm Petri dish (Black, 1964). The efficiency of adsorption is higher in suspension cultures than in monolayer cultures.

After adsorption (and if necessary suspension) the infected BHK21 cells are suitably diluted and plated in Petri dishes for colony formation. To differentiate and count the normal and transformed colonies it is essential that they should be discrete so as to avoid inhibition by crowding. The overall plating efficiency of BHK21 cells on bare substrate is 10–20% in standard growth medium, or 30–60% on feeder layers. Therefore, 1000–2000 cells may be plated on bare substrate, or 200–500 on feeder layers, in 60-mm Petri dishes. For better differentiation of normal and transformed colonies it is advisable to use glass, rather than plastic Petri dishes on which the cells form more diffuse colonies.

After 7 days of growth (or 10 days in the absence of feeder layers) and subsequent staining, transformed colonies can be differentiated by the random orientation of cells and rounded shape of the colony (see Fig. 2). Some otherwise normal colonies contain sectors of transformed cells due to delay in the transformation process (Stoker, 1963). It is customary to score such colonies as transformed.

b. *3T3 Cells.* These are an epithelial, aneuploid line of mouse cells (Todaro and Green, 1963). They show a high degree of growth inhibition in confluent cultures and thus form very thin monolayers of cells with a low saturation density. After exposure to polyomavirus there is some cytopathic effect, but transformations occur and give rise to rounded refractile cells which grow to a higher saturation density than the unaffected cells. The colonies of these transformed cells are dense areas which show up against the background monolayer, particularly after staining. For assay by this method, monolayers in 50-mm plastic Petri dishes were infected for 3 hours with 0.5 ml of virus, then washed 3 times with phosphate-buffered saline, and fresh medium added.

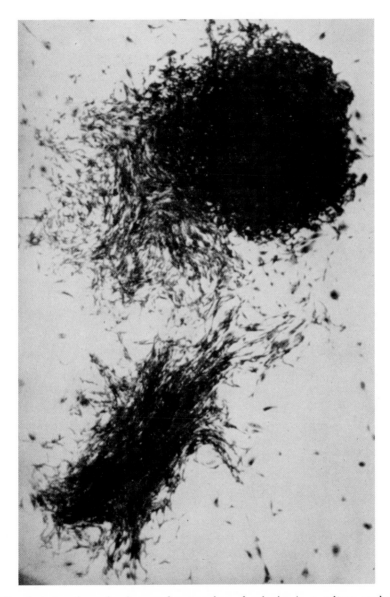

Fig. 2. A transformed colony and untransformed colonies in a culture seeded 7 days previously with polyoma-infected BHK21/13 cells. The transformed cells form a dense rounded colony in which the cells pile upon each other at random. Giemsa stain. × 25.

The methods of assay described thus far are nonselective or partly selective. For example, untransformed BHK21 cells grow as fast and with almost as high a colony-forming efficiency as the transformed cells. With freshly isolated hamster fibroblasts and the 3T3 line of mouse cells, the transformed cells are selected because they grow faster and to a higher saturation density, but the untransformed cells also grow to some extent.

The continued growth of untransformed cells, especially in the BHK21 system, leads to some degree of interference with development and expression of transformed clones. Therefore it is not possible to increase proportionately the number of countable, transformed colonies per culture simply by increasing the total number of cells initially plated. For this reason it is difficult to detect very small numbers of transformed cells, such as are obtained, for example, with low multiplicity of infection or with viral DNA. For these situations a highly selective method is needed which allows only transformed cells to grow. Such selection is provided by the agar suspension method.

4. *Agar Suspension Assay*

Following observations by Sanders and Burford (1964) with an ascites-adapted line, Macpherson and Montagnier (1964) found that hamster cells exposed to polyomavirus and held in suspension in soft agar medium gave rise to spherical colonies of transformed cells, whereas untransformed cells did not form colonies (see Fig. 3).

Either BHK21 cells or freshly isolated hamster fibroblasts are used and exposed to virus in suspension or as monolayers as described previously. (Alternatively, virus may be added to the surface of preformed agar cultures containing the susceptible cells.) Following virus adsorption, appropriate numbers of suspended cells are added to medium containing 0.5% agar at 44°C to give a final agar concentration of 0.34%. Then 1.5 ml of the suspension is immediately added to a 60-mm Petri dish containing a preformed base layer of 6 ml of 0.5% agar in medium. After the agar has set the cultures are incubated for about 10 days and examined at low magnification for colonies in the agar. These show up as dark spheres by transmitted light and may be counted easily.

Uninfected BHK21 cells, but not fresh hamster fibroblasts, may give rise to a background of scanty, small colonies in agar usually amounting to ten to twenty colonies per million cells plated (although higher if the cell suspensions are clumped or if the agar contains particulate material). A few of these background colonies are spontaneous genetic variants, but the majority fail to grow in agar suspension when propagated. For assay of polyoma transformation it is customary to plate

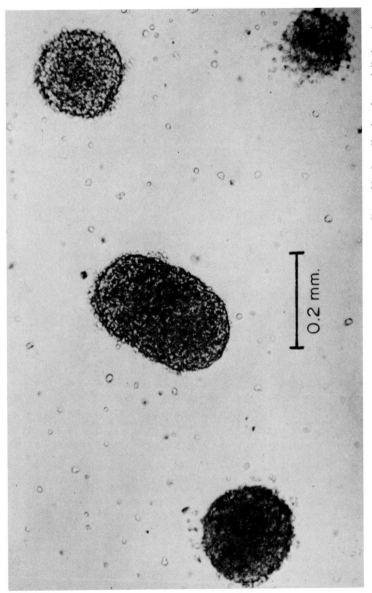

Fig. 3. Colonies of polyoma-transformed BHK21/13 cells in agar medium. Single cells that have failed to form colonies are also seen. Unstained. × 125.

10^4–10^5 cells/Petri dish, so that the background of normal colonies should be negligible. Figure 4 shows a dose–response curve in agar.

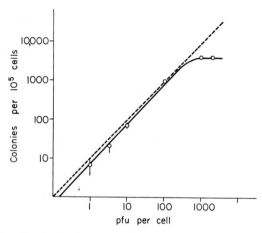

Fig. 4. Colonies developing in agar medium 10 days after seeding cultures with BHK21/13 cells that has been infected with different amounts of polyomavirus. The vertical line through each point represents the standard error of the estimate. The broken line is a slope of 1. (From Macpherson and Montagnier, 1964.)

5. *Assay for Transformation by Polyoma DNA*

The efficiency of transformation by viral DNA is about one-thousandth that of intact virus, so it is necessary to culture large numbers of infected cells under conditions selective for transformants. This has been done with rat fibroblast, monolayer cultures, but a more satisfactory quantitative method is with the BHK21 agar suspension assay (Crawford *et al.*, 1964; Bourgaux *et al.*, 1965).

Just-confluent monolayer cultures of about two million BHK21 cells in 60-mm Petri dishes are washed successively with 0.37 M NaCl and 0.55 M NaCl (all containing 0.002 M MgCl$_2$), and are then exposed for 30 minutes to a 0.1-ml volume of virus DNA in 0.55 M NaCl at 29°C. Medium with extra serum (20%) is added carefully to avoid dislodging shocked cells, and after incubation at room temperature for 30 minutes and 37°C for 1 hour the cells are suspended in trypsin–Versene and plated in agar with 2×10^5 cells/culture, as described above.

6. *Comparison of Assay Methods for Polyoma Transformation*

Not all systems have been used in the same laboratory, so that it is impossible to make precise comparisons because virus strains used and local conditions may vary. In all systems the number of transformations is proportional to the virus dose up to concentrations of 10^9 pfu per milliliter. At higher concentrations no further transformations are obtained (Fig. 4). The efficiency of transformation, compiled from various published results using different cell systems is shown in Table III. The BHK21 cells are more sensitive for assay than the fresh hamster cells but not necessarily more than rat cells or 3T3 cells. For ease of counting and quantitative reliability, the agar suspension method is superior and has the additional advantage that it allows detection of small numbers of transformed cells. It should be noted that in rat and hamster embryo cells and BHK21 cells there is decline in transformation frequency at virus concentrations above 10^9 pfu per milliliter. The reason for this is not known.

TABLE III

POLYOMAVIRUS—RELATIVE TRANSFORMATION RATES IN VARIOUS CELLS

Cells[a]	Method of culturing	No. of transformed colonies / No. of cells plated (%)
Hamster embryo		
Primary	Colonies on glass	0.006
	Agar suspension	0.007
Fifth passage	Colonies on glass	0.004
	Agar suspension	0.003
BHK21/13	Colonies on glass	0.8
	Agar suspension	4.0
Rat embryo, secondary[b]	Colonies on confluent monolayer	0.45

[a] Multiplicity of infection (pfu per cell) 10^3 in each case, and approximately 10^3 for the rat embryo cells.

[b] Data from Williams and Till (1964).

D. SV40 VIRUS

The SV40 virus is similar in physical properties to polyomavirus and also causes rapidly growing sarcomas after inoculation of newborn hamsters. Vegetative growth of the virus may be assayed by plaque formation in cultures of green monkey kidney cells.

1. Transformation of Hamster and Human Cells

In vitro transformation can also be obtained after infection of hamster and human cells (Shein and Enders, 1962; Koprowski et al., 1962).

In neither of these cell types, however, do transformed cells grow into recognizable clones immediately following infection either on solid substrates or in agar suspension as occurs with polyomavirus in hamster cells. It is, therefore, not possible to assay the number of transforming units in the original virus inoculum by direct colony counts using these cells. Transformed cells may appear after some early, unknown, virus–cell interactions, and eventually the culture as a whole is seen to be transformed (in the case of human cells many weeks after the original infection). Transformed cultures as a whole are identified from the rapid growth of the cells and high acid production, or, more significantly, the presence of SV40 tumor cell antigen by complement fixation or immunofluorescence.

Thus the transforming activity of a virus suspension at present can be measured only in hamster and human cells by an end-point titration method, scoring transformed or untransformed cultures several weeks after inoculation of various virus concentrations or alternatively by relating virus dose to the time of appearance of detectable change in the cultures. Such assay methods are obviously unsatisfactory, and, despite the fact that mice are not susceptible to the oncogenic effect of the virus, the method of choice for assay is in the 3T3 line of mouse cells.

2. Assay in 3T3 Cells

As previously mentioned, the 3T3 line of cells is highly sensitive to growth inhibition in culture and forms very thin sheets of cells. After exposure of sparse cultures to SV40 virus, transformed colonies appear which may be recognized by their loss of growth inhibition leading to dense piled-up colonies of epitheloid-like cells (see Fig. 5). The SV40-transformed 3T3 cells may be distinguished from their polyoma-transformed counterparts by their colonial morphology, and it has been possible to identify double transformants after sequential infection by both viruses. The procedure is as follows (Todaro and Green, 1964): Subconfluent monolayers of $2–5 \times 10^5$ cells per 50-mm Petri dish are exposed to 0.5 ml of virus suspension for 5 hours. After overnight incubation in growth medium the cells are suspended and plated at 100–500 cells/dish. Cultures are examined after fixing and staining 10–14 days later. The plating efficiency of 3T3 cells is 30–50% without feeder layers, and this is undiminished after SV40 virus infection. By 14 days the normal cells form a confluent sheet against which the multilayered transformed clones can easily be seen and counted. Over the range tested, up to $10^{8.4}$ infectious units (cytopathic) of virus per milliliter, the number of transformations was approxi-

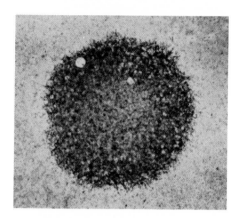

Fig. 5. A colony of SV40-transformed 3T3 cells against a background of un-transformed cells 14 days after plating 500 virus-infected cells. Hematoxylin stain. × 5. (From Todaro and Green, 1964.)

mately proportional to virus dose, and the transforming efficiency in terms of infective particles was of the same order as that found with polyomavirus.

E. Papilloma Viruses

1. *Bovine Papilloma Virus*

Bovine papilloma virus causes transformations in cultured bovine embryo or in newborn calf conjunctiva or skin cells (Black *et al.*, 1963) and in mouse embryo cells (Thomas *et al.*, 1963, 1964), and end-point titrations have been used satisfactorily to assay the activity both of virus and of viral DNA (Boiron *et al.*, 1965). Although morphologically altered colonies appear after plating separated infected cells, it has not yet been possible to develop a satisfactory quantitative assay method because of the heterogeneity of the colonies on solid substrate, some of which are difficult to distinguish from normal colonies. Moreover, there is as yet no positive means for distinguishing transformed cells, such as by their transplantability or presence of a specific tumor cell antigen. Recently, however, bovine papilloma virus suspensions have been found to initiate growth of bovine embryo skin cells in agar suspension cultures (LeBouvier and Thomas, personal communication). Although the proportion of colony-forming cells is low (0.06–0.17%, maximum) and requires rather precise conditions such as high humidity, it should provide a satisfactory assay method for this virus.

2. *Human Papilloma Virus*

Human papilloma virus has been reported to cause *in vitro* transformation of human embryo skin and muscle cultures leading to irregular multilayered foci of cells visible 10 days after infection (Noyes, 1965). No quantitative assay has been described, but transformation was only found with undiluted wart suspension containing 10^9–10^{10} particles per milliliter and not with a 1 : 10 dilution of this suspension.

3. *Shope Papilloma Virus*

No *in vitro* transformation systems have yet been reported for Shope papilloma virus, although the virus may be assayed by end-point titrations in rabbit skin. Following the finding by Rogers (1959) of arginase activity in rabbit papilloma tissue, Passen and Schultz (1965) have reported the induction of arginase in rabbit cells by Shope papilloma virus *in vitro*. It is possible that this may lead to a transformation assay system based on the induced enzyme.

F. ONCOGENIC ADENOVIRUSES

McBride and Wiener (1964) reported transformation of hamster embryo fibroblasts by adenovirus Type 12 virus. The transformation was only identified in the whole culture after a long delay, however, and was, therefore, unsuitable for quantitative assay. More recently Yamane and Kusano (personal communication) have used hamster brain cultures to demonstrate adenovirus transformation. In these cultures foci of transformed cells appear from 15 days after infection, and this system may provide the basis for a suitable quantitative assay procedure.

G. POXVIRUSES—YABA AND SHOPE FIBROMA VIRUSES

Several poxviruses cause tumors, but it is not certain if they are true neoplasms since they frequently regress. The most active viruses in this respect are the Yaba tumor virus of monkeys and the Shope fibroma virus of rabbits. The possible transforming activity of Yaba virus *in vitro* has been studied by Yohn *et al.* (1964) using the BSC stable line of *Cercopithecus* monkey kidney cells. At low multiplicity of infection, Yaba virus causes piled-up foci of cells as well as small degenerative plaques, both of which can be counted. The changes are only observed if growth of unaffected cells is slowed, for example, by incubation at 33°C. It is not yet clear whether the piled-up foci of cells are due to proliferation resulting from viral transformation of the type found with other tumor viruses or whether they are due to cell migration and aggregation such as may occur with certain strains of herpesvirus on monolayer cultures.

Similar piled-up foci are found in rabbit kidney cultures infected with Shope fibroma virus, and these could be used for virus assay. However, Israeli and Sachs (1964) have recently failed to find evidence of cell division in the Shope fibroma foci and have come to the conclusion that the effect with this virus is due to cell aggregation. It is, therefore, not yet justifiable to talk of cell transformation by these poxviruses.

REFERENCES

Adams, E. V., and Groupé, V. (1963). *Virology* **21**, 271.
Baluda, M. A., and Goetz, I. E. (1961). *Virology* **15**, 185.
Bayreuther, K. (1965). Personal communication.
Black, P. H. (1964). *Virology* **24**, 179.
Black, P. H., and Rowe, W. P. (1963a). *Virology* **19**, 107.
Black, P. H., and Rowe, W. P. (1963b). *Proc. Soc. Exptl. Biol. Med.* **114**, 721.
Black, P. H., Hartley, J. W., Rowe, W. P., and Huebner, R. J. (1963). *Nature* **199**, 1016.
Boiron, M., Thomas, M., and Chenaille, Ph. (1965). *Virology* **26**, 150.
Bourgaux, P. (1964). *Virology* **24**, 120.
Bourgaux, P., Bourgaux-Ramoisy, D., and Stoker, M. (1965). *Virology* **25**, 364.
Crawford, L., Dulbecco, R., Fried, M., Montagnier, L., and Stoker, M. (1964). *Proc. Natl. Acad. Sci. U.S.* **52**, 148.
Dougherty, R. M., and Rasmussen, R. (1964). *Natl. Cancer Inst. Monograph* **17**, 337.
Dougherty, R. M., and Simons, P. J. (1962). *Virology* **18**, 559.
Dougherty, R. M., Simons, P. J., and Chesterman, F. C. (1963). *J. Natl. Cancer Inst.* **31**, 1285.
Fraser, K. B., and Gharpure, M. (1962). *Virology* **18**, 505.
Hayflick, L., and Moorhead, P. S. (1961). *Exptl. Cell Res.* **25**, 585.
Israeli, E., and Sachs, L. (1964). *Virology* **23**, 473.
Jensen, F., Koprowski, H., and Pontén, J. A. (1963). *Proc. Natl. Acad. Sci. U.S.* **50**, 343.
Koprowski, H., Pontén, J., Jensen, F., Ravdin, R. G., Moorhead, P. S., and Saksela, E. (1962). *J. Cellular Comp. Physiol.* **59**, 281.
LeBouvier, G., and Thomas, M. (1965). Personal communication.
McBride, W. D., and Wiener, A. (1964). *Proc. Soc. Exptl. Biol. Med.* **115**, 870.
Macpherson, I. A. (1963). *J. Natl. Can. Inst.* **30**, 795.
Macpherson, I. A. (1965). *Science* **148**, 1731.
Macpherson, I. A. (1966). *Recent Results Cancer Res.* **6**, 1.
Macpherson, I. A., and Montagnier, L. (1964). *Virology* **23**, 291.
Macpherson, I. A., and Stoker, M. (1962). *Virology* **16**, 147.
Manaker, R. A., and Groupé, W. (1956). *Virology* **2**, 838.
Morgan, H. R. (1964). *Natl. Cancer Inst. Monograph* **17**, 395.
Moses, E., and Kolin, A. (1963). *Exptl. Cell Res.* **32**, 182.
Noyes, W. F. (1965). *Virology* **25**, 358.
Passen, S., and Schultz, R. B. (1965). *Virology* **26**, 122.

Pontén, J. A., and Macpherson, I. A. (1966). *Ann. Med. Exptl. Fenn.* **44**, 260.

Rogers, S. (1959). *Nature* **183**, 1815.

Rubin, H. (1960a). *Proc. Natl. Acad. Sci. U.S.* **46**, 1105.

Rubin, H. (1960b). *Virology* **12**, 14.

Sachs, L., and Medina, D. (1961). *Nature* **189**, 457.

Sanders, F. K., and Burford, B. O. (1964). *Nature* **201**, 786.

Sarma, P. S., Huebner, R. J., and Armstrong, D. (1964a). *Proc. Soc. Exptl. Biol. Med.* **115**, 481.

Sarma, P. S., Turner, H. C., and Huebner, R. J. (1964b). *Natl. Cancer Inst. Monograph* **17**, 481.

Shein, H. M., and Enders, J. F. (1962). *Proc. Natl. Acad. Sci. U.S.* **48**, 1164.

Somerson, N. L., and Cook, M. K. (1965). *J. Bacteriol.* **90**, 534.

Stoker, M. G. P. (1962). *Ciba Found. Symp. Tumour Viruses Murine Origin, 1961,* 365.

Stoker, M. G. P. (1963). *Virology* **20**, 366.

Stoker, M. G. P., and Abel, P. (1962). *Cold Spring Harbor Symp. Quant. Biol.* **27**, 375.

Stoker, M. G. P., and Macpherson, I. (1961). *Virology* **14**, 359.

Stoker, M. G. P., and Smith, A. (1964). *Virology* **24**, 175.

Temin, H. M. (1960). *Virology* **10**, 182.

Temin, H. M., and Rubin, H. (1958). *Virology* **6**, 669.

Thomas, M., Levy, J. P., Tanzer, J., Boiron, M., and Bernard, J. (1963). *Compt. Rend.* **257**, 2155.

Thomas, M., Boiron, M., Tanzer, J., Levy, J. P., and Bernard, J. (1964). *Nature* **202**, 709.

Todaro, G. J., and Green, H. (1963). *J. Cell Biol.* **17**, 299.

Todaro, G. J., and Green, H. (1964). *Virology* **23**, 117.

Vogt, M., and Dulbecco, R. (1960). *Proc. Natl. Acad. Sci. U.S.* **46**, 365.

Vogt, M., and Dulbecco, R. (1962). *Cold Spring Harbor Symp. Quant. Biol.* **27**, 367.

Vogt, P. K. (1965). *Advan. Virus Res.* **11**, 293.

Vogt, P. K., and Rubin, H. (1963). *Virology* **19**, 92.

Williams, J. F., and Till, J. E. (1964). *Virology* **24**, 505.

Yamane, I., and Kusano, T. (1965). Personal communication.

Yohn, D. S., Grace, J. T., and Haendiges, V. A. (1964). *Nature* **202**, 881.

8 Methods for Selecting RNA Bacteriophage*

Mamoru Watanabe and J. Thomas August

I. Introduction

A bacteriophage, f2, containing ribonucleic acid as its genetic material, was first isolated by Loeb (1960) and Loeb and Zinder (1961). Many investigators have since described other bacteriophages related to f2 in their biophysical (Table I) and serological characteristics (Scott, 1965). These RNA phages infect only male strains (Hfr and F$^+$) of *Escherichia coli* or other bacteria that have received the *E. coli* F$^+$ episome. These phages are small and circular and contain a single-stranded, linear RNA

* This is Communication No. 62 from the Joan and Lester Avnet Institute of Molecular Biology, Albert Einstein College of Medicine, New York, New York. Dr. M. Watanabe is a recipient of the Research Fellowship of the American College of Physicians, 1964–1967. Dr. J. T. August is a recipient of an Investigatorship of the Health Research Council of the City of New York under contract I-346.

TABLE I
CHARACTERISTICS OF RNA BACTERIOPHAGES

Phage	Molecular weight (gm)		$S_{20,w}$		Density in CsCl (gm/ml)	Base composition (moles %)				Reference
	Phage	RNA	Phage	RNA		A	U	G	C	
f2		$0.7\text{-}1 \times 10^6$				22.2	25.1	25.9	26.8	Loeb and Zinder (1961)
MS 2	3.6×10^6	1×10^6	81	27	1.46	22.4	25.6	27.5	24.5	Strauss and Sinsheimer (1963)
R17	3.6×10^6	1.1×10^6	79	27		22.6	25.5	27.1	24.8	Paranchych and Graham (1962) Gesteland and Boedtker (1964)
fr	4.4×10^6	1.2×10^6	79	21		24.3	23.7	27.1	24.9	Marvin and Hoffmann-Perling (1963)
β			75, 90			23.3	28.0	21.6	27.2	Nonoyama et al. (1963)
f_can			79.5		1.42					Davern (1964)
R23		1×10^6	75	25		23.4	26.0	25.6	25.1	Watanabe and August (1967)
Qβ	4.2×10^6		84.3		1.439					Overby et al. (1966)

of molecular weight approximately 1×10^6. Their diameter is 25 mμ; particle weight $3\text{--}4 \times 10^6$; sedimentation coefficient ($S_{20,w}$) 80; and buoyant density in cesium chloride 1.46. RNA-containing bacteriophages have also been reported for *Pseudomonas aeruginosa* (Feary *et al.*, 1963) and for *Caulobacter* (Schmidt and Stanier, 1965).

II. General Techniques

A. Assay of Phage

Phage titer and host range are determined by plaque formation with the agar-layer method (Adams, 1959). Bacteria used for plating are harvested during early log-phase growth. Male-specific RNA bacteriophages do not produce plaques on organisms harvested during stationary growth, presumably because they become F$^-$ phenocopies.

B. Media and Solutions

1. A suitable plating medium for RNA bacteriophages contains (per liter) 10 gm of Bacto-Tryptone, 8 gm of NaCl, and 1 gm of glucose. The base layer is supplemented with 10 gm of agar, and the top layer with 6 gm of agar. After melting the agar, 1.5 ml of 1 N NaOH and 2 ml of 1 M CaCl$_2$ are added per liter.

2. Several media may be used for preparation of phage stocks. Medium A (Davern, 1964) contains (per liter) 7 gm of Na$_2$HPO$_4$, 3 gm of KH$_2$PO$_4$, 1 gm of NH$_4$Cl, and 0.5 gm of NaCl. This basic salt medium is supplemented with 10 ml of 30% glycerol in 0.5 M MgSO$_4$, 50 ml of 12% Difco casamino acids, and 2 ml of 0.5 M CaCl$_2$. LB medium (Loeb and Zinder, 1961) contains (per liter) 10 gm of Bacto-Tryptone, 1 gm of yeast extract, 1 gm of glucose, 8 gm of NaCl, and 0.22 gm of CaCl$_2$.

3. Diluent used for titering RNA phage contains (per liter) 10 ml of 1 M Tris at pH 7.5, 1 ml of 1 M MgCl$_2$, 5 gm of NaCl, and 1 ml of 1% gelatin.

4. Lysing medium contains (per 100 ml) 10 mg of lysozyme, 1 ml of 1 M EDTA at pH 8.0, and 96.5 ml of 1 M Tris at pH 8.0.

C. Source of Phage

Sewage samples may be treated by centrifugation or filtration to remove particulate material, and the clear solution is stored over chloroform (1%, v/v) at 2°–4°C. Soil samples may be mixed with water, allowed to stand at room temperature, filtered, and stored in a similar manner. These samples are used for selection of RNA bacteriophages, as described in subsequent sections.

D. Preparation of Phage Stock

Phage stocks are prepared by picking single plaques from samples plated on appropriate bacteria. Plaques are suspended in phage diluent and replated several times to ensure homogeneity. An early log-phase culture of bacteria, 25–50 ml, is then infected with a single phage plaque. Infected cultures are incubated at 37°C with vigorous aeration for 3–6 hours. Lysing solution, 0.1 volumes, and chloroform (1%, v/v) are then added, and the culture is shaken vigorously. Bacterial debris is removed by centrifugation or filtration, and the lysate is stored over chloroform.

E. Purification of Phage

A procedure based on the liquid-polymer-phase technique of Albertsson (1960) has been devised to provide a simple, nonlaborious means of phage purification. The chief advantages of this technique are that it concentrates the phage with good yield without need for centrifugation of large volumes, and it has been applicable to purification of many different types of bacteriophages.

A large volume of culture in early log phase (2×10^8 cells/ml) is infected with the phage stock at a multiplicity of 10. After incubation for 3–6 hours, lysis is completed as described above. Lysates prepared in medium A contain little bacterial debris and do not require centrifugation. When lysates are prepared in LB medium, bacterial debris is removed by adding Celite (Johns-Manville) and centrifuging at 11,000 rpm for 10 minutes. To each liter of lysate are added 17.5 gm of NaCl, 69 gm of polyethylene glycol (Carbowax 6000, Union Carbide Corporation, New York), and 2 gm of sodium dextran sulfate 500 (Pharmacia, Uppsala, Sweden). After the ingredients are completely dissolved, the phases are allowed to form at 2°–4°C. The lower dextran phase containing the bacteriophage, 50- to 100-fold concentrated, is collected after 48 hours. To remove the sodium dextran sulfate, KCl is added to a final concentration of 1 M, and the precipitate is removed by centrifugation at 17,000 rpm for 5 minutes. The supernatant from this centrifugation is dialyzed for 24 hours against SSC (0.15 M NaCl, 0.015 M sodium citrate) and fractionated by a second liquid-polymer phase separation. Sodium chloride, 5.85 gm, and sodium dextran sulfate, 16.8 gm, are added to each 100 ml of the phage suspension, and the phases are allowed to separate at 2°–4°C. After 24–48 hours, the upper phase containing the bacteriophage is collected. To remove sodium dextran sulfate, 0.67 volumes of 3 M KCl is added, and after mixing the precipitate is removed by centrifugation at 17,000 rpm for 5 minutes. The bacteriophage suspension is then centrifuged in the Spinco 40 rotor at 40,000 rpm for 3 hours, and the pellet of bacteriophage is resuspended in a small volume of SSC, usually around 1 ml per tube. The phage is then banded by centrifugation in CsCl in the Spinco 40 or 50 angle-head rotor at maximum speed for 48 hours. Cesium chloride is added to the phage suspension to a final density of about 1.4 (approximately 0.6 gm/ml), and the solution is added to the cellulose nitrate tubes. These tubes are completely filled with paraffin oil to prevent collapse during centrifugation. When solutions of density greater than 1.2 gm/ml are centrifuged, the allowed maximum speed is determined in the following manner:

$$\text{Allowed maximum speed} = \sqrt{1.2 \text{ gm/ml/density of sample}}$$
$$\times \text{ maximum rated speed}$$

After centrifugation the phage layer is removed and dialyzed against SSC for 24 hours.

The purification procedure using ^{32}P-labeled RNA phage is illustrated in Table II. Phage lysate was prepared as described, except that ^{32}P was added to the medium at the time of infection. Phage recovery has usually been higher than that seen in this particular experiment. The specific activity of the phage particle was constant for the last two steps of the purification procedure, indicating radiochemical homogeneity. The purity of the final preparation was also confirmed by electron microscopy and analytical ultracentrifugation.

III. Selection Techniques

The techniques for isolation of RNA bacteriophages depend on one or more of the known characteristics of these organisms, such as host specificity, size, ribonuclease sensitivity, serologic behavior, and resistance to inhibitors of DNA synthesis. Procedures based on these characteristics have resulted in the isolation of many RNA bacteriophages of *E. coli*, all of which appear to be related to f2 (Table I), with the exception of Qβ (Overby *et al.*, 1966).

Although these phages are all similar in type of RNA, size and shape, and male specificity, RNA bacteriophages present in nature need not all exhibit these same characteristics. If totally unrelated RNA bacteriophages do exist, most of the selection techniques described here may in fact select against them. Perhaps the best procedure for selecting new RNA bacteriophages is resistance to inhibitors of DNA synthesis. With these considerations in mind, the following selection techniques may be utilized singly or in combinations, in a

TABLE II

PURIFICATION OF AN RNA BACTERIOPHAGE

Step	Total volume (ml)	Phage titer (pfu/ml $\times 10^{-12}$)	Phage recovery (%)	^{32}P Radioactivity (cpm/ml $\times 10^{-6}$)	Specific activity (cpm/pfu $\times 10^{6}$)
Lysate	1850	1.5	100	12.8	8.5
Phase 1 (bottom)	56	50	100	160	3.2
KCl precipitation	100	18	64	42	2.3
Phase 2 (top)	77	20	54	42	2.1
High-speed pellet	16	140	79	210	1.5
CsCl banding	3.7	200	26	300	1.5

sequence most convenient to the individual investigator. The use of these techniques does not guarantee the isolation of an RNA bacteriophage, but greatly enhances the likelihood of success in such a search.

A. HOST SPECIFICITY

All known RNA coliphage are specific for male-strain organisms. An RNA bacteriophage may therefore be isolated by the ability to grow on male but not on female organisms (Loeb, 1960; Marvin and Hoffmann-Berling, 1963). This criterion is not absolute, however, since there are also male-specific DNA phages (Loeb, 1960; Marvin and Hoffmann-Berling, 1963), and selection by this technique is therefore best used in conjunction with one or more of the other isolation procedures. The likelihood of selecting a DNA phage may also be reduced by use of a bacterial strain resistant to DNA phage (Bishop and Bradley, 1965).

Method. Mixtures of bacteriophage may be screened rapidly by replica plating. Samples to be tested are plated in the usual manner by the agar-overlay method. A sterile toothpick is stabbed through the center of the phage plaque on the original plate and successively stabbed through each of several plates containing different bacterial strains, both male and female. Several plaques may be tested on a single plate. After incubation, a clear area of lysis on male but not on female organisms indicates male specificity.

B. RIBONUCLEASE SENSITIVITY

Infection by the single-stranded RNA coliphage is inhibited by ribonuclease (RNase), and this effect has been used for isolation of RNA phages (Bishop and Bradley, 1965; Schmidt and Stanier, 1965). It has been reported that 10 μg of RNase per milliliter of top layer reduces the plaque yield by 90%, and that concentrations of 50 μg/ml or higher result in complete suppression of plaque formation (Knolle and Kaudewitz, 1963).

Method. To test for RNase sensitivity, 100 μg of RNase is added to each 2 ml of top agar. Identical aliquots of an appropriate dilution of phage are plated, one with and one without RNase, in order to determine the inhibition of plaque formation by RNase. Replica-plating techniques may also be employed. A sterile toothpick is stabbed through the center of the phage plaque on the original plate and successively stabbed through two plates containing the host organism, one plate also containing 50 μg/ml of RNase in the top agar.

C. RESISTANCE TO INHIBITORS OF DNA SYNTHESIS

Isolation of RNA phages may be facilitated by the use of agents that inhibit DNA synthesis. Such a technique utilizing 5-fluorodeoxyuridine was reported by Davern (1964). Because many DNA phages are resistant to 5-fluorodeoxyuridine, other inhibitors of DNA synthesis may be preferred. Mitomycin D, streptonigrin, rubidomycin, and nalidixic acid have been found to be potent inhibitors of DNA phage multiplication but not of RNA synthesis or RNA phage replication. These agents inhibit the yield of both single- and double-stranded DNA phages by 97–99% at a concentration of 10 μg/ml or more in the culture medium, whereas the multiplication of RNA phages is not affected at concentrations up to 40 μg/ml (Fig. 1).

If these agents are to be used with bacteria other than E. coli, their effect on DNA and RNA synthesis must be determined. Otherwise, a bacteriophage resistant to a given antibiotic need not necessarily contain RNA. Organisms such as Pseudomonas and Staphylococcus are resistant to the action of certain of these drugs, perhaps due to impermeability. Other mechanisms for antibiotic resistance may also alter the effect of these agents on bacteriophage replication. In order to circumvent such limitations, sewage samples may be enriched sequentially through several inhibitors of DNA synthesis.

1. Enrichment Technique with Fluorodeoxyuridine

A log-phase culture of the host organism (2×10^8 cells/ml) grown in medium A is harvested by centrifugation and resuspended in medium A supplemented with 10^{-4} M fluorodeoxyuridine and 10^{-3} M uridine. A suitable aliquot of sewage sample is added and the culture is incubated at 37°C with aeration for 3 hours. The culture is then lysed as previously described.

2. Enrichment Techniques with Nalidixic Acid, Streptonigrin, Rubidomycin, or Mitomycin C*

E. coli are grown in either medium A or LB to a density of 2×10^8 cells/ml. An aliquot of sewage sample and the inhibitor, 20 μg/ml, are added. The culture is incubated for 3–4 hours at 37°C and then lysed.

* Rubidomycin was kindly supplied by Dr. K. E. Price of Bristol Laboratories, Syracuse, New York. Nalidixic acid was the gift of Dr. W. A. Goss of Sterling-Winthrop Research Institute, Rensselaer, New York. Streptonigrin was a gift of Dr. T. McBride of Charles Pfizer and Co., Maywood, New Jersey. Mitomycin C was generously supplied by Dr. Y. Takagi of Kyushu University Medical School, Fukuoka, Japan.

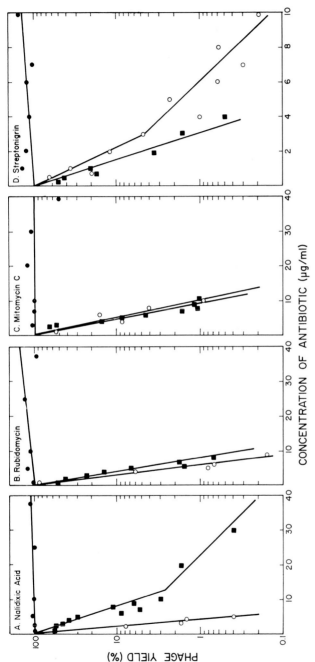

FIG. 1. Bacteria were grown in LB medium to a density of 2×10^8 cells/ml at 37°C in a gyrotory shaker. Phages were then added at a multiplicity of infection of 10^{-3}–10^{-5}, and 3 minutes after infection the various inhibitors were added in concentrations indicated in the figure. After incubation for 60 minutes at 37°C the cultures were lysed by the addition of 0.1 volumes of lysing solution and chloroform (1%, v/v), and the phage yield was determined by plaque assay. (●) RNA phage R23; (■) phage T2; (○) single-stranded DNA phage.

An aliquot of drug-treated lysate may be processed by several ad
ditional enrichment procedures in order to increase the likelihood o
selecting an RNA bacteriophage. The same or different antibiotic agen
may be used. The multiplicity of infection in these procedures shoul
be below 1, because replication of RNA bacteriophage is inhibited b'
superinfection with the T-even phages (Neubauer and Zavada, 1965)

The lysates obtained after successive enrichment procedures wit
inhibitors of DNA synthesis are diluted and plated on the host organ
ism. Phage stocks are prepared from each distinctive phage type presen
in high titer by picking a single plaque. Each phage can then be examine
for its host specificity and ribonuclease sensitivity. In addition, the exten
of suppression of each phage by inhibitors of DNA synthesis should b
analyzed quantitatively as follows:

$E.$ $coli$ are grown to a density of 2×10^8 cells/ml. The bacteriophag
is then added to 5 ml of culture at a multiplicity of infection of 10^{-}
to 10^{-4}. Three minutes after the addition of phage, 1-ml aliquot
are added to 20 μg of each antibiotic to be tested, and the culture
are incubated at 37°C for 3 hours. The cells are then lysed and th
phage titer is determined. The yield of inhibitor-resistant RNA phag
should be identical to that of the untreated control sample.

D. SIZE OF PHAGE

RNA bacteriophages of $E.$ $coli$ are small and can be separated b
virtue of size from larger DNA phages. The smaller DNA phages ar
not separable on this basis. Several investigators have used sucrose
density gradient sedimentation techniques for isolating small phage
(Paranchych and Graham, 1962; Bishop and Bradley, 1965). Theoreti
cally, separation on the basis of size may be obtained by other tech
niques as well, such as agarose and acrylamide gel filtration.

$Method.$ About 0.1 ml of sewage sample or phage suspension i
layered on top of a solution containing a 5–20% sucrose gradien
and centrifuged for 30 minutes at 30,000 rpm (SW 39 rotor) in
Spinco Model L ultracentrifuge. After centrifugation, the base of th
tube is pierced and 20 fractions of 0.25 ml are collected. The fraction
are then tested by the agar-layer technique. The small phages ar
located in the upper quarter of the gradient.

E. SEROLOGICAL BEHAVIOR

The RNA bacteriophages of $E.$ $coli$ presently fall into two serologi
groups (Scott, 1965; Overby et al., 1966). Newly isolated RNA phage

may thus be selected and categorized by their immunologic behavior. Nonoyama *et al.* (1963) have isolated several RNA-containing bacteriophages from sewage, selecting those phages that were inactivated by antiserum of phage MS2.

1. Preparation of Phage Antiserum

Antiserum is prepared as described by Adams (1959). Rabbits were immunized with RNA bacteriophage purified by the procedure previously described (Section II,E). The rabbit is given an intravenous injection containing about 10^{11} plaque-forming units in 1 ml of sterile saline at 3- to 4-day intervals for a period of 1 month.

2. Assay of Phage Antiserum

The rate constant k for neutralization of phage infectivity is calculated as described by Adams (1959). The k value of an antiserum when tested with various viruses can be taken as an indication of the degree of relatedness of the viruses.

3. Use of Antiserum for Phage Selection

To test whether phage is inactivated by antiserum, an appropriate concentration of antiserum is added to the top agar. Identical aliquots of an appropriate dilution of phage are plated, one with and one without antiserum. Replica-plating techniques may also be employed, the method being to stab successively through a sensitive organism in the presence and absence of antiserum in the top agar.

Immunologically unrelated bacteriophage may be selected by plating sewage samples in the presence of antiserum or by incubation of sewage samples with antiserum, the appropriate antiserum concentration and duration of incubation having been determined by the rate-constant k for neutralization of phage infectivity. Each phage isolated in this manner must be tested subsequently with the antiserum to confirm its immunologic unrelatedness.

IV. Identification of the Nucleic Acid

A bacteriophage isolated by one or a combination of the above techniques need not necessarily contain RNA. The phage characteristics used in selection are of relative value in making a tentative identification. Specificity for male bacteria and smallness of size are not sufficient criteria. Resistance of the phage to various inhibitors of DNA synthesis is a useful criteria, but it should be stressed that these inhibitors do not completely suppress the growth of DNA phages. The best indication of an RNA phage is serological relatedness to previously known RNA phages or inhibition of plaque formation by RNase. On the other hand, serologic unrelatedness and ribonuclease resistance do not preclude an RNA bacteriophage. Antigenically different RNA phages are to be expected, and double-stranded RNA phages, if such exist, may be resistant to the action of RNase. Other procedures are necessary to confirm that the bacteriophage does indeed contain RNA as its nucleic acid.

The method by which the phage nucleic acid is identified depends upon the speed and accuracy desired for the experiment. When a single phage is being examined, it is feasible to purify the phage and to examine the purified nucleic acid by a number of techniques. When large numbers of potential RNA phages are being examined, a more rapid screening procedure may be desirable.

A. Screening Procedure

Phage lysate is prepared in 50 ml of medium A as previously described (Section II,D). RNase and DNase are added to a final concentration of 10 μg/ml, and the lysate is incubated at 37°C for 18 hours. The debris is removed by centrifugation at 17,000 rpm for 10 minutes. To the supernatant 0.1 volume of 3 M trichloroacetic acid (TCA) is added, and the suspension is allowed to remain at 4°C for 30 minutes. The phage precipitate is collected by centrifugation at 17,000 rpm for 10 minutes, and the phage pellet is washed twice with 0.3 M TCA. The washed pellet is resuspended in 1 ml of 1 N KOH and incubated at 37°C for 18 hours. DNA is precipitated with 4 ml of an aqueous solution containing 0.3 M HCl and 0.3 M TCA. After 30 minutes at 4°C the suspension is centrifuged at 10,000 rpm for 10 minutes. The supernatant is analyzed for RNA by the orcinol method (Schneider, 1957). The precipitate is washed once with 0.3 M TCA, resuspended in 1 ml of 0.1 N NH$_4$OH, and analyzed for DNA by the diphenylamine reaction (Schneider, 1957). Depending upon the size of the phage and its nucleic acid content, about 10^{12}–10^{13} phage particles are required to determine the nucleic acid by this screening procedure. The result of this screening procedure should always be verified by analysis of a pure phage preparation.

B. Examination of Nucleic Acid from Purified Phage

The phage is purified as previously described (Section II,E), and the nucleic acid is prepared by phenol extraction of the phage. Freshly redistilled phenol is equilibrated with 0.1 M potassium phosphate buffer pH 7.0. The purified phage suspended in SSC is gently mixed with an equal volume of phenol. The nucleic acid in the aqueous layer is precipitated with 2 volumes of cold 95% ethanol and stored at −20°C for 1 hour. The precipitate is then collected by centrifugation at 10,000 rpm for 10 minutes, and the pellet is resuspended in SSC. The ethanol precipitation is repeated twice more in order to remove all traces of phenol. If necessary, the last traces of phenol may be removed by gently washing the aqueous layer with ether.

The nucleic acid isolated in this way may be identified by one or more of the following techniques:

1. Color reactions of nucleic acid components (Dische, 1955)
2. Sensitivity to alkaline hydrolysis (Loring, 1955)
3. Increases in absorption maxima following depolymerization with RNase or DNase (Beaven et al., 1955)
4. Template activity in DNA-dependent reactions such as DNA polymerase (Lehman, 1963) and RNA polymerase (Hurwitz, 1963) or RNA-dependent reactions such as viral RNA polymerase (August et al., 1965) or poly A polymerase (August et al., 1962)

REFERENCES

Adams, M. H. (1959). "Bacteriophages." Wiley (Interscience), New York.

Albertsson, P. A. (1960). "Partition of Cell Particles and Macromolecules." Wiley, New York.

August, J. T., Ortiz, P. J., and Hurwitz, J. (1962). J. Biol. Chem. 237, 3786.

August, J. T., Shapiro, L., and Eoyang, L. (1965). J. Mol. Biol. 11, 257.

Beaven, G. H., Holiday, E. R., and Johnson, E. A. (1955). In "The Nucleic Acids" (E. Chargaff and J. N. Davidson, eds.). Vol. 1, pp. 493–553. Academic Press, New York.

Bishop, D. H. L., and Bradley, D. E. (1965). Biochem. J. 95, 82.

Davern, C. I. (1964). Australian J. Biol. Sci. 17, 719.

Dische, Z. (1955). In "The Nucleic Acids" (E. Chargaff and J. N. Davidson, eds.), Vol. 1, pp. 285–305. Academic Press, New York.

Feary, T. W., Fisher, E., Jr., and Fisher, T. N. (1963). Biochem. Biophys. Res. Commun. 10, 359.

Gesteland, R. F., and Boedtker, H. (1964). J. Mol. Biol. 8, 496.

Hurwitz, J. (1963). Methods Enzymol. 6, 23–27.

Knolle, P., and Kaudewitz, F. (1963). Biochem. Biophys. Res. Commun. 11, 383.

Lehman, I. R. (1963). Methods Enzymol. 6, 34–39.

Loeb, T. (1960). Science 131, 932.

Loeb, T., and Zinder, N. D. (1961). Proc. Natl. Acad. Sci. U.S. 47, 282.

Loring, H. S. (1955). In "The Nucleic Acids" (E. Chargaff and J. N. Davidson, eds.), Vol. 1, pp. 191–209. Academic Press, New York.

Marvin, D. A., and Hoffmann-Berling, H. (1963). Nature 197, 517.

Neubauer, A., and Zavada, V. (1965). Biochem. Biophys. Res. Commun. 20, 1.

Nonoyama, M., Yuki, A., and Ikeda, Y. (1963). *J. Gen. Appl. Microbiol.* **9,** 299

Overby, L. R., Barlow, G. H., Doi, R. H., Jacob, M., and Spiegelmann, S. (1966) *J. Bacteriol.* **91,** 442.

Paranchych W., and Graham, A. F. (1962). *J. Cellular Comp. Physiol.* **60,** 199.

Schmidt, J., and Stanier, Y. A. (1965). *J. Gen. Microbiol.* **39,** 95.

Schneider, W. C. (1957) *Methods Enzymol.* **3,** 680–684.

Scott, D. W. (1965). *Virology* **26,** 85.

Strauss, J. H., Jr., and Sinsheimer, R. L. (1963). *J. Mol. Biol.* **7,** 43.

Watanabe, M., and August, J. T. (1967). Unpublished observations.

9 *Structural Studies of Viruses*

J. T. Finch and K. C. Holmes

I. The Scope of the Article

The highly regular nature of small viruses makes it possible to ask very detailed questions about their anatomy. For the small spherical viruses our knowledge now permits description of the gross outline of the protein and nucleic acid moieties of each particles. In one rod virus, namely, tobacco mosaic virus, knowledge of the structure is now approaching atomic resolution.

The two techniques that have made possible such detailed examination of the structure of the small regular viruses are electron microscopy of negatively stained particles and x-ray diffraction. In this chapter we consider both these techniques and attempt to give a detailed account of those aspects of the more general techniques of x-ray diffraction and electron microscopy that are applicable to the problem of virus structure. For example, we cannot attempt to cover the whole field of x-ray crystallography even as it is now being applied to protein crystals; however, we can attempt to describe how the special techniques of preparing and mounting virus crystals are carried out, and point out any special problems that arise in the theoretical treatment of the diffraction from viruses. A short account of diffraction theory is given. However, the aim of this is not to provide a detailed working knowledge of x-ray diffraction but rather to provide a logical basis into which such knowledge can be fitted. Of necessity, other textbooks must be consulted for a full understanding of this large subject (e.g., Guinier, 1963; Buerger, 1942; James, 1954; Lipson and Cochran, 1966; Holmes and Blow, 1965; D. C. Phillips, 1966; International Tables for X-ray Crystallography 1952, 1959, 1962).

We also show how the related techniques of light scattering and low-angle x-ray scattering are logically connected in order that the worker may decide which technique suits the problem that besets him.

The negative-staining method of electron microscopy is a much newer technique than x-ray crystallography and therefore is not nearly as well documented in textbooks. We have, therefore, given more space to elaborating the techniques of interpretation with regard to this method. Moreover, these techniques do not have the difficult theoretical basis of the method of x-ray crystallography and are therefore more amenable to treatment in a short article. However, the ramifications of the negative-staining method are beginning to become considerable, as is shown in work on the two-sided images and the interpretation of the resultant superposition patterns.

The aim of the fine structural examination of small viruses has been to establish the architectural principles upon which these viruses are built. Moreover, the small viruses are most probably model self-assembling systems and will display the nature of the bonding between protein subunits, which is necessary for self-assembly to take place. They also provide examples of the regular combination of nucleic acid with protein. The answers to some of the architectural problems have already been found, for example, in the theory of quasiequivalence, but the answers to many of the more detailed problems about the interaction between protein subunits and nucleic acids on a molecular level are known only in the broadest outline.

II. Principles of Design of Viruses

A. GENERAL

The infective agent of all viruses is a high molecular weight nucleic acid component, and for transmission to a susceptible host cell this is wrapped in a protective container to form the complete virus particle. Although the sizes and shapes of virus particles vary considerably, all those causing any particular disease look strikingly similar in electron micrographs. For all the small viruses for which the protective container consists almost entirely of protein, this similarity goes further than just overall appearance; all the virus particles of any one type have the same components in exactly the same symmetrical arrangement. The particular arrangements found for any of these regular virus particles are all based on a design principle closely related to the way in which the particles are assembled. The method of design is important, since a knowledge of the possible designs is a great help in predicting those features to be sought in structural studies.

The protein components of the small viruses consist of a large number of identical subunits of molecular weight around 20,000. In tobacco mosaic virus, for example, there are about 2000 identical subunits. Larger viruses may have several different types of protein, but each protein component again consists of many identical small subunits. The reason for this lies in the necessity of economical and efficient use of the coding mechanism in protein synthesis. The design of virus particles is thus based on the need to build a protein container out of many small identical subunits, and this can be done in only a limited number of ways (Caspar and Klug, 1962). If only one protein component is present, the protein subunits can be arranged either on a helix to form a rod-shaped particle or on an icosahedral surface lattice to form an isometric particle. The larger viruses with more than one protein component can combine these two types of arrangement.

B. Rod-Shaped Viruses

The structure of tobacco mosaic virus (TMV) has been worked out in detail from x-ray diffraction results (see Klug and Caspar, 1960). It is rod-shaped, with a length of 3000 Å and a mean diameter of 150 Å. It contains about 2000 identical protein subunits arranged helically about the long axis ($16\frac{1}{3}$ per turn of the helix), and the RNA chain is buried between turns of the helix at a radius of 40 Å. From the drawing in Fig. 1a it can be seen that the subunits are structurally all equivalent; that is, not only are they all chemically identical but each subunit makes the same contacts with its neighbors as any other. The structure is built using the same bonds between

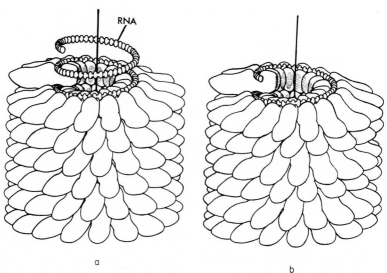

RNA

a

b

Fig. 1. Drawings of the structures of: a, the common strain of TMV; and b, the dahlemense strain (Caspar and Holmes, 1968). In each case about one twentieth of the particle length is shown. Each particle is built from a large number of chemically identical protein subunits. In (a) the subunits are all structurally equivalent; they exist in identical environments and use the same chemical bonds between units over and over again. In (b) adjacent turns of the helix are alternately closer together and farther apart around the particle; the subunits are structurally quasi-equivalent.

units over and over again. A helical arrangement is the only way of putting together a large number of subunits in structurally equivalent positions; the helix need not be so compact as in TMV—the longer, more flexible viruses, potato X and bacteriophage fd, for example, are probably also based on helical arrangements of identical subunits.

One strain of TMV (dahlemense) has an interesting variation on the TMV structure (Fig. 1b) (Caspar and Holmes, 1968). There is a periodic distortion of the helical arrangement, so that the subunits in adjacent turns of the helix are alternately closer together and farther apart around the particle. The subunits are not now structurally equivalent, since they have many slightly different environments, but because the same bonds act between them—varying slightly in length and angle—they are called quasiequivalent.

C. Isometric Viruses

1. *Icosahedral Symmetry*

The largest number of identical subunits that can build an isometric shell with all subunits structurally equivalent is 60, arranged with icosahedral symmetry (three units in identical positions and dispositions on each face of the regular icosahedron) (Crick and Watson, 1956). Although many isometric viruses have been shown by x-ray diffraction and electron microscopy to possess icosahedral symmetry, the number of subunits is always larger than 60. To resolve this problem, Caspar and Klug (1962) proposed a theory for the construction of protein shells built from identical protein molecules in quasiequivalent positions; for isometric particles, this accounts for the preference for shells with icosahedral symmetry.

2. *Quasiequivalence Theory*

The spherical icosahedron (the projection of an icosahedron onto a concentric sphere) partitions the surface of a sphere into the maximum number of equivalent (spherical) triangles, that is, 20. The positions of 60 equivalent asymmetric units represented by commas, three per triangle, are shown in Fig. 2. The process can be extended if the surface of the sphere is partitioned into a larger number of triangles, but now the triangles will no longer be in equivalent positions or have equivalent shapes, and thus the asymmetric units assigned (three per triangle) cannot be in equivalent environments. The departures from equivalence are minimized, however, if the spherical polyhedron formed by triangulation, called the *surface lattice*, has icosahedral symmetry. Thus the device of triangulating the sphere with icosahedral symmetry represents the optimum design for a state of minimum energy of a closed shell built of regularly bonded identical structure units, and the units can be said to be in quasiequivalent positions. Caspar and Klug (1962) enumerated all the possible icosahedral surface lattices and the numbers of structure units involved in each case in terms of a triangulation number, T. The number of triangles in the surface lattice is $20T$ and the number of structure units is $60T$. The possible values of T are given by the rule $T = H^2 + HK + K^2$, where H and K are any pair of integers (Fig. 3). The positions of 180 identical units (represented by commas) in quasiequivalent positions on the icosahedral surface lattice $T = 3$ are shown in Fig. 5a.

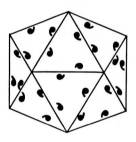

Fig. 2. Sixty asymmetric units (represented by commas) arranged with icosahedral symmetry on the surface of an icosahedron. Each triangle has an identical arrangement of three units related by its 3-fold axis. All 60 asymmetric units are in identical environments and thus indistinguishable from each other. The arrangement represents the largest number of asymmetric objects that can be placed together with complete equivalence of environment to form an isometric group.

The triangulation number can be factorized by writing $T = Pf^2$, where f is any integer and $P = h^2 + hk + k^2$ (h and k are now any integers having no common factor). Each value of P represents a particular class of icosahedral surface lattice; the classes $P = 1$ and 3 (on the lines OA and OB in Fig. 3) give rise to arrangements of lattice points related by the planes of symmetry of the regular icosahedron. Only the lattice points, not the structure units, are so related. All other values of P give rise to skew lattices that can be built in either left- or right-handed versions.

Since the structure units have radial extent, the precise representation of a surface lattice is not too significant. Two convenient representations (illustrated for $T = 7$ in Fig. 4) are the geodesic shell, in which all the vertices are at the same radius but the edge lengths of the triangular facets are not all the same, and the deltahedron, in which all the edge lengths are the same but the vertices are not

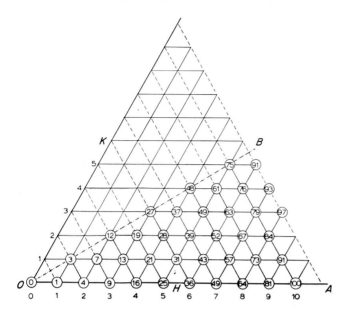

FIG. 3. Triangulation numbers $T = H^2 + HK + K^2$, giving the number of possible ways of triangulating a sphere to produce an icosahedral surface lattice, are shown in the small circles. For any particular value of T the number of triangles is $20T$, and the number of surface lattice points $10T + 2$. If the points O and T represent the 5-coordinated surface lattice points, the arrangement of 6-coordinated lattice points in their vicinity is given in the figure by the arrangement of net points between O and T. Values of T on the lines OA ($P = 1$, see text) and OB ($P = 3$) give surface lattices that are symmetrical about these lines; the rest give skew arrangements.

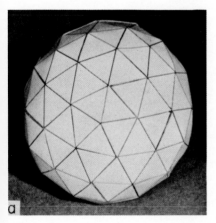 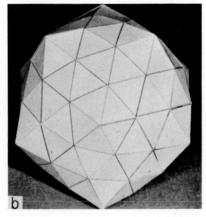

FIG. 4. Two representations of the icosahedral surface lattice $T = 7d$: a, the geodesic sphere, in which all the vertices are at the same radius but the edge lengths of the triangular facets are not all the same; b, the deltahedron, in which all the edge lengths are the same but the vertices are not all at the same radius.

357

at the same radius. The geodesic shell would be a more appropriate representation for a spherically shaped particle and the deltahedron for an icosahedral-shaped particle.

The number of morphological units seen in electron micrographs need not be the same as the number of structure units. The morphological units seen will depend on the physical packing of the protein structure units and on the resolution of the electron micrographs. The different appearances that can arise are illustrated for $T = 3$ in Fig. 5, but the same *local* appearances could occur for any T value. The

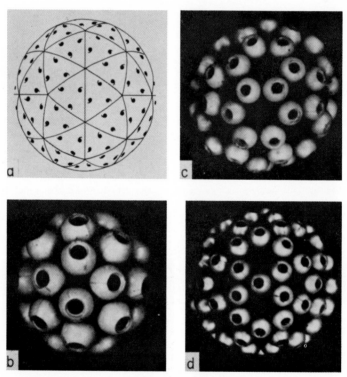

Fig. 5. Clustering patterns arising from different positions of the structure units on the $T = 3$ icosahedral surface lattice. In (a) is shown a drawing of a fairly uniform distribution of 180 asymmetric units (commas) on the $T = 3$ icosahedral surface lattice. The units are present in three different, but quasiequivalent, environments. If, instead of being uniformly distributed over the lattice, the units were clustered in 32 unresolved groups of five and six (hexamer–pentamer clustering) at the lattice points (the vertices of the triangles), the appearance would be as in (b) (compare Fig. 13b). If the units were clustered in 60 unresolved groups of three at the centers of the triangles (trimer clustering) the appearance would be as in (c). Clustering in unresolved pairs at the centers of the edges of the lattice triangles (dimer clustering) would produce the appearance shown in (d) (compare Fig. 14ii).

$T = 3$ surface lattice, shown in Fig. 5a, is composed of 60 (in general, $20T$) triangles, on each of which three structure units (represented by commas) can be arranged, related by the local 3-fold rotation axis through the center of the triangle; the arrangement on all the triangles is identical. If the structure units occur near the vertices of the triangles (the surface-lattice points) so that they are clustered in unresolved groups of five or six, the number of morphological units (hexamers and pentamers) is 32 ($= 10T + 2$), with the appearance shown in Fig. 5b. If the structure units are clustered in unresolved groups of three near the centers of the triangles, there are 60 ($= 20T$) morphological units (trimers), as in Fig. 5c. If the structure units are clustered in unresolved pairs at the centers of the edges of the triangles (the local 2-fold axes), there are 90 ($= 30T$) morphological units (dimers), as in Fig. 5d. The larger the morphological units, the easier is their resolution in the electron microscope, and thus hexamer–pentamer clustering arrangements have been the most commonly reported. If the structure units lie in general positions in the surface lattice with no tendency to cluster, it would require the resolution of the individual subunits over the entire particle image to determine the arrangement, and this would be quite difficult even in the seldomly obtained, completely one-sided image, and probably prohibitive in two-sided images.

D. Other Viruses

The larger, less regular viruses all have components that are rather similar to the regular viruses. The large bacteriophages, for example, have heads built of identical subunits, probably with icosahedral symmetry, and tails that are helical arrangements of other subunits. Apart from the determination of the structure of the various components, there is additionally the problem of finding out how these parts fit together.

III. *Interpretation of Electron Micrographs*

A. Negative-Staining Method

The technique that reveals by far the most structural detail in electron micrographs of virus particles is that of negative staining. The procedures used for specimen preparation are described in Chapter 11 by Horne and we shall confine ourselves in this section to the techniques used to interpret the resulting electron microscope images in terms of particle substructure. The most detailed results have been obtained with some of the smaller viruses and we describe these in detail since the methods used are generally applicable. The particular results obtained, especially with regard to the distribution of stain around the virus particle, will however vary from virus to virus, and for a given virus with the particular negative stain employed and the method of preparation for electron microscopy. While similar viruses under similar conditions may be expected to behave similarly, the possibility of variations should be borne in mind.

1. *Choice of Stain*

The amount of detail visible in the electron microscope images of negatively stained virus preparations varies considerably with the particular negative stain used. A comparison of the surface detail visible in images of TMV particles negatively stained with sodium phosphotungstate, uranyl acetate, and uranyl formate is shown in Fig. 6.

Fig. 6. Comparison of electron microscope images of TMV negatively stained with: a, sodium phosphotungstate; in places on the periphery a serration with a 23-Å period can be seen corresponding to the pitch of the basic TMV helix; b, uranyl acetate; the 23-Å serration can be seen more clearly, and occasionally the lines of the basic helix across the image; c, uranyl formate; the basic helix can be clearly seen and occasionally the lines of the higher 16- and 17-fold helices (Finch, 1964). The clarity of these lines varies along the image owing to superposition of varying amounts of the detail from the two sides of the particle (see Fig. 12).

With sodium phosphotungstate no detail can be seen in the image except an occasional serrated edge with a periodicity of 23 Å, which corresponds to the pitch of the helical arrangement of subunits. This serration can be seen more clearly with uranyl acetate, but little other surface detail can be seen. With uranyl formate, however, the basic helix is clearly visible, as are occasionally the higher 16- and 17-fold helices (Finch, 1964). These differences can be related to the relative sizes of the molecules or ions of the negative stain used, although other factors must also be involved. Sodium phosphotungstate is the largest molecule of the three and may not be able to penetrate sufficiently into the crevices between the subunits of the virus to render them visible in the particle image. Uranyl formate is the smallest molecule and can penetrate fairly deeply into the surface grooves, to an inner radius of about 60 Å (this has been shown by making the optical transform of the electron micrograph; see Section III,A,3). Uranyl acetate lies between these two in size, and likewise the appearance of the particle image is intermediate. A similar result has been obtained for the rod-shaped tobacco rattle virus by Offord (1966), who found that more detail is present in the particle images obtained with uranyl formate than with other stains.

In the case of spherical viruses, no difference has been reported between the images obtained with uranyl formate and uranyl acetate (the latter is preferred, since it is more stable in solution), but both give better resolution than sodium phosphotungstate. For example, from electron micrographs of turnip yellow mosaic virus negatively stained with sodium phosphotungstate (Huxley and Zubay, 1960a), the arrangement of the 32 large morphological units visible in the particle images has been found, and (after Caspar and Klug, 1962) the $T = 3$ surface lattice, on which the structure of the protein shell is based, deduced. With uranyl acetate as a negative stain the large morphological units occasionally show signs of a regular substructure, and the arrangement of the 180 individual protein subunits on the $T = 3$ surface lattice can be deduced (Finch and Klug, 1966; see Section III,D,1). In the case of the human wart virus (Klug and Finch, 1965), the arrangement of large morphological units on the surface of the virus particles was seen most clearly in, and deduced from, electron micrographs of preparations negatively stained with sodium phosphotungstate, and it is likely that the greater resolution of uranyl acetate is a hindrance in this case.

Another example of the differing effects of negative stains is shown ing Fig. 7. These are electron micrographs of the lighter protein layer obtained when a human wart virus preparation is fractionated by cesium chloride density-gradient centrifugation. In Fig. 7a, in which the specimen was negatively stained with sodium phosphotungstate, two main types of particle image are seen. One appears to be a hollow protein shell into which the negative stain has penetrated, and the other appears to be similar to the particle images of the complete virus particle and shows little penetration of the outer protein shell by the phosphotungstate. In Fig. 7b uranyl acetate was used as the negative stain. Again, two main types of particle are seen and again one of these appears to be a hollow protein shell into which the uranyl acetate has penetrated. However, the other type of particle image is of a shell with a similar external diameter, also penetrated by the negative stain but with an unpenetrated core. Electron micrographs of complete virus particles show no appreciable penetration of

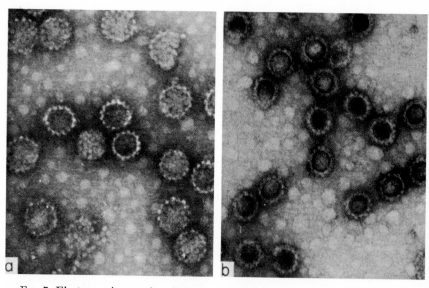

Fig. 7. Electron micrographs of the protein fraction of a human papilloma virus preparation separated by cesium chloride density-gradient centrifugation and negatively stained: a, with sodium phosphotungstate; and b, with uranyl acetate. In (a) can be seen two classes of particles, empty shells and apparently full particles; in (b) the latter class of particles has been penetrated by the uranyl acetate, revealing an inner protein core.

the outer shell by uranyl acetate. These results strongly suggest that there is a protein core present in the intact human wart virus particles that is sometimes lost when the particles lose DNA (Klug *et al.,* 1966a).

In summary, sodium phosphotungstate and similar compounds (e.g., borotungstate) are probably the most useful negative stains where gross external detail only is required. For the resolution of fine detail and where maximum penetration of the particle is an advantage, the uranyl salts are to be preferred; uranyl formate shows some advantage over uranyl acetate for the rod-shaped viruses so far investigated in detail, but at this time no advantage has been reported for this stain when applied to spherical viruses. However, these are only rough rules and it is always worth trying many different negative stain solutions on any virus in case one should prove particularly useful in a special situation.

2. Topology of Staining

In all the work described here that has given information on the distribution of negative stain around virus particles, the specimens have been prepared on the electron microscope grids by the drop method of Huxley and Zubay (1960b). In this method a drop of the virus solution is placed on the carbon film on the grid, washed with a few drops of 0.1 M KCl, and then with a few drops of the negative staining solution; the excess solution is then removed by touching the grid with filter paper. It is possible that other methods of specimen preparation may produce different stain distributions, but this discussion is limited to the method outlined above. The distribution of stain is different for particles on the carbon substrate and over holes in this substrate, and we shall consider these cases separately.

Since virus particles often have skew structures, in order to be able to determine the particular hand present it is imperative to have a convention for the loading of the electron microscope grid and the printing of the photographic plates. The convention adopted by Klug and Finch (1965)—loading the grids into the electron microscope specimen side away from the electron source (Fig. 8) and loading the plates into the photographic enlarger with the emulsion away from the

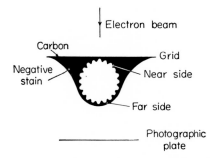

FIG. 8. Diagram showing how negative stain in general encloses an isolated virus particle on the electron microscope grid and produces contrast of detail from both the near and far sides of the particle, giving rise to two-sided images in electron micrographs.

bromide paper—ensured that for their investigation of the structure of papilloma virus particles, dominantly one-sided images were reproduced on photographic prints in such a way that the virus particles were represented as if they were opaque and one were seeing the surface structure from the outside.

a. *On the Substrate.* The first experimental results on the distribution of negative stain were those of Klug and Berger (1964). Using the optical transform technique (see Section III,A,3), the optical-diffraction patterns of electron microscope images of particles of tobacco mosaic virus negatively stained with uranyl formate showed that, in general, the negative stain completely enclosed the virus particle. Since the structure of TMV is helical and thus of a particular hand, the structure of the side nearest the carbon substrate (the near side; see Fig. 8) and the far side appear to be of opposite hands in the particle image. If the distribution of stain on the two sides of the particle were the same, the optical-diffraction patterns from the two sides would be mirror images of each other. In the case of TMV, the two patterns are well separated (see Section III,A,3 for details), and a comparison can be made between corresponding intensity maxima arising from the two sides. It is found that they are, in general, unequal in intensity and in spacing. The intensity difference arises from unequal development of contrast on the two sides of the particle, i.e., unequal distribution of the negative stain. The spacing of an intensity maximum relates to the radius (or mean radius) within the particle of the periodicity giving rise to the diffracted intensity, and it is found that this radius is smaller when the diffracted intensity is greater, i.e., the negative stain has penetrated more deeply into the particle. The high degree of correspondence between the optical-transform pattern and the x-ray diffraction patterns from the wet intact virus particles shows that there is remarkably good preservation of the structure of the TMV particles on the electron microscope grid; and the apparent disorder visible in the particle images arises from the superposition of varying proportions of contrast from the two sides of the particle.

In the case of TMV, it has not been possible to determine which side of the particle corresponds to which of the two superposed patterns, i.e., to determine the hand of the structure. This has been possible with the isometric human and rabbit papilloma viruses. Klug and Finch (1965) and Finch and Klug (1965) have shown (Section III,C,1) that with sodium phosphotungstate as a negative stain almost all of the images of the virus particles arise from contrast developed on both the near and far sides of the particle. For only about 1% of the images is the detail a result of contrast dominantly from one side, and from these both human and rabbit viruses are found to have the $T = 7$ skew structure; the human virus, however, appears consistently right-handed $(T = 7d)$ and the rabbit virus left-handed $(T = 7l)$. Thus it may be concluded that these images always arise by contrast dominantly from the same sides of the particles. By tilting the electron microscope grid [using a Valdrè stereo cartridge (Valdrè, 1962)] through angles up to 45°, it has been possible occasionally to identify the same (5-coordinated) morphological unit on the images before and after tilting (Fig. 9). From the direction of the apparent shift in the position of this unit relative to the circumference of the particle image, the unit was always found to be on the side nearest the carbon substrate. In the case of the papilloma viruses, therefore, the negative stain always encloses the near side of the virus particle, and there is a variable covering of the far side of the virus—sometimes so little as to produce negligible effect in the image and sometimes sufficient to produce contrast of detail equal to that on the near side. In this case the particle is completely enclosed in negative stain.

From the magnitude of the shift of the unit in Fig. 9 and the known angle of tilt, Finch and Klug (1965) showed that for isolated particles and those near the edge of a pool of negative stain there is considerable flattening of papilloma virus particles on the substrate, with probably more flattening on the near side. However, in close-packed arrays of particles, there is little flattening, and the particle structure is well preserved: this has been shown by following the changes in the two-sided images as the grid is tilted.

With the small turnip yellow mosaic virus negatively stained with uranyl acetate, Finch and Klug (1966) found recognizable two-sided images on the carbon substrate only where the stain was particularly thick, suggesting that in the normal fields the particles are appreciably contrasted only on one side. The images do not change appreciably when the grid is tilted through 45°, indicating that they arise from considerably flattened particles.

b. Over Holes in the Carbon Substrate. In the case of turnip yellow mosaic virus negatively stained with uranyl acetate, Finch and Klug (1966) found that all the particles over holes in the substrate were completely embedded in negative stain. They were able to account for many of the appearances of the particle images as superposition patterns of detail from the two sides of the particle (see Section III,C) and were able to compare the changes in appearance of the images as the grid was tilted with those expected from the postulated surface structure of the particle, as shown in Fig. 10. They found that for a tilt angle of 45°, the change in appearance corresponded to an

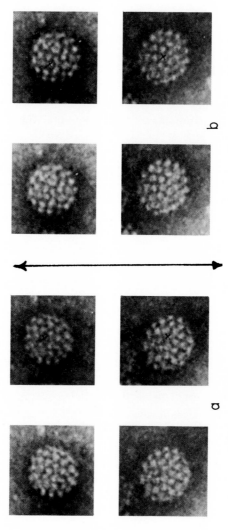

FIG. 9. a, Duplicate prints of electron micrographs of rabbit papilloma virus particles showing a clear 5-coordinated morphological unit, which is marked by X on the right-hand copies. b, Duplicate prints of electron micrographs of the same virus particles after the grid has been tilted through an angle of 45° about an axis parallel to the arrow. The new position of the 5-coordinated unit is again marked by X on the right-hand copies. In both cases the position of the marked unit relative to the circumference of the particle image has moved from right to left on going from (a) to (b). From the direction of this shift it can be shown that the marked unit lay on the side of the particle nearest the carbon substrate (Finch and Klug, 1965).

angle of 35°–40° for an undistorted isometric particle, corresponding to a small amount of flattening (10–20%) perpendicular to the plane of the hole.

3. Extraction of Periodic Detail

a. Artificial Superposition Methods. All virus particles possess local surface symmetry and the more regular viruses have, in addition, strict (helical or icosahedral) symmetry. As a consequence of this symmetry there is much repetitive detail in the electron microscope images. Markham *et al.* (1963) devised a method by which this detail can be enhanced in comparison with a random background. For rotational symmetry the image in question is superposed on itself n times at angles $360°/n$ to each other, where n is varied until appreciable enhancement of detail is obtained in the superposed image. For translational repetition, superposition is made of images successively translated a given distance; the distance is varied for maximum enhancement. While the method is clearly a good one in principle, there are certain dangers in its use. For example, false symmetry may arise in the reinforced version of a particle image which has an artifactual harmonic (Agrawal *et al.*, 1965). The process should, therefore, be repeated on many different images. Second, for the rotational case, if the symmetry axis is not in the center of the image, false impressions of symmetry can arise—for example, a unit that by analysis of the remainder of the image must be 5-coordinated can look 6-coordinated toward the edge of the image. There is also the possibility of pseudorepetition being mistaken for true repetition, and above all the effect of superposition of detail from both sides of the particle in the original image. It would, therefore, be safest to use this method only when the symmetry is known and in the rotational case when the symmetry axis is exactly through the center of the image and can be accurately located. Even in the latter case local distortion and stain variations can produce false symmetry, as has been demonstrated by Caspar (1966) with analog images of negatively stained models (Section III,C,2).

b. Use of Optical Transforms. The extraction of repetitive detail in electron micrographs can also be made by using the optical-transform method of Klug and Berger (1964). The experimental arrangement is shown diagrammatically in Fig. 11; the electron microscope image to be analyzed, E (the subject), is illuminated by a parallel beam of monochromatic light, the diffracted rays are brought to a focus in the back focal plane, H, of a lens situated behind the subject, and the diffraction pattern observed or photographed. Klug and Berger

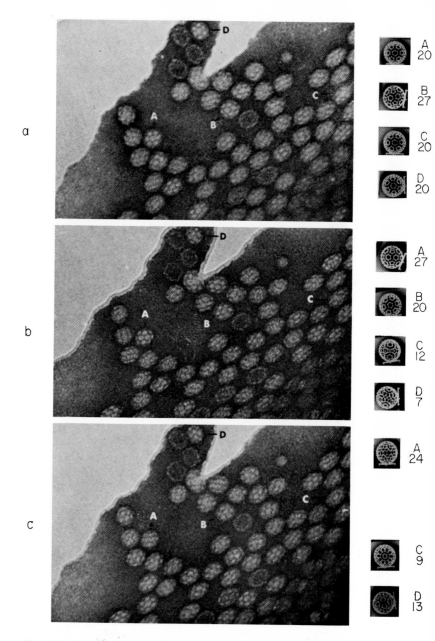

Fig. 10. Electron micrographs of the same field of TYMV negatively stained with uranyl acetate over a hole in the carbon substrate. The grid was tilted by about 45° between taking the micrographs (a) and (c); (b) is taken at an angle roughly halfway between. The direction of the tilt axis is shown by the arrow. The images

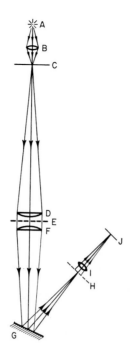

Fig. 11. Diagrammatic representation of the optical diffractometer (from Taylor and Lipson, 1964). The subject (the image to be analyzed) is placed at E in a parallel beam of light between lenses D and F. The optical transform of the subject is produced at H, the focal point of lens F, and can be recorded on a film placed at H. The transform can be recombined by the lens I to produce a real image of the subject at J. Parts of the transform (e.g., that from one side of a two-sided image) can be selected for recombination by an appropriate filter at H (see Fig. 12).

used a standard optical diffractometer (of the type manufactured by R. B. Pullin & Co., Ltd.); a full description of the apparatus and method is given by Taylor and Lipson (1964). The subjects used are copies on film of the electron micrographs mounted in a dish with an optically flat base containing immersion oil so that irregularities in the surface of the film do not affect the diffraction pattern. With the

---

of individual particles change dramatically between micrographs and, where the particle orientation is favorable, can be followed in terms of two-sided images using the gallery of shadowgraphs shown in Fig. 15. In the case of the four particles marked A, B, C, and D, the shadowgraphs (numbered as in Fig. 15) corresponding to the particle images are shown on the right of each of the fields, except for B in (c) for which no shadowgraph is available in the limited gallery.

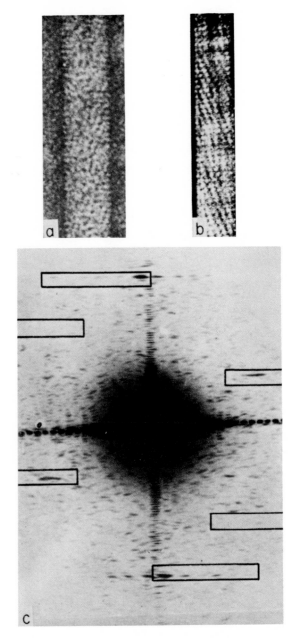

Fig. 12. One-sided image of TMV produced by reconstruction from a filtered optical transform of a two-sided electron microscope image. a, The subject—part of an electron micrograph of a TMV particle negatively stained with urany

standard source of light, a mercury arc lamp with an appropriate gelatin filter, the exposure times required are rather long (some hours); however, experiments with lasers show that a reduction of some orders of magnitude in the exposure time is possible.

A typical optical-diffraction pattern from an electron micrograph of TMV is shown in Fig. 12. Each spot or streak along a layer line of the pattern corresponds to a direction in which a regular periodicity occurs in the subject, and the distance of the spot from the center corresponds to the inverse of the spacing in the subject. The similarity between the optical- and x-ray diffraction patterns shows that the particle structure is very well preserved in the negative stain (to a resolution of 20 Å). The nonperiodicity of background grain in the electron micrograph only contributes a fairly random blackening to the diffraction pattern. The diffraction pattern shows that detail from both sides of the particle is present in the image; the contribution from one side is indicated in Fig. 12c. By comparing corresponding intensity maxima from the two sides, it is possible to compare the distribution of the negative stain on the two sides. It is generally found that the intensity maxima are stronger from one side of the particle and further from the meridian. This is because the negative stain has penetrated more deeply into the particle on this side, giving a greater amount of stain in the crevices of the particle surface, at a smaller mean radius from the particle axis.

The diffraction pattern of TMV is particularly favorable to such investigations because, apart from the equator, there is no overlap of the diffraction patterns of the two sides. In other cases there may be overlap between the two patterns or it may prove difficult to decide which diffraction spots refer to which side. There are two rules that help in the latter case: first, for a helical structure the patterns

---

formate. c, The optical transform of (a). The diffraction pattern of the particle is confined to equally spaced layer-line lines; as in the x-ray diagram (Fig. 60), the near-meridional intensity occurs on the third layer line. Unlike the x-ray diagram, however, the intensities on the left- and right-hand sides are unequal, since for a given layer line they arise from detail on opposite sides of the particle, and the distribution of stain on the two sides is not the same. The part of the pattern enclosed in boxes arises from the detail on one side of the particle. The strong intensity along the equator and meridian is due to the overall shape of the subject. b, The image of one side of the original particle obtained by recombining only that part of the optical transform arising from that side, i.e., the boxed region in (c) plus the intensity along the meridian and equator reduced to half strength by covering this region with a wire mesh. The image in (b) is much less confused than that in (a), and the regular substructure can be seen quite clearly.

of the two sides must be approximately related by mirror symmetry about the meridian (they would be exact mirror images if the distribution of stain were the same on the two sides of the particle); and second, the maxima of one side must lie on a reciprocal lattice (Section IV,A,4) corresponding to the surface lattice of the structure. The latter rule must be modified, however, if, say, two discrete surfaces (the inner and outer surfaces of a hollow particle, for example) are being contrasted; in this case there would be two related surface lattices with corresponding reciprocal lattices for each side of the particle.

The optical transform pattern can be recombined by a lens (I in Fig. 11) to give a real image of the subject at J. By placing an opaque mask (the filter) at the plane of the transform, H, with holes to allow through only the pattern of diffraction spots, the recombined real image will reproduce only the periodic part of the subject, i.e., the original subject minus background grain. Further, if the diffraction patterns of the two sides are well separated, a filter can be made to allow through only the pattern from one side of the particle, and the recombined image will correspond to one side of the particle only. A recombined image of one side of TMV is shown in Fig. 12b (Klug and De Rosier, 1966). In Fig. 12c is shown the optical transform from the original electron micrograph (Fig. 12a) and the pattern corresponding to one side is shown boxed, indicating the sizes of the holes made in the filter. The pattern around the origin and extending some way up the meridian and along the equator includes the shape function of the particle and has contributions from the patterns of both sides; it is, therefore, allowed through the filter at half strength by covering the hole in the filter with a fine wire mesh. The three major helices can be clearly seen in the recombined image.

B. One-Sided Images of Particles

Although most of the images of virus particles seen in electron micrographs arise by superposition of detail from both the near and far sides of the particle, a small proportion of dominantly one-sided images occur, and it is from these that the triangulation number, T, can be most easily determined. In addition, for symmetrical surface lattices ($P = 1$ or 3) the surface lattice has a mirror plane perpendicular to each strict 2-fold axis. If the arrangement of the structural units is also symmetrical (which is true for hexamer–pentamer, trimer, and dimer clustering) their positions are also related by the mirror symmetry, and thus the image of a particle seen down a 2-fold axis is the same whether it is one- or two-sided.

1. Hexamer–Pentamer Clustering

a. *Determination of the Triangulation Number.* Caspar and Klug (1962) have given the following criteria for regarding an icosahedral structure of the hexamer–pentamer clustering type as established: (1) at least two neighboring 5-coordinated morphological units must be unequivocally identified; (2) the arrangement of the 6-coordinated morphological units in their neighborhood must be discernible. (For a given triangulation number T, the 5-coordinated morphological units can be identified with the points O and T in Fig. 3, and the neighboring 6-coordinated morphological units with the lattice points in the region between O and T.) Some examples in which these criteria were satisfied are shown in Fig. 13. In the case of adenovirus shown in Fig. 13a (Horne *et al.*, 1959), the structure is clearly hexamer–pentamer clustering, with $T = 25$; in Fig. 13b turnip yellow mosaic virus can be seen to have the $T = 3$ arrangement of hexamer–pentamer morphological units (Huxley and Zubay, 1960a; Nixon and Gibbs, 1960). In both these cases the surface lattice is symmetrical, and for the images from which the structure was deduced it was not critical whether they were one- or two-sided. For rabbit papilloma virus, however (Finch and Klug, 1965), the arrangement found was hexamer–pentamer clustering for $T = 7$ (Fig. 13c), a skew arrangement, the recognition of which required particles in a favorable orientation to show at least two unequivocally 5-coordinated morphological units, and sufficiently one-sided to show the arrangement of morphological units around them. These conditions limited the possible number of images to quite a small proportion of the total.

b. *Size of Particles and Structure Units.* The maximum diameter of a virus particle is measured most accurately as the interparticle distance in close-packed arrays; these can usually be easily produced by using a suitably concentrated solution of the virus. The diameter measured across the particle image is often less than this unless the particles have appreciably flattened or collapsed. A third diameter (the surface of apparent end-on contrast) is deduced by knowing the arrangement of morphological units (the surface lattice) and measuring the distance between them in the center of the particle image (the distance between lattice points). This gives the diameter of the surface at which the contrast is apparently developed, although it is in fact developed over some depth and averaged. For human wart

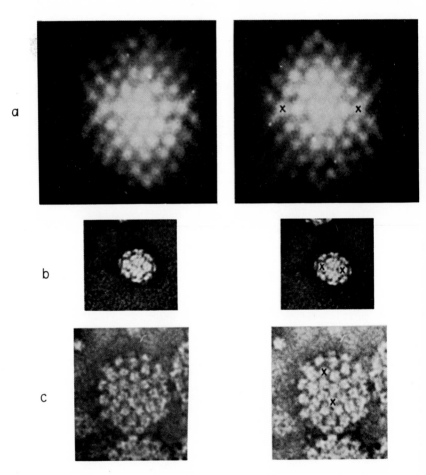

Fig. 13. Electron micrographs of virus particles (at roughly the same size) show-ing hexamer–pentamer clustering patterns from which the triangulation number can be determined from the arrangement of 5-coordinated (marked by X on right-hand copies) and 6-coordinated morphological units: a, adenovirus, $T = 25$, an example of the symmetrical class $P = 1$; b, turnip yellow mosaic virus, $T = 3$, an example of the symmetrical class $P = 3$; c, rabbit papilloma virus, $T = 7l$, an example of a skew class (see legend to Fig. 3). In both (a) and (b) the view is in the direction of a 2-fold axis of the particle; for these symmetrical classes and for this view one-sided and two-sided images are identical as far as the positions of the large morphological units are concerned, and the images shown could be either. However (c) must be a dominantly one-sided image, since in no view of a skew arrangement do the surface lattice points (the positions of the large morphological units) on the two sides of the particle superpose over the whole particle.

virus (Klug and Finch, 1965), the maximum diameter (from arrays) is 560 Å, the diameter of images of uncollapsed particles is about 530 Å, and the diameter of the surface of apparent end-on contrast is 435 Å. Thus the structure units extend about 60 Å beyond the surface of mean (end-on) contrast and probably about the same distance inside this to the main body of the particle, inside which the stain cannot penetrate. The distance between structure units is about 30 Å, and thus each subunit is roughly an ellipsoid, with a revolution of dimensions 120 × 30 Å.

2. Other Clustering Patterns

Clustering arrangements other than hexamer–pentamer lead to a larger number of smaller morphological units on the surface of a virus particle. The surface patterns are more complex and for interpretation require more stringent conditions of resolution and stain distribution. The particle images of turnip crinkle virus, however, do show clear evidence of dimer clustering based on the $T = 3$ surface lattice; some of these particle images are shown in Fig. 14.

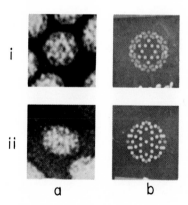

Fig. 14. a, Electron micrographs of particles of turnip crinkle virus negatively stained with uranyl acetate. b, Computed two-sided superposition pattern for dimer clustering of structure units on a $T = 3$ icosahedral surface lattice: the appearances are very similar to those in (a). In both cases, (i) is a view in the direction of a 3-fold axis and (ii) a 2-fold axis.

C. Two-Sided Images of Particles

1. Comparison with Shadowgraphs

When virus particles are completely enveloped in negative stain, the particle image owes to the superposition of detail from both the

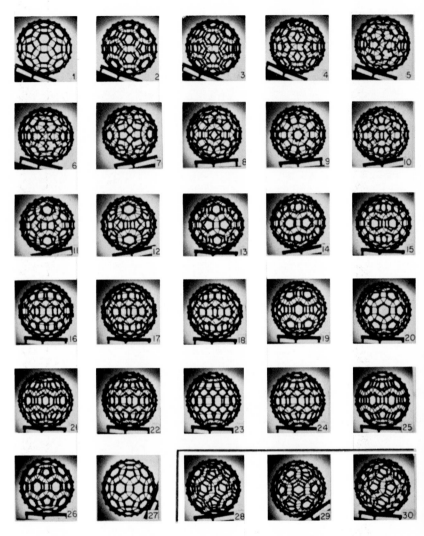

Fɪɢ. 15. Shadowgraphs (photographs of the shadow cast in parallel light) of a model of 180 units (balls) on the surface of a sphere, having the angular coordinates of the centers of the structure units of turnip yellow mosaic virus (Finch and Klug, 1966). (1) shows the shadowgraph taken down a 2-fold axis of the model with another 2-fold axis vertical, and (27) shows a shadowgraph of the model rotated through 90° about the vertical axis to another 2-fold view. Shadowgraphs (2–26) were taken at approximately equal intervals. Three other distinctive shadowgraphs that do not arise in the above set are also shown (28–30). The lines on the shadowgraphs are the shadows of the top of the stand on which the model was placed and which was reset at various points in the series, e.g., between (6) and (7).

near and far sides of the particle. In order to recognize these images, it is of great help to know the types of superposition pattern likely to arise. One method of producing these patterns that has proved quite useful is the method of shadowgraphs. Knowing the surface structure of the particle, a skeletal model can be built and its shadow cast in parallel light observed as the orientation of the model is changed. A limited gallery of shadowgraphs obtained in this way from a model of the arrangement of subunits in turnip yellow mosaic virus is shown in Fig. 15. Some of the more striking two-sided images of turnip yellow mosaic virus particles are shown in Fig. 16 compared with the corresponding shadowgraphs. Finch and Klug (1966) demonstrated that

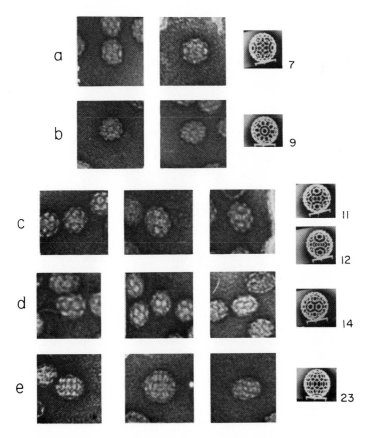

Fig. 16. Sets of distinctive two-sided images of particles of TYMV with accompanying shadowgraphs from the gallery in Fig. 15 showing how the various appearances arise (Finch and Klug, 1966). Set (b) shows views in the direction of 5-fold axes of the particles.

these are two-sided images by following the change in appearance of the image as the grid is tilted—the changes observed are exactly those observed for shadowgraphs of the model rotated by a corresponding angle about a corresponding axis. Some striking two-sided images are also observed in the case of human wart virus (Klug and Finch, 1965), and a selection of these is shown in Fig. 17 compared with the corresponding shadowgraphs of a skeletal model of the $T = 7$ surface structure. One of the most striking and commonly occurring image appearances is that shown in Fig. 17a, which is close to a 3-fold axis of the particle; only in a skew arrangement can the three morphological units in the center of the particle on one side superpose almost exactly

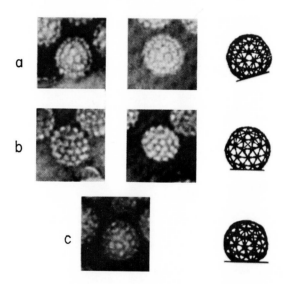

Fig. 17. Two-sided images of human wart virus particles compared with corresponding shadowgraphs of a $T = 7$ Geodestix model (Klug and Finch, 1965). (a) View down a 3-fold axis. The three central morphological units on the near and far sides of the particle almost exactly superpose in this view, giving rise to the three dominant central apparent morphological units in the images. The morphological units surrounding these on the two sides of the particle interleave, producing the appearance of terraces of smaller "units." (b) View down a local 2-fold axis between a 5- and a 6-coordinated morphological unit. The morphological units on the two sides of the particle superpose over the lower half of the image, giving the appearance of clear apparent morphological units in this region. They tend to interleave in the top half of the image, giving a confused region of relatively low contrast. (c) An image showing distinctive dominant morphological units (eyes). These units appear where morphological units on the two sides of the particle superpose, and they are separated in the images by more confused regions where exact superposition does not occur. Many different types of "eye" patterns are observed.

on the three central morphological units on the opposite side to produce the three clear, apparent, large units in the center of the image. Around these central units the morphological units on opposite sides of the particle interleave in projection to give the appearance of roughly triangular terraces of smaller units (the overlap regions). These two-sided images cannot, of course, distinguish between the two possible hands of a skew arrangement—the same superposition patterns occur for both hands and the same types of two-sided images occur for both human and rabbit papilloma, which have opposite hands.

2. Analog Method for Negative Staining

A basic deficiency in the shadowgraph representation of two-sided images is that the shadow of two superposed units is no stronger than that of a single unit, whereas the optical density in an electron micrograph would be doubled. A more realistic image can be obtained using the analog method for negative staining devised by Caspar (1966). The procedure used in this method is to coat a supposedly realistic model of the virus with plaster of paris (the negative stain) and radiograph it with x-rays of a wavelength for which the components of the model are relatively transparent compared with the plaster. The excellent correspondence of the analog images of proposed models with the electron microscope images obtained in the cases of human wart virus and turnip yellow mosaic virus is shown in Fig. 18.

3. Computed Superposition Patterns

While the analog method is clearly the best for testing a proposed model, both it and the method of shadowgraphs suffer the limitation that it is impossible to vary the parameters of a model without making a new one. Rapid examination of different models is, however, the most important requirement during the early stages of a structure determination. A new computational method has, therefore, been used by Finch and Klug (1967). The coordinates corresponding to a particular model are supplied to a computer with a program that calculates the superposition pattern corresponding to any required direction of view and displays it on a cathode-ray tube screen; the pattern is then photographed. Some typical computed patterns for a structure based on the icosahedral surface lattice $T = 3$ are shown in Fig. 19. The results are an improvement on shadowgraphs, since at places where units superpose the intensity is increased, and, furthermore, the extraneous components that are used in model construction and that confuse the shadow patterns are absent. However, the patterns obtained are not analog images, since no account is taken of the distribution of negative stain, which in particular affects the periphery of the electron microscope image.

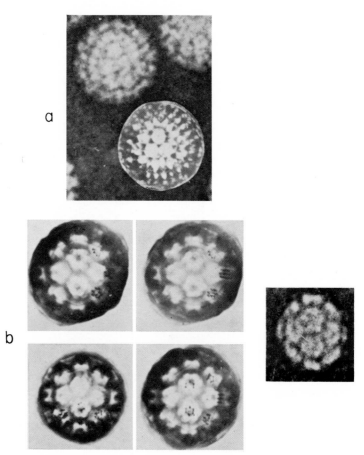

FIG. 18. Analog images of negatively stained particles (Caspar, 1966). (a) A two-sided electron microscope image of a negatively stained particle of human wart virus seen in a direction about 2° off a 3-fold axis. The inset is an analog two-sided image obtained by radiographing a model of the virus particle completely coated with plaster of paris, the analog negative stain. (b) On the left are four analog two-sided negative stain images obtained by radiographing a model of a particle of turnip yellow mosaic virus coated with plaster of paris, in the directions of 2-fold axes. These images show variations in detail similar to those found in the electron microscope images of the virus particles, one of which is shown for comparison on the right.

D. The Detailed Structure of Turnip Yellow Mosaic Virus

Although the gross features of many viruses have been reported, only for turnip yellow mosaic virus (Finch and Klug, 1966) has the detailed surface morphology and the arrangement of RNA been derived from electron micrographs. The various methods employed in this work are described below.

1. The Number and Arrangement of Structure Units

In order to locate the individual structure units on the surface of a virus particle in terms of their position on the surface lattice, a much higher degree of resolution is required than for the determination of the triangulation number, when only clusters of units need be considered. The resolution in images of turnip yellow mosaic virus is much improved by using uranyl acetate as a negative stain rather than sodium phosphotungstate. The 32 large morphological units seen at

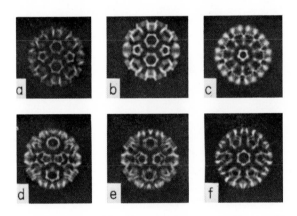

Fig. 19. Computed patterns arising from 180 structure units on a $T = 3$ icosahedral surface lattice. Each structure unit is represented in this case by a series of points at three different radii; the structure units are joined into hexagons and pentagons to give a result rather similar to the model used to produce the shadowgraphs in Fig. 15, but without the extraneous model components which also give rise to unwanted shadows in that gallery. The coordinates chosen for the computed patterns were skew, as is evident in (a), and this gives rise to structurally significant differences between them and the corresponding shadowgraphs produced by a symmetrical model. (a) and (b) are projections down a 2-fold axis, (a) showing the detail from one side only and (b) from two sides superposed. (c) is a two-sided superposition pattern seen in the direction of a 5-fold axis [shadowgraph (9) in Fig. 15]. (d) and (e) are a two-sided superposition pattern seen in directions close to a local 2-fold axis between a hexagon and a pentagon [shadowgraphs (12) and (13) in Fig. 15]. (f) is a two-sided superposition pattern seen in the direction of a 3-fold axis [shadowgraph (20) in Fig. 15].

low resolution, from which the triangulation number $T = 3$ is determinable, can occasionally be seen to be polygonal in shape, sometimes with discrete units at the vertices of the polygons. The 6-coordinated morphological units appear hexagonal and the 5-coordinated units pentagonal (Fig. 20). Although the proportion of images in which these polygons

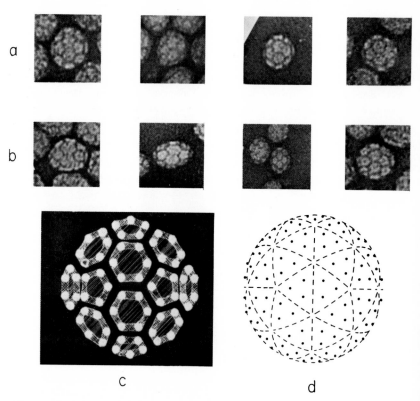

Fig. 20. Parts (a) and (b) are electron microscope images of particles of TYMV negatively stained with uranyl acetate, corresponding to views down or close to a 2-fold axis of the particles, in which regular substructure can be seen within the large morphological units. Group (a) shows one 6-coordinated morphological unit (the upper morphological unit of the central four units), which can be seen to be composed of six discrete smaller units at the vertices of a hexagon. Group (b) shows one 5-coordinated morphological unit (the right-hand morphological unit of the central four units), which can be seen to be either pentagonal in shape or composed of five discrete smaller units at the vertices of a pentagon. In both groups the vertices of the hexagon or pentagon point between the neighboring morphological units. (c) A drawing of the idealized distribution of intensity seen in the images of particles of TYMV seen down a 2-fold axis. (d) The positions of the vertices of the polygons in (c) shown as coordinates in the icosahedral surface lattice $T = 3$.

can be seen is quite small, their orientation is consistent and the vertices of a polygon point between neighboring polygons, as shown in the drawing of the ideal particle image in Fig. 20c. The fact that only on a very small proportion of images can this arrangement be seen is attributed to the fact that only in views *exactly* down the 2-fold axes of completely undistorted particles is there superposition of the centers of structure units on the near and far sides of the particles. However, for there to be superposition at all, a symmetrical disposition of structure units, as shown in Fig. 20d, is required.

This symmetrical arrangement of units was confirmed by study of the particles in square crystalline arrays. Not only is the particle structure better preserved in these arrays, but the particles are present in definite orientations. Thus any structurally significant regularity on a particle image repeats from particle image to particle image, and its effect on the fine structure of the image of the whole array is made abundantly clear. Thus the regular features in the particle images can be followed by the eye across the array and distinguished from the noise and local variations in contrast and distortion. One such array over a hole in the carbon substrate is shown in Fig. 21a. In this case, the collapse of the film has resulted in a compression of both the lattice and the particles approximately parallel to an edge of the lattice. Pairs of lines can be seen in places passing through the centers of the images and joining neighboring particles in the direction of the lattice rows, giving the appearance of a railway track of gage about 0.14 of the interparticle distance. Similar lines can be seen on arrays of the RNA-free top component particles (Fig. 21b). These lines appear to be produced by the joining up of structure units lying in a row, and the only arrangement of structural units that can produce such lines is the symmetrical one shown in Fig. 20d, which was derived from the single-particle images.

2. Location of the RNA

The positions of the structure units derived from the TYMV particle images show no particular clumping into hexagons or pentagons. In fact, the 32 large morphological units so dominant in appearance in images of the virus-component particles (Fig. 21a) are not nearly so apparent in images of the top-component particles (Fig. 21b). Thus, provided that conditions of preparation for electron microscopy do not affect the two types of particle differently, the contrast giving rise to the dominant appearance of the 32 morphological units in the images of virus particles must be the result of the presence of RNA—the space formerly occupied by the RNA in the virus particle becomes accessible

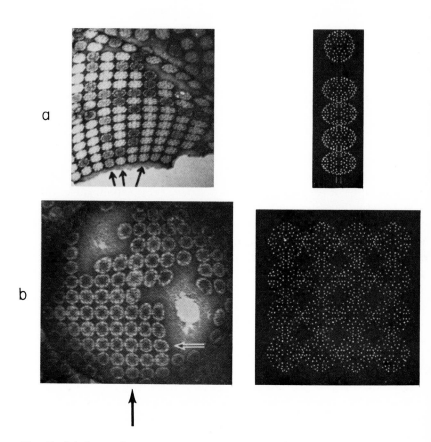

Fɪɢ. 21. (a) A two-dimensional crystal of particles of TYMV that is compressed in the direction of a lattice row owing to the breaking of the film of negative stain over a hole in the substrate. Pairs of lines having the appearance of a railway track can be seen linking adjacent particles in the rows in the direction of compression, and in some cases running right across the individual particle images. The rows in which these are most clear are marked by arrows. On the right is a linear array of 2-fold projections of 180 units in the arrangement shown in Fig. 20d; alternate projections are turned through 90°, as are the virus particles along a row line of the crystal; the row has been compressed by about the same amount as the virus crystal. Two rows of units (indicated by lines) can be seen running centrally across the particle drawing and connecting them. The distance between these lines corresponds closely to the gage of the "railway track" in the electron micrograph. (b) A similar crystal of TYMV top component in which "railway lines" can also be seen, more particularly in the rows marked by arrows. On the right is a drawing of particles, each with the surface distribution shown in Fig. 20d, arranged in the same lattice as the top component particles in the crystal. The clarity of the "railway lines" is similar to that on the particle images in (a).

to the negative stain in the RNA-free top-component particles. Thus this comparison of images suggests that a high proportion of the RNA is wound in such a way that it joins the structural units into hexamers and pentamers around the 32 lattice points.

3. Morphology of the Particle

The diagram in Fig. 20d shows the positions of the centers of contrast (by the negative stain) of the 180 structure units on the surface of the TYMV particle. It is possible from the detailed intensity distribution in the image to deduce information on two aspects of the particle morphology, namely, the "splay" and the radial extension of the structure units.

By "splay" is meant the broad distribution of matter about the center of contrast: can the structure unit be said to be directed toward or away from the lattice point closest to it? In the images of well-preserved top-component particles (Fig. 21b), the four central units forming the characteristic rhombus of this view can be seen as thin rings. The side of a ring farther from the center of the image always appears brighter, indicating that in this region there is a greater depth of matter and thus that the structure units are being viewed more nearly from end-on. On this reasoning the structure units are splayed away from the radial direction through an angle of about 30° toward the lattice points at an outer radius. While this effect could also be explained by overlapping from the bases of other units more distally situated, independent confirmation of the splay comes from a consideration of the various interparticle distances found for various modes of packing in arrays and crystals. This distance is greatest when the particles meet in the direction of lattice points.

The radial extent of the structure units from the body of the particle or, in other words, the depths of the grooves on the particle surface accessible to the staining material can be deduced from the images showing 5-fold views of particles (Fig. 16). The periphery of these images shows 10 promontories projecting into the stain, since in this view the morphological units around the periphery occur in 10 super-posed pairs. Thus each promontory is a region of double contrast, and the distance they project into the stain from the body of the image should provide a reliable measure of the extent to which the corresponding morphological units in the particle protrude at the surface of the particle. The clearest 5-fold particle images occur over holes in the substrate, and so absolute measurements of dimension are doubtful, but the promontories consistently project a distance 15% farther than the main body of the image. Assuming that the circularly averaged diameter of the particle images is the same as the spherically averaged diameter of the particle (known to be 280 Å from low-angle x-ray diffraction studies), the tips of the morphological units would be at a radius of about 150 Å and the valleys between at a radius of 130 Å.

All the facts regarding the surface morphology of TYMV are summarized in the drawing in Fig. 22, and, as mentioned in Section III,C,2, a model of the structure based on these results has been tested by the analog method of negative staining (Caspar, 1966), yielding results in very good agreement with the electron microscope images.

Fig. 22. A drawing of the outer surface of the TYMV particle as revealed by negative staining (approximately 2 million ×). The 180 structure units protrude about 20 Å from the main body of the particle, but their exact shape is not known. They are tilted somewhat out of the radial direction toward the directions of the 3- and 5-fold axes of the particle. The RNA is associated closely with the hexamers and pentamers at an inner radius (see Fig. 47c).

IV. Introduction to the Theory of Diffraction

A. General Diffraction Theory

1. The Physical Basis of Scattering of Light and X-rays

A beam of electromagnetic radiations interacts with matter by the oscillating electric vector of the radiation, causing the electrons of the material to oscillate. The movement of the electrons sets up small oscillating dipoles in the material, and these oscillating dipoles in turn reradiate an electromagnetic wave. Neglecting for the moment problems of polarization, we can say that each dipole radiates isotropically a spherical wavelet much in the manner of the Huygens elementary wavelet in physical optics. Since the electrons in the material are not free but are bound to the nuclei of the atoms by electrostatic forces, the degree to which they respond to the incoming wavelength will obviously depend on the frequency of the incoming wave, and this degree of response is known as the polarizability. Apart from variations in the polarizability, the physical basis of the scattering is identical for light and x-rays. In the following sections, therefore, we will present in outline a theory that is applicable to both of these phenomena, although emphasis will be laid on the x-ray application.

The aim of scattering studies is to find out the internal structure of a material by observing the scattered radiation. The amount of structural data available from such an investigation depends upon the state of order of the initial sample; for example, if we are studying a virus in solution, then each virus particle is randomly orientated with respect to its neighbors and, in general, we will not obtain a great deal of information about the internal structure of the particle, but only about overall parameters describing its general size and shape. However, if we are studying a crystalline array, there is a fixed relationship between the positions and orientations of the particles, and it is, in principle, possible to retrace the process of scattering in order to compute from the scattered intensity distribution the structure from which it arose. This, of course, is the basis of structural x-ray crystallography. In the following sections we will first derive general formulas for calculating the scattering from any object; second, we will show how it is, in principle, possible to invert this process in favorable cases; and third, in studies of viruses in solution, either by light scattering or low-angle x-ray scattering, we will show how it is possible to derive general parameters describing the size and shape of the virus particle.

2. A Simple Diffraction Grating

Since the geometry of scattering is not altogether straightforward, it is helpful to consider cases in order of increasing complexity, and we start with the simple problem of diffraction by a linear grating. Consider a set of scattering points, spacing d, arranged at right angles to the direction of propagation of a plane wave of radiation of wavelength λ (Fig. 23). If the angle between the incident radiation and the scattered radiation is α, then, as is well known, there will be a strong scattering in directions given by

$$n\lambda = d \sin \alpha$$

This equation describes the condition that the scattering from each of the points shall be an integral number of wavelengths before or behind that of its neighbor. Then all scattered waves add together in the direction of α. In other directions they interfere destructively to give a very low or zero scattering. Let us now consider a more realistic problem, in which each of the point scatterers is replaced by something with arbitrary scattering power. We must evaluate the scattering from an element of the length of the object and then sum the scattering from all such elements. The two variables to be evaluated are the strength of the scattering from each element and its phase with respect to the standard wave (which will be taken as that passing through the origin). The strength of the scattering is simply given by whatever function we choose to use to designate this quantity; for example, in this case we have used ρ (for x-rays ρ is proportional to the electron density). The path difference, and hence the phase angle, may be calculated (see Fig. 23) and is $x \sin \alpha$.* The sum of many

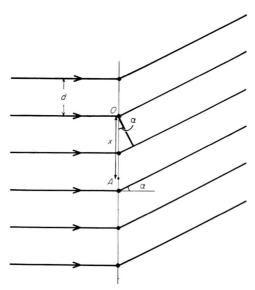

FIG. 23. Scattering from a row of points. The incident radiation is shown coming from the left. In order to work out the scattering in a general direction, α, it is necessary to know the path difference for a ray passing through a general point A as compared with a ray passing through the origin, O. This is $x \sin \alpha$ and therefore the phase-angle difference is $2\pi x \sin \alpha/\lambda$.

* In this treatment and those that follow we are assuming that the diffraction we are considering is essentially Fraunhofer diffraction, that is, we are far enough away from the scattering object that all rays leaving at a given angle α can be considered to come to one point and interfere. In the case of light, this condition is often achieved by inserting a lens to bring all such rays to a common focal point. In the case of x-rays, the radiation wavelength is so short that this condition is easily realizable in practice.

waves is conveniently arrived at by using the device that a wave can be represented as a complex number. In the complex number representation the amplitude of the complex number is put equal to the amplitude of the wave, and the phase angle of the complex number (i.e., its polar coordinate in the Argand diagram) is put equal to the phase of the wave. The sum of many waves is then simply given by the algebraic sum of the complex numbers representing the waves. In this representation the scattering from the point A in Fig. 23 would be written:

$$\rho(x) \exp \frac{2\pi i x \sin \alpha}{\lambda}$$

and the total scattering in the direction α is simply given by the integral of this quantity:

$$F(\alpha) = \int_{x=0}^{W} \rho(x) \exp \frac{2\pi i x \sin \alpha}{\lambda} dx \qquad (1)$$

Alternatively, Eq. (1) can be written in terms of its real and imaginary parts:

$$F(\alpha) = \int_{x=0}^{W} \rho(x) \cos \frac{2\pi x \sin \alpha}{\lambda} dx + i \int_{x=0}^{W} \rho(x) \sin \frac{2\pi x \sin \alpha}{\lambda} dx$$

This is the form that would be used for numerical computation. The result of the integration is a complex number, $A + iB$, whose amplitude $(A^2 + B^2)^{1/2}$ is the amplitude of the scattered wave in the direction α and phase, $\tan^{-1} B/A$, is the phase angle of the scattered wave in the direction α. Note that the integration has been taken over the length of the scattering object, which we have written as W.

3. *The Relationship between Scattering and Fourier Transforms*

Let us rewrite Eq. (1), but put s in place of $(\sin \alpha)/\lambda$. We have:

$$F(s) = \int_0^{\cdot} \rho(x) \exp (2\pi i x s) dx \qquad (2)$$

If W is sufficiently large to be replaced by infinity, Eq. (2) is the definition of the important mathematical operation known as the *Fourier transform*, so that we may say that F is a transform of ρ. Therefore, apart from the trivial change of variable of putting s instead of $(\sin \alpha)/\lambda$, we may say that the observed optical-diffraction pattern is the transform of the scattering density ρ. This statement needs qualification, because the film or device used for recording records the energy flux that is given by F^2 (more properly, since F

is complex, it is given by FF^*, which is real, since energy flux is independent of phase). The importance of identifying Eq. (2) as a Fourier transformation is that it allows the many powerful theorems known about Fourier transforms to be applied to the problem of scattering. The central and most important of these is the inversion theorem: *If F is the transform of ρ, then ρ is the transform of F.* Therefore, if we can measure the scattering amplitude and phase, we may compute the scattering density.

The light microscope is helpful in illustrating these concepts. The light incident upon an object on the stage of the microscope is scattered by the object in a manner similar to that which we have just described. In the microscope the objective lens gathers together the scattered radiation and combines it to form an image. The second step is exactly analogous to taking a Fourier transform of the scattered radiation. These concepts form the basis of the Abbé theory of the microscope. Unfortunately, with x-rays there is nothing that will take the place of the objective lens of the microscope, and the best we can do is to collect the scattered radiation and form the image from this by computation.

4. Some Properties of Fourier Transforms

1. The first and most important property of Fourier transforms, the inversion theorem, has already been mentioned.

2. The second most important property is the convolution theorem. To understand this it is first necessary to define convolution. The convolution of two functions is illustrated in Fig. 24. The first function is the drawing of a duck with a point marked in it to designate an origin. The second function is a two-dimensional lattice of points,

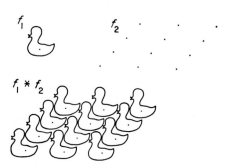

FIG. 24. A simple example of convolution. One function is a drawing of a duck, the other is a two-dimensional lattice. The convolution of these functions (shown by the * sign) is accomplished by putting the duck on every lattice point From Holmes and Blow (1965).

each point having weight unity. To convolute these two functions we put down the duck function on each of the lattice points giving the results shown. The operation is particularly simple because we have chosen a simple form (a lattice) for one of the functions. A general statement of the operation of convolution of two functions is: *Set down the origin of the first function in every possible position of the second, multiply the first function in each position by the value of the second at that point, and take the sum of all such possible operations.* If one of the functions is a lattice, which is only nonzero at widely separated points, then it is seen that this and the first procedure are equivalent.

The concept of convolution is useful because it considers a periodic structure, such as a crystal, to be made from two separable parts, the lattice and the density function describing the component molecules. In the example of Fig. 24, the lattice of ducks may be said to be a duck function convoluted with a lattice function. If we consider the Fourier transform of the convolution of two functions we find the following important result: *the Fourier transform of the convolution of two functions is the product of their Fourier transforms.* The converse theorem states: *the Fourier transform of a product of two functions is equal to the convolution of the transforms of the individual functions.*

3. In general terms the Fourier transform analyzes an arbitrary function in terms of all possible periodicities d and is, in fact, a graph with $1/d$ as ordinate of the amount of periodicity d in the arbitrary function. It is fairly obvious that if the arbitrary function itself is periodic, then only periodicities that are submultiples of the basic period will be representable in the Fourier transform. In other places the Fourier transform will be zero. Stated formally: *if a function repeats indefinitely with repeat period d, then its Fourier transform is zero except at points that are at integral multiples of 1/d from the origin of the Fourier transform.* Returning to the diffraction grating, we see that a knowledge of the connection between the scattering and the Fourier transform allows us to predict that the scattering from the grating will be zero except at integral multiples of $1/d$ of the variable we have called s (i.e., sin α/λ). Moreover, the theory we have given above allows us to calculate the strength of each of these orders of diffraction.

5. *Diffraction from a Three-Dimensional Object*

While the physics of scattering of x-rays or light is no more complex for a three-dimensional object than for the one-dimensional grating, the geometrical problems of calculating the path length are not so straightforward. Therefore, we give, without proof, the following construction due to Ewald (see Buerger, 1942; or Holmes and Blow, 1965) for calculating the scattering from a three-dimensional object.

1. Compute the Fourier transform of ρ (the density) in three dimensions. Call this F. Note that if ρ is periodic, with period d in any direction, then F is nonzero only on points at distances of $1/d$ from the origin in that direction; hence, if ρ is periodic in three dimensions, i.e., as in a crystal, F is nonzero only at discrete points (reciprocal lattice points).

2. Draw a sphere of radius $1/\lambda$ passing through the origin of F, making the line from the center of the sphere to the origin of F parallel to the direct beam.

3. To find the scattering in any direction, mark off the radius of the sphere parallel to the required direction. The value of F at the end of the radius vector is the scattered amplitude in the required direction. The Ewald construction shows how to relate a three-dimensional function (the Fourier transform of a three-dimensional object) to a two-dimensional diffraction pattern. It can be seen that the Ewald sphere cuts a spherically shaped section through the Fourier transform. In the drawing of the Ewald construction shown in Fig. 25, the object has been taken to be a crystal, and its Fourier transform is shown as a lattice of points. Because of the reciprocal nature of the relationship between the distance between these points and the spacing of

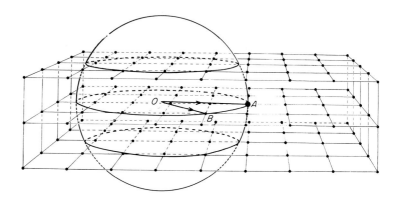

Fig. 25. The Ewald construction. A sphere of radius $1/\lambda$ is drawn so as to pass through the origin of the reciprocal lattice at A. If the reciprocal lattice point B lies on the sphere, there will be a diffracted beam in the direction of the line joining the center of the sphere to this point.

repeating planes in the crystal, this lattice is frequently known as the *reciprocal lattice,* and the Fourier transform space is often known as reciprocal space.

A simple way of thinking of the diffraction pattern from a three-dimensional object that is valid for small angles of scattering is to consider the projection of the object down a set of lines parallel to the incident-beam direction onto a plane at right angles to the incident beam; then the scattering calculated from such a projection is the same as the scattering that would be seen from a three-dimensional object in this orientation. Thus, as the specimen is rotated, the nature of the projection alters and the diffraction pattern alters.

The extension of the Fourier transform to three dimensions is:

$$F(\mathbf{s}) = \int_{-\infty}^{\infty} \rho(\mathbf{x}) \exp (2\pi i \mathbf{s} \cdot \mathbf{x}) d\mathbf{x} \tag{3}$$

Notice the scalar product between two vectors inside the exponent, which replaces the scalar product between two scalars in Eq. (2). The expression of this scalar product in numerically useful terms will be effected when a convenient coordinate system for the diffraction problem in hand has been chosen.

B. DIFFRACTION BY CRYSTALS

1. *Bragg's Law*

In Fig. 25 it can be seen that in general there will be no diffraction from a perfect crystal, since the Ewald sphere does not, of necessity, intersect any reciprocal lattice point.* However, if the crystal is rotated about any axis, then it is obvious that reciprocal lattice points will sweep through the Ewald sphere, and as they do this a beam of x-rays in the requisite direction will shine out and reach the photographic film or counter, i.e., the condition for reflection is that a reciprocal lattice point shall lie on the Ewald sphere. Fig. 26a shows an equatorial section of the Ewald sphere drawn to show a reciprocal lattice plane passing through the origin of the reciprocal space A. In this drawing one of the reciprocal lattice points, B, lies on the Ewald sphere. The distance of this point from the origin of the reciprocal lattice is $1/d$. If we consider for a moment the point B in isolation, the Fourier transform of the point B is a set of plane waves of spacing d. The

---

* In fact, for virus crystals the reciprocal lattice points are so close together that many will lie on the Ewald sphere whatever the orientation, giving rise to the still photographs; see Section V,C,1.

nodal surfaces of these plane waves are shown in Fig. 26b. Therefore, we can say that the point B *arises* from planes of spacing d with orientation shown in Fig. 26b. It is interesting that the incident and diffracted ray directions that we have found from the Ewald construction can be seen to make equal angles with the planes in Fig. 26b. If we call this grazing angle of incidence or diffraction θ_1, then by consideration of the diagrams it is simple to see that we can write $\lambda = 2d \sin \theta_1$, since the radius of the Ewald sphere is $1/\lambda$. This is the basis of the famous Bragg formulation of crystal diffraction. Bragg's simplifying idea is that the diffracted ray can be thought of as a reflection of the incident ray in a plane of high electron density in the crystal. As well as the condition for reflection (i.e., angle of incidence = angle of diffraction), on account of the periodic nature of the crystal there is the extra condition $\lambda = 2d \sin \theta$. Furthermore, if we consider the point C in Fig. 26a and imagine the diagram rotated so that this point lies on

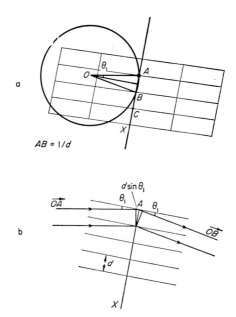

Fig. 26. The relation between real space and the Ewald construction. (a) An equatorial section through the Ewald sphere containing the zero layer of a reciprocal lattice. The point B has been drawn so as to lie in the Ewald sphere, and therefore OB represents the direction of a diffracted ray. OA represents the incident ray. (b) The point B is reciprocal to a set of planes of spacing d (since AB is of length $1/d$) at right angles to the line AB. These are shown in (b). The directions OA and OB from (a) are also shown; it can be seen that these make equal angles (θ_1) with the planes and that θ_1 obeys the Bragg relationship $1/d = 2 \sin \theta_1/\lambda$.

he Ewald sphere (Fig. 27a), we will find that the same conditions prevail
except that now we have $2\lambda = 2d \sin \theta_2$. θ_2 is now the angle of diffraction
when the point C is brought into reflecting position. In general, we have
$n\lambda = 2d \sin \theta$, which is Bragg's equation. The points along the line
AX in Fig. 26a, i.e., the points A, B, C, and the rest, form a series
that are all orders of diffraction from a set of Bragg planes of spacing
1 and that are quite analogous to the orders of diffraction from a
grating of spacing d. Following Bragg, the diffracted rays are called
x-ray reflections and the Ewald sphere the sphere of reflection.

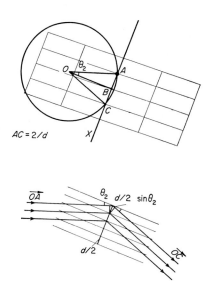

FIG. 27. The same as Fig. 26 except that the point C has now been brought onto
the reflecting sphere instead of point B. In (b) the corresponding real space situation
is shown. Again OA and OC make equal angles for the planes reciprocal to the point
C. Notes that since AC is now of length $2/d$, the spacing of the planes is $d/2$, thus
the Bragg relationship obeyed by these planes is $2/d = 2 \sin \theta_2/\lambda$.

2. Symmetry in Crystals

In the preceding analysis of three-dimensional diffraction, expressions
for the phase angle of a scattered wave have been presented as the
scalar product of two vectors [Eq. (3)]. This needs expression in
a coordinate system for any numerical work. Of necessity, unless one
is going to generate fearsome-looking expressions, it is necessary to
choose a coordinate system that reflects the natural symmetry of the
problem. Therefore, before giving a formula that can be used for

evaluating diffraction in a practical case, it is necessary to discuss the kinds of crystal symmetry that will be encountered. Moreover crystal symmetry is of great interest *per se*, since the external morphology of the crystal reflects the internal symmetry of the object making up the crystal.

A crystal consists of a set of molecules or perhaps virus particle arranged regularly on a lattice. A lattice is a geometrical abstraction of the arrangement of any regularly repeating system, which could for example, be a protein crystal or wallpaper. In order to find the lattice of, say, wallpaper, one would choose a conspicuous point on a design and put down a mark every time one came to it. This set of marks constitutes the lattice. By joining up neighboring marks, we would outline a repeating section of the wallpaper. This repeating section is known as the unit cell of the structure. The wallpaper may now be described as a lattice function convoluted with a density function representing the pattern inside one unit cell. For a three-dimensional object the unit cell is a parallelepiped from which the whole body of the crystal can be built up by repetition. Each block is identical in shape and contents with all the others and is in the same orientation However, it usually happens that the unit cell is built up of a number of identical units that are in different orientations. If these units still obey the condition that each one is indistinguishable in its environment from any other, they are said to be related by crystallographic symmetry and are called crystallographic asymmetric units. The unit cell may display certain kinds of symmetry, and this symmetry will also refer to the relationship between the asymmetric units within the unit cell. Three kinds of symmetry are possible—rotational symmetry mirror symmetry, and centers of symmetry. Of these only the first kind is found in protein crystals, since the other two require mirror-image relationships that are impossible for protein molecules because of the existence of only *l*-amino acids. Two kinds of rotational symmetry are possible. The simple kind could be explained by the example of considering a 4-fold axis. If an object is turned through $360°/4$, i.e., $90°$, about the symmetry axis and looks identical, then it is said to possess a 4-fold symmetry axis. Fig. 28 shows an example of the second kind of rotational axis, the 4-fold screw axis. In this case the object is essentially turned through $90°$, but raised through a quarter of the unit cell so that after operating with the 4-fold axis four times we come back to the original position, but one unit cell removed in a vertical direction. Since all unit cells are equivalent, this is a legitimate symmetry operation. By way of further example, a 2-fold axis produces an identical view if the object is turned through $180°$ and

he 2-fold screw axis lifts the object up through half the unit cell and
urns it through 180° so that after two operations of the 2-fold screw
ιxis one regenerates the same view of the object only one unit cell
emoved. Only certain kinds of symmetry axes are compatible with
ιroduction of a three-dimensional crystal; these are 1-fold, 2-fold,
ι-fold, 4-fold, and 6-fold. Such symmetry axes express themselves by
·equiring the unit cell of the crystal to be of compatible rotational
ιymmetry, which in turn leads to display of this rotational symmetry
n the external morphology of the crystal. There is only a strictly
imited number of ways of combining symmetry operators in space in
ι consistent manner, and these have all been enumerated. There are,
n fact, 230. The presence of the asymmetric α-carbon atom in proteins
mplies that we must leave out any space group with mirror sym-
netry. There are 65 such possible space groups available for proteins
(Table I). A complete list of space groups can be found in the "Inter-
ιational Tables of Crystallography," Vol. I (1952). The existence of
·ertain symmetry elements requires certain relationship in length be-
ween the base vectors of the unit cell. Space groups are divided into
·rystal systems according to these dimensional requirements, and these
ιre indicated in Table II. The base vectors of the unit cell are con-
·entionally written as **a, b,** and **c.** A subdivision of the crystal system
.s the crystal class that describes the external morphology of the crystal
.n terms of a group of symmetry operators called a point group. It
.s, of course, logical and quite proper to choose as the unit cell of
·he crystal that repeating unit that has the minimum volume. This
s known as the primitive unit cell. However, it frequently appears
·hat the primitive cell does not display the full symmetry of the crys-
·al, and it is, therefore, worthwhile to choose a cell of larger volume

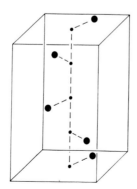

FIG. 28. A 4-fold screw axis.

TABLE I

ENANTIOMORPHIC SPACE GROUPS

System	Class	Space-group symbols
Triclinic	1	$P1$
Monoclinic	2	$P2$, $P2_1$, $C2$
Orthorhombic	222	$C222$, $P222$, $P2_12_12_1$, $P2_12_12$, $P222_1$, $C222_1$, $F222$, $I222$, $I2_12_12_1$
Tetragonal	4	$P4$, $P4_1$, $P4_2$, $P4_3$, $I4$, $I4_1$
	422	$P422$, $P42_12$, $P4_122$, $P4_12_12$, $P4_222$, $P4_22_12$, $P4_32_12$, $P4_322$, $I422$, $I4_122$
Trigonal	3	$P3$, $P3_1$, $P3_2$, $R3$
	32	$P312$, $P321$, $P3_121$, $P3_112$, $P3_212$, $P3_221$, $R32$
Hexagonal	6	$P6$, $P6_5$, $P6_4$, $P6_3$, $P6_2$, $P6_1$
	622	$P622$, $P6_122$, $P6_222$, $P6_322$, $P6_422$, $P6_522$
Cubic	23	$P23$, $F23$, $I23$, $P2_13$, $I2_13$
	432	$P432$, $P4_132$, $P4_232$, $P4_332$, $F432$, $F4_132$, $I432$, $I4_132$

which does display this symmetry. This leads to the concept of lattice type, which can best be illustrated by example. Let us consider an arrangement in which there is an atom at each corner of a cubic unit cell and one at the center of each cube (Fig. 29). One can check that each atom represents a lattice point by seeing that the environment of an atom at the corner of the cell is identical to the environment of the atom at the center. It is quite possible to choose a unit cell whose volume is only half that of the cube, so that the body-centered atoms also come at the corners of the cell. To do this. however, masks

TABLE II

CRYSTAL SYSTEMS

System	Minimum symmetry (with conventional choice for naming axes)	Dimensional requirements for unit cell
Triclinic	None	None
Monoclinic	2-fold axis (parallel to **b**)	**a** and **c** both perpendicular to **b** (but not to each other)
Orthorhombic	Three mutually perpendicular 2-fold axes	**a**, **b**, and **c** all perpendicular
Tetragonal	4-fold axis (parallel to **c**)	**a**, **b**, and **c** all perpendicular; **a** and **b** equal in length
Trigonal	3-fold axis (parallel to **c**)	**a** and **b** perpendicular to **c** and at 120° to each other; **a** and **b** equal
Hexagonal	6-fold axis (parallel to **c**)	Same as trigonal
Cubic	3-fold axes along cube diagonals	**a**, **b**, and **c** perpendicular and equal in length

he essential symmetry of the cubic arrangement, and it is inconsistent
vith the axial relationships in the cubic system. Rather than do this,
t is preferable to say that a different type of lattice, a body-centered
attice, exists. The different lattice types, called Bravais lattices, are
isted in Table III. In the tables we have used space-group symbols.

TABLE III
Bravais Lattices

Symbol	Name	Description
P	Primitive	Lattice points only at corners of unit cell
A B C	Face centered	Lattice point at center of one face of unit cell
F	All face centered	Lattice point at center of all faces of unit cell
I	Body centered	Lattice point at body center of cell
R	Rhombohedral	Lattice points only at corners of rhombohedral cell so that 3-fold axis of symmetry passes through body diagonal

The first symbol in a space-group symbol denotes the lattice type;
for example, P is primitive. The remaining symbols show rotation axes
that vary somewhat from system to system, and we will consider, by
way of example, the orthorhombic system. The orthorhombic system
has a unit cell whose axes are at right angles to each other but which
are unequal in length. The symmetry of the orthorhombic system consists of three 2-fold axes at right angles, each lying along the axes
of the unit cell. Consider the space-group symbol $P222_1$; this means

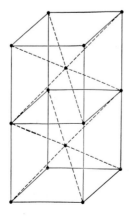

Fig. 29. Two-unit cell of a body-centered cubic lattice.

that the unit cell is primitive and that there is a 2-fold axis along the x direction, a 2-fold axis along the y direction, and a 2_1, or screw 2-fold, axis along the z direction.

The brief account given above can do no more than give a general idea of the types of symmetry that exist in crystals. For a more complete account and an understanding of space-group symbols the reader is referred to elementary textbooks of crystallography e.g., F. C Phillips, 1963; or a good review article by Lipscomb, 1960) and to the complete list with diagrams of all the space groups in the International Tables, Vol. I (1952).

3. *Structure-Factor Formula*

It is conventional to choose the symbols **a, b, c,** to refer to the unit cell edges. We mentioned above that the Fourier transform of a regularly three-dimensional repeating object is nonzero only at discrete points that are known as reciprocal lattice points. Conventionally symbols are allocated to the reciprocal lattice dimensions in the same way as to the unit cell, so that **a*** is the reciprocal lattice dimension corresponding to **a,** etc. (the direction of **a*** is always perpendicular to the directions of **b** and **c** in the real lattice). An individual reciprocal lattice point can be referred to by its coordinates in this lattice. The three symbols h, k and l are quite generally used in crystallography to identify a reciprocal lattice point, and they are written (hkl). For example, the position of the reciprocal lattice point (324) would be $3\mathbf{a^*} + 2\mathbf{b^*} + 4\mathbf{c^*}$, and that of (hkl) would be $h\mathbf{a^*} + k\mathbf{b^*} + l\mathbf{c^*}$. Now consider the equation relating the electron density to the scattering amplitude, which is the inverse of the equation relating the scattering amplitude to the electron density [Eq. (3)].

$$\rho(\mathbf{x}) = \int_{-\infty}^{\infty} F(\mathbf{s}) \exp\left[-2\pi i \mathbf{s} \cdot \mathbf{x} \, d\mathbf{s}\right] \tag{4}$$

For a crystal, $F(\mathbf{s})$ is zero, except at the reciprocal lattice points, and the integral of Eq. (4) could equally well be replaced by a summation over all values of hkl. Such a summation is called a Fourier series. For a reciprocal lattice with axes **a***, **b***, **c***, **s** may be written in terms of the lattice indices hkl, $s = h\mathbf{a^*} + k\mathbf{b^*} + l\mathbf{c^*}$. Similarly, **x** may be written in terms of the crystal cell axes $\mathbf{x} = x\mathbf{a} + y\mathbf{b} + z\mathbf{c}$. xyz are called the fractional unit-cell coordinates. Because the vectors **a** and **a*** are reciprocal, the form of the scalar product turns out to be simple and we have

$$\rho(xyz) = \sum_h \sum_k \sum_l F(hkl) \exp\left[-2\pi i(hx + ky + lz)\right] \tag{5}$$

This is the basis of the formula used in practice for evaluation of Fourier series in crystal structures, that is, for working out the electron density as a function of the observed scattering. The inverse formula can also be written as a series, if desired; in this case because the electron-density distribution consists of a finite number of atoms, $\rho(\mathbf{x})$ may be expressed in these terms. Because of the repetitive nature of the structure, the summation is taken only of the one unit cell and we have

$$F(hkl) = 1/V \sum_{j}^{n} f_j \exp\left[2\pi i(hx_j + ky_j + lz_j)\right] \qquad (6)$$

where the fractional atomic coordinates are $x_j,\ y_j,\ z_j\ (j = 1 \ldots N)$ and f_j is the atomic-scattering factor. V is the volume of the unit cell, and at low angles of scattering f_j is equal to the number of electrons in the atom.

4. The Effects of Symmetry on the Structure Factor

If a rotation operation leaves the structure unchanged, it must also leave the diffraction pattern unchanged. This can be expressed in more general terms. If a structure has an n-fold symmetry axis of rotation, then its Fourier transform also has an n-fold symmetry axis.

An n-fold screw axis causes the x-ray diffraction pattern, as far as the intensities are concerned, to have n-fold rotational symmetry. In addition, it has one other effect that enables screw symmetry and rotational symmetry to be distinguished. If the whole structure is projected onto the screw axis, the projected structure repeats itself n times within one unit cell (see Fig. 28). As far as this particular projection is concerned, the unit-repeat distance is $1/n$ of the unit-cell dimension, and this causes the lattice points in this direction of the reciprocal lattice to be spaced n times as far apart as they would be for a simple rotation axis. There can be no intensity at intermediate points. Therefore, if one observes systematically missing reflections, one finds evidence for existence of screw axes.

It is always possible to work in terms of a primitive lattice, and the primitive lattice will always have a smaller volume than a lattice showing the full symmetry. The x-ray pattern, which knows nothing about our choice of lattice, can be considered in terms of the primitive cell. If this has half the volume of the nonprimitive cell, there will be only half as many reciprocal lattice points. At other points there can be no diffraction. For example, in a cubic body-centered lattice with the indexes of the lattice hkl allocated on a cubic frame of reference, there is no diffraction if $h + k + l$ is odd. The systematic absences for each space group are recorded in the "International Tables of Crystallography," Vol. I (1952).

C. Solving Crystal Structures

1. *The Phase Problem*

In x-ray diffraction by any experimental technique available to us we can find the modulus of the scattered wave by recording its intensity, but we have no knowledge of the phase angle of the scattered radiation. Unless we can supply this missing information about the phase from some other experimental source, we cannot invert the process of Fourier transformation in order to calculate the electron density from the observed scattering amplitudes. Most of the history of crystallography has been concerned with attempts to solve the phase problem.

2. *The Patterson Function*

Since experimentally we have available only the intensity of the radiation, we might consider the possibility of taking the Fourier transform of the intensity. It can be shown that this gives us the Patterson function, which bears the following relationship to the actual structure. The Patterson of an object consists of the convolution of the object with itself inverted through a center of symmetry. Necessarily, if the object itself has a center of symmetry, then the Patterson function consists of the convolution of an object with itself. In general crystallography it is not usual to consider the Patterson as being a convolution function, but rather to make use of the following result. *If a density function consists of point atoms, then the convolution of this function with its inverse is equivalent to producing a map of all possible vectors between atoms.* In the case of low-angle x-ray scattering and light scattering, it is frequently necessary to consider the Patterson function, and then it is generally more useful to consider it in terms of the convolution function, as defined above.

An illustration of the meaning of a Patterson or vector map for a simple structure consisting of three point atoms is shown in Fig. 30. The structure is shown on the left and its Patterson on the right. If the structure is simple, for example, a small organic molecule, then it can be envisaged that the availability of the Patterson function shown on the right would enable one to postulate the shape of the original structure, and this is, in fact, how most simple crystallographic problems have been solved. With something having the complexity of a protein molecule, this procedure is quite impossible, and for a virus

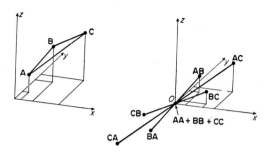

Fig. 30. The Patterson function: the object shown on the left gives rise to the interatomic vectors shown on the right. For example, vector **AB** becomes the vector **OAB** and vector **BA** becomes vector **OBA**.

is unthinkable. However, a low resolution Patterson, that is, one using data only up to limited angles of diffraction, might be useful for testing a certain simple virus model; for example, the model might produce a high number of vectors of a similar length between protein subunits and these would be expected to show up in the Patterson. Patterson methods are also useful in locating heavy atom positions.

3. The Method of Isomorphous Replacement

In proteins the phase problem has been solved by adding onto the protein very heavy metal atoms that scatter x-rays much more strongly than the light atoms of the protein. If the positions of the additional atoms can be established by comparison of the scattering intensities from the protein and from the protein with the heavy atom, it is possible to find the phase of the scattered radiation from the protein (Holmes and Blow, 1965). It is not yet clearly established whether such a method can work for crystalline viruses, but one hopes that it may. Success has been obtained by applying this method to the rod virus, tobacco mosaic virus (Section III,D).

D. Diffraction in Systems with Cylindrical Symmetry

1. Diffraction from Orientated Virus Sols and Gels

A few members of the class of rigid rod viruses have been induced to form specimens in which all the virus particles are accurately aligned along the axis of a capillary tube, but in which the azimuthal orientation of the virus particle is completely random. The archetype of such systems is the sol of tobacco mosaic virus (TMV), and most of the discussion hereafter will be concerned with TMV. The conditions for forming orientated sols of TMV will be discussed below. Here we are

concerned with describing the nature of the diffraction pattern produced by such virus specimens. TMV and other similar rodlike viruses
are known from preliminary x-ray studies to be helical; therefore, the
problem of understanding the diffraction from TMV sols really breaks
into two parts. The first is to understand the diffraction pattern from
a helix, and the second is to know the effects of cylindrical averaging
on this diffraction pattern. Both problems have their simplest mathematical form if one expresses coordinates and diffraction patterns in
terms of cylindrical polar coordinates (Fig. 31). The results given
below may be fairly readily obtained by expressing the equations for
the Fourier transform [Eq. (3)] in cylindrical polar coordinates (Klug
et al., 1958). Since this derivation is beyond the scope of the present
article, the results are quoted without proof.

   The nature of the diffraction problem is well illustrated by making
use of the "optical transform." In the x-ray experiment, a beam of
x-rays is shone at right angles to the long axis of the specimen of a
TMV sol, and the diffraction pattern is recorded upon a film at right
angles to the x-ray beam at a suitable distance from the specimen.
Making use of the analogy between light and x-rays, if a parallel
beam of light is shone onto a drawing of a helix at right angles to
the beam of light and the diffraction pattern is recorded on a film,
one obtains a pattern such as that shown in Fig. 32. On the left is
shown a diagram of a helix and on the right its diffraction pattern.
Note that the diffraction pattern is broken into layer lines of intensity
that occur in reciprocal space perpendicular to the particle axis at
spacings that are integral multiples of $1/c$, where c is the helix pitch.
A more realistic example is shown in the next diagram (Fig. 33).
Here we have the diffraction pattern produced by a helix of discrete

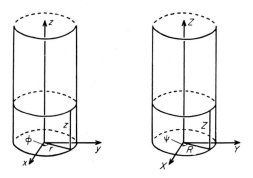

FIG. 31. Cylindrical polar coordinates. On the left are shown real coordinates; on
the right, reciprocal space coordinates.

points, and we see that the diffraction pattern, while retaining many of the features of that of the continuous helix, is more complicated.

The mathematical form of the Fourier transform from a simple helix may be shown to be (Cochran *et al.*, 1952)

$$F(R,\psi,n/c) = J_n(2\pi R r_o) \exp[in(\psi - \phi_o + \pi/2)] \tag{7}$$

where r_o is the radius of the helix, R is the reciprocal space radius, ϕ_o is an angle giving the origin of coordinates for the helix, ψ is the azimuthal angle measured in reciprocal space, and c is the pitch of the helix. J_n is a Bessel function of order n. Bessel functions are oscillating functions rather like a cosine, but they attenuate as one goes to higher arguments. One interesting and important property of Bessel

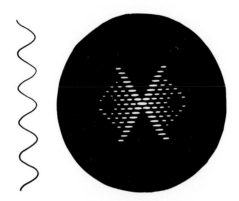

Fig. 32. Optical transform of a continuous helix. From Holmes and Blow (1965).

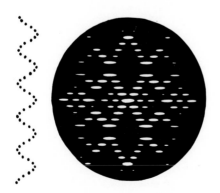

Fig. 33. Optical transform of a helix with 10 points in one turn. From Holmes and Blow (1965).

functions is shown in Fig. 34. This diagram shows that, as the order of the Bessel function increases, the value of the Bessel function stays near zero until the argument becomes nearly equal to the order. Low-order Bessel functions assume a nonzero value very near the origin, but high-order Bessel functions are essentially zero for a long range of the argument. When the argument is about equal to the order, the Bessel function starts with a strong bump and then behaves as an attenuated sine wave. It may be shown, for a simple helix, that the order of a Bessel function found on layer line l is l; for example, on the third layer line one would find the Bessel function of order 3, etc.

To relate the Fourier transfrom to x-ray- or light-diffraction photograph it is necessary to use the Ewald construction (Section IV,A,5). The construction appropriate for the experimental arrangement discussed here is shown in Fig. 35. Each of the discs represents a layer of reciprocal space intensity that varies as a function of the distance R from the axis of the Fourier transform. The Ewald sphere essentially cuts a section through each layer of intensity. We see on the photograph the projection of this spherical section onto the film as a set of layer lines. In Fig. 35b is shown the effect of tilting the specimen. Regions of the diffraction pattern otherwise not visible are obtainable by a suitable specimen tilt, since the Fourier transform tilts with the specimen.

Returning to Fig. 33, we may relate the optical transform to the mathematical expression of the Fourier transform [Eq. (7)]. Each of the strong spots arises from the first peak of a Bessel function whose order is equal to the layer-line number. Therefore, on high layer lines

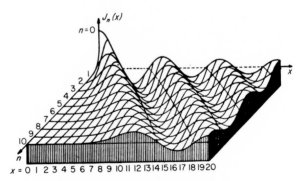

Fig. 34. The Bessel function $J_n(x)$ as functions of n and x. Note that J_0 is large at the origin, but that all other orders are zero at the origin. At large values of n the first maximum value of the Bessel function $J_n(x)$ occurs at a value of x close to n. After the first maximum all the Bessel functions oscillate like an attenuated sine wave (Jahnke and Emde, 1945).

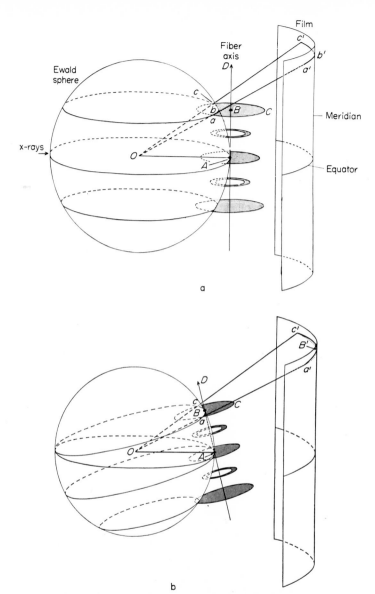

FIG. 35. Fiber diffraction geometry. (a) The shaded discs represent the Fourier transform of a fiber. The lines drawn through the intersection of the discs with the Ewald sphere from the center O of the sphere represent the scattered ray directions. The points of intersection of the disc C with the sphere, which are a, b, and c, give a', b', and c' on the film. The points a', b', and c' form a layer line. Note that the point B does not give rise to any point on the film. (b) The same as (a), but the fiber axis has been tilted so as to bring the point B into the reflecting position. Note that the point B projects onto the meridian at B' and that the layer line is no longer straight. From Holmes and Blow (1965).

the diffraction occurs far out, but on low layer lines the diffraction is near the meridian (axis of reciprocal space), thereby forming the characteristic cross that is associated with the diffraction from the helix. In the more complex case of diffraction from a helix made up of points, the orders of Bessel functions occurring on various layer lines are given by the following selection rule:

$$l = tn + um \tag{8}$$

Here l is the layer-line number, n is the order of Bessel function, m is any positive, negative, or zero integer, and u and t are numbers such that there are u scattering units in t turns of the helix. For example, in TMV there are 49 subunits arranged in three turns of the helix. After three turns the structure repeats exactly. The form of the Fourier transform of a helix of discrete point scatterers is a little more complex and is

$$F(R,\psi,l/c) = \sum_n J_n(2\pi R r_o) \exp(2\pi i l z_o/c) \exp in(\psi - \phi_o + \pi/2) \tag{9}$$

z_o is the coordinate of the point on the helix taken as origin and n is given by the selection rule. Note that there is an extra phase term taking account of the variable z_o. The term c is now the distance in which the structure repeats exactly. From this we see that, knowing the geometrical parameters of the helix, i.e., t, u, and c, it is possible to predict the general shape of the diffraction pattern. The detailed appearance must, of course, depend upon the arrangement of all the atoms in the structure, but the occurrence of certain Bessel function terms on certain layer lines is determined only by the helical parameters. Conversely, in favorable cases, it is possible to determine the helical parameters by observing the general shape of the diffraction pattern. Generalizing Eq. (9), the transform of a real structure consisting of many atoms may be written as

$$F(R,\psi,l/c) = \sum_n \sum_j f_j J_n(2\pi R r_j) \exp i[n(\psi - \phi_j + \pi/2) + 2\pi l z_j/c]$$

where f_i is the scattering power of atom j and the subscript j on coordinates refers to atom j. Frequently it is useful to think of the electron density not as concentrated in atoms but as a continuous function of position in the structure, in which case the equation assumes a slightly different form,

$$F(R,\psi,l/c) = \sum_n \int_o^\infty \int_o^{2\pi} \int_o^c \rho(r,\psi,Z) J_n(2\pi R r) \exp i[n(\psi - \phi + \pi/2) \\ + 2\pi l z/c] \, dz \, rd\phi \, dr$$

This equation may be simplified by making the substitution

$$g_{nl}(r) = 1/2\pi \int_o^c \int_o^{2\pi} \rho(r,\psi,z) \exp\left[-i(n\phi - 2\pi lz/c)\right] d\phi dz \qquad (10)$$

in which case we may write

$$F(R,\psi,l/c) = \sum_n \exp in(\psi + \pi/2) \int_o^\infty g_{nl}(r) J_n(2\pi Rr) 2\pi r dr \qquad (11)$$

Klug et $al.$ (1958) define

$$G_{nl}(R) = \int_o^\infty g_{nl}(r) J_n(2\pi Rr) 2\pi r dr \qquad (12)$$

whereupon we have

$$F(R,\psi,l/c) = \sum_n G_{nl}(R) \exp in(\psi + \pi/2) \qquad (13)$$

showing that G_{nl} is the n'th azimuthal harmonic of F on layer line l. From the point of view of the work on the structure on TMV, which we will describe below, the most important consequence of these equations is that one can write down their inverse equations, that is, the equations relating the electron density to the observed Fourier transform or scattering factors. In full this is

$$\rho(r,\phi,z) = 1/c \sum_l \sum_n \int_o^{2\pi} \int_o^\infty F(R,\psi,l/c) J_n(2\pi Rr) \exp i[n(\phi - \psi + \pi/2) - 2\pi lz/c]RdRd\psi \qquad (14)$$

To prove Eq. (14), Klug et $al.$ proceed in steps and first show that the inverse of Eq. (12) is true, $viz.$,

$$g_{nl}(r) = \int_o^\infty G_{nl}(R) J_n(2\pi Rr) 2\pi R dR \qquad (15)$$

and then find the inverse to Eq. (10) as

$$\rho(r,\phi,z) = 1/c \sum_n \sum_l g_{nl}(r) \exp\left[i(n\phi - 2\pi lz/c)\right] \qquad (16)$$

Eqs. (14) and (16) are, in effect, identical. Therefore, if one can find experimentally the values of the various terms G_{nl}, then from Eqs. (15) and (16) it is possible to compute the electron density of the virus. This has been successfully completed at limited resolution for tobacco mosaic virus (Section VII,D,4). Hence in favorable circumstances, by studying the fiber-diffraction patterns, it is possible to find out facts about the structure of the protein subunits of the virus.

2. *The Effects of Cylindrical Averaging*

Thus far we have ignored one important experimental difficulty; that is, we observe not the diffraction pattern from a regular crystalline array of virus particles, but rather that from an orientated sol in which the virus particles are randomly arranged about their long axis. The effect of this random arrangement is that we record on the diffraction pattern not the square of the Fourier transform from an array of virus particles but a quantity proportional to the cylindrical average of the square of the Fourier transform from an individual virus particle. We may see what this means by considering the effects of cylindrical averaging on the square of Eq. (13), which becomes

$$<F(R,\psi,l/c)F^*(R,\psi,l/c)>_\psi = \sum_n G_{nl}(R)G_{nl}^*(R) \qquad (17)$$

where $< >_\psi$ denotes cylindrical averaging over the reciprocal space azimuthal coordinate ψ. Hence the observed intensity along any layer line in reciprocal space is made up of the sum of the squares of various terms $|G_{nl}^2(R)|$. However, in order to build up the electron density, we must know the values of each of the G_{nl} terms independently. In general, there is no way of finding these out from the observed intensities. Fortunately, however, because of the properties of Bessel functions that we outlined above, viz., that a Bessel function is zero until the argument is about equal to the order, terms G_{nl} where n is large cannot occur near the middle of the diffraction pattern and therefore in this region there is frequently a geometrical sorting out of the G_{nl} terms.

The argument just presented may be illustrated by use of optical transforms. In Fig. 36a is shown an optical-diffraction mask consisting of a ring of 100 points, and in Fig. 36b is shown its optical-diffraction pattern made by shining the light beam normal to the plane of the ring. Note that the inner part of the ring has cylindrical symmetry and is the region where only the term $J_o(2\pi Rr_o)$ is contributing. Further out the term $J_{100}(2\pi Rr_o)$ starts to contribute (where $2\pi Rr_o \cong 100$) and the pattern has 100-fold symmetry.*

In an x-ray diffraction experiment the direction of the x-ray beam would be at right angles to the direction of the light beam in these

---

* This aspect of the diffraction pattern is easily related to the Abbé theory of resolving power of the microscope. At low angles of scattering (small numerical aperture) the resolving power is insufficient to tell that the 100-fold ring is not continuous. If it is continuous, it will have cylindrical symmetry. At a resolving power sufficient to tell that the ring is made from 100 points, the diffraction pattern quite suddenly assumes 100-fold symmetry.

figures, but the resulting diffraction intensity can be derived from the optical transforms of Fig. 36b by use of the Ewald construction. The x-ray beam would be in the plane of the paper and the trace of the Ewald sphere in this plane is simply a circle. Therefore, on the x-ray diffraction photograph we would see a projection of the intensity on a circular section cut through the optical transform. The effect of cylindrical averaging on the optical transform is difficult to demonstrate, but the character of the intensity on one layer line of the x-ray film is clearly seen by referring to Fig. 36. Near in, there will be many oscillations of the Bessel function $J_o{}^2$; further out there will be combined intensity arising from the terms $J_o{}^2$ and $J_{100}{}^2$; and even further out there will be terms $J_o{}^2 + J_{100}{}^2 + J_{200}{}^2$. Note that the region in which the $J_o{}^2$ term occurs singly is quite extensive. In this region and in corresponding regions on higher layer lines there is no ambiguity as to how to interpret the x-ray–diffraction photograph. The interpretation of the photograph where two or more terms overlap is extremely difficult.

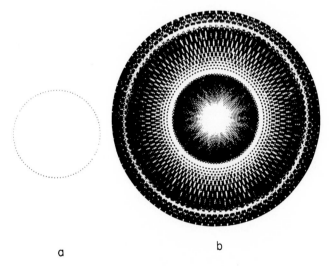

a   b

FIG. 36. Optical transform of a ring of 100 points (after Whitaker, 1955).

E. DIFFRACTION IN SYSTEMS WITH SPHERICAL SYMMETRY

1. *The Effect of Spherical Averaging*

In discussing problems having helical symmetry and random cylindrical orientation it was advantageous to introduce cylindrical polar coordinates. Likewise, when discussing problems with, for example, icosahedral symmetry and spherical averaging, it is often worthwhile to use spherical polar coordinates. A definition of spherical polar coordinates for real and reciprocal space is given in Fig. 37.

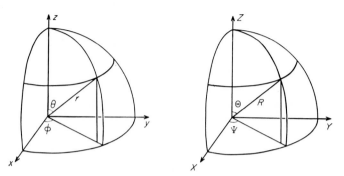

FIG. 37. Spherical polar coordinates: (a) shows real space coordinates and (b) right reciprocal space coordinates.

The form of the Fourier transform in spherical polar coordinates

$$F(R,\Theta,\Psi) = \sum_{n=-\infty}^{\infty} \int_{r=0}^{\infty} g_n(r) \, j_n(2\pi R r) \left[\sum_{m=-n}^{n} i^n \, a_{nm} \, P_n^{\,m}(\cos\Theta) \right.$$
$$\left. \exp \, im(\Psi + \pi/2) \right] 4\pi r^2 dr \quad (18)$$

In Eq. (18) the radial variation is governed by the term $j_n(x)$ [*], which is a spherical Bessel function analogous to the cylindrical Bessel functions discussed above. $P_n^{\,m}$ is an associated Legendre polynomial (see Sommerfeld, 1949; Stratton, 1941). Each term

$$P_n^{\,m}(\cos\Theta) \, \exp[im(\Psi + \pi/2)]$$

is called a tesseral harmonic. Tesseral harmonics are waves on the surface of a sphere having lines of latitude and longitude as nodal lines (see Stratton, 1941, p. 402). The azimuthal symmetry of each tesseral harmonic is m; n is the total number of nodal lines, so that $n - m$ is the number of divisions of the surface made by nodal lines of latitude.

The values of n which can occur depend upon the symmetry of the particle. Thus for icosahedral symmetry (point group 532), Klug (1968) has shown that the values of n are given by the selection rule

---

[*] Unlike cylindrical Bessel functions, all spherical Bessel functions can be expressed in elementary form with the help of sine and cosine functions (see Sommerfeld, 1949). In particular $j_0(x) = \sin x/x$.

$$n = 6p + 10q + 15r$$

where p and q are any positive or zero integers, and r can have the value 0 or 1. The first five values of n are 0, 6, 10, 12, and 15. The values of m that can occur in Eq. (18) depend upon which symmetry axis is taken to be the z direction. For example, if one chooses the 2-fold axis, m can only take the values 0, ± 2, $\pm 4 \cdots \pm n$. If a 5-fold axis were chosen to be the z direction, m can take the values 0, ± 5, $\pm 10 \cdots \pm n$. It is clear the m relates to the azimuthal symmetry in the same way that n is used for the azimuthal symmetry of one term in the transform of a helix [Eq. (9)]. By adding together all tesseral harmonics of the same n (where n is 0, 6, 10, 12, or 15, etc.) with the appropriate coefficients a_{nm}, one produces a solution of the wave equation on the surface of a sphere with icosahedral symmetry. These are known as icosahedral harmonics. The term enclosed in square brackets in Eq. (18) is an icosahedral harmonic. The values of a_{nm} have been evaluated by Cohen (1958) and the expansion of two low-order icosahedral harmonics in terms of tesseral harmonics is given in Table IV (after Klug, 1968).

TABLE IV

The Expansion of the Icosahedral Harmonics $\mathcal{J}_6$ and $\mathcal{J}_{10}$ about a 5-fold Axis in Terms of Tesseral Harmonics[a]

$\mathcal{J}_6(\Theta,\psi) = 7920 P_6^0(\cos\Theta) + 2 P_6^5(\cos\Theta)\cos 5\psi$
$\mathcal{J}_{10}(\Theta,\psi) = 1793 \times 10^6\, P_{10}^0(\cos\Theta) - 54720\, P_{10}^5(\cos\Theta)\cos 5\psi + 2 P_{10}^{10}(\cos\Theta)\cos 10\psi$

[a] After Klug (1968).

In order to use the theory outlined above to evaluate the scattering from a particular object, one must determine the amount of each icosahedral harmonic present in the structure at each radius. These coefficients we have called $g_n(r)$; all $g_n(r)$ are real numbers. The method of evaluating coefficients $g_n(r)$ is beyond the scope of this article (see Klug, 1967) but, by way of example, if the structure consists only of points at the vertices of an icosahedron all even-order harmonics are present in the transform and all odd order icosahedral harmonics are missing.

The spherical average of the square of the modulus of Eq. (18) (i.e., after squaring, its average over the angular coordinates Θ, ψ) has a simple form if we consider just one atom, f_o; then

$$<F^2(R)>_{\Theta,\psi} = g_o^2 j_o^2(2\pi R r_o) + g_o^2 j_n^2(2\pi R r_o) + \text{etc.} \tag{19}$$

where g_o, g_n, etc. are functions only of the angular coordinates of the atoms.

Where n takes any of the values allowed by the symmetry. This is strikingly similar to the result obtained for cylindrical coordinates, only in place of the cylindrical Bessel functions we have spherical Bessel functions. For a real structure consisting of many atoms grouped on each surface lattice point, the computational problem is more complex, but in essence it is the same. At small angles of scattering, since Bessel functions of order other than zero are zero for zero argument, all terms of the expression above must be zero except the $j_o{}^2$ term. The intensity in the diffraction pattern depends solely on the $j_o{}^2$ term until the first $j_n{}^2$ term starts to contribute. For an arrangement of points with icosahedral symmetry, the first nonzero term is $j_6{}^2$, and this will start to contribute at $2\pi Rr \cong 8$. If the radius of the particle is 130 Å, the limiting value of R below which only the zero-order term contributes, is

$$R \cong 8/2\pi130 \cong 0.01 \text{ Å}^{-1}$$

The nodes of $j_o(x)$ are at π, 2π, 3π, etc.; therefore as R goes from zero to 0.010 Å^{-1}, $j_o{}^2(2\pi Rr)$ will oscillate twice. The situation should be contrasted with the situation in a system having high rotational symmetry (see Section IV,D,2), where the $J_o{}^2(2\pi Rr)$ term makes many oscillations before the $J_n{}^2(2\pi Rr)$ term becomes appreciable. Thus the sorting out of Bessel function terms, which is possible out to a 10-Å resolving power for a cylindrical rod virus (e.g., TMV), is possible only at very low resolution (about 100 Å) for a spherical virus.

We may illustrate these ideas by recourse to the method of the optical transform. Figure 38a shows points arranged on the surface lattice $T = 3$, and Fig. 38b shows the optical transform of this drawing with the light beam normal to the paper. Note that the inner region has cylindrical symmetry in section and therefore in three dimensions has spherical symmetry. However, even at quite small angles of scattering the pattern is pseudohexagonal, indicating that high-order Bessel functions such as $j_6{}^2$, $j_{10}{}^2$, $j_{12}{}^2$ are beginning to make a significant contribution to the intensity. When attempting to interpret diffraction patterns from spherically averaged distributions of particles (see Section VI) the possible overlap of high-order Bessel functions with the $j_o{}^2$ term should be borne in mind, for it is clear that serious errors will arise if one attempts to interpret the fourth and fifth peaks of Fig. 38b as arising from the j_o term. While in practice the contributions of $j_n{}^2$ may be smaller for a more uniform shell built of units of finite size rather than points, there is a limit to the scattering that can be considered as purely $j_o{}^2$.

FIG. 38. Optical diffraction pattern of a $T = 3$ surface lattice. The surface lattice is shown in (a) and its diffraction pattern in (b). Note that the peak at the origin, the first subsidiary and second subsidiary maxima of the diffraction pattern, have near cylindrical symmetry, and therefore the full transform of the particle must have spherical symmetry at this resolving power. It is clear that beyond the second subsidiary maxima it is not valid to assume that the particle transform has spherical symmetry.

2. The Formula of Debye

By algebraic manipulation of Eq. (19) or by returning to first principles, it is possible to arrive at the following simple and general result due to Debye (see Prock and McConkey, 1962; Guinier and Fournet, 1955):

$$<F^2(R)>_{\theta, \psi} = \sum_k \sum_j f_k f_j \frac{\sin (2\pi R r_{kj})}{2\pi R r_{kj}} \tag{20}$$

The summations extend over all atoms in the particle. The term r_{kj} is the distance between atom j and atom k. The Debye formula is very convenient for numerical evaluation of $<F^2>$. The long form [Eq. (19)] is often convenient for algebraic analysis of $<F^2>$, since not only are the coordinates simpler but the influence of symmetry on the diffraction pattern is clearly seen.

The formula of Debye is usually taken as the basis of the development of the theory of low-angle x-ray scattering. In the theory of Kratky and Porod (1949), the summation over discrete atoms is replaced by a continuous electron-density function $\rho(\mathbf{r})$. From this they define what is essentially a spherically averaged Patterson function for each particle $P(r)$ (for explanation of Patterson, see Section IV,C,2). $P(r)$ is computed by finding the convolution of $\rho(\mathbf{r})$ with $\rho(-\mathbf{r})$ and spherically averaging. Then Eq. (20) may be written

$$<F^2(R)>_{\theta,\psi} = \int_0^\infty P(r) \frac{\sin 2\pi Rr}{2\pi Rr} \, dr \qquad (21)$$

Often it is simpler to consider the spherically averaged Patterson density

$$g(r) = P(r)/4\pi r^2$$

then

$$<F^2(R)>_{\theta,\psi} = \int_0^\infty g(r) \frac{\sin 2\pi Rr}{2\pi Rr} 4\pi r^2 dr$$

Using the symbol $i(R)$ for $<F^2(R)>_{\theta,\psi}$ one obtains

$$i(R) = \frac{2}{R} \int_0^\infty g(r) \sin (2\pi Rr) r \, dr \qquad (22)$$

Use will be made of this result in Section VI.

V. X-ray Diffraction from Virus Crystals

A. APPARATUS

For an x-ray diffraction study of a single crystal one must measure the intensities of as many of the Bragg reflections as possible. The intensities can be measured directly using counter methods or indirectly by exposing a sensitive film to the diffracted x-ray beams; the blackening produced is measured by a densitometer. Both methods have their advantages and disadvantages (see the review by Holmes and Blow, 1965), and both have been used for protein crystallography, with counter methods now becoming more popular in conjunction with automated techniques. No counter methods have yet been used with virus crystals; the difficulty lies in the high resolution required (the angular separation between diffracted beams is very small) and the relatively low intensity of the reflections. Therefore, at present all data are collected on photographic film. The basic apparatus required is an x-ray source and a camera incorporating a collimator for defining the x-ray beam incident on the crystal, a goniometer by which the crystal can be oriented, a film holder, and a mechanism by which the crystal can be rotated completely through the reflecting position of each reflection.

In this way the blackening on the film is proportional to the diffraction from the complete crystal and not to some part of the mosaic of small crystallites of which all crystals are, in fact, composed.

The actual arrangement adopted for virus crystallography is determined mainly by the large size of the unit cell of a virus crystal. All virus particles that have been crystallized and studied by x-ray diffraction are about 200–300 Å in diameter. In each case the unit cell sides are also of this order except for turnip yellow mosaic virus, in which case the cell side is 700 Å. Because of these large spacings, the density of the reciprocal lattice points is high, i.e., the x-ray diffraction–patterns are densely packed with reflections, and since the total diffracted intensity is proportional to the number of electrons irradiated by the x-ray beam, the greater the number of reflections, the lower their average intensity. Thus there is a need for both high-resolution and high-intensity x-ray sources. In all the studies so far made, pinhole collimation has been used to produce the required fine x-ray beam. A design for a collimator with pinholes (platinum electron microscope apertures) that are adjustable for ease of centering has been described by Longley (1963) and is shown diagrammatically in Fig. 39. The size of pinhole used varies with the particular case, but a common arrangement used an entrance pinhole (A) of 200-μ diameter, a defining pinhole (B) of 100-μ diameter, and a guard pinhole (C) of 150-μ diameter; this arrangement gives a resolution between reflections of 400 Å at a specimen–film distance of 5 cm. The ideal size of x-ray tube source that can be employed with such a collimator is about 0.3 × 3 mm, which is generally viewed at an angle of 6° to the plane of the anode face, so that it has apparent dimensions 0.3 × 0.3 mm. The maximum loading

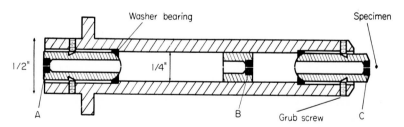

Fig. 39. Diagram of x-ray collimator for use with virus crystals (Longley, 1963). A, B, and C are the entrance, defining, and guard apertures, respectively—electron microscope platinum apertures of required sizes (see text). B is mounted in a brass holder, which is a stiff sliding fit inside the collimator. The holders of A and C have rounded ends that are pressed against spherical seatings by grub screws. By adjustment of these grub screws the pinholes A and C can be centered by observing with the camera microscope a light beam directed through the collimator.

that can be developed in such a focal size for a stationary copper anode is 5 mÅ at 40 kV. An arrangement in which this can be achieved with a fairly uniform focus was described by Longley (1963). This arrangement was based on the Beaudouin demountable tube and is shown diagrammatically in Fig. 40; the main modifications are to the focusing cap and back plate both at bias potential, with the plate as close to the filament as possible. Recently the same cathode has been combined with the Broad-type rotating anode (Broad, 1956), in which the loading can be increased to 20 mA/40 kV (Holmes and Longley, 1964; see Fig. 41). In both cases the Raymax 60 power supply is used, and for most uniform focus the gun is run in a space-charge limited way rather than filament-temperature limited.

The x-ray diffraction camera that has been used almost exclusively for single crystal studies is the Buerger precession camera, produced

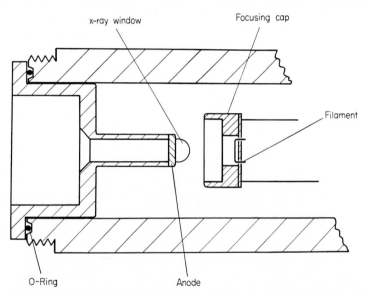

FIG. 40. Diagram showing the anode and cathode arrangement for producing a semimicrofocus x-ray source. The filament is mounted as close to the back plate of the focusing cap as possible. With the filament axis vertical, as in the diagram, a verticle line focus is produced on the anode (a reduced image of the filament), which when viewed through the window is effectively a fine vertical line source of x-rays suitable for use with a bent quartz crystal focusing monochromator for studies requiring fine horizontal resolution (e.g., along the layer lines of the x-ray diagram of TMV). With the filament axis horizontal, the focus seen through the window is foreshortened effectively to a square x-ray source for use with pinhole collimators and single crystals. The anode is water cooled and the anode–cathode distance is variable for optimum focusing.

by Charles Supper Co., with some modification. Briefly (the technique has been fully described by Buerger, 1964), a crystal is set on the camera with a prominent zone axis parallel to the x-ray beam. Zone axes are the directions of vectors between lattice points in the crystal and are perpendicular to planes of reciprocal lattice points. With the crystal thus set, the reciprocal lattice plane perpendicular to the zone axis, and containing the origin (the zero layer), is tangential to the sphere of reflection at the origin, and parallel planes nearer the x-ray source (higher layers) intersect the sphere in a system of circles. In the precession method the crystal is offset by an angle μ (the zero-layer inter-

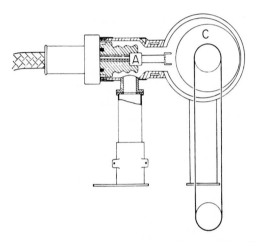

Fig. 41. Diagram of a semimicrofocus rotating-anode x-ray tube. C is a Broad-type, water-cooled rotating anode and A is a Beaudouin-type cathode modified as shown in Fig. 40. With this combination a loading of 10 kW/mm² can be achieved in a focal size of 1 × 0.1 mm.

section becoming a circle of angular diameter 2 μ) and precessed about the x-ray beam; all reflections on the zero layer within an angular radius 2 μ thus pass through the sphere of reflection twice per cycle (360° precession). Reflections on higher layers also pass through the sphere twice. Mechanically linked to the crystal is an annular screen that allows only reflections from one of the reciprocal lattice planes to reach the film. Moreover, the film holder is coupled to move so that the recorded reflections lie on an undistorted representation of the reciprocal lattice. The latter coupling is adjustable, so that for any given layer the diffracted beams arising from the two reflecting positions per cycle are recorded at the same point on the film. The undistorted record of the reciprocal lattice is a great advantage, since the x-ray diffraction photographs obtained display the symmetry within the crystal. Another advantage of the precession method is that it lends itself to the investigation of the reciprocal lattice from the center outward; small precession angles can be used for a low-resolution study with short exposure times.

The standard precession camera for protein study has specimen–film distances of 5, 7.5, and 10 cm. The main modifications employed in the authors' laboratory for virus work are as follows:

1. The collimator holder has been bored out to one-half inch in diameter to take the collimator type shown in Fig. 39.

2. A hole has been bored along the camera axis through the drive shaft to the rear of the camera to facilitate collimator alignment.

3. The layer-line screen arm carries a cross slide for accurate setting of the fine layer-line screens required for virus work.

4. An oscillation device has been fitted so that the precession motion can be limited to any fraction of a complete rotation. This is useful in reducing the exposure time required; if the complete x-ray pattern has, for example, 4-fold symmetry, only a quarter of the pattern need be recorded. In practice, this device has not been of great help, since to record a quadrant of the pattern at full intensity (each reflection passing through the sphere of reflection twice, as in the normal precession photograph) requires an oscillation of magnitude 270° compared with the complete 360° normal rotation; thus the saving is not great.

The crystal is centered in the collimated beam by shining a light through the collimator and observing the crystal through a microscope mounted vertically in the dovetail slide of the cassette holder. Mounted on the objective of the microscope is a 45° prism, so that one looks at the crystal in the direction of the collimator and one can center it in the light beam.

The backstop used to prevent the direct x-ray beam from reaching the film is a lead sphere squashed to a disc of about 1 mm in diameter and mounted on thin Melinex foil, which has no appreciable x-ray absorption; the foil holder is mounted on a cross slide for ease of positioning the backstop. The dimensions of the layer-line screen depend on the particular unit-cell dimensions, but a typical screen for a 3° precession photograph has an annulus of 1.7-mm inner radius and of 2.5-mm outer radius. The possible annulus thickness (in the example, 0.8 mm) varies (directly) with the distance between reciprocal lattice layers in the direction in question and (inversely) with the precession angle. The finer the annulus, the more accurate must be the crystal setting.

An oscillation camera, in which the crystal is oscillated through a small angle about an axis perpendicular to a zone axis, has been used to collect low-angle reflections from virus crystals; the advantage is that for a pattern with four identical quadrants only one quadrant need be recorded, and for this one oscillation is almost sufficient. Longley (1963) showed that the oscillation angle can be extended by a factor beyond that which would normally give overlap of zero- and first-layer patterns by using a layer screen oscillating with the crystal.

Both precession and oscillation methods give patterns of reflections on straight lines that lend themselves to easy measurement of intensity. The Joyce-Loebl microdensitometer is commonly employed for this purpose using a fine slit width (about a tenth of the spot width) and a slit height equal to spot width. Resolution must be sufficient to enable a clear background to be drawn between the reflections.

B. GROWING AND MOUNTING CRYSTALS

1. *Size of Crystals*

Virus crystals diffract x-rays fairly weakly; they also are disordered by prolonged exposure to x-rays, and thus crystals must be sufficiently large so that they diffract strongly enough to record the required x-ray pattern before appreciable radiation damage occurs. Normally this sets a minimum size limit of about 0.3 mm to crystals, although limited investigations requiring shorter exposures can be made on crystals smaller than this. Since the x-ray beams used are in general smaller than the crystals, the latter can be translated during long exposures to expose fresh regions to the x-ray beam.

2. *Crystallization*

The most commonly used method of growing crystals is by salting out the virus from a solution (1–5%), usually with ammonium sulfate, but other salts have also been used. The required concentration of salt is found roughly by adding drops of saturated salt solution until the solution is just turbid. A few bottles are then set up with varying salt concentrations below this turbidity level, and after a few days at room temperature the suitable range of salt concentration can be narrowed further. The solution of highest salt concentration will have precipitated the virus completely, generally as microcrystals, and at the lowest salt concentration the virus remains in solution. Some of the bottles between these extremes may show some small crystals, and the conditions are now varied more finely in this region. Some hundreds of bottles may be necessary to study a sufficient range of salt concentration, virus concentration, buffer strength, and pH. Crystals may take one to a few months to grow to a suitable size; the best crystals are usually obtained at room temperature, although on occasions suitable crystals have been grown at 4°C.

The following are the conditions that have been used to crystallize viruses for x-ray work:

Turnip yellow mosaic virus: 1–6% virus solution in phosphate buffer ($I = 0.1$, pH 7) with a final ammonium sulfate concentration of 0.75–0.70 M at room temperature (Klug et al., 1966b).

Turnip crinkle virus: 1% virus solution in phosphate buffer ($I = 0.1$, pH 7) with a final ammonium sulfate concentration of 1.5–1.7 M at room temperature (Longley, 1963). The crystals produced in this way are large (2 mm) thin plates and difficult to handle. More isometric crystals have been grown in 0.6 saturated sodium citrate pH 6.4.

Broad bean mottle virus: 1% virus solution in 0.33 saturated sodium citrate solution at pH 6.5 (Finch et al., 1967).

Human wart virus: 1% virus solution in 0.8 M ammonium sulfate (Leberman, 1965).

Other methods have been used to crystallize the following viruses:

Tomato bushy stunt virus: Like most other viruses, this has a negative temperature–solubility coefficient. Ammonium sulfate was therefore added at room temperature until the solution was turbid. When this solution was refrigerated it cleared and crystals grew over a period of weeks (Bawden and Pirie, 1938).

Southern bean mosaic virus: This virus was crystallized by slow isoelectric precipitation (Miller and Price, 1946) by dialyzing the virus solution extensively against acetate buffer at pH 5.5.

Coxsackie virus: This virus has been crystallized in an orthorhombic form from 5% ammonium acetate. Apparent cubic forms have been crystallized using other conditions (Mattern, 1962; Mattern and du Buy, 1956), but these have not proved suitable for x-ray work.

Poliovirus: 0.5% virus solution in phosphate–saline (0.01 M Na_2HPO_4, 0.1 M NaCl, pH 7.5) was left at 4°C for 1 year (Steere and Schaffer, 1958).

Satellite tobacco necrosis virus: 1.65% virus solution in 0.001 M $MgSO_4$ was allowed to evaporate slowly over a few weeks at room temperature (Fridborg et al., 1965).

3. Crystal Mounting

In order to preserve their structure, crystals are mounted wet in thin-walled capillary tubes of either glass or quartz. The glass capillary tubes, although they have a high alkali content, are satisfactory for most virus crystals in which the salt concentration is moderate. With crystals of poliovirus, however, in which the salt concentration was particularly low, the crystals were unstable in glass capillaries but stable in quartz. Moreover, the quartz tubes are much more robust than glass and the relative ease of handling makes them preferable.

A well-shaped crystal can be selected in the crystallization bottle under a low-power stereomicroscope and sucked into the thin-walled capillary tube using a hyperdermic syringe for pressure control. Most of the mother liquor surrounding the crystal is withdrawn using a very fine capillary tube. Since by the method of crystallization the conditions inside the bottle are on the borderline between crystallization and solution, crystals are stabilized by increasing the salt concentration (say by 0.1 M). The mounted crystal is washed by this stronger salt solution, which is then withdrawn, and a small reservoir (about 1 mm in length) of the solution is kept about 1 cm from the crystal; this acts as a buffer against possible salt variations while sealing the tube. The capillary tube is then cut to the required length (about 1 inch), with the crystal centrally placed, and sealed with wax. Usually virus crystals are so soft that this is all the manipulation that is possible; sometimes, however, harder crystals can be gently persuaded into a convenient orientation if the morphology is recognized.

4. Crystal Setting

Usually virus crystals have a well-defined morphology and can be set by optical examination to within a few degrees of a desired orientation. In the case of crystals with cubic symmetry (e.g., octahedral TYMV crystals), the relationship between the morphology and the reciprocal lattice is quite simple. For less symmetric or less well-defined crystals, this relationship has to be established, and for a new crystal type it is worth sketching each crystal for later correlation with the x-ray diagrams. For x-ray work the capillary tube is mounted on a goniometer providing rotation ($\pm 25°$) about two mutually perpendicular axes.

The exact orientation setting by x-rays is made in two stages, by "still" photographs and by low-angle precession photographs. The exposure times required vary considerably with the intensity of the x-ray beam, the size and type of crystal, and the particular zone axis required. Roughly, still photographs taken with a 3-cm specimen–film distance will take about an hour, and by this means crystals can be set to well within 1° of a zone axis. Low-angle precession photographs with a 5-cm specimen–film distance also take about an hour for precession angle, say 1° or less (the minimum angle that gives a recognizable pattern clear of the backstop); the final setting by means of these is within about 2 minutes of arc. Such accuracy of setting is required for larger-angle precession photographs requiring layer-line screens, since these must have fine annuli for the large unit cells of virus crystals. A precession photograph with angle (μ) $3°$ requires about 2 days exposure time with a 5-cm specimen–film distance and fine-focus Beaudouin x-ray tube.

Below we consider in detail the different types of x-ray photographs and the information obtainable from them.

C. Types of X-ray Diffraction Photographs

1. *Still Photographs*

The initial setting is made by taking "still" photographs, in which the crystal is kept stationary with respect to the x-ray beam. These can be taken with quite small specimen–film distances (3 cm, say) so as to minimize exposure time. In general, the pattern obtained consists of sets of concentric circles (or strictly ellipses), as shown in Fig. 42. These circles are the intersection of planes of reciprocal lattice points with the sphere of reflection. The greater the distance between these reciprocal lattice planes the denser are the reciprocal lattice points on the planes and the more dominant in appearance are the circles on the x-ray diagram. The direction of the vector normal to the planes of reciprocal lattice points, i.e., that going from the crystal to the center of a set of circles, is a zone axis; it is the direction of a dominant vector between lattice points within the crystal. The ratio of the distance on the film between the origin and the center of a set of circles to the specimen–film distance is the tangent of the angle required to bring into coincidence the zone axis and the x-ray beam. This angular correction can be split into horizontal [to be made on the goniometer arc(s)] and vertical (to be made on the precession camera dial) components. If the angles involved are large, corrections should be calculated by using a stereogram (Finch, 1959).

Apart from their use in setting crystals in preparation for precession photography, still photographs can give a great deal of information on the crystal structure for a relatively short exposure. In the case of poliovirus crystals, the unit cell, lattice type, and mode of packing were determined solely from still photographs (Finch, 1959; Finch and Klug, 1959). The simplest information that can be derived is the distance between the planes of the reciprocal lattice at right angles to the given zone axis. If this is parallel to the x-ray beam, the specimen–film distance is F, and D_n is the diameter of the nth circle; the distance between the reciprocal layers is $d^* = (1/n)(1 - \cos \tan^{-1} D_n/2F)$. An approximate formula that holds for small angles of offset is $d^* = (D_{n+1}{}^2$

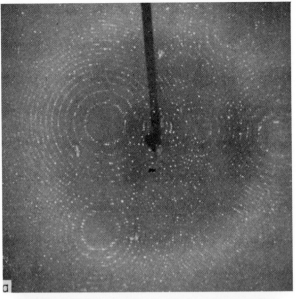

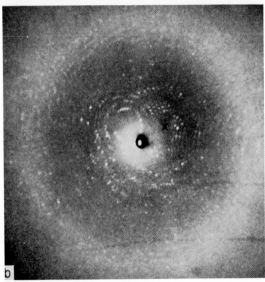

Fig. 42. X-ray diffraction "still" photographs from virus crystals. (a) Still from poliovirus crystal. The reflections lie on systems of interleaving circles. The center of each system of circles corresponds to the direction of a zone axis of the crystal—the direction of a vector between lattice points of the crystal structure. The shorter this vector is in length the further apart are the circles on the x-ray diagram and the more dominant is its appearance. (b) Still from broad bean mottle virus crystal. The system of circles of reflections surrounding the point marked X does not correspond to a true zone axis, since it interleaves with the circles from other true zone axes over several reflections and not over one or two reflections in a small, well-defined region as in (a). The direction of this pseudozone axis is that between virus particles in the same orientation, but not at equivalent crystal structure positions.

$- D_n{}^2)/8F^2$ (Carlisle and Dornberger, 1948). For a zone in the direction of a side of the unit cell, the length of the side is given directly as $a = \lambda/d^*$ (λ is the x-ray wavelength).

Still photographs can also show the absence of classes of reflections. For a reflection of index hkl on the nth reciprocal lattice layer from the origin of a zone axis uvw, $uh + vk + wl = n$. Thus, for a body-centered lattice, $h + k + l$ can only be even, and for the [111] zone axis alternate layers in reciprocal space are absent—the value of d^* is twice as large as expected for a primitive lattice. For a face-centered lattice, $h + k$, $k + l$, and $l + h$ must all be even, and thus the zone axes of the type [110] have alternate missing layers.

Two circles from two different zone axes in general intersect at only one or perhaps two common reflections. In the case of still photographs from crystals of broad bean mottle virus, one zone axis persistently interleaves with others at multiple reflections, as indicated in Fig. 42b. The presence of this pseudozone axis indicates a vector between virus particles that are in the same orientation but that are not at equivalent points in the unit cell, and its appearance and location were of great help in the determination of the arrangement of particles in the crystal (Finch et al., 1967).

Accurately set still photographs also display the symmetry about the zone axis, both in the positions of reflections and in their intensity distribution. This has not been used in practice, since the symmetry is more easily seen in precession photographs, but the intensity distribution around still circles was used by Klug et al. (1966b) to show that the x-ray pattern of turnip yellow mosaic virus at relatively high angles was not affected by salt concentration, and thus that the structure of the protein shell of the virus was unaffected by salt.

2. Precession Photographs

Having set the crystal by still photographs with a zone axis close to the direction of the x-ray beam, the final setting is made by taking low-angle precession photographs. The crystal is precessed by an angle μ (say $1°$ or less for setting purposes) about the beam direction, and all the reflections on the zero layer of the reciprocal lattice (i.e., that reciprocal plane passing through the origin) perpendicular to the zone axis within a cone of semiangle 2μ are recorded on the x-ray film as a circle containing the origin. The position of the center of this circle relative to the direct beam is very sensitive to the exact crystal orientation; the angle (measured from the crystal) is twice the angle between the zone axis and x-ray beam. This angle can be calculated and the crystal set to within 2 minutes of arc, which allows larger-angle precession photographs to be taken using a layer-line screen to select reflections from a particular plane of the reciprocal lattice perpendicular to the zone axis. Zero-layer patterns are both the most easily obtained and the most useful, since they relate to the crystal structure projected in the direction of the zone axis. For virus crystals the recording of higher (nonzero) layers is particularly inefficient by precession photography, since for the small angles of precession possible there are large "blind" regions in the centers of higher layers. However, these regions can be recorded on zero-layer photographs for other zone axes.

D. CRYSTAL STRUCTURE

The spacings of the reflections on zero-layer precession photographs taken in the directions of the main zone axes, and the angular relationship between these, enables the reciprocal lattice and hence the unit cell size and shape to be determined. The space group can be determined from the symmetry of these diagrams and from the absence of any particular classes of reflections.

Standard procedures are used that may be found in crystallographic textbooks (e.g., Buerger, 1942). However, it is worth discussing some of the particular techniques that have proved useful in virus crystallography.

It is possible that the space group completely determines the arrangement of virus particles. For example, crystals of tomato bushy stunt virus were shown to be body-centered cubic of 386-Å cell side (Caspar, 1956a). There is sufficient room in this unit cell for only one virus particle per lattice point, and it must be oriented so that it has 2-fold axes parallel to the 2-fold axes of the crystal. However, for turnip yellow mosaic virus, the face-centered cubic space group $F4_132$ of 695-Å cell side allows two possible arrangements with virus particles (with at least 23 symmetry) of 300-Å diameter; these are shown in Fig. 43. In Fig. 43a there are 8 particles per unit cell, arranged as the carbon atoms in diamond, and in Fig. 43b 16 particles per unit cell, with centers lying on a body-centered cubic lattice of side half that of the true unit cell; in both structures the particles are found in two orientations rotated 90° to each other about the cell edge. The two structures can be immediately differentiated by their low-angle patterns. The lower the angle of diffraction (i.e., the nearer the reflection to the origin), the greater is the real spacing to which the reflection corresponds, and thus the lower the resolution. At angles sufficiently low that differences in orientation of the virus particles are not resolved, i.e., the particles scatter as a spherically averaged particle, the

16-particle structure should produce only reflections corresponding t
the small body-centered unit cell, i.e., with $h + k + l = 4n$. This wa
found to be the case for the crystals investigated by Klug *et al.* (1957)
However, freshly grown crystals investigated by Klug *et al.* (1966b
showed quite strong reflections of the class $h + k + l = 4n + 2$ at lo
angles, showing that these crystals had the 8-particle structure. In fact
by considering the structure factors of these two structures, Klug *et a*
(1966b) showed that all the reflections of the class $h + k + l =$
$4n + 2$ should be strictly absent for the 16-particle structure, and i
this case this is the stronger criterion for differentiating the two struc
tures. Nevertheless, the absence of classes of reflections at low angle

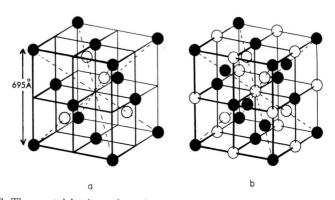

a   b

Fɪɢ. 43. The crystal lattices of turnip yellow mosaic virus. One cubic unit cell o
edge length 695 Å is shown in each case: (a) 8 particles per cell; (b) 16 particles pe
cell. Black and white represent the two orientations of the particles, rotated 90° tc
each other about the cube edge.

in indicating a small pseudocell at low resolution is very useful where
the arrangement of several virus particles in a unit cell is to be determined. For example, it was used to determine the arrangement of particles in the crystals of poliovirus (Finch and Klug, 1959). Here the orthorhombic cell appeared at low resolution to be body centered, and
reflections for which $h + k + l$ is odd were absent. However, these reflections were present at higher angles, showing that the "centering"
particle is shifted slightly from the strict body center and also perhaps
is slightly different in orientation from the particles at the lattice
points.

The determination of the space group and the location of the centers
of the virus particles do not necessarily fix the orientation of the virus
particles. In the cases of the cubic crystals of tomato bushy stunt virus

nd turnip yellow mosaic virus, the icosahedral virus particles lie at
points of special symmetry within the unit cell and must be oriented
o that 2-fold axes lie in the directions of the unit-cell edges. In the
ase of poliovirus, the space group was determined as $P2_12_12$, and the
educed arrangement required only that a 2-fold axis of the particle
e in the direction of the crystallographic 2-fold axis. With the limited
-ray data available, it was not possible to identify this crystallo-
raphic 2-fold axis with one of the cell-side directions, but the inten-
ity pattern of spikes (see the next section) showed that in fact the
articles are all oriented with 2-fold axes close to the directions of the
nit-cell sides.

If there is only one orientation of particle, the spike pattern (Section
,E,1) clearly enables this to be determined. The two orientations re-
ated by a 90° rotation found in turnip yellow mosaic virus are also
learly visible from the spike pattern, but for a crystal structure in-
olving several orientations the x-ray pattern might not be so easily
nterpretable in terms of spike patterns; fortunately, however, such
tructures have not yet been found, virus structures tending to be
ather simple.

E. PARTICLE STRUCTURE

No detailed three-dimensional structural study of an isometric virus
as yet been published. The difficulty lies in the collection of the data;
eflections occur on still photographs to spacings of 2 Å, but since the
seful life of a crystal can be spent in giving one 3° precession photo-
raph of a zero layer (a resolution of about 15 Å), it has not yet
roved possible to collect three-dimensional data to a worthwhile reso-
ution. Were this possible, the standard methods of protein crystallog-
aphy (isomorphous replacement) could be applied using heavy atom
erivatives and making use of the symmetry of the particle (see
Iolmes and Blow, 1965). However, with the limited data available, it
s possible to obtain some structural information, and in the case of
TYMV the arrangement of the protein subunits and the distribution of
RNA has been deduced. The methods used in that investigation are
escribed here, since most of them would be applicable to virus crystals
n general, but some are peculiar to TYMV for the two following rea-
ons. First, the existence of the RNA-free top component, which forms
rystals isomorphous with those of virus, enables structural informa-
ion on the RNA to be deduced by a comparison of corresponding x-ray
iagrams of the two components. Second, the large unit cell of TYMV
vith two orientations of virus particle enables a distinction to be made

between various classes of reflections. However, corresponding deduc-
tions may well be obtained for other crystal structures.

1. *Particle Symmetry*

The possession of icosahedral symmetry by a virus particle shows up
in the x-ray diagram as "spikes" of reflections of strong intensity in the
directions of the rotational symmetry axes of the icosahedral point
group 532. Figure 44a shows the spikes that occur on the zero-layer
precession photograph of tomato bushy stunt virus (Caspar, 1956a)
taken in the direction of a 2-fold axis of the crystal (and particle);
the directions of the 2-, 3-, and 5-fold axes corresponding to icosahedral symmetry that lie in the zero layer of the reciprocal lattice are
shown. In the corresponding pattern of TYMV shown in Fig. 44b two
orientations of the particle are present, and as the number of spikes
is doubled, they are less easily picked out.

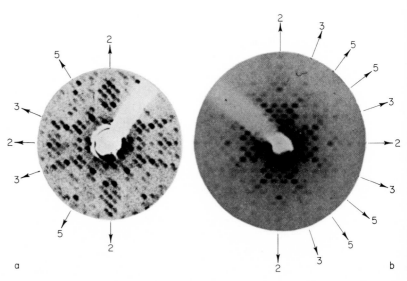

Fig. 44. X-ray diffraction (precession) photographs of crystals of (a) tomato bushy
stunt virus (BSV) (Caspar, 1956a) and (b) turnip yellow mosaic virus (TYMV) taken
with the x-ray beam parallel to the edge of the cubic unit cell. The directions of the
2-fold, 3-fold, and 5-fold rotation symmetry axes corresponding to icosahedral symmetry, which lie in the plane of the photograph, are marked by arrows. There is a
concentration of strong reflections ("spikes") in these directions. For BSV all the
virus particles have the same orientation. In TYMV crystals the virus particles are
present in two orientations (rotated 90° to each other about the cube edge) and thus
the number of 3-fold and 5-fold spikes is double that of BSV.

2. Comparison of X-ray Diagrams with Computed Transforms of Models

As mentioned above, a great advantage of TYMV is the existence of the RNA-free top-component particles which can be crystallized; the crystals are isomorphous with those of the complete virus. The physicochemical data (Markham, 1959) are consistent with there being about 160 protein subunits in the protein shell, and this figure points to the icosahedral surface lattice $T = 3$ with 180 subunits. The coordinates of these units on the surface lattice are to be determined. The $T = 3$ icosahedral surface lattice is shown in Fig. 45a. In order to investigate the possible positions of the structure units, computations were made of the transforms that would correspond to various arrangements of 180 units arranged quasiequivalently on the $T = 3$ surface lattice. The possible arrangements were investigated systematically by covering half the asymmetric unit of the surface lattice with grid points, as shown in Fig. 45b; only half the asymmetric unit need be considered, since the projection in the direction of a 2-fold axis has mirror symmetry. The transform corresponding to subunits (represented by points) at each of these grid points in turn was computed. At low angles (low resolution) the models have transforms like those of a spherical shell. At higher angles departures from spherical symmetry occur due to clusters of units or large holes in the structure. Farther out, the effect of interunit spacing shows. Comparison with the x-ray pattern is limited to a resolution of about 30 Å, since beyond this no agreement can be expected between the x-ray data and a model in which the protuberances of the protein units are represented merely by points.

Comparison with the top-component x-ray diagrams gives good agreement for grid points X and 3 (Fig. 45b) at a radius of 145 Å, both of which lead to arrangements of 180 points fairly evenly distributed over the surface. A choice can be made between these, since X leads to a skew arrangement and 3 to a centrosymmetric arrangement. It can be shown that the class of reflections hhl for the crystal structure have amplitudes giving the modulus of the imaginary part of the transform directly; the absence of such reflections to spacings of 18 Å shows that to this resolution the particle structure is centrosymmetric, inconsistent with the X arrangement. The point representing the protuberances of the subunit is therefore located near the grid point 3; the corresponding arrangement of 180 points is shown in Fig. 45c.

Comparison with the x-ray diagrams of the complete virus gave best agreement for grid points producing arrangements with 32 clusters; the agreement is shown in Fig. 46 for grid point 6 at a radius of 125 Å. At

high angles (beyond 20 Å) the x-ray diagrams of the virus and top
component are very similar, and thus the protein arrangement in both
cases must be the same. The strong concentrations of matter in the
region of the 32 lattice points for the virus must correspond to the
distribution of RNA.

3. RNA Distribution

The investigation of the gross distribution of the RNA within the
virus particle was made possible by the greater scattering power of

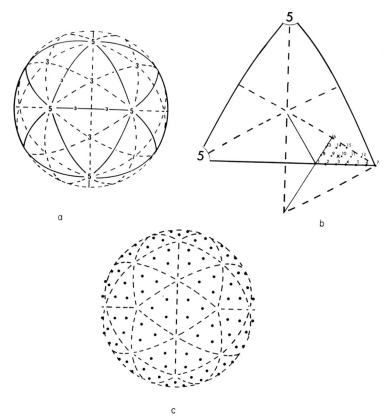

Fig. 45. (a) Orthogonal projection down a 2-fold axis of the icosahedral surface
lattice $T = 3$ (dotted lines) shown in relation to the spherical icosahedron ($T = 1$).
The figures in large type denote strict symmetry axes; those in small type the quasi-
or local, symmetry axes (Caspar and Klug, 1962). (b) A grid of points covering half
the asymmetric unit of the surface lattice $T = 3$ shown in (a). (c) The arrangement
of points produced by the action of the strict and quasisymmetry elements on the
grid point 3 of (b). This is the arrangement deduced from the x-ray diagrams for the
protuberances of the 180 protein subunits in TYMV. Grid point X in (b) leads to
the most skew arrangement of points, and grid point 6 to 32 clusters of points around
the lattice points.

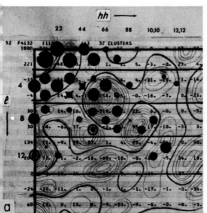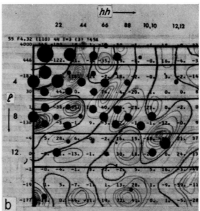

FIG. 46. Comparison of observed and calculated diffracted intensities in the [110] zone of TYMV (Klug *et al.*, 1966b). (a) The black circles represent in diameter the intensity of the x-ray reflections on the [110] zone-axis layer x-ray diagram of the virus. The pattern is superposed on the calculated intensity pattern ($|F|^2$) for 32 clusters of units at a radius of 125 Å (grid point 6 in Fig. 45b). (b) A similar representation of the [110] x-ray pattern of the TYMV top component superposed on the calculated pattern for 180 points at a radius of 145 Å, corresponding to grid point 3 of Fig. 45b.

RNA compared with that of protein; the average electron densities of RNA and protein relative to that of water are roughly in the ratio 2 : 1. Confirmation of the RNA distribution indicated by comparison of virus and top-component x-ray diagrams can be sought by methods enhancing this ratio. Two methods have been used: the first is to stain the RNA with heavy-metal salts (e.g., uranyl acetate, which is known to combine with nucleic acid); and the second is to increase the salt concentration in the crystals to an electron density approximately matching that of the protein.

a. Uranyl Acetate Staining. Crystals of the virus soaked for some weeks in 2% uranyl acetate were found to be rather fragile, but small-angle precession photographs ($\mu = 0.75°$) were obtained. Comparison of these with the normal virus x-ray diagrams showed that the uranyl acetate-stained virus had a transform rather more like that of a 32-cluster model than the untreated virus, which is evidence that the nucleic acid has a configuration resembling this model.

b. Salt Changes. Crystals of the virus were soaked in various concentrations of ammonium sulfate up to 4 M and x-ray photographs were taken. At high salt concentrations the crystals are more stable, but the low-angle x-ray pattern is much weaker because the scattering density of both the protein and RNA is reduced—an exposure time of days is required for even small precession angles.

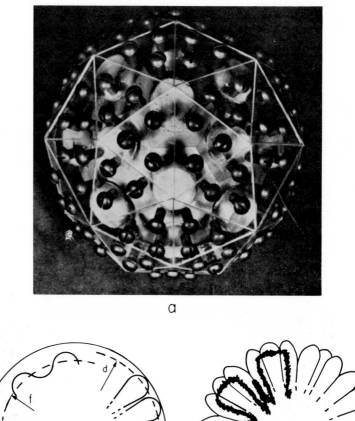

a

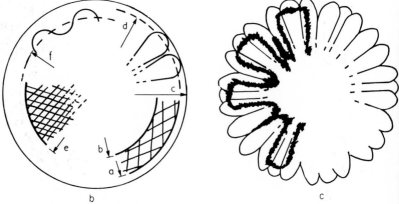

b   c

FIG. 47. A summary of the results of x-ray diffraction from TYMV (Klug *et al*
1966b). (a) A model of the structure of the virus, which gives agreement with th
x-ray patterns. The Perspex polyhedron represents the icosahedral surface lattic
$T = 3$. The position of the 180 protein subunits at an outer radius (approximatel
140 Å) are represented by black screws and the 32 bunches of RNA (at a radius c
125 Å) are represented by the plastic knobs inside. (b) Diagram incorporating th
significant radii deduced from the x-ray work. The right-hand half of the diagrar
refers to the distribution of the protein and the left to that of the RNA. The to
half of the diagram refers (schematically) to the fluctuations of density, while th

No changes in the x-ray diagram were observed beyond the 20-Å region, and since this high-angle part of the pattern is due to protein alone, its structure is unaltered by varying the salt concentration. As the salt concentration is increased, the reflections with $h + k + l = 4n + 2$ decrease in intensity until at 4 M they are absent out to 20-Å spacings. For these reflections the structural factor is the difference between the transforms of the two orientations of particle, and their absence indicates that to 20-Å resolution the particles appear spherically symmetric. The RNA has thus lost the lumpiness it shows at low salt concentration. The radial scattering curve derived from the single crystal photographs shows that at 4 M ammonium sulfate the RNA scatters as a solid sphere (or thick spherical shell) of 117-Å radius. Thus either this reflects the position of the bulk of the RNA in the virus—the 32 bumps seen at low salt concentrations have a smaller average density—or there is a real physical collapse of the RNA from the 32 bumps to a roughly spherical mass. The effect is reversible and the normal x-ray diagram is obtained if the ammonium sulfate concentration is reduced from 4 to 1 M. The x-ray diagram at high salt concentration shows a marked fading of the pattern at spacings about 50 Å, thus the RNA distribution is more disordered than at 1 M concentration.

4. Model of Structure of Turnip Yellow Mosaic Virus

The results of these x-ray diffraction studies are summarized in Fig. 47a, in which the positions of the 180 protein subunits are represented by black screws and the 32 bunches of RNA are represented by the plastic knobs inside. The radial dimensions are shown in Fig. 47b, and in Fig. 47c is shown the relation of the gross RNA distribution in the virus to the arrangement of subunits.

---

bottom half refers to spherically averaged dimensions; a and b refer to outer and inner radii of the spherically averaged uniform density approximation to the protein shell, 140 Å and 105 Å, respectively (Schmidt et al., 1954); c is half the interparticle distance in the crystal, 150 Å; d is the effective scattering radius of the protuberances corresponding to the protein subunits, 145 Å (not significantly different from the value of 140 Å for a); e is the radius of the RNA distribution deduced from the studies on salt changes, 117 Å; and f is the effective radius of the 32 bumps of RNA, 95 Å. (c) Schematic drawing, based on the diagram in (a), to indicate the relation of the gross RNA distribution in the virus to the arrangement of protein subunits. A section through a diametric plane of the virus particle is shown. The precise shape of the protein subunits and the detailed path of the RNA chain are not known, and neither is the distribution of protein and RNA known toward the center of the particle.

VI. Low-Angle X-ray Diffraction in Solution

A. LOW-ANGLE X-RAY SCATTERING AND LIGHT SCATTERING

A dilute solution of virus particles will contain the particles in completely random orientation, since the interactions between the particles will be slight. Thus in any diffraction experiment we record essentially the spherical average of the square of the Fourier transform
from one virus particle multiplied by the number of virus particles
in the beam. In such situations the theory developed in Section IV,F
is applicable. Frequently such examinations are restricted merely to
the first peak (the origin peak) of the particle transform (see Fig. 38).
From such studies it is possible to get overall parameters describing
the size, shape, and weight of the particle. However, the origin peak
of the particle transform may be explored by two techniques that
differ considerably in their experimental method. These are light scattering and low-angle x-ray scattering. In practice, their use is largely
complementary. The short wavelength of x-rays allows one to explore
a large region of the particle transform but will miss variations in the
shape of the origin peak close to the direct beam, whereas visible light
is used to explore fine structure of the origin peak. Moreover, visible
light is more generally used for molecular weight determinations (see
Section V,D); thus, in order to measure large dimensions (for example
the length of a rod virus ~3000 Å), one would use light scattering
but for measuring its breadth (ca. 150 Å) and for measuring the
dimensions of a small spherical virus one would, of necessity, use x-rays.
Clearly, it would be desirable to use intermediate wavelengths. Unfortunately, the intermediate spectrum of wavelengths presents a considerable number of experimental problems.

By the use of light scattering and low-angle x-ray scattering it
is possible to determine the molecular weight of the particle. As the
scattering is observed at angles nearer and nearer to zero, the effect
of the shape of the particle on the scattering factor becomes less and
less important and ultimately the intercept extrapolated for zero-angle
scattering depends only upon the particle molecular weight and the
concentration of particles. In Fig. 48a is shown a graph of the transform of a hypothetical isodimensional particle shown as a function of
the reciprocal space radius R ($R = 2 \sin \theta/\lambda$, where θ is the half
scattering angle and λ is the wavelength). The regions available for
study by low-angle x-ray scattering and by light scattering are shown.
It is clear that the molecular weight found from the intercept of this
graph is more accurately determined by light scattering, since the extrap-

ɔlation is much more readily made, but the width of the peak and ıence the "radius of gyration" (see Section VI,C,3) may be found ıccurately by x-ray scattering. In Fig. 48b is shown the origin peak ɔf the spherically averaged transform of a rod virus. In this situation ʰe extrapolated values from light scattering and from low-angle x-ray

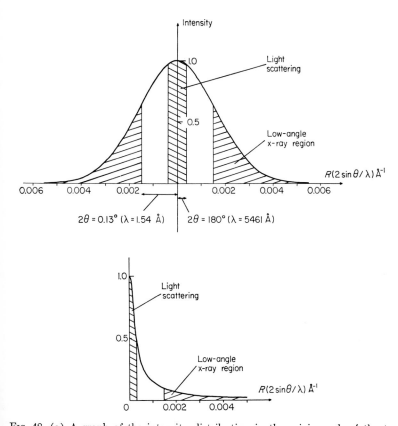

Fig. 48. (a) A graph of the intensity distribution in the origin peak of the transʰorm of the small spherical particle (radius 100 Å). 2θ is the scattering angle. The ₥olecular weight of the particle may be found by extrapolating the scattering curve ₯ack to the origin. With light scattering this extrapolation is easy, since the scatₑering curve of the particle alters very little in the light-scattering region. By the use ₯f the Guinier approximation it is possible to extrapolate the low-angle x-ray region ₗo the origin and hence obtain a molecular weight for such an isodimensional partiₑle. (b) A graph of the origin peak of the spherically averaged scattering curve from ₐ rod particle of length 3000 Å and diameter 150 Å. Note that in this case light ₛcattering can give important information about shape (length) of the particle. The ₗow-angle x-ray scattering cannot be extrapolated to give molecular weight for such ₐ particle; however, the mass per unit length may be deduced from measurements ₙ this region.

scattering are wildly different; the value extrapolated from light scat
tering will be, correctly, the molecular weight, whereas the value ex
trapolated from low-angle x-ray scattering can be shown to be relate
to the weight per unit length of the virus (see Section VI,D,4).

B. Apparatus

The basic problem is the measurement of the scattered intensity a
angles as close to the direct beam as possible. The latter must, there
fore, be very narrow and well defined in the region of the detecto
To this end many different kinds of low-angle scattering apparatu
find favor in various laboratories, and of these we will describe tw
that have been well developed in their respective laboratories.

The apparatus described by Anderegg et al. (1955) is, in essence
the simplest (see Fig. 49). It consists of a high-power x-ray sourc

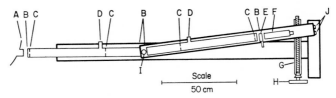

Fig. 49. A low-angle diffractometer using slit collimators: A, x-ray tube exit win
dow; B, mica window; C, collimating slits; D, vacuum connections; E, Ross filter
on slide; F, Geiger counter; G, precision lead screw; H, calibrated wheel; I, pivo
and sample holder; J, rollers (Anderegg et al., 1955).

at A (a rotating anode tube), followed by an evacuatable tube fo
holding two collimating slits, C and C. The sample is fitted at
and the scattered radiation is observed with a Geiger counter mounte
upon another evacuatable tube that can swing around an axis unde
the specimen. Two more slits in the Geiger counter tube act as
Geiger counter collimator. The angular setting of a counter arm i
achieved with a micrometer screw. Characteristic CuKα radiation i
used, and monochromatization is achieved by means of the balanced
filter method. In a more recent paper (Anderegg et al., 1961) mono
chromatization was achieved by using a proportional counter rathe
than a Geiger counter and a single-channel pulse-height analyzer i
the counting circuit.

An alternative kind of apparatus capable of making absolute inten
sity measurements has been developed by Luzzati et al. (1963). Thi
is based on the Guinier focusing monochromator, it is shown diagram
matically in Fig. 50. The apparatus consists of a modified Philip

oniometer mounted on a Philips-stabilized x-ray generator using a
ne-focus tube with a copper target. A bent quartz monochromator
olates the CuKα₁ radiation and focuses it onto the entrance slit of
Geiger counter. The width of the beam is defined by a slit close to
ιe monochromator, and secondary scatter is stopped by another slit
et just clear of the beam. Just behind the counter-entrance slit is
xed another slit to reduce the amount of scattered radiation entering
ιe counter.

In both these experimental arrangements, in order that the intensity
ecorded on the Geiger counter or proportional counter be at a reason-
ble level, the authors find it necessary to use a rectangular x-ray
eam relatively high compared with its width, derived from slits as
ollimators, rather than a round beam derived from pinhole collimators.
'he interpretation of the resulting data is thereby made more difficult.
n the work described by Anderegg *et al.* the effects of smearing caused

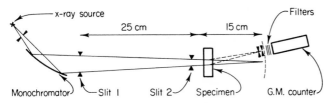

Fig. 50. Low-angle absolute scattering apparatus: the curved monochromator
rovides a focused beam of monochromatic radiation. The counter is arranged to
ving around the specimen in the focal plane of the monochromator. Collimation is
rovided by two sets of slits (after Luzzati *et al.*, 1963).

y the use of a beam of finite height are eliminated as far as possible
y making corrections. These are described, for example, by Beeman
t al. (1957). However, Luzzati (1960) prefers to use a very long x-ray
eam and makes no correction to the measured intensity. Rather, he
ιodifies the theoretical equations that would be used to interpret the
ιtensity to fit the experimental arrangement (Section VI,D,4).

C. Shape Analysis of the Scattering Curves

1. *Scattering by a Sphere*

The shape factor for scattering from a spherical particle of radius
is given by

$$i_n(R) = \left(3 \frac{\sin 2\pi R r_o - 2\pi R r_o \cos 2\pi R r_o}{(2\pi R r_o)^3} \right)^2 \tag{23}$$

This function has a strong central peak surrounded by evenly spaced maxima that decay very rapidly. The plot of this function on a semi logarithmic scale for $r_o = 140$ Å is shown by a broken line in Fig. 51. The solid line curve in this figure represents the scattering from a solution of wild cucumber mosaic virus (WCMV) (Anderegg et al. 1961). Out to the fourth subsidiary maximum these two curves are very like each other, showing that at low resolution the structure of WCMV may be represented by a solid sphere of 140-Å radius. This

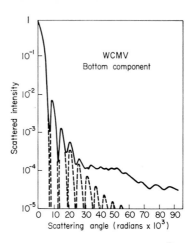

Fig. 51. The scattering from a solution of wild cucumber mosaic virus (WCMV). The logarithm of the intensity is plotted as a function of the scattering angle (solid line); the broken line is the theoretical scattering from the uniform sphere of 148-Å radius (Anderegg et al., 1961).

method of analysis may, of course, be extended by comparing the experimental scattering curve with the computed scattering from more detailed models suggested by other techniques, but it remains most powerful for particles with near spherical symmetry.

2. Fourier Transform Method

Returning to Eq. (18) in Section IV,E,1, which gives the form of the Fourier transform in spherical polar coordinates, we see that if the particle to be considered has spherical symmetry and the angular terms disappear, the form of the spherical average of the square of the Fourier transform is simple:

$$i(R) = \left[\int_o^\infty \rho_o(r) j_o(2\pi Rr) 4\pi r^2 dr \right]^2 \qquad (24$$

By taking square roots of both sides, we have

$$F_o(R) = \int_0^\infty \rho_o(r) j_o(2\pi Rr) 4\pi r^2 dr \tag{25}$$

Subscript o is to point out that these quantities are spherically averaged quantities or refer to a situation in which there is spherical symmetry; [$j_o(x)$ is a zero-order spherical Bessel function and is equal to sin x/x]. Furthermore, the inverse of this equation may be written down, i.e.,

$$\rho_o(r) = \int_0^\infty F_o(R) j_o(2\pi Rr) 4\pi R^2 dR \tag{26}$$

Thus, the radial density of the particle may be computed from the observed scattering amplitudes if these are experimentally available.

For an icosahedral particle the spherically averaged scattering may be written

$$i(R) = \left[\int_0^\infty g_0(r) j_o(2\pi Rr) 4\pi r^2 \, dr \right]^2 + \sum_n \left[\int_0^\infty g_n(r) j_n(2\pi Rr) 4\pi r^2 \, dr \right] \tag{27}$$

If our examination is limited to sufficiently small angles of scattering, then all the high-order Bessel function terms may be ignored and the equation for the spherically averaged scattering then becomes simply

$$i(R) = \left[\int_0^\infty \rho_o(r) j_o(2\pi Rr) 4\pi r^2 dr \right]^2 \tag{28}$$

where ρ_0 is the spherically averaged electron density. If we take the square roots of both sides of this equation, we have

$$F_o(R) = \int_0^\infty \rho_o(r) j_o(2\pi Rr) 4\pi r^2 dr$$

In doing this there is, of course, the problem of determining the sign of F. If this can be done, then, by similarity with the process described in Eqs. (25) and (26), we may write down the spherically averaged electron density as a function of the observed structure amplitudes, viz.,

$$\rho_o(r) = \int_0^\infty F_o(R) j_o(2\pi Rr) 4\pi r^2 dr \tag{29}$$

This method has been applied to both top and bottom components of WCMV with interesting results (Anderegg et al., 1961). Here the authors considered that the data out to 0.02 Å^{-1} was spherically symmetrical, the intensity peaks alternating in sign so that the spherically averaged electron-density distribution to about 50-Å resolving power

could be calculated by the use of Eq. (29). The results are shown in
Fig. 52. The solid line is the curve derived from the WCMV bottom
component, i.e., the intact virus particle, and the broken line from
the WCMV top component, i.e., the empty protein shell. From these
two curves it seems clear that the RNA component of the virus must
be located within a protein shell. However, it is doubtful whether the
dip in the middle of the electron-density distribution of the bottom
component can be taken as meaningful because of the low resolving
power employed and the fact that in such calculations errors accumulate at the origin.

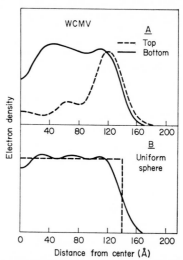

FIG. 52. (a) The radial distribution of electron density inside WCMV (solid line)
and the associated top-component particle (broken line) as calculated from the
Fourier transform of the scattering amplitudes. (b) The Fourier transform (solid
line) of the theoretically calculated scattering amplitudes from a uniform sphere of
140-Å radius. For a comparison with (a) the amplitude curve has been cut off at the
same angle and multiplied by the same artificial temperature factor as was used in
(a). The broken line is the true density distribution in a uniform sphere, 140-Å
radius (Anderegg et al., 1961).

3. The Guinier Approximation

For very low angles of scattering the shape of the origin peak of
the spherically averaged and squared Fourier transform is independent
of the exact nature of the particle shape. Guinier (see Guinier and
Fournet, 1955) showed that the shape of the origin peak could be
approximated by a Gaussian curve

$$I = I_o \exp\left(-\tfrac{4}{3}\pi^2 R^2 r_g^2\right)$$

n this equation I is the scattered intensity, I_o is the scattered inten-
ty extrapolated to zero angle, and r_g is the radius of gyration of the
article. By expressing R in terms of the half-scattering angle θ and
aking suitable rearrangements, we find

$$I = I_o \exp(-kr_g{}^2 \sin^2 \theta) \qquad (30)$$

here $k = 16\pi^2/3\lambda^2$. In this context, the radius of gyration is defined
s

$$r_g{}^2 = \frac{\Sigma m \mathbf{r} \cdot \mathbf{r}}{\Sigma m}$$

y taking the logarithm of Eq. (30), we have

$$\log (I/I_o) = -kr_g{}^2 \sin^2 \theta$$

ence, the logarithm of the observed scattering intensity should be
roportional to $\sin^2 \theta$ for small $\sin \theta$, and the slope of this line is
ven by $-kr_g{}^2$. Hence, it is possible to determine the radius of gyration
f the particle from measurements on the origin peak alone. At the
w angles of scattering necessary for the use of such a theory the
ssumption that all the particles in solution are scattering independ-
ntly is often no longer strictly valid. Therefore, it is advisable to
ake measurements of the radius of gyration at a range of concentra-
ons and extrapolate this to zero concentration. This has been done
or WCMV (Anderegg *et al.*, 1961), and the results are shown in
ig. 53. The extrapolated value of the radius of the gyration is 118 Å,
nd a uniform sphere with this radius of gyration would have a

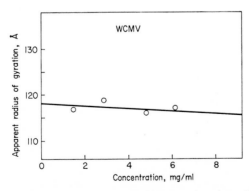

FIG. 53. Apparent radius of gyration of WCMV, as a function of the virus concen-
ation. To obtain a correct radius of gyration free of interference effects the radius
gyration extrapolated to zero concentration should be taken (Anderegg *et al.*,
61).

diameter of 290 Å, which compares well with the value of 280 Å given by the methods of Section VI,C,2.

In the case of a highly anisotropic particle, such as tobacco mosaic virus, the situation is more complex and will be discussed below (Section VI,D,4).

D. Mass Determination from Measurements of the Absolute Intensity of Scattering

1. *The Rayleigh Scattering Formula*

Up to this point in the development we have avoided using the absolute formula for the amount of x-rays or light scattered, since measurements on an arbitrary scale are sufficient to give information about shape. However, to find the *quantity* of material in the particle, absolute intensity measurements are necessary.

If I is the scattered intensity (energy flux per unit area) at a distance x from the scattering particles, which are illuminated with a beam of energy flux I_o, then

$$\frac{I}{I_o} = \frac{nk^4}{x^2} \alpha^2 \frac{(1 + \cos^2 2\theta)}{2} i_n(R) \tag{31}$$

if we consider a unit volume of the sample at low concentration of solute. Other variables are defined in Table V. Equation (31) was first derived by Rayleigh and is discussed, for example, by Debye (1962), Born (1933), and Stratton (1941). The function $i_n(R)$ differs from the definition of $i(R)$ given in Eq. (22) in that it is normalized

TABLE V
Notation for Absolute Scattering

n = Number of particles per unit volume
α = Polarizability of each particle
N = Avogadro's number
M = Molecular weight of particle (particle mass in grams = M/N)
$i(R)$ = Particle-scattering factor (see Eq. 22)
$i_n(R)$ = $i(R)$ normalized to unity at $R = 0$ (i.e., $i_n(R) = [i(R)]/[i(0)]$)
k = Wave number ($2\pi/\lambda$) of radiation
2θ = Scattering angle
R = $2 \sin \theta/\lambda$ reciprocal space radius
I = Scattered intensity (energy per unit area at x)
x = Specimen–detector distance
I_o = Direct beam intensity (energy per unit area at specimen)
C = Concentration of solute in gm/100 ml

o unity. This allows one to define α as the polarizability per particle rather than the polarizability per electron or atom. The use of a particle-shape factor normalized to unity is general in light scattering. The term $(1 + \cos^2 2\theta)/2$ is to take account of the effects of polarization.

2. Light Scattering

As the scattering angle becomes small the term

$$\frac{(1 + \cos^2 2\theta)}{2} \, i_n(R)$$

tends to unity, so that it may be neglected if we extrapolate to zero angle. Under these conditions

$$n\alpha^2 = \frac{I}{I_o} \frac{x^2}{k^4}$$

Therefore the quantity that can be determined from a light-scattering experiment is $n\alpha^2$ (n is the number of particles per unit volume). By expressing the polarizability in terms of refractive index and finding the relation between the refractive index and the concentration (the refractive increment), it is possible, therefore, to use $n\alpha^2$ to find the mass of the particle.

We assume that the particles of a solute in a solution of low concentration act as though they were molecules of a gas suspended in a medium of dielectric constant ϵ_o. Using the law which is valid for a gas, we have

$$\epsilon - \epsilon_o = 4\pi n\alpha$$

If we substitute the square of the refractive index (μ) for the dielectric constant, ϵ, we obtain as a good approximation:

$$\alpha = \frac{\mu^2 - \mu_o{}^2}{4\pi n} = \frac{(\mu - \mu_o)(\mu + \mu_o)}{4\pi n} \simeq \frac{\Delta\mu\mu_o}{2\pi n}$$

Moreover,

$$n = CN/M$$

Therefore,

$$\alpha = \mu_o M \Delta\mu/2\pi N C = \mu_o M [d\mu/dC]/2\pi N$$

Hence

$$n\alpha^2 = \frac{CM}{N} \left(\frac{\mu_o \, d\mu/dC}{2\pi}\right)^2$$

And finally

$$M = \frac{I x^2 \, 4\pi^2 \, N}{I_o k^4 C \mu_o{}^2 \, (d\mu/dC)^2} \tag{32}$$

3. X-ray Scattering—General

The polarizability of an electron is

$$\alpha_{el} = e^2/m\omega^2$$

where e is the charge on an electron, m is its mass, and ω is th[e] angular frequency of the radiation; if there are ρ electrons in a particl[e] the polarizability of the particle is (see Table VI)

$$\alpha = \rho e^2/m\omega^2$$

TABLE VI

NOTATION FOR ABSOLUTE X-RAY SCATTERING[a]

ρ	= Number of electrons in the particle
$\bar{v}$	= Partial specific volume
ρ_e	= Electron density of solvent (electrons/$\mathring{A}^3$)
z	= Average value of (atomic number/atomic weight)
e	= Charge of an electron
m	= Mass of an electron
ω	= Angular frequency
c	= Velocity of light
M'	= Molecular weight per $\mathring{A}$ of rod
r_g	= Radius of gyration $\Sigma mr \cdot r/\Sigma m$ where r is a vector measured from the particle center of gravity (isodimensional particles) or from the particle axis (rods)

[a] The definitions given in Table V are used together with those listed here.

Filling in these values in the Rayleigh expression given above, we fin[d]

$$\frac{I}{I_o} = \frac{nk^4\rho^2e^4}{x^2m^2\omega^4} \frac{(1 + \cos^2 2\theta)}{2} i_n(R) \tag{33}$$

In the low-angle studies considered here, the value of the polarizatio[n] term $(1 + \cos^2 2\theta)/2$ is essentially 1 and can be neglected from th[e] equations from now on; hence Eq. (33) simplifies to

$$I/I_o = (n\rho^2/x^2)(e^2/mc^2)^2 i_n(R) \tag{34}$$

since ω/k is c, the velocity of light. The value of $(e^2/mc^2)^2$ in cgs unit[s] is 7.9×10^{-26}, so that

$$I/I_o = (n\rho^2/x^2) \, 7.9 \times 10^{-26} \, i_n(R)$$

If we illuminate a unit volume of solution, as before we can write

$$n = CN/M$$

Furthermore, from the composition of the material we can find a number z so that

$$\rho = zM$$

Hence

$$I/I_o = (7.9 \times 10^{-26}/x^2)CNz^2Mi_n(R) \tag{35}$$

This expression is for particles in a vacuum, and so far we have ignored the contribution of the solvent to the scattering. Since at low resolving power the solvent is essentially a continuum, we would expect very little scattering. This, however, is an oversimplification, since there are holes in the solvent to contain each particle. To take account of the holes we must subtract from the number of electrons in the particle the number of electrons in the volume of solvent displaced by the particle. Therefore, in place of Mz^2 we have (see Table VI for definition of variables)

$$\rho_{\text{effective}} = Mz - (\bar{v}M/N)\rho e \times 10^{24}$$
$$= M(z - \bar{v}\rho e \times 10^{24}/N) \tag{36}$$

Therefore

$$I/I_o = (7.9 \times 10^{-26}/x^2)(CNM^2/M)(z - \bar{v}\rho e \times 10^{24}/N)i_n(R)$$

or, simplifying this equation and putting $R = 2\sin\theta/\lambda$,

$$I/I_o = (7.9 \times 10^{-26}/x^2)\ CNM(z - \bar{v}\rho e \times 10^{24}/N)^2 i_n(2\sin\theta/\lambda) \tag{37}$$

Hence, we can find M from a series of measurements in which θ is varied and the values of I/I_o are extrapolated to zero θ. Since the basic assumption of the theory presented here is that all particles scatter independently, it is important to conduct such scattering measurements at a range of concentrations and extrapolate the molecular weight to zero concentration.

4. X-ray Scattering from Randomly Orientated Rods

In cylindrical coordinates, the square of the Fourier transform (normalized to unity) of a uniform rod of radius r_o and half length h is

$$F^2(R,Z) = \frac{\sin^2(2\pi Zh)}{(2\pi Zh)^2}\ \frac{4J_1^2(2\pi Rr_o)}{(2\pi Rr_o)^2} \tag{38}$$

J_1 is a first-order cylindrical Bessel function. The spherical average of this is (see Guinier and Fournet, 1955, p. 19)

$$i_n(R) = \int_o^{\pi/2} \frac{\sin^2(2\pi Rh\cos\theta)}{(2\pi Rh\cos\theta)^2}\ \frac{4J_1^2(2\pi Rr_o\sin\theta)}{(2\pi Rr_o\sin\theta)^2}\ \sin\theta\ d\theta \tag{39}$$

If we are considering light scattering, then Rr_o is very small, since R depends inversely on the wavelength. Therefore, the second term in Eq. (39) will be unity for a rod virus since the radius will be much less than a wavelength. Therefore

$$i_n(R) = \int_o^{\pi/2} \frac{\sin^2(2\pi Rh \cos \theta)}{(2\pi Rh \cos \theta)^2} \sin \theta \, d\theta \qquad (40$$

and we note that $i_n(R)$ does not depend in any way upon the radius of the particle, and therefore no information about radius can be obtained by light scattering. Eq. (40) may be integrated by parts to give (see Guinier and Fournet, 1955)

$$i_n(R) = \frac{Si(4\pi hR)}{2\pi hR} - \frac{\sin^2(2\pi hR)}{(2\pi hR)^2}$$

where

$$Si(x) = \int_o^x (\sin t/t) dt$$

This is the form of the shape factor for thin rods and is frequently used in light scattering.

In the x-ray region

$$\sin^2(2\pi Rh \cos \theta)/(2\pi Rh \cos \theta)^2$$

will be zero unless $\theta \cong 90°$, since $2\pi Rh$ will be numerically very large so that we can write

$$i_n(R) = \frac{4J_1^2(2\pi Rr_o)}{(2\pi Rr_o)^2} \int_o^{\pi/2} \frac{\sin^2(2\pi Rh \cos \theta)}{(2\pi Rh \cos \theta)^2} d\theta$$

Putting

$$\cos \theta \cong \frac{\pi}{2} - \theta \qquad \text{for} \qquad \theta \cong \frac{\pi}{2}$$

and using the standard integral

$$\int_o^\infty \frac{\sin^2 ax}{(ax)^2} dx = \frac{\pi}{2a}$$

we have

$$i_n(R) = \frac{1}{4Rh} \frac{4J_1^2(2\pi Rr_o)}{(2\pi Rr_o)^2}$$

[Guinier and Fournet, 1955, p. 27, Eq. (40)].

We have chosen a simple model (uniform rod) in order to keep the derivation simple, but the only effect, at low angles of scattering, of using a rod of arbitrary cross section is to replace

$$\frac{4J_1^2(2\pi R r_o)}{(2\pi R r_o)^2} \qquad \text{by} \qquad \exp\left(-2\pi^2 r_g^2 R^2\right)$$

if we use the appropriate Guinier approximation (see Section VI,C,3) for rods. Here r_g is the radius of gyration measured in a plane at right angles to the axis of the rod. Hence

$$i_n(R) = \frac{1}{4Rh} \exp\left(-2\pi^2 r_g^2 R^2\right)$$

so that if we extrapolate a plot of log $[Ri_n(R)]$ against R^2 the slope will be $-2\pi^2 r_g^2$ and the intercept will be $1/4h$. Continuing as above [Eq. (34)], we can write

$$x^2 \frac{I}{I_o} = 7.9 \times 10^{-26} n \rho^2 i_n(R)$$

If M' is the molecular weight per Å of the rod, then

$$\rho^2 = 4h^2 z^2 M'^2 \qquad \text{and} \qquad n = \frac{CN}{2hM'}$$

Therefore

$$x^2 \frac{I}{I_o} = \frac{7.9 \times 10^{-26} CN z^2 M'}{2R} \exp(-2\pi^2 r_g^2 R^2) \qquad (41)$$

which for r depends only upon the mass per unit length divided by R.

The correction for the excluded volume of solvent is made in the same way as in Section VI,D,3. Putting

$$\rho_{\text{effective}} = 2hzM' - \frac{2hM'}{N} \bar{v}\rho e \times 10^{24}$$

$$= 2hM'\left(z - \frac{\bar{v}\rho e}{N} \times 10^{24}\right)$$

we have

$$x^2 \frac{I}{I_o} = \frac{7.9 \times 10^{-26} CNM'\left(z - \dfrac{\bar{v}\rho e}{N} \times 10^{24}\right)}{2R} \times \exp(-2\pi^2 R^2 r_g^2) \qquad (42)$$

5. Effect of Using Long-Slit Collimation

The effect of using a long-slit x-ray beam to illuminate the specimen rather than a pencil beam of x-rays is shown in Fig. 54. Under conditions of point collimation, the pattern chosen for an example is just two rings. In order to simulate long-slit collimation, we have drawn the rings many times with the centers displaced along the axis. The nature of the resulting pattern can be envisaged from Fig. 54. It will be recognized that this operation is the convolution of the original pattern with the trace of the direct beam.

The use of slit collimation for absolute intensity measurements is generally necessary for dilute solutions, and therefore the effect of convoluting the intensity distribution with the line along Z must be taken into account.

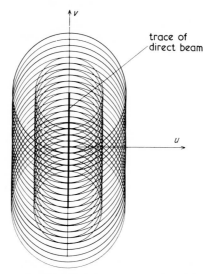

FIG. 54. Diagram showing the effect of slit collimation. The effect of using a slit finite height as an x-ray source rather than as a point is found by convoluting the point intensity pattern with a line that is as long as the x-ray beam. As an example for this diagram the point x-ray–diffraction pattern has been taken as two circles. The effect of convoluting these with a line representing the trace of the direct beam is shown. Directions u and v are the direction of axes used in calculations given in the text.

This problem has been treated fully by Luzzati (1960) for the case where the scattering can be represented as a Gaussian (exp $-2\pi^2 r_g^2 R^2$) divided by $2R$ (for rodlike particles) and the x-ray beam is of infinite height. The following derivation is a sketch of part of the argument given by Luzzati for the case of rods.

We have

$$x^2 \frac{I}{I_o} = 7.9 \times 10^{-26} CNM'(z - \bar{v}\rho e/N \times 10^{24}) \frac{\exp(-2\pi^2 R^2 r_g^{\,2})}{2R} \quad (42)$$

and if we put k for the whole of the first part of the expression, then:

$$x^2 I/I_o = k \exp(-2\pi^2 r_g^2 R^2)/2R \qquad (43)$$

If distances from the center of the direct beam in the plane of the detector are u and v (as in Fig. 54), for the intensity at u arising from all the specimen we can put

$$x^2 \frac{I_{total}}{I_o} = \lambda x k \int_o^\infty \frac{\exp\left(\dfrac{-2\pi^2 r_g^2 (u^2 + v^2)}{\lambda^2 x^2}\right)}{(u^2 + v^2)^{1/2}} \, dv \qquad (44)$$

if the specimen is of unit thickness and unit width. Luzzati (1960) shows how to integrate the expression, giving

$$x^2 \frac{I_{total}}{I_o} = \frac{\lambda x k}{2} \exp\left(\frac{-\pi^2 r_g^2 u^2}{\lambda^2 x^2}\right) K_o \left(\frac{\pi^2 r_g^2 u^2}{\lambda^2 x^2}\right) \qquad (45)$$

where K_o is a cylindrical Bessel function of the second kind, of order zero (see G. N. Watson, 1952, p. 181). This expression can be used for slit heights (at the detector) greater than 2 u_{min}.

Longley (1963) has used the above method on dilute solutions of TMV (see also Luzzati, 1960) and has found $r_g = 63.5$ Å, which is in good agreement with what is known about the virus structrue. He has also evaluated the mass per unit length M' from absolute intensity measurements using the "infinite-slit" theory outlined above and finds $M' = 11,800$ per Å, which is within 12% of the known value (13,200). The errors in the method as much result from inaccuracies of concentration determination as from errors in intensity measurement.

VII. X-ray Diffraction from Orientated Rod Viruses

A. MAKING SPECIMENS

1. Orientated Sols

The major problem encountered when working on biological systems that cannot be induced to crystallize is to find some way of obtaining partial ordering of the system. The best hope of doing this is to form liquid crystals, and the most highly ordered liquid crystal known in the biological field is that formed by tobacco mosaic virus (TMV). We therefore consider this virus in detail, since we hope that other viruses of the TMV type (i.e., with rigid rodlike particles) will behave in the same way as TMV when the correct conditions of salt concentration, pH, etc., are found.

TMV forms colloidal solutions over a considerable range of both pH and ionic strength that are spontaneously birefringent at high virus concentrations. A detailed study of the colloidal system was made by Bernal and Fankuchen (1941). For the purposes of x-ray work, the most important observation made by these authors is that the TMV particles may be induced to form orientated "gels," wherein the particles are accurately aligned parallel to each other. The perfection of these gels is such that the x-ray diffraction measurements may be made with an accuracy comparable to that obtained from single crystals. Since the term "gel" is usually reserved for a rigid colloidal suspension capable of sustaining shear, it is more accurate to use the term "sol" to describe the TMV solutions that can be orientated. However, the behavior of highly hydrated gels is thixotropic and the distinction is, therefore, only a rough one.

On leaving a solution of TMV of about 5–10% concentration at low ionic strength, it separates into two phases, top and bottom. Between crossed polaroids the top phase is nonbirefringent, but the bottom phase is spontaneously and strongly birefringent (see Fig. 55). The top phase is an isotropic sol in which the virus particle axes are completely randomly arranged. The bottom phase is a typical nematic mesophase—an anisotropic sol consisting of an aggregate of tactoids, spindle-shaped assemblies of particles, the majority of which are aligned parallel to the long axis of the tactoid. Since the tactoids are of small size they tend to be isodimensional. At higher virus concentrations (15%) only the bottom layer anisotropic sol forms; as the virus concentration is raised this becomes a highly viscous gel, but without a phase transition. The interparticle separation is 380 Å for a 20% sol (Bernal and Fankuchen, 1941).

Fig. 55. The appearance of sols and gels of TMV between crossed polaroids at various degrees of orientation of the virus. In each case the picture at the left was obtained with the specimen axis at 45° to polarizer direction and that at the right with the specimen in the extinction position. The upper specimen in the top plate shows TMV gel taken from a centrifuge pellet mixing with buffer (on the left). The second plate shows the appearance of the same specimen after the gel has been dispersed in the buffer to give a fairly homogenous sol. After waiting a few weeks the appearance of the same specimen is shown in the third plate (upper specimen). Note that the extinction is now very good. This specimen is quite suitable for x-ray diffraction. Other specimens show various pathological states that may be induced in the gel by the wrong choice of concentration or by too much flow in capillary tubes (see Gregory and Holmes, 1965).

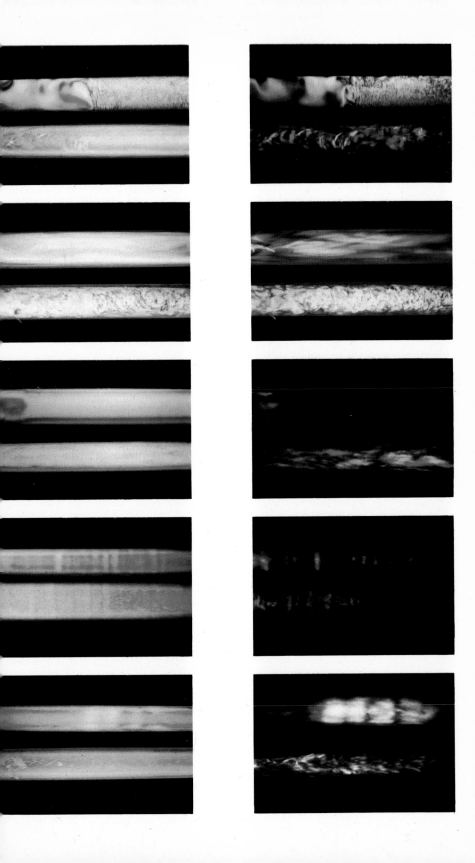

Neighboring tactoids readily fuse if their axes are parallel; we will refer to these large fused systems as domains. As they become larger, surface effects become less and less important and these large domains have, eventually, poorly defined boundaries. One can induce the formation of domains by passing the sol through a capillary tube, thereby setting up a velocity gradient in the sol (Bernal and Fankuchen, 1941). On standing, the domains in such a sol may coalesce and the particles *interact cooperatively in the absence of flow* to give a highly ordered homogeneous phase.

A theoretical treatment of the mechanism of the top and bottom layer phenomena has been given by Onsager (1949), a more readily comprehensible but a qualitative account has been given by Oster (1950), and an experimental description of the process has been given by Gregory and Holmes (1965). In order to form sols suitable for x-ray diffraction studies the following requirements must be met: (1) The viscosity of the sol must be low enough to allow free flow through a capillary tube of diameter 0.5–1 mm (such as is used for x-ray work), so that orientation may be initiated by the shear. (2) The concentration must be high, otherwise the orientation so induced is not stable. (3) The pH must be far from the isoelectric point in order to prevent the virus particles from becoming sticky and aggregating. (4) Time must be allowed after a specimen has been set up for cooperative interaction between the particles to improve the orientation. Aging can sometimes bring about a dramatic improvement even in samples that are initially poor. A detailed description of the technique used for orientating samples is given by Gregory and Holmes.

In Fig. 55 we show the appearance of various orientated and partly orientated specimens in capillary tubes of about 1 mm in diameter as seen between crossed polaroids in a polarizing microscope. In each case the left picture is shown with the specimen at 45° to the polarizer direction, and the right picture is with the specimen in the extinction position. The upper specimen of the third plate of Fig. 55 is a very good specimen suitable for x-ray diffraction. Note that in the extinction position virtually no light is transmitted. In the top plate the top specimen shows the appearance of TMV gel taken from a centrifuge pellet in the process of mixing with some buffer in order to form a TMV sol. The upper specimen of the second plate shows the same specimen after this mixing has taken place, and one can see already that a considerable degree of orientation has been achieved. The lower plates show examples of various pathological conditions produced by aggregation of the TMV particles or by too much working up and down the capillary tube. For a full explanation the original paper (Gregory and Holmes, 1965) should be consulted.

Orientated gels of tobacco rattle virus have been prepared by Finch (1965). These were made by diluting a centrifuge pellet of the purified virus with 0.1 M borate buffer at pH 7 until the solution, when sucked into a thin-walled quartz capillary tube, showed large areas of uniform birefringence. The solutions never became as uniformly birefringent as the best orientated gels of tobacco mosaic virus, and only small areas of extinction were observed. The bext x-ray diagrams were obtained by selecting one of the most uniform areas of birefringence and extinction toward the edge of the capillary tube and illuminating this with a finely collimated x-ray beam (0.1 mm in diameter). Better results have been obtained with barley stripe mosaic virus. Orientated gels for x-ray diffraction work were made by diluting a centrifuge pellet of purified virus with 0.1 M borate buffer at pH 7.5 and sucking the solution into a thin-walled capillary tube. After sealing the capillary tubes and leaving them for a few hours, some of the specimen showed fairly uniform birefringence and extinction. X-ray diffraction photographs of these were considerably better in quality than those obtained from tobacco rattle virus (Finch, 1965). It seems possible that this virus is capable of being analyzed in the same way as TMV.

Other methods of orientating virus particles, for example, by flow or by use of the Kerr effect, are never satisfactory for detailed x-ray diffraction studies. Only in those specimens where orientation is spontaneous is the ordering good enough to make possible the kind of analysis to be described below.

2. *Fiber Specimens*

In the case of the longer, flexible viruses, no well-orientated solutions have so far been produced and these may well be impossible to produce. A method of producing orientated samples that has been very successful in the examination of the structure of DNA (Langridge *et al.*, 1960) is to pull fibers from a sticky gel of the sample. This method has recently been applied successfully to preparing samples of orientated fd virus by Marvin (1966). Purified gels of fd phage were prepared and the following procedure was then used to bring about orientation. Glass rods 2.5 mm in diameter were placed with their tips opposite one another about 2 mm apart. A drop of concentrated phage gel (10–15 mg/ml) was placed between the rods and allowed to dry slowly. The distance between the rods was increased slightly during drying. Highly birefringent fibers of fd were prepared in this way.

B. APPARATUS

A useful general apparatus for work on the orientated dried fibers and for preliminary work on orientated wet sols is the x-ray micro-camera described by Langridge *et al.* (1960), which was devised for work on DNA fibers. The camera consists of a piece of lead-glass capillary 50–100 μ in diameter, which must be selected for uniformity and parallelism of bore. Mounted behind the capillary is the specimen, and 2–3 cm away from this is the film. Frequently the body of the camera is hydrogen filled during operation in order to cut down air scattering. Alternatively, the lead-glass capillary may be replaced by a set of three concentric apertures arranged as in Fig. 56. The camera is designed for use with a very fine x-ray source, such as the 50-μ spot produced by the Hilger microfocus x-ray tube. For the accurate intensity measurements needed for the work on the structure of TMV to be described below, it is desirable to use strictly monochromatic radiation in order to cut

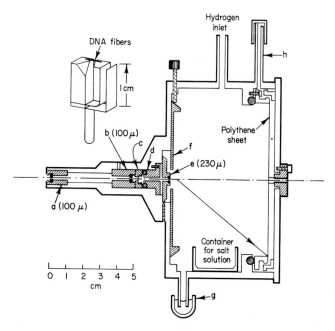

FIG. 56. A scale drawing of an x-ray camera suitable for work with fibers and spacing up to 100 Å. Parts a, b, and c carry the collimating apertures. There is a mica sheet at c to seal the camera. The specimen is mounted against the plate f. The camera is filled with hydrogen to reduce air scatter. The film is protected from the atmosphere of the camera by a polythene sheet. The insert shows a holder for the DNA fibers (after Langridge *et al.*, 1960).

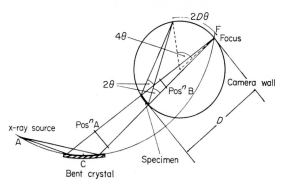

FIG. 57. The Guinier monochromator and focusing camera: a long thin slab of quartz is elastically bent; x-rays reflected by the 10$\bar{1}$1 Bragg planes are thereby brought to a focus. If the specimen and the film lie on the same circle, it can be seen that the diffraction pattern will be in focus on this circle.

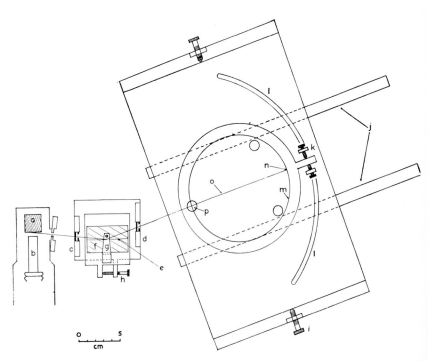

FIG. 58. Diagram showing an x-ray tube, bent quartz crystal monochromator and stand, and Guinier focusing camera and stand. a, Copper target; b, cathode assembly; c, monochromator entrance slit; d, monochromator exit slit; e, quartz crystal; f, press; g, clamp; h, monochromator fine-rotation adjustment; i, camera transverse adjustment; j, rails for camera carriage; k, fine-rotation adjustment for camera; l, rails for k; m, inner wall of camera; n, focus of monochromator beam; o, middle ray of beam; p, pivot for rotation of camera, the specimen is located over this point (Holmes, 1959).

down extraneous scattering. Adequate intensities are available from bent quartz crystal monochromators used with a fine-focus rotating anode tube. A diagram of a fine-focus rotating anode tube developed in the authors' laboratory specifically for such purposes is shown in Fig. 41. Very high specific intensities (10 kW/mm^2) are available from this tube when used as a source of dimensions 1 $\times$ 0.1 mm. Viewed at 6° to the target surface this becomes a 100-μ^2 x-ray source. Figure 57 shows the principle of the focusing monochromator and focusing camera used with this tube. A quartz crystal is elastically bent in a press and arranged so that planes of high reflecting power are in the Bragg reflecting position (see Guinier, 1952). The converging beam comes to a focus on the cylindrical film. If the specimen is on the circumference of this cylinder, all corresponding diffracted beams from different parts of the specimen are also brought to a common focus on the film. Figure 58 shows a practical version of the apparatus built by the late Dr. R. E. Franklin. In order to cut down the scattering still further, the cylindrical camera is evacuated.

C. INTERPRETATION OF FIBER DIAGRAMS

1. *The Lattice Parameters*

The low-angle equatorial diffraction from either orientated fibers or orientated sols will be strongly influenced by interference effects between the particles. If the particles are roughly cylindrical in shape, then it is very probable that they tend to an hexagonal arrangement, and thus the low-angle interference will take the form of the orders of diffraction from a pseudohexagonal lattice. Therefore, a measurement of the positions of low-angle diffraction maxima can give fairly directly a measure of the interparticle distance. As the sols become more concentrated or the fibers are dried, such interparticle interference effects become more and more marked. Moreover, their spacing varies inversely as a function of the water content of the gel. If the interparticle distance is measured accurately as a function of the degree of hydration of the gel, then it is possible to get a measure of the mass per unit length of the virus (see Klug and Caspar, 1960, p. 241).

2. *Identifying the Geometrical Parameters of the Helix*

At wider angles on the equator and in other parts of the diffraction pattern, in general, interference effects will be negligible; therefore, the fiber-diffraction pattern records the cylindrical average of the square of the scattering from essentially one virus particle. By direct inspection of this pattern it is possible to identify some of the important geometrical parameters in the helix. In a simple helix that repeats in one turn, the layer-line separation is proportional to the reciprocal of the pitch of the helix. In addition, the height of the first *meridional* intensity is the reciprocal of the vertical separation of the repeating atoms of the helix. Thus, by direct inspection one can obtain two important stereochemical parameters. If the diagrams were as simple as those shown in the optical transforms (Section IV,D,1; Figs. 32 and 33), a measurement of the position of the first maxima of each Bessel function on each layer line would give the helix radius. For example, if we know that there is a J_4 term on the fourth layer line having a maximum value at R_{max} we can refer to tables to find that the first maximum of $J_4(x)$ is at $x = 5.3$; since $x = 2\pi R_{max} r_0$, we therby obtain r_0, the helix radius. However, to do this we should need to be sure of the value of n on layer line 4. In practice, with a complex structure consisting of atoms at many radii, the value of the radius obtained in this way would not need to be the same for each layer line.

The pitch of the helix, P, may not be simply the reciprocal of the layer-line separation, since there might be one, two, or more turns of the helix in one repeat, c. In these circumstances, the layer lines will break up into groups in a way that is most easily explained by an example. Suppose a helix repeats exactly after three turns (i.e., $t = 3$ and $c = 3P$); then the first and second layer lines will involve relatively high-order Bessel function terms and will have no intensity near the meridian, whereas the third layer line will involve a low-order Bessel function and the intensity will be near, but not on, the meridian. Likewise, the fourth and fifth will be away from the meridian, and the sixth near, and so on. The reciprocal of the separation of the near-meridional layer lines will give the pitch P, and the ratio of this to the repeat distance c gives t, the number of turns in which the structure repeats.

By arguments such as these J. D. Watson (1954) was able to show that for TMV there must be $3n + 1$ subunits in one repeat and that the structure must repeat in three turns (n is any positive integer). However, it was never possible to find unambiguously a meridional layer line corresponding to the z rise per residue. The value of n was therefore established by the following method. Reference to Fig. 36 will show that for a structure consisting of 100 points in a ring there will be a strong diffraction peak at a reciprocal space radius given by R_{max} where

$$2\pi R_{max} r_0 \cong 102$$

which indicated that if this diffraction maximum could be located in the virus-diffraction pattern on the zero layer line, then the value of the rotational period $(3n + 1)$, and hence of n, could be determined. For a structure as complex as TMV this is clearly impossible. However, it is fairly simple to mark the TMV particle regularly with mercury atoms by attaching one to each of the sulfhydryls in each of the protein subunits. Then if an accurate comparison is made between the diffraction on the zero layer line from normal TMV and TMV substituted with mercury, it is found that there is a new intensity maximum at a position that corresponds to the $(3n + 1)$-fold scattering from the mercury atoms; this is shown in Fig. 59. Against the difference between the moduli of the two scattering curves is shown the expected scattering from mercury atoms grouped with 46-fold, 49-fold, and 52-fold symmetry. It is clear that the observed differences fit 49 very much better than the other two possible values of $3n + 1$ in the

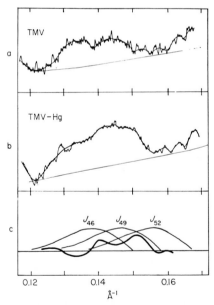

Fig. 59. Determination of the helical parameter, u. (a) Photometer trace of I_{TMV} on the equator for values of R from 0.12 to 0.17 Å^{-1}. The smooth curve shows the values read. (b) Photometer trace of $I_{\text{TMV-Hg}}$ on the equator for values of R from 0.12 to 0.17 Å^{-1}. The intensity scale is here 1.4 times greater than that of (a). (c) The difference between $|F_{\text{TMV-Hg}}|$ and $|F_{\text{TMV}}|$ (heavy curve) is compared with the first peak of the functions $J_{46}(2\pi R \times 56.2)$, $J_{49}(2\pi R \times 56.2)$, and $J_{52}(2\pi R \times 56.2)$. It is clear that the largest values of $|F_{\text{TMV-Hg}}| - |F_{\text{TMV}}|$ occur in the region of the first peak of $J_{49}(2\pi R \times 56.2)$, indicating that there are 49 units of TMV protein in the axial repeat period of 69 Å (Franklin and Holmes, 1958).

region. Thus, the number of subunits in one repeat of the TMV particle was established as 49. Since the structure repeats in 69 Å ($c = 69$ Å,
$t = 3$, $u = 49$), the rise per residue is 1.4 Å.

D. Fourier Methods Applied to Tobacco Mosaic Virus

1. Special Methods of Data Collection

In Section IV,C,3 we mentioned how the method of isomorphous
replacement may be used to solve the phase problem in crystalline proteins. The same method has been applied to the cylindrically averaged
data from tobacco mosaic virus sols (Holmes and Klug, 1968a). However, it has been necessary to develop special methods of collecting the
data so as to ensure that the results of these calculations are significant. The reasons for this are 2-fold: (1) it has been possible to use
data only out to a limited resolving power (10 Å) and therefore one has
had considerable trouble in locating the heavy atoms; and (2) the
magnitude of the changes to the diffracted intensity caused by heavy
atoms is not very great and would be easily swamped by errors.

The data have been collected with an evacuated focusing camera
with a specimen–film distance of 11.2 cm [the camera, designed by
the late Dr. R. E. Franklin, is described by Holmes (1959); see Fig.
58]. The camera has been used with a Guinier curved quartz crystal
monochromator and CuKα radiation from a fine-focus rotating anode
tube, as shown in Fig. 41. A typical x-ray photograph is shown in
Fig. 60. Such photographs are photometered with a Joyce Loebl microdensitometer using a 0–1 wedge and a 20 × linear magnification.
A photometer trace of the zero layer line with the water background
added is shown in Fig. 61. The scattering caused by water and glass in
a specimen is measured up the meridian of the photograph where there
is little scattering from the TMV sample, and this is subtracted from
all the data after various geometrical corrections have been applied.
The data are measured off the photometer traces every half centimeter
and are punched on cards and fed to an IBM 7090. The calculation of
the reciprocal space coordinate corresponding to any given length
measured on the film along a layer line (a Bernal chart calculation) is
performed in the computer, and the necessary interpolations are made.
In addition, the tilt of the specimen (which is difficult to align to an
accuracy of better than 1°–2°) is found by a least-squares analysis of
the data. In order to aid in the problem of recording very intense diffracted intensity near the meridian of the photograph, part of the film
is shielded with an aluminum screen of known absorption (see Fig. 60).
A number of films of the same specimen are taken at exposure times

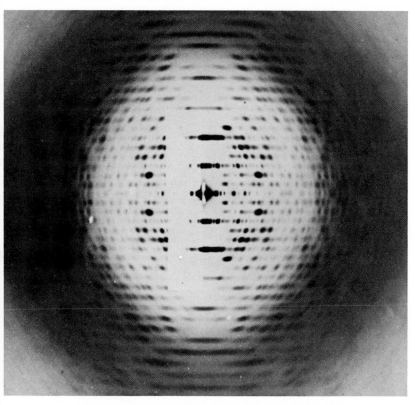

FIG. 60. X-ray fiber diagram of orientated TMV solution with axis of specimen vertical. For this photograph a bent quartz line focusing monochromator was used with a vacuum camera having a specimen–film distance of 12 cm. Since the range of intensity recorded on the photograph is very large, an aluminum screen was used to screen out part of the intense diffraction pattern.

varying from 2 to 50 hours in order to cover the necessary exposure range; after treatment the data from all these films are scaled together and standard deviations are calculated. These standard deviations are important in that in all subsequent calculations the weight given to any item of data is calculated from the standard deviation.

2. The Interpretation of Cylindrically Averaged Data

In Section IV,D,2 it was shown how cylindrically averaged data could be analyzed into the sum of terms G_{nl}^2. If we write $I_l(R)$ for the intensity on layer line l we have

$$I_l(R) = \sum_n G_{nl}^2(R)$$

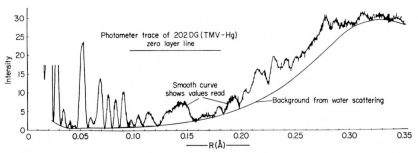

Fig. 61. Photometer trace of the zero layer line of a mercury-substituted derivative of TMV (TMV–Hg). The trace was made from a film similar to that shown in Fig. 60. The scattering arising from water and glass in the specimen is shown as a slowly varying curve. A smooth curve is drawn through the noise (caused by film grain) of the photometer trace, and the intensity of scattering from the virus sol may be read off.

TABLE VII

Low-Order Values of n for the TMV Helix

Layer line (l)	Rotational symmetry (n)		
0	−49	0	49
1	−16	33	—
2	−32	17	—
3	−48	1	50
4	−15	34	—
5	−31	18	—
6	−47	2	51
7	−14	35	—
8	−30	19	—
9	−46	3	52

where the possible values of n are given by the selection rule [Eq. (8)] for the given helix. The values of n for TMV are given in Table VII; note that on the zero layer line the only allowed values are 0, 49, 98, etc. Remembering that each term G_{nl} is the sum of many Bessel functions, i.e.,

$$G_{nl}(R) = \sum_{j} J_n(2\pi R r_j) \exp i(-n\phi_j + 2\pi l z_j/c)$$

we can see that if the maximum radius of the particle is known (in the case of TMV it is about 80 Å), then we can predict that the minimum value of R for which the term $G_{49,0}$ can contribute to the zero layer-line intensity is at a value of R given by

$$2\pi 80 R \cong 51$$

Thus, out to a value of $R = 0.1$ (10-Å resolving power) the zero layer line of TMV can be made up only of the term $G_{0,0}{}^2$. Likewise, by making the same kind of calculation on the other layer lines, the maximum value of R where it may be safely assumed that the contribution to the intensity arises solely from one G_{nl} term may be found. These values are shown in the Table VIII. We see that the situation is best for the 0th, 3rd, and 6th layer lines of TMV, but is not intolerably bad for the intermediate layer lines. If we restrict our attention to these parts of the diffraction pattern, we lose nothing by having cylindrically averaged data, since if the data were not cylindrically averaged we would, in any case, record the same value of the intensity. These con-

TABLE VIII

MAXIMUM R VALUE FOR WHICH THE DIFFRACTION PATTERN OF TMV HAS CYLINDRICAL SYMMETRY (see Text)

Layer line (l)	R_{max}
0	0.102
1	0.070
2	0.068
3	0.100
4	0.072
5	0.066
6	0.098
7	0.074
8	0.064
9	0.096

clusions may be restated by saying that the high rotational symmetry of the TMV particle means that out to about 10-Å spacing the intensity of the diffraction pattern has complete cylindrical symmetry.

At the moment the work on the structure of TMV has been deliberately limited to this part of the diffraction pattern; however, as a result of being limited to what is, for x-ray-diffraction purposes, very low resolving power, considerable difficulty has been found in locating heavy atom positions. The radius of attachment of the heavy atom may readily be found by an examination of the zero layer-line data in a manner to be described in Section VII,D,3, but the other coordinates have proved much more elusive. These problems have been solved (Holmes and Klug, 1968b) by an application of the method of Bragg ellipses (Bragg, 1958). These methods are rather too crystallographically technical to be described here, but the problem of finding heavy atoms in three dimensions *can* be solved with low-resolution fiber-dif-

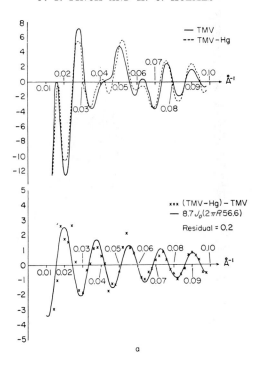

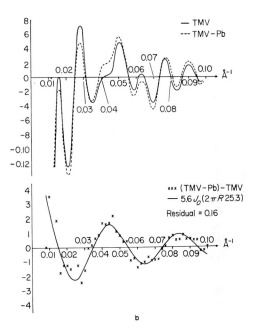

raction data on condition that the heavy atoms are added to the virus
 one at a time. Multiple substitution makes the problem virtually
nsoluble.

3. *The Zero Layer Line*

It is possible to write the cylindrically averaged square of a Fourier
ransform of one particle in cylindrical coordinates in terms of the
unctions g_{nl} in the following way:

$$<F^2(R)>\psi = \left[\int_0^\infty g_{0,0}(r)J_0(2\pi Rr)2\pi R dR\right]^2$$
$$+ \sum_n \left[\int_0^\infty g_{nl}(r)J_n(2\pi Rr)2\pi R dR\right]^2 \quad (46)$$

where each of the integrals is one of the terms G_{nl}^2. On the zero
ayer line, therefore, out to reciprocal spacings of 0.1 Å^{-1} we can write

$$<F^2(R)>\psi = \left[\int_{0\mathfrak{l}}^\infty g_{0,0}(r)J_0(2\pi Rr)2\pi R dR\right]^2$$

ince all the other terms must be zero. On condition that the signs of
F can be found, we may take the square root of this equation to give:

$$F(R) = \int_0^\infty g_{0,0}(r)J_0(2\pi Rr)2\pi r dr \quad (47)$$

nd directly from this it is possible to deduce the inverse relationship:

$$g_{0,0}(r) = \int_0^\infty F(R)J_0(2\pi Rr)2\pi R dR \quad (48)$$

Hence we may calculate the coefficient $g_{0,0}(r)$ from observations of the
zero layer-line data. $g_{0,0}(r)$ expresses the variation of the density in
he particle as a function of radius only, i.e., it is cylindrically averaged
nd vertically averaged.

In order to find the signs of F, a number of heavy atoms have been
sed (Caspar, 1956b; Franklin and Holmes, 1958). Two examples of
he changes caused by the addition of a single heavy atom to each pro-
ein subunit are shown in Fig. 62. Here the F values are plotted both

---

FIG. 62. (a) The upper curves show the amplitude of scattering on the zero layer
ne from TMV and TMV with mercury attached (TMV–Hg). The difference be-
ween these amplitudes is shown in the lower curves (crosses), with the theoretical
cattering from a mercury atom at 56.6 Å radius. (b) Same as (a) except that the
hemically attached atom is lead and the theoretical scattering shown is from half
lead atom at 25.3 Å radius.

for the native virus and for the virus with the heavy atom attached The data are taken from the inner portion of the zero layer line. It ca be seen that the difference between these two curves, which is the scat tering caused by the heavy atom, fits along the theoretical curves of th heavy atom at a single radius. Knowing only the moduli of the dat given in Fig. 62 but knowing that the difference between these modu should lie upon a regular oscillating curve, it is clear that, with a littl trial and error manipulation, the signs of the zero layer-line data ma be unequivocally determined.

The scattering data on the zero layer line from the native virus ma be used to compute the radial-density function [Eq. (48)] for the vi rus. This was first done by Caspar (1956b), and a typical curve i shown in Fig. 63. About the same time Franklin (1956) proceeded in similar way using repolymerized protein of tobacco mosaic virus, bu with no RNA; the resultant radial-density function is also shown i Fig. 63. The radial-density functions are very similar except in th 40-Å region, where the native TMV is much higher than the repoly merized protein. This indicates quite clearly that the nucleic acid located at 40-Å radius in the particle. It is also of interest that there

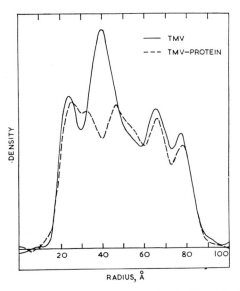

FIG. 63. The average density as a function of radius in TMV (solid line curve) ar repolymerized protein (broken line curve) calculated to Fourier–Bessel inversion the zero layer line [Eq. (48)] amplitudes. Note that the particle is hollow and th the outside radius is 85 Å. The large density difference between TMV and TMV protein at a radius of 40 Å indicates the position of the RNA (Franklin, 1956).

hole of 40-Å diameter in the middle of the particle. The maximum radius of the particle, about 85 Å, is also fairly evident from these radial-density functions.

Once the signs of the parent virus have been discovered, then examination of any new heavy atom compound is a fairly routine matter. This may proceed in one of two ways. First, curves very similar to those shown in Fig. 62 may be prepared, which usually show at once the radius and occupancy of any new heavy atom, or we may compute the radial-density function [using Eq. (48)] and see where this differs from that of standard TMV (Fig. 64). Of these two procedures, the first is preferable unless the heavy atom is fairly heavy, since fre-

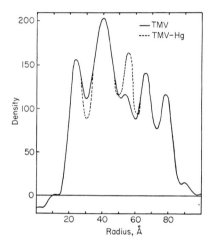

FIG. 64. The average density as a function of radius in TMV (solid line curve) and TMV with mercury attached (TMV–Hg, broken line curve). Difference in density may be seen at a radius of 30 and 56 Å. The 56-Å difference shows the location of the heavy atom (Holmes, 1959).

quently small heavy atom sites may be obscured by errors in the density map. Moreover, a least-squares analysis of the data in reciprocal space is possible using the known standard deviations of this data, and this gives the most accurate possible estimate of heavy atom radius and occupancy. Proceeding in this way it is possible to locate a heavy atom radius to within 0.5 Å and its occupancy to within 10–20 electrons.

4. *The Determination of the Electron Density in Three Dimensions*

Once heavy atom coordinates have been located in three dimensions, then the phase of the scattering of all layer lines may be computed and this phased data may be used in order to compute a three-dimen-

sional electron-density map of the subunit of tobacco mosaic virus
Such three-dimensional work is at present in progress (Holmes *et al.*
1966), and provisional three-dimensional electron-density maps at
10-Å resolution have been computed. Since these maps have yet to be
interpreted in terms of the folding of the polypeptide chain and in any
case do not lend themselves easily to representation on the printed
page, we will not attempt to demonstrate them here; rather, we show a
two-dimensional electron density map which is computed from zero
third, and sixth layer-line data. The choice of only some of the diffraction data can be shown to amount to computing a projection of the
structure in a direction specified by the way the choice of data was
made. Since we are working with a helical structure and cylindrical coordinates, the projection computed is a helical projection, the
meaning of which is explained by Fig. 65. We choose a family of helices
that is specified only by their pitch. Consider the point A; we choose a
helix of given pitch that passes through this point and follow this helix
down until it intersects the vertical plane, producing the point A_1

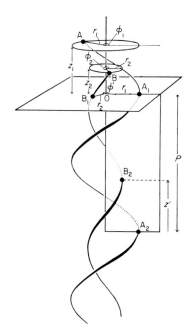

Fig. 65. A helical projection: the point A projected down a helix of pitch P be
comes the point A_1 on the horizontal plane, and the point B becomes B_1. Alterna
tively, the projection may be made onto a vertical plane, giving the points A_2 and
B_2. From Holmes and Blow (1965).

equally, we could follow this through a complete turn of the helix to produce the point A_2. This provides a way of working out one repeat in the projected view of the structure. Likewise, the point B would produce the point B_2 on the vertical helical projection. It is equally valid to make the projection on to a horizontal plane producing the points B_1 and A_1, as shown. However, this view of the projection is not very useful for our purpose. As an example of a helical projection, by choosing the layer lines at height zero, $\frac{1}{23}$, and $\frac{2}{23}$ Å^{-1} (i.e., zero, third, and sixth) we define the pitch of the helix along which we project to be 23 Å. This is, in fact, the basic or genetic helix of the virus (see Fig. 1a) which is very flat. Therefore, this is a rather useful view of the virus, since it is virtually a view sideways through the subunit. Some results are shown in Fig. 66. Figure 66a shows the helical projection computed using mercury and a uranyl ion as the heavy atoms. Figure 66b shows the same helical projection computed using osmium and lead as the heavy atoms. The similarity between these two projections gives one confidence as to the correctness of the methods. The combined pro-

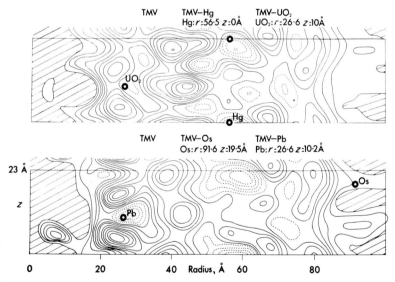

FIG. 66. Helical projections of TMV down the basic helix of pitch 23 Å computed from data on the zero, third, and sixth layer lines. The upper density map was computed with phase angles derived from methyl mercury and uranyl pentafluoride ions as heavy atoms. The lower density map was computed with osmium and lead ions as heavy atoms. The similarity between these two maps, which are based on independently determined heavy atom coordinates, gives confidence in the reliability of the method. The broken contours show valleys in the electron density, which would otherwise be indistinguishable from hills.

jection computed using all the heavy atom data at once, and which
may be assumed to be more accurate, is shown in Fig. 67.

In interpreting low-resolution electron-density maps any ancillary
information that can provide restrictions on the way that the chain
can fold is of great value. One of the most helpful ways of providing
restrictions on the possible positions of various segments of the protein
chain is to use some of the many artificial mutants of TMV created by
the use of nitrous acid. In particular, one nitrous acid mutation replaces residue No. 139, a tyrosine, by a cysteine residue, which may
then be marked with a mercury atom (Wittmann-Liebold and Wittman, 1965). In this way the radius of residue 139 is found to be 72 Å.
Moreover, it has been possible to locate this mercury atom with respect
to the other heavy atoms in three dimensions.

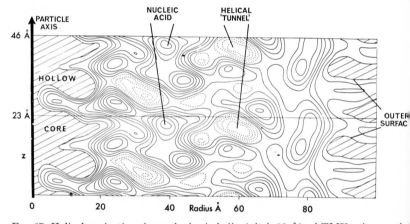

Fig. 67. Helical projection down the basic helix (pitch 23 Å) of TMV using methyl
mercury, osmium, lead, and uranyl pentafluoride ions all together as heavy atoms.
Recognizable features of the pattern are marked.

VIII. Comparison of X-ray and Electron Microscope Techniques

The investigation of the structure of viruses by the negative-staining
method of electron microscopy is limited to those regions of the virus
accessible to the negative stain and to a resolution of about 20 Å. This
resolution is barely sufficient to resolve individual protein subunits,
and the determination of a surface lattice is based in the case of spherical viruses on the grouping of units into larger, more easily resolved
morphological units, and in the rod-shaped viruses on the repetitive
detail along the helical lines of units that can be picked out by eye or
more readily, by optical transformation.

The potential of the x-ray diffraction method is much greater (in theory to atomic resolution) provided (1) well-ordered crystals can be grown, (2) the intensity of all reflections to the required resolution can be recorded, and (3) the intensity data can be interpreted or processed with that from necessary heavy atom derivatives. The second condition is more easily satisfied for the rod-shaped viruses, since the x-ray diagram from an orientated sol or gel corresponds to the cylindrically averaged transform, and thus almost all the available data from a specimen can be recorded on one film. Thus in the case of TMV the helical parameters and location of RNA were found quite early in the investigation; more detailed work has been limited by the need for more heavy atom derivatives and the problems of handling the cylindrically averaged data. However, for rod viruses of this type, provided that sufficient material is available and orientated gels can be prepared, an x-ray investigation is structurally much more rewarding. In other cases, and particularly for the long flexible viruses which have not yet provided well-orientated specimens, the surface lattice may be obtained by electron microscopy.

In the case of the spherical viruses, only very limited x-ray data from a few viruses have so far been collected. Such data can show the presence of icosahedral symmetry, and in favorable cases (e.g., TYMV) the positions of the structural units and the broad distribution of RNA can be determined by comparison with models. All this information and more, however, has been obtained from electron micrographs; note the detailed surface morphology of the particle shown in Fig. 22. In fact, both the x-ray and electron microscope investigations on this virus were conducted in parallel, each helping the other, and this would seem to be the ideal method of attack until such time as the x-ray technique can be applied more fully.

Acknowledgments

We are indebted to Dr. A. Klug for many ideas and helpful discussions. We thank Dr. D. L. D. Caspar for permission to reproduce his drawings in Figs. 1 and 22. We are grateful to Mrs. Angela Mott for the line drawings.

References

Agrawal, H. O., Kent, J. W., and MacKay, D. M. (1965). *Science* **148**, 638.
Anderegg, J. W., Beeman, W. W., Shulman, S., and Kaesberg, P. (1955). *J. Am. Chem. Soc.* **77**, 2927.
Anderegg, J. W., Geil, P. H., Beeman, W. W., and Kaesberg, P. (1961). *Biophys. J.* **1**, 657–667.

Bawden, F. C., and Pirie, N. W. (1938). *Brit. J. Exptl. Pathol.* **19**, 251.

Beeman, W. W., Kaesberg, P., Anderegg, J. W., and Webb, M. B. (1957). *In* "Handbuch der Physik" (S. Flügge, ed.), Vol. 32, p. 321. Springer, Berlin.

Bernal, J. D., and Fankuchen, I. (1941). *J. Gen. Physiol.* **25**, 111.

Born, M. (1933). "Optik." Springer, Berlin.

Bragg, W. L. (1958). *Acta Cryst.* **11**, 70–75.

Broad, D. A. G. (1956). U.K. Patent Appl. Nos. 5172, 5173, 12761, 38938, 10984, and 13376.

Buerger, M. J. (1942). "X-ray Crystallography." Wiley, New York.

Buerger, M. J. (1964). "The Precession Method in X-ray Crystallography." Wiley, New York.

Carlisle, C. H., and Dornberger, K. (1948). *Acta Cryst.* **1**, 194.

Caspar, D. L. D. (1956a). *Nature* **177**, 475.

Caspar, D. L. D. (1956b). *Nature* **177**, 928.

Caspar, D. L. D. (1966). *J. Mol. Biol.* **15**, 365.

Caspar, D. L. D., and Holmes, K. C. (1968). *J. Mol. Biol.*, in press.

Caspar, D. L. D., and Klug, A. (1962). *Cold Spring Harbor Symp. Quant. Biol.* **27**, 1.

Cochran, W., Crick, F. H. C., and Vand, V. (1952). *Acta Cryst.* **5**, 581.

Cohen, N. V. (1958). *Proc. Cambridge Phil. Soc.* **54**, 28–38.

Crick, F. H. C., and Watson, J. D. (1956). *Nature* **177**, 473.

Debye, P. (1962). See Prock and McConkey (1962).

Finch, J. T. (1959) Ph.D. Thesis, London University.

Finch, J. T. (1964). *J. Mol. Biol.* **8**, 872.

Finch, J. T. (1965). *J. Mol. Biol.* **12**, 612–619.

Finch, J. T., and Klug, A. (1959). *Nature* **183**, 1709.

Finch, J. T., and Klug, A. (1965). *J. Mol. Biol.* **13**, 1.

Finch, J. T., and Klug, A. (1966). *J. Mol. Biol.* **15**, 344.

Finch, J. T., and Klug, A. (1967). *J. Mol. Biol.* **24**, 289.

Finch, J. T., Leberman, R., and Berger, J. E. (1967). *J. Mol. Biol.*, **27**, 17.

Franklin, R. E. (1956). *Nature* **177**, 928–930.

Franklin, R. E., and Holmes, K. C. (1958). *Acta Cryst.* **11**, 213.

Fridborg, K., Hjertén, S., Höglund, S., Liljas, A., Lundberg, B. K. S., Oxelfelt, P., Philipson, L., and Strandberg, B. (1965). *Proc. Natl. Acad. Sci. U.S.* **54**, 513.

Gregory, J., and Holmes, K. C. (1965). *J. Mol. Biol.* **13**, 796–801.

Guinier, A. (1952). "X-ray Crystallographic Technology." Hilger & Watts, London.

Guinier, A. (1963). "X-ray Diffraction" (English ed. transl. by P. Lorrain and D. Sainte-Marie Lorrain). Freeman, San Francisco, California.

Guinier, A., and Fournet, G. (1955). "Small Angle Scattering of X-rays" (English ed. transl. by C. B. Walker). Wiley, New York.

Holmes, K. C. (1959). Ph.D. Thesis, London University.

Holmes, K. C., and Blow, D. M. (1965). *Methods Biochem. Anal.* **13**, 113.

Holmes, K. C., and Klug, A. (1968a). To be published.

Holmes, K. C., and Klug, A. (1968b). In preparation.

Holmes, K. C., and Longley, W. (1964). Unpublished data.

Holmes, K. C., Klug, A., Leberman, R., and von Sengbusch, P. (1966). *Abstr. 2nd Intern. Biophys. Congr., Vienna, 1966* No. 205.

Horne, R. W., Brenner, S., Waterson, A. P., and Wildy, P. (1959). *J. Mol. Biol.* **1**, 84

Huxley, H. E., and Zubay, G. (1960a). *J. Mol. Biol.* **2**, 189.

Huxley, H. E., and Zubay, G. (1960b). *J. Mol. Biol.* **2**, 10.

International Tables for X-ray Crystallography." (1952). Vol. I. Kynock Press, Birmingham, England.

International Tables for X-ray Crystallography." (1959). Vol. II. Kynock Press, Birmingham, England.

International Tables for X-ray Crystallography." (1962). Vol. III. Kynock Press, Birmingham, England.

ahnke, E., and Emde, F. (1945). "Tables of Functions with Formulae and Curves," 4th ed. Dover, New York.

ames, R. W. (1954). "The Optical Principles of the Diffraction of X-rays," 2nd ed. Bell, London.

Klug, A. (1956). International Union of Crystallography Symposium, Madrid.

Klug, A. (1968). In preparation.

Klug, A., and Berger, J. E. (1964). J. Mol. Biol. 10, 565.

Klug, A., and Caspar, D. L. D. (1960). Advan. Virus Res. 7, 225.

Klug, A., and De Rosier, D. J. (1966). Nature 212, 29.

Klug, A., and Finch, J. T. (1965). J. Mol. Biol. 11, 403.

Klug, A., Finch, J. T., and Franklin, R. E. (1957). Biochim. Biophys. Acta 25, 242.

Klug, A., Crick, F. H. C., and Wyckoff, H. W. (1958). Acta Cryst. 11, 199.

Klug, A., Finch, J. T., Leberman, R., and Longley, W. (1966a). Ciba Found. Symp., Principles Biomol. Organ. p. 158.

Klug, A., Longley, W., and Leberman, R. (1966b). J. Mol. Biol. 15, 315.

Kratky, O., and Porod, A. (1949). J. Colloid Sci. 4, 35–70.

Langridge, R., Wilson, H. R., Hooper, C. W., Wilkins, M. H. F., and Hamilton, L. D. (1960). J. Mol. Biol. 2, 19–37.

Leberman, R. (1965). Unpublished data.

Lipscomb, W. N. (1960). In "Techniques of Organic Chemistry" (A. Weissberger, ed.), 3rd ed., Vol. I, Part II, pp. 1641–1738. Wiley (Interscience), New York.

Lipson, H., and Cochran, W. (1966). "The Determination of Crystal Structures," 2nd ed. Bell, London.

Longley, W. (1963). Ph.D. Thesis, London University.

Luzzati, V. (1960). Acta Cryst. 13, 939.

Luzzati, V., Witz, J., and Baro, R. (1963). J. Phys. (Paris) 24, 141A.

Markham, R. (1959). In "The Viruses" (F. M. Burnet and W. M. Stanley, eds.), Vol. 2, p. 33. Academic Press, New York.

Markham, R., Frey, S., and Hills, G. J. (1963). Virology 20, 88.

Marvin, D. A. (1966). J. Mol. Biol. 15, 8–17.

Mattern, C. F. T. (1962). Virology 17, 520.

Mattern, C. F. T., and du Buy, H. G. (1956). Science 123, 1037.

Miller, G. L., and Price, W. C. (1946). Arch. Biochem. 11, 329 and 337.

Nixon, H. L., and Gibbs, A. J. (1960). J. Mol. Biol. 2, 197.

Offord, R. E. (1966). J. Mol. Biol. 17, 370.

Onsager, L. (1949). Ann. N.Y. Acad. Sci. 51, 627.

Oster, G. (1950). J. Gen. Physiol. 33, 445.

Phillips, D. C. (1966). In "Advances in Structure Research by Diffraction Methods" (R. Brill and R. Mason, eds.), Vol. 2, p. 75. Interscience, New York.

Phillips, F. C. (1963). "An Introduction in Crystallography," 2nd ed. Longmans, Green, London.

Prock, A., and McConkey, G. (1962). "Topics in Chemical Physics" (based on the Harvard lectures of P. Debye). Elsevier, Amsterdam.

Schmidt, P., Kaesberg, P., and Beeman, W. W. (1954). Biochim. Biophys. Acta 14, 1.

Sommerfeld, A. (1949). "Partial Differential Equations in Physics." Academic Pre New York.

Steere, R. L., and Schaffer, F. L. (1958). *Biochim. Biophys. Acta* **28,** 241.

Stratton, J. A. (1941). "Electromagnetic Theory." McGraw-Hill, New York.

Taylor, C. A., and Lipson, H. (1964). "Optical Transforms, Their Preparation a Application to X-ray Diffraction Problems." Bell, London.

Valdrè, U. (1962). *J. Sci. Instr.* **39,** 278.

Watson, G. N. (1952). "A Treatise on the Theory of Bessel Functions." Cambrid Univ. Press, London.

Watson, J. D. (1954). *Biochim. Biophys. Acta* **13,** 10.

Whittaker, E. J. W. (1955). *Acta Cryst.* **8,** 255.

Wittmann-Liebold, B., and Wittman, H. G. (1965). *Z. Vererbungslehre* **97,** 305–32

10 *Microscopic Techniques*

Rex S. Spendlove

This chapter will discuss the use of fluorescence microscopy to demonstrate virus or viral material in cells or tissues. The techniques include fluorescent-antibody staining, a serologically specific staining method, and fluorochrome staining with acridine orange, a method that will differentially stain nucleic acids. Some histochemical stains that can be used to confirm and complement results obtained with fluorescent antibody and acridine orange staining will be described.

The vast literature pertaining to the use of these techniques will not be reviewed, since a number of excellent reviews have been written. An attempt will be made to give sufficient theoretical background to enable the reader to gain a general understanding of the methods discussed; procedures will then be described in detail.

G. R. Price and Schwartz (1956), Ornstein *et al.* (1957), Young (1961), and Nairn (1964a) have published articles describing the the theoretical aspects and applications of fluorescence and fluorescence microscopy as applied to the study of biological problems. Only a brief discussion of these considerations will be presented here.

Radiations of the electromagnetic spectrum (see Table I for partial list) consist of packets of energy, called quanta, which travel in wave motion. All quanta of a specific wavelength travel at a uniform velocity and have the same energy; the velocity and energy are inversely proportional to the wavelength of the quantum. Radiations must be absorbed if they are to affect matter. The effect that an absorbed quantum has is a function of its energy content; thus, a quantum of visible light will have less effect than a quantum of ultraviolet light of shorter wavelength.

In conventional light microscopy the specimen is illuminated with white light (radiations of visible light). Quanta of white light are reflected, refracted, or absorbed; the molecules that absorb quanta are energized and are said to be excited. Since the energy per quantum of visible light is small, it is usually transferred to neighboring molecules without inducing chemical change or without emitting further

TABLE I

Wavelengths in $m\mu$ of Various Radiations of Interest in Fluorescence Microscopy[a]

Radiations	Representative	Spectrum
Ultraviolet		Below 400
Visible spectrum		400–700
Violet	410	400–424
Blue	470	424–491
Green	520	491–575
Maximum visibility	556	
Yellow	580	575–585
Orange	600	585–647
Red	650	647–700
Infrared		>700

[a] Adopted from Hodgman, 1949.

adiations. The unabsorbed portion of the spectrum constitutes the color that is seen in the specimen.

The techniques of fluorescence microscopy described in this chapter use the ultraviolet, violet, and/or blue parts of the spectrum for illumination (exciting radiation). Molecules that have electrons raised to higher energy levels by excitation with ultraviolet or near ultraviolet light may transfer the energy to neighboring molecules, or the electrons may return to their original energy level with the emission of a secondary radiation. This phenomenon is known as fluorescence. A compound is highly fluorescent if the molecules are highly absorbent for the ultraviolet radiations and if most of the excited molecules emit energy in a range equal to or somewhat less than the excitation energy. The fluorescence of many materials is too low to be useful, and the autofluorescence of some tissues and microscope components is sometimes undesirable.

One principal advantage of fluorescence microscopy is the sensitivity resulting from the high contrast that is obtainable. In conventional light microscopy the intensity of the light coming from the specimen is compared with that of the surrounding material. Many unstained biological materials examined by light microscopy have refractive indexes near those of the mounting media and therefore have little contrast. The contrast, and consequently the sensitivity, obtainable with fluorescence microscopy on the other hand is remarkable.

The ultraviolet light used for illumination (excitation) is cross-filtered by excitation and barrier filters (see Fig. 1). The excitation filters transmit only ultraviolet or near ultraviolet exciting light, while the barrier filters are used to exclude stray exciting ultraviolet light from reaching the eye. Theoretically with the appropriate filter system the only light observed is the fluorescence emitted from the specimen, the microscope, the mounting medium, and the immersion oil. The background light can be further reduced by the use of a dark-field condenser.

The microscope employed in fluorescence microscopy depends on the nature of the fluorescence to be studied. Most microscopes commonly used in laboratory work are suitable for fluorochrome and fluorescent-antibody studies if they are equipped with a dark-field condenser. Difficulty may be encountered from fluorescing lenses if a bright-field condenser is used. More refined equipment may be required for certain studies, viz., the investigation of weakly autofluorescent, biological materials.

A binocular body tube is preferred for convenience and comfort of operation if the observed fluorescence is of sufficient intensity. Light emitted from a specimen is split for viewing with a binocular micro-

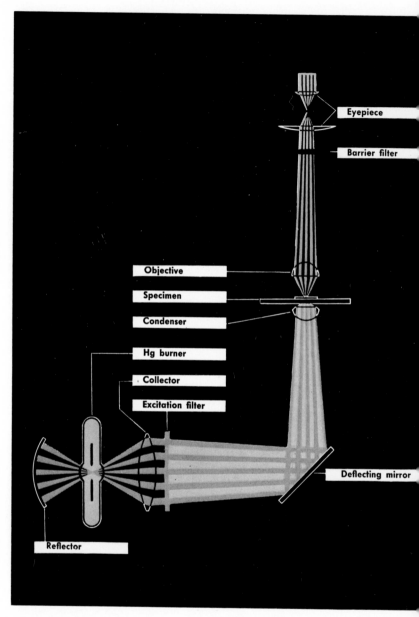

Fɪɢ. 1. Fluorescence microscope. Diagrammatic representation of the path of rays and of the action of excitation and barrier filters. (Courtesy of Carl Zeiss, Inc., 708 Oberkochen, Germany.)

cope, so the intensity of light reaching each eye is less than would
e observed with a monocular microscope.

Most manufacturers sell fluorescence microscopes equipped with the
ppropriate optics, light source, and filters.

At present, high-pressure mercury vapor lamps are the most com-
only used sources of illumination in fluorescence microscopy. Most
uorescence microscopes available commercially come equipped to
ouse the Osram HBO 200 mercury vapor lamp manufactured by the
)sram Company, Munich, Germany. A comparable burner with adapt-
rs to fit the various lamp holders is manufactured by PEK Labs,
nc., 4024 Transport Street, Palo Alto, California.

The General Electric A-H6 mercury arc lamp has a luminous output
f 195,000 candles per square inch as compared to 155,000 candles
er square inch for the Osram HBO 200 (Tobie, 1958). However, enough
nfrared light is produced by the A-H6 that water cooling is required.
'obie (1958) and L. H. Price (1965) have described housings for this
urner.

Several factors are involved in the selection of the most appropriate
lter system. These include: (1) the source of illumination, (2) the
bsorption and emission spectra of fluorescent materials being exam-
ned, and (3) the presence of undesirable background autofluorescence.

For ease of use, exciting radiations should be capable of passing
hrough glass and should differ sufficiently in wavelength from the
uorescent emissions so as to be easily separable from them. Thus,
he radiations of the mercury arc lamps that are most useful are
hose emitted at 366 and 435 mμ, and those at 405 mμ, which are less
ntense.

The emission spectra and sources of many fluorescent dyes used in
iological studies can be found in publications by Porro et al. (1963)
nd Porro and Morse (1965). Steiner and Edelhoch (1962) listed from
he literature the absorption and emission spectra of the more im-
ortant fluorescent dyes when they were conjugated to protein. Some
igures taken from their list are found in Table II.

It can be seen from the absorption spectra given that fluors are not
xcited optimally with a mercury lamp. The main purpose of filters,
hen, is to obtain the best possible excitation from the 366, 405, and
35 mμ radiations without having the exciting light interfere with the
bservation of the fluorescent emissions. An examination of the transmission characteristics of the excitation (primary) filters, which are
tandard equipment on the Zeiss fluorescence microscope, will serve
s an example of primary filter systems commonly used. The heat-
bsorption filter KG 1 is placed between the light source and the

excitation filters. This or a comparable filter should always be used to protect the primary filters from breaking. The primary filters are two BG 12 filters, a UG 2, and a UG 5 filter. The BG 12 filter transmit well at all three wavelengths, the UG 2 filter transmits mainly a 366 mμ, and the UG 5 transmits strongly at 366 and moderately a 405 mμ.

The instructions with the microscope recommend the BG 12 and the UG 2 for observation of fluorescence in the entire visible spectra range, the UG 2 and UG 5 for intense UV excitation for observation of blue and green fluorescences (in combination with a blue barrier filter), and two BG 12 filters for intense excitation for observation o yellow and red fluorescence.

Virus-infected tissues stained with fluorescein-labeled antibodies are usually examined under dark field with a primary filter system that passes 366 mμ light but excludes the 435 mμ band. Excitation by light of 435 mμ results in intense blue autofluorescence of the tissues which tends to obscure the specific fluorescence. A yellow barrier filter can be used to remove the blue fluorescence, but areas of intense blue emissions appear yellow and do not give good contrast with yellow-green dyes such as fluorescein. If the 435-mμ wavelength is excluded from the exciting radiations, the only barrier filter usually needed is a colorless filter to remove stray ultraviolet light that may injure the eyes. The best filter system should be determined by experimentation. The specimen can be excited with various wavelengths of light, and the most appropriate barrier filter(s) to use with different exciting radiations can be determined.

Table I shows the wavelength of radiations of the electromagnetic spectrum that are of particular interest in fluorescence microscopy. This

TABLE II

SOME ABSORPTION AND EMISSION MAXIMA OF LABELED PROTEINS[a]

Protein label	Absorption maxima (mμ)	Emission maxima (mμ)
DANS[b]	340	500 (525)[e]
FITC[c]	325, 495	500 (520)[e]
RB200[d]	350, 420	(595, 710)[e]

[a] Taken from Steiner and Edelhoch, 1962.
[b] 1-Dimethylaminonaphthalene-5-sulfonic acid.
[c] Fluorescein isothiocyanate.
[d] Lissamine rhodamine B.
[e] Reported by Fothergill, 1964b.

information, used with transmission data for filters, should enable one to select the appropriate primary and secondary filters for any given fluorochrome and tissue.

The quality of a microscope is, in addition to its ability to compensate for certain aberrations, judged by its resolving power. Resolving power is the shortest distance between two adjacent points at which they can be distinguished as distinct images. Stated differently, resolving power is the ability of the microscope to render visible the fine detail of an object. It is expressed as

$$RP = 0.6\lambda/N \sin \alpha$$

where RP = resolving power, λ = wavelength of light used for illumination, N = refractive index of the medium between the specimen and the objective, and α = one-half the aperture of the objective lens, as shown in Fig. 1 (an angle forming one-half the cone of light between the specimen and the objective). $N \sin \alpha$ is called the numerical aperture. The best resolving power is obtained by the use of illuminating light of short wavelength, immersion oils with high refractive indexes, and by lenses with large apertures. The aperture can be increased by the use of lenses with short focal lengths, but one half of the aperture cannot exceed 90°.

Achromats, fluorites, and apochromats are the three major types of microscope objectives. The achromats are the least expensive, and with low power they generally give good control of chromatic and spherical aberration. The fluorites, also called semiapochromats, are intermediate in price and quality. The apochromats are the most expensive and give the best control of aberration. Achromatic objectives are usually suitable for fluorescence studies of virus-infected materials, since high resolution is not usually a necessity.

Microscope mirrors that are made by coating the back side of the mirror glass with silver are inefficient reflectors of ultraviolet light. Light is lost both in the inferior reflecting properties of the silver surface and also by the double passage of light through the glass of the mirror. First-surface mirrors made by coating the front surface of the mirror glass with an aluminum alloy will reflect almost all ultraviolet light.

The ordinary optical glass found in most condensers is quite efficient in passing light of wavelengths used in most acridine orange and fluorescent-antibody studies. The type of condenser used is dependent on the kind of specimen to be examined and is best determined by experiment. If the object to be examined is large, best results may be obtained with the bright-field condenser since the fluorescence will be more intense. In addition, the relatively large microscopic field seen with low-power objectives is more uniformly illuminated by a bright-field condenser or a dry dark-field condenser rather than an oil immersion dark-field condenser. The fluorescence of small intracellular objects, such as viral inclusions, may be observed best against the dark background of a dark-field condenser.

When good resolution and good contrast are both required, a cardioid condenser, the most refined form of dark-field illumination, is preferred. It is a reflecting condenser that is free from both spherical and chromatic aberration and produces concentrated light brought to a mathematically correct focus.

I. Fluorescent-Antibody Techniques

To the investigator who desires to use the fluorescent-antibody technique, the two most important aspects are the preparation of labeled antibody and the procedures used in preparing and staining specimens. The many modifications of the procedures that constitute the basic technique signify that there is no single procedure that is best for all investigators or investigations. A few of the commonly used procedures are discussed in this section on fluorescent antibody; they are taken in sequence as they would be performed in using the technique. Precautions used in preparing specific immune serums are first discussed, followed by procedures used to prepare labeled antibodies that stain specifically, specimen preparation, methods of staining, specificity testing, and concluding with a rapid and accurate assay method for viruses.

Further information can be obtained from the literature. A monograph has been published recently (Nairn, 1964a), and several shorter reviews are available describing in detail the technique and its applications (Coons, 1956, 1958, 1964; Cherry et al., 1960; Beutner, 1961a,b; C. W. Smith et al., 1962; Steiner and Edelhoch, 1962; Liu, 1963, 1964; Hers, 1963; Cheever, 1964; Mims, 1964; Schaeffer et al., 1964).

In fluorescent-antibody staining an appropriately prepared antigen is incubated with antibody labeled with a fluorescent dye; labeled serum proteins that have not reacted serologically with the specimen are removed by washing, and the preparation is mounted and examined by fluorescence microscopy. Labeled antibody that has combined with viral antigen is excited by ultraviolet light and fluoresces a color characteristic of the antibody label, while tissue that is not stained will usually emit a low level of blue-white autofluorescence.

A. PREPARATION OF ANTIBODY

Unknown or undesirable antibodies present in serums to be conjugated can contribute to nonspecific staining. The following list describes ways to minimize this problem. It should be pointed out, however, that none or only part of these precautions may be required to produce a good specific immune serum for labeling. The requirements for different host–virus systems must be determined individually.

1. Reduce the possibility of immunization with a mixed culture by purification of the viral antigen, preferentially by a plaque procedure or by three successive terminal dilution passages if the virus does not readily form plaques.

2. Purify the immunizing virus to remove antigenic components of the host cells and growth medium.

3. Take rigorous precautions to prevent introduction of undesirable virus from subclinical or latent viral infections in the animal to be immunized, in the host system used for the preparation of viral antigen, and in the tissues stained with the labeled antibody. Serums should be screened for antibodies against adventitious viruses such as SV40, RIF, K, polyoma, or others that may be encountered in the investigation. If undesirable antibodies are detected, they should be removed by absorption with the homologous antigen.

4. Prepare virus in cells of the species of animal to be immunized, since antibodies are less likely to be induced by contaminating tissue from the same species.

5. Obtain a preimmunization serum for control purposes.

6. Immunize susceptible animals or use convalescent serums from animals with natural infections.

7. When feasible, cells or tissues to be stained should be of a different species of plant or animal from those used for preparing the immunizing antigen.

8. The immunization schedule should be sufficient to allow for good antibody response without sacrificing specificity. Prolonged immunization can enhance minor antigenic components, which may give rise to undesirable cross-reactions.

9. Absorb conjugates with suspensions of tissues or cells used in the preparation of the immunizing virus and/or tissues or cells to be stained.

10. Use only the fraction of serum globulin that contains the specific antibody.

B. Serum Fractionation

Some investigators have conjugated whole serum while others have used almost every serum fractionation technique that has been described in the literature. The essential objective is to obtain specifically staining antibody of high titer. How this is achieved operationally depends on a variety of factors. If the antibody titer of a conjugate is high enough, nonspecific staining can be removed by dilution without the use of any special serum-fractionation technique. On the other hand, refined methods of fractionation can be used if it is known that undesirable antibodies are present in globulin fractions that are easily separable from specific antibody. Another circumstance that calls for a special method of serum fractionation is the use of diethylaminoethyl-(DEAE) cellulose chromatography to remove the highly labeled proteins from a conjugate. Overlabeled serum proteins stain nonspecifically and their most effective chromatographic removal from conjugates requires that chromatographically homogeneous globulin be used for conjugation (Wood et al., 1965). Finally, little of the total serum protein is antibody, so removal of most of the nonantibody protein substantially reduces the amount of nonspecific staining due to overlabeled proteins.

Ammonium sulfate fractionation, a widely used method, and DEAE-cellulose and DEAE-Sephadex, two currently popular procedures, will be described in detail.

1. *Ammonium Sulfate Precipitation*

When a concentrated solution of ammonium sulfate is added to a serum, proteins precipitate from solution. Serum proteins precipitated by salting out with ammonium sulfate are unaltered and usually redissolve in fresh portions of the original solvent. Globulins are precipitated from solution upon half saturation with the salt, and albumins are precipitated by complete saturation; if less salt is used, less globulin precipitates and more of the albumin remains in solution. Most fractionation has been done with half-saturated sulfate, although various investigators have used sulfate at concentrations between one-half and one-third of saturation.

Recently Sinha and Reddy (1964) reported that better results were obtained in the preparation of wound-tumor virus conjugates if the ammonium sulfate were neutralized with NaOH before fractionation. We have used neutralized ammonium sulfate at 50% saturation for several years with immune serums from several species of animals prepared against several viruses and have found the method to be highly satisfactory. It has been our experience that the low pH of the salt results in denaturation of some of the globulins during fractionation. These denatured proteins precipitate when the preparations are dialyzed to remove the salt.

If difficulty is encountered with conjugates that stain nonspecifically, the use of neutralized sulfate, sulfate of reduced concentration, or the use of specific globulin fractions obtained by other methods should be considered. The steps in serum fractionation with half-saturated $(NH_4)_2SO_4$ are outlined below:

1. Prepare a saturated salt solution by adding 760 gm of CP sulfate to 1 liter of distilled water at room temperature, or weigh out 542 gm and bring the volume to 1 liter with distilled water. (Neutralization of the solution with 1 N NaOH is optional.)

2. Place the serum to be fractionated in a suitable container and cool to 0°–5°C. While the serum is stirred with a magnetic mixer, add dropwise a volume of saturated salt solution equal to the volume of serum used.

3. Mix 1 hour or longer (some workers recommend that the solution stand overnight at 4°C). Sediment the precipitated globulins by centrifugation at 1000 g for 30 minutes and decant the supernatant fluid.

4. Dissolve the precipitated globulins in distilled water to approximate the original serum volume. Reprecipitate the globulins at one-half saturation with salt according to steps 2 and 3; the precipitate can be centrifuged immediately after the ammonium sulfate is added. Three precipitations will usually remove most of the hemoglobin. The last precipitate should be dissolved in a volume of distilled water approximately one half to two thirds of the initial volume of the serum.

Residual sulfate is removed by dialysis against saline or by passage through a Sephadex column (see Section I,F for the Sephadex procedure). It is often more convenient to dialyze overnight than it is to use Sephadex. The procedure for dialysis is as follows:

1. Boil a piece of dialyzing tubing for 15 minutes and rinse several times in distilled water. This removes substances that absorb light at 280 mμ and interfere with the spectrophotometric estimation of protein content. This step is unnecessary if protein analyses at 280 mμ are not to be made.

2. Dialyze in the cold against 0.85% NaCl until the sulfate is removed. Kaufman and Cherry (1961) found conjugates labeled in the

presence of contaminating ammonium sulfate to fluoresce weakly and to have poor staining titers when compared to salt-free controls. They reported that complete removal of ammonium sulfate from 20-ml aliquots of albumin was achieved by dialysis for 4 hours with or without agitation, using either $^{20}/_{32}$- or $^{27}/_{32}$-inch diameter dialyzing tubing. Test for the presence of sulfate by adding a few drops of saturated barium chloride solution to several milliliters of the dialyzing fluid. Absence of a precipitate indicates sufficient dialysis. If phosphate-buffered saline is used as a dialyzing medium, it must be acidified before testing for sulfate.

2. *Separation of γ-Globulin on DEAE-Cellulose Columns*

Levy and Sober (1960) described a simple chromatographic method for preparing γ-globulin from whole serum.

1. DEAE-cellulose, reagent grade, 0.09 ± 0.1 mEq/gm exchange (Standard) capacity (C. Schleicher and Schuell, 543 Washington Street, Keene, New Hampshire) is washed with 1 N NaOH and rinsed with water on a coarse-sintered glass filter until the filtrate is free of alkali (Peterson and Chiazze, 1962). The slurry is adjusted to pH 6.3 with 0.2 M NaH_2PO_4 and is washed several times with 0.0175 M phosphate (Na^+) at pH 6.3.

2. The serum is dialyzed overnight in the cold against 100–200 volumes of 0.0175 M phosphate buffer at pH 6.3.

3. For each 2 ml of dialyzed serum a column of DEAE-cellulose 1 cm in diameter and 5 cm in height is prepared using nitrogen pressure not to exceed 10 psi. The column is washed with 50 ml of the buffer used in step 2.

4. The dialyzed serum is added to the column when the liquid level of the buffer is level with the DEAE-cellulose.

5. The γ-globulin is not absorbed, and the majority in 2 ml of serum will pass through the column with 6 ml of the pH 6.3 buffer, but approximately 20 ml is required for complete recovery.

6. Two molar NaCl in 0.4 M sodium phosphate pH 5.2 can be used to remove the absorbed proteins if the antibody recovery is poor.

3. *Separation of γ-Globulin on DEAE-Sephadex Columns*

Dedmon *et al.* (1965) used DEAE-Sephadex A-50 medium grade (Pharmacia Fine Chemicals, 501 Fifth Avenue, New York) for the isolation of γ-globulin from whole serum.

1. The Sephadex is allowed to swell in distilled water for 24 hours

with repeated decantations to remove the "fines." It is washed with 0.1 N NaOH and then with distilled water until neutrality is reached, and finally with 0.02 M phosphate buffer at pH 7.6.

2. Sixty to 80 ml of whole, undialyzed serum is added to a 4×40 cm column that has been equilibrated with the buffer just described.

3. The γ-globulin passes through the column; the other serum proteins can be eluted with 2 M NaCl.

Baumstark *et al.* (1964) have described a preparative, two-stage batch method for the separation of 7S γ-globulin from undialyzed human serum using the chloride form of DEAE-Sephadex. The procedure is simple, rapid, economical, and gives high yields of immunoelectrophoretically pure γ-globulin. Six hundred milligrams of γ-globulin were obtained within 3 hours from 50 ml of undialyzed serum.

The extension of this method to serums of other species would provide investigators with a useful additional tool for preparing satisfactory fluorescent-antibody preparations.

C. PROTEIN DETERMINATION

The determination of protein concentration by the biuret method described by Gornall *et al.* (1949) is widely used and relatively simple. The procedure for establishing a standard protein curve, and a modification of the biuret method as used in the Viral and Rickettsial Disease Laboratory of the California State Department of Public Health are given below.

1. *Procedure for Establishing a Standard Protein Curve*

1. Prepare a 1 : 10 dilution of the standard protein solution (Armour Laboratories Standard Solution, crystalline bovine albumin containing 10.2 mg of protein nitrogen/ml) in 0.85% NaCl.

2. Introduce the indicated amounts of 0.85% NaCl (see Table III) into each of seven cuvettes. Replicate tubes should be used if possible.

3. Add the indicated volumes of standard protein dilutions.

4. Add 8.0 ml of biuret reagent (see following section) and mix thoroughly.

5. Allow to stand 30 minutes at room temperature.

6. Read percent transmission ($\%T$) on a spectrophotometer at 540 mμ.

7. Record and plot $\%T$ against calculated gram percent protein on semilog graph paper.

TABLE III
PROCEDURE FOR ESTABLISHING A STANDARD PROTEIN CURVE

Cuvette	0.85% NaCl (ml)	Protein standard (1 : 10 dilution) (ml)	Biuret reagent (ml)	Calculated gm–% protein[a]	%T
1	2.00	0.00	8.0	0.000	100
2	1.85	0.15	8.0	0.956	—
3	1.70	0.30	8.0	1.910	—
4	1.55	0.45	8.0	2.870	—
5	1.40	0.60	8.0	3.795	—
6	1.20	0.80	8.0	5.100	—
7	1.00	1.00	8.0	6.375	—

[a] Gram-percent protein = volume of protein standard $\times$ 10.2 mg of nitrogen/ml $\times$ 6.25 (the factor used for calculating protein from the nitrogen content).

2. Preparation of Biuret Reagent

1. Place 1.5 gm of $CuSO_4 \cdot 5H_2O$ in a dry 1-liter volumetric flask and dissolve in about 250 ml of distilled water.

2. Add 6.0 gm of sodium potassium tartrate ($NaKC_4H_4O_6 \cdot 4H_2O$) and dissolve by adding more distilled water.

3. With constant mixing add 300 ml of 10% sodium hydroxide. (The NaOH should be prepared from carbonate-free water that has been boiled and cooled in a stoppered flask.)

4. Bring to 1-liter volume with distilled water.

5. Store in a paraffin-lined, polyethylene, or Pyrex bottle. The reagent is stable for a considerable time if properly prepared, but must be discarded if a black or reddish precipitate appears.

3. Determination of Protein Content of Globulin Solutions

1. Prepare a 1 : 20 dilution of globulin with 0.85% NaCl by mixing 0.5 ml of globulin with 9.5 ml of saline.

2. Transfer 2.0 ml of the globulin dilution into each of two cuvettes.

3. Add 8.0 ml of biuret reagent and mix.

4. Prepare a control tube by mixing 2.0 ml of saline with 8.0 ml of biuret reagent.

5. Allow to stand 30 minutes at room temperature.

6. Read in the spectrophotometer at a wavelength of 540 mμ.

7. The grams percent protein can be determined directly using the %T reading and the standard curve.

D. LABELING OF ANTIBODY WITH FLUORESCEIN ISOTHIOCYANATE (FITC)

Overlabeling of serum protein molecules has been found to be one of the most important causes of nonspecific staining by fluorescent-antibody preparations (Curtain, 1958; Nairn et al., 1960; Griffin et al., 1961; Goldstein et al., 1961; Spendlove and Lennette, 1962). Serum proteins have a relatively high negative charge when they are highly labeled with FITC, and as a consequence acquire an avidity for certain tissue components.

Approaches that have been used to prepare conjugates which stain specifically include the following: (1) Conjugation with the fluorescent label at a reduced level so there is little if any overlabeling (Spendlove and Lennette, 1962). Although conjugates prepared in this way do not have to be treated to selectively remove highly labeled proteins, they cannot be used at high dilution, since unlabeled antibody present in these preparations will combine with the antigen and block specific staining (Goldstein et al., 1962). (2) Conjugates may be slightly to moderately overlabeled with subsequent removal of the overlabeled (Goldstein et al., 1961; Griffin et al., 1961) and underlabeled (Goldstein et al., 1962) protein. Techniques to remove highly labeled proteins include convection electrophoresis (Curtain, 1958), chromatography on DEAE-cellulose (Riggs et al., 1960; Curtain, 1961; Goldstein et al., 1961; McDevitt et al., 1963), and chromatography on DEAE-Sephadex (Dedmon et al., 1965; P. L. Wolf et al., 1965). Other less selective methods are absorption with tissue powder (Coons and Kaplan, 1950), activated charcoal (Fothergill and Nairn, 1961), silk hydrolyzate (Rappaport et al., 1964), or with suspensions of tissues or cells. Many of these methods are time consuming and all may result in considerable loss of antibody activity. (3) The serum proteins can be conjugated with a concentration of FITC that has been predetermined to be optimal (Spendlove, 1966). This method is described in Section I,D,2.

To control the degree of labeling of a fluorescent-antibody preparation, it is important that FITC of high quality be used. In the past there has been considerable variation in the purity of FITC obtained commercially. McKinney et al. (1964a) described the determination of the FITC content of products obtained from commercial sources by the use of infrared absorption measurements. They prepared FITC reference standards and compared them with 12 commercial preparations obtained from eight different sources. Five of the 12 preparations contained less than 50% FITC, and 10 of the 12 contained less than 75%. We have consistently prepared satisfactory conjugates with crystalline FITC (Baltimore Biological Laboratory, Baltimore, Maryland).

Care should be taken to prevent degradation of the FITC (Frommhagen and Spendlove, 1962; McKinney et al., 1964b). No significant deterioration occurs during storage of FITC in an open bottle in a desiccator over Drierite (McKinney et al., 1964b).

1. Labeling by the Method of Marshall et al.

Riggs et al. (1958) prepared FITC and found that it was superior to fluorescein isocyanate (Coons and Kaplan, 1950) for labeling antibody. Marshall and co-workers (1958) modified the method of Riggs and associates by adding powdered FITC to the reaction mixture to minimize protein denaturation associated with solution of FITC in acetone. This modification has been widely used.

1. The serum proteins to be labeled are diluted with 0.15 M NaCl and carbonate–bicarbonate buffer, 0.5 M, pH 9, so the final solution contains 10 mg of protein/ml and 10% buffer solution.

2. The solution is cooled to 4°C, and 50 mg of FITC/gm of protein is added (most workers would agree that 20 mg of FITC or less per gram of protein would be more satisfactory).

3. The mixture is stirred at 4°C for 12–18 hours.

Unconjugated FITC is removed by gel filtration or by dialysis.

2. Optimal Labeling of Antibody with FITC .

McKinney et al. (1964c) reported an extensive study of the factors controlling antibody labeling with FITC. They found conjugation of rabbit γ-globulin was essentially complete in 30 minutes if a reaction temperature of 25°C, a protein concentration of 2.5%, and a 0.05 M phosphate buffer at pH 9.5 were used. With these reaction conditions, the degree of labeling was accurately controlled by the initial amount of dye added. Controlled antibody labeling is used in the procedure described below for optimal labeling. When serum proteins are overlabeled and subsequently treated to remove the highly labeled protein molecules, considerable time and effort are expended, and the loss of antibody may be excessive. An alternative method is to determine the optimal degree of labeling (Spendlove, 1966). The optimal concentration of FITC implies that the conjugate can be used at a dilution that will give strong specific with no nonspecific staining.

A large batch of conjugate is prepared after the optimal concentration of FITC to use is determined by conjugating small aliquots of serum protein with different concentrations of FITC.

1. Dissolve 2.5 mg or more of crystalline FITC (Baltimore Bilogical Laboratory, Baltimore, Maryland) in 0.1 M Na_2HPO_4 at a rate of 1.25 mg/ml. Difficulty may be encountered in getting the FITC into solution if the phosphate has absorbed CO_2 from the air. Dissolution of the FITC can be facilitated by adding several drops of phosphate and then breaking up the FITC with a stirring rod or the end of a pipet.

2. Add 0.8 ml of the FITC solution to a beaker containing 1 ml of 5% serum globulin while the solution is being stirred.

3. Adjust the pH of the solution to 9.5 using 0.04 N NaOH. The final volume should be approximately 2 ml.

4. Conjugate for 30 minutes at room temperature without stirring, pass the conjugate through Sephadex to remove the free FITC, and stain infected and uninfected specimens to determine whether non-specific staining is excessive. If so, repeat the procedure using 0.6 ml of FITC. The volume of the reaction mixture is brought to 1.8 ml with 0.1 M Na_2HPO_4 before the pH adjustment.

Results to date indicate that a single coupling of an immune globulin with 20 mg of FITC/gm of protein is statisfactory for preliminary labeling. The optimal FITC concentration to be used by different investigators may be greater or less than 20 mg/gm of protein owing to variations in purity of the FITC, ambient temperature, and pH used in conjugation.

E. OTHER ANTIBODY LABELS

The following is the procedure described by Fothergill (1964a) for the conjugation of whole serum or serum protein fractions with lissamine rhodamine B (RB 200) (Chadwick *et al.*, 1958a,b) and with the sulfonyl chloride of 1-dimethylaminonaphthalene-5-sulfonic acid (DANS) (Weber, 1952; Clayton, 1954; Mayersbach, 1958).

1. *Preparation of the Sulfonyl Chloride of RB 200*

1. Convert to the sulfonyl chloride by grinding 0.5 gm of RB 200 (George T. Gurr, Ltd., 136–140 New King's Road, London, England) with 1.0 gm of PCl_5 in a mortar in a fume hood.

2. Add 5 ml of acetone and stir for several minutes.

3. Filter and store in a sealed tube at −20°C in the presence of a little anhydrous calcium sulfate.

2. Conjugation Procedure

1. Add 2 volumes of carbonate–bicarbonate buffer for each volume of 5–6% serum protein being conjugated. The buffer (pH 9.0, 0.5 M is prepared by dissolving 3.6 gm of $NaHCO_3$ and 0.6 gm of Na_2CO (anhydrous) in sufficient distilled water to make 100 ml of solution and is stored in small quantities in closed containers.

2. (a) Cool to 0°–2°C, stir equal volumes of the RB 200 sulfony chloride solution and 5–6% protein for 0.5 hour. (b) Dissolve th sulfonyl chloride of DANS (A. G. Fluka, Chemische Fabrik, St. Gal Canton, Buchs, Switzerland) in a minimum volume of acetone. Us at a rate of 3 mg of the sulfonyl chloride for every milliliter o 5–6% protein being conjugated.

The fluorochromes should be added slowly while the reaction mix ture is being stirred. Vigorous stirring without frothing is continued for 6 hours; the alkaline pH should be maintained.

The isothiocyanate derivative of tetramethyl rhodamine (Balti more Biological Laboratory, Baltimore, Maryland) is another usefu antibody label; it has been chromatographically purified (Felton and McMillion, 1961) and used for the conjugation of serum proteins by M. L. Smith et al. (1962), Hiramoto and Hamlin (1965), and Cebra and Goldstein (1965). Conjugation may be achieved by procedure used for FITC.

F. REMOVAL OF UNCOUPLED DYES FROM CONJUGATES

Fluorescent dyes not coupled to serum proteins have an affinity for certain tissue components, and if present, will stain nonspecifically Uncoupled dyes can be removed rapidly and efficiently by gel filtration (Porath and Flodin, 1959) through G-25 or G-50 Sephadex (Phar macia Fine Chemicals, Inc., 501 Fifth Avenue, New York). The col umns should have a 1 : 10 diameter to height ratio, with the sample load 20–25% of the bed volume.

1. Wash the Sephadex three times with phosphate-buffered saline (0.01 M phosphate, 0.15 M NaCl, pH 7.5) to remove the "fines." After the third wash the gel beads are allowed to swell for 6 hours or longer.

2. If a glass tube with a constricted end is used as a column place a small amount of glass wool in the bottom of the tube to contain the Sephadex. Add a slurry of Sephadex in buffered saline (see step 1) to the tube. When the desired bed height is reached. remove the excess buffer or allow it to percolate through the column

3. Add conjugate when the buffer is level with the bed surface, taking care to prevent drying of the Sephadex. The conjugate is allowed to enter the bed completely before additional buffer is added. Collection of eluate is begun when the first visible band of dye elutes from the column and ceases with the last material from the first band.

G. REMOVAL OF HIGHLY LABELED PROTEINS FROM CONJUGATES

1. *DEAE-Cellulose Chromatography*

Goldstein and co-workers (1961, 1962; Wood and associates, 1965) have stressed the importance of removing unlabeled antibodies as well as overlabeled proteins from conjugates. Unlabeled antibodies block specific staining, while overlabeled proteins stain nonspecifically. The procedure recommended for removing undesirable proteins is given below:

1. Fractionate the serum with 40% saturated ammonium sulfate.

2. Obtain γ-globulin chromatographically on DEAE-cellulose using 0.01 M sodium phosphate at pH 7.5 to equilibrate the column and to elute the γ-globulin.

3. After coupling the γ-globulin with FITC, dilute the reaction mixture 10-fold with the buffer used in step 2 and add to a column of DEAE-cellulose equilibrated with the same buffer.

4. Use step elution to remove fractions of γ-globulin labeled with varying amounts of FITC. (a) Lightly labeled globulin is not bound and is washed through with the 0.01 M phosphate buffer. (b) The globulin that is most satisfactory for specific fluorescent-antibody staining is eluted with 0.03 M sodium phosphate buffer at pH 7.2–7.5. (c) The highly labeled globulin which stains nonspecifically is eluted with 0.05 M and 0.1 M sodium phosphate at pH 7.2–7.5. (d) Free FITC which has not combined with protein is very strongly bound to the column.

2. *DEAE-Sephadex Chromatography* (Dedmon *et al.*, 1965)

1. After conjugation, remove the unbound FITC by gel filtration through a column of G-25 Sephadex coarse beads equilibrated with phosphate-buffered saline (0.01 M phosphate, 0.14 M NaCl, pH 7.3).

2. Equilibrate a 2×5 cm column of DEAE-Sephadex (see Section I,B,3) with the same buffered saline; this column is satisfactory for approximately 20 ml of conjugate containing 6 mg of protein/ml.

3. A fraction with good specific staining and negligible nonspecific staining is eluted with the buffer used in step 1.

H. Specimen Preparation

The preparation of viral specimens for fluorescent-antibody examination should preserve the morphological structure of the host
tissues and the localization and antigenic determinants of the virus.
Methods for demonstrating viral antigens in cells in culture, in
smears of infected cells, in tissue sections, and as soluble antigens
incorporated into cellulose acetate discs or agar are described below.

1. Cells in Culture

Cells can be grown on cover glasses or on microscope slides (whole
or broken pieces) in test tubes, Leighton tubes, Petri dishes, or in
plastic boxes. We routinely use Trophy brand 15 mm circular, No. 1,
cover glasses (LaPine Scientific Co., 6001 South Knox Avenue, Chicago, Illinois). The Trophy brand cover glasses are transferred to Petri
dishes with forceps and then sterilized by autoclaving or dry heat sterilization.

One to five cover glasses are placed in a 60-mm glass Petri dish,
and each cover glass is seeded with 0.2 ml of cell suspension (mammalian, avian, fish, etc.) containing $2-4 \times 10^5$ cells/ml. Some cells at
this concentration have a tendency to aggregate when serum is present
in the medium, so for these, serum is omitted. The cover glasses can
be held at room temperature or at 37°C in a CO_2 incubator to allow
the cells to attach. Four milliliters of outgrowth medium containing
serum is then added to each Petri dish; the cell layers are usually
confluent after overnight incubation at 37°C in a 5% CO_2 atmosphere.

It is a common practice to wash the cultures prior to infection to
remove any viral inhibitors that may be present in the serum used
in the outgrowth medium. After removal of the wash fluid, cultures
are inoculated, incubated for an appropriate time period to permit
virus absorption, and covered with maintenance medium. The cultures
are then incubated to allow for development of the virus. For a
detailed discussion of the manipulation of infected cover glass cultures see Section I,L.

2. Smears

Smears of infected tissue can be prepared by making impressions
of cut surfaces or by crushing the tissue on a microscope slide. Small
samples of infected cells grown in monolayer or suspension and ex-
foliative cells or exudates can be dried on microscope slides or on
cover glasses. Such preparations should be air dried before fixing.

3. Tissue Sections

Nearly all investigators preparing tissues for fluorescent-antibody staining have sectioned frozen tissue. The method of Coons and Kaplan (1950) and Coons et al. (1951) is given below.

Four to five millimeter pieces of tissue are placed in a test tube and frozen at −70°C by immersing the tube in a Dry Ice–alcohol bath. The frozen tissue is stored at −20°C and is sectioned on a microtome held at −16° to −18°C in a mechanically refrigerated cryostat. The sections are prevented from rolling or curling as they are cut by a glass support held by a device suspended from the top of the knife. Nairn (1964b) used Perspex rather than glass as a support to minimize adhesion of sections from static charge effects.

To minimize rolling of frozen sections as they were cut, Louis (1957) altered the angle of the knife to 60° from the horizontal position and kept the knife absolutely dry and cooled to a temperature below −13°C. By this method serial sections of 4–5-μ thickness can be cut with a slow steady rotation of the microtome. The sections are picked up from the side of the knife by touching with a slide that has been scrupulously cleaned and moistened by dipping the slide, which has been previously cooled to −20°C, in absolute alcohol cooled to the same temperature. Care is taken not to wet the edge of the knife with alcohol from the moistened slide.

The sections are dried for 1 hour at 0°–2°C in front of a fan prior to staining with fluorescent antibody.

Distortion of the tissue and loss of immunological reactivity of the antigen may occur when the frozen sections are held at low temperatures. George and Walton (1962) found this could be prevented if the sections were mounted on cover glasses and dipped immediately into polyethylene glycol, molecular weight 285–315 (Carbowax, Union Carbide Corp., Chemical Division, New York) for 5 seconds. The polyethylene glycol-coated cover glasses are stored at −20°C. Before use, the cover glasses are warmed on the finger and are given three to five 1-minute washes with physiological saline.

Rahman and Luttrell (1962) described a method whereby crude egg albumin is utilized for frozen embedding and sectioning of fresh tissue in the cryostat. They were able to obtain quality sections of varying thickness from different organs, and reported that the sections were suitable for histochemical, autoradiographic, and fluorescent-antibody studies.

Sainte-Marie (1962) used a paraffin-embedding procedure and reported that bovine serum albumin, bovine γ-globulin, horse ferritin, influenza A viral antigens, diphtheria and tetanus toxoids, and antibody in mouse spleen were all well preserved for fluorescent-antibody staining.

Although Liu (1964) maintains that paraffin sections are generally not suitable for rickettsial and viral agents owing to the loss of antigenicity during embedding, this technique may have greater application if appropriate fixatives are used.

Other methods that have been used in the preparation of tissues for sectioning for fluorescent antibody are: (1) freeze-drying and (2) freeze substitution, in which tissues are dehydrated at low temperatures in organic solvents. In both methods the tissues are subsequently embedded in wax. These techniques, which to date have had little use in virological studies, are reviewed by Nairn (1964b).

4. *Preparation of Soluble Antigens*

Cellulose acetate and agar have been used as supporting mediums for soluble antigens and antibodies in fluorescent-antibody staining by Paronetto (1963) and Allen (1963). The following procedure for cellulose acetate was taken from that of Paronetto (1963).

1. Draw and number nine squares 12 mm wide on cellulose acetate filter discs (Consolidated Laboratories, Chicago, Illinois).

2. Add the discs to the surface of antigen solutions containing 10 mg/ml of antigen; when the discs are wet, submerge them for 30 seconds.

3. Blot the discs lightly and place them in a vacuum desiccator for 10–15 minutes.

4. Fix for 10 minutes at 5°C (Paronetto used 95% ethanol for human γ-globulin and horse serum and 1% acetic acid in 95% ethanol for bovine serum albumin) and wash three times for 3 minutes with phosphate-buffered saline at pH 7.2.

The impregnated discs can be stained by the direct and indirect staining methods. Positive reactions appear as apple-green spots, the brightness of which decreases with the dilution of antigen or antiserum. Negative reactions appear blue-gray or are nonfluorescing.

Allen (1963) described a method for the entrapment of soluble antigen in agar.

1. Melt a 3% solution of agar in saline and cool to 45°C; mix rapidly with 2 volumes of aqueous antigen solution.

2. Pour into a circular plastic mold 15 mm in depth and 20 mm in diameter.

3. After gelling, freeze the agar onto a microtome specimen holder.

4. Cut 32-μ sections in a cryostat at $-20°C$.

5. Transfer the sections to cold microscope slides coated with a dry film of 0.5% agar in water.

6. Remove the slides from the cryostat and allow the sections to thaw; dry at room temperature.

Allen (1963) incorporated human serum albumin, human γ-globulin, diphtheria toxin, and botulism toxin in agar and was able to demonstrate specific fluorescent-antibody staining with each antigen. Identical results were obtained when unfixed slides were stained or when the slides were fixed for 10 minutes in acetone or absolute ethanol.

Positive staining appeared as bright green strands crisscrossing a black or dark background. At higher magnification this bright fluorescence was seen to be composed of many fluorescent dots, presumably representing antigen–antibody aggregates, scattered throughout the agar strands.

Toussaint and Anderson (1965) devised an indirect fluorescent-antibody test for soluble antigens. Two cellulose acetate filter paper discs one-quarter inch in diameter were used in each test. One disc was impregnated with soluble antigen which had been diluted in 1% bovine serum albumin; the other disc contained only 1% bovine serum albumin and served as a control. The two discs were stained by the indirect fluorescent-antibody procedure and the results were quantitated by reading on a fluorometer fitted with a paper chromatogram door.

I. Fixation

Fixation should make the cell membranes permeable to the labeled antibody as well as preserve antigenic determinants and cell morphology. Acetone is the most widely used fixative for viral specimens. For thin smears and cell monolayers, 5–10 minutes fixation at $4°C$ is usually adequate, but the times and temperatures used have been varied considerably. Goldwasser et al. (1959), for example, fixed rabies virus smears by dropping them into Coplin jars filled with acetone at $-15°$ to $-20°C$. After 4 hours fixation, the slides were removed from the acetone and were drained and dried without being taken from the freezer.

We have found Formalin to be not entirely suitable for fixing vaccinia and the reoviruses and to be a poor fixative for poliovirus. Fixatives that are satisfactory for use with the reoviruses are acetone,

benzene, chloroform, ether, and xylene (Spendlove *et al.*, 1964). The
fixatives are suitable only when infected cells have been dried prior
to fixation.

Mayor and Jordan (1963) found that acrolein could be used as a
fixative in preparing infected cells for fluorescent-antibody and
acridine orange staining and would also preserve the fine structure of
cells for electron microscopy. This fixative permits consecutive sections
of tissue to be stained with fluorescent antibody, acridine orange, and
with the electron-dense ferritin antibody label.

J. FLUORESCENT-ANTIBODY STAINING

A specimen (tissue section, smear, or monolayer of cells) properly
prepared on a microscope slide or cover glass and appropriately fixed
is ready for fluorescent-antibody staining.

The preparation is flooded with labeled antibody and is incubated
to allow for serologic reaction between the antigen, held firmly in the
specimen, and the conjugated antibody. Uncombined conjugate is removed by washing, and the specimen is mounted in buffered glycerol
and examined under a fluorescence microscope. The antigen will be
coated (stained) with the fluorescent antibody and will fluoresce brilliantly, while the unstained surroundings will usually emit a low level
of blue-white autofluorescence. The glycerol mounting medium contains 90% glycerol and 10% buffered saline at pH 7.5 (0.01 M phosphate
and 0.15 M NaCl). If immersion oil is used, it should have low fluorescence (Cargille's immersion oil, low fluorescence; mix equal amounts
of types A and B).

It is necessary to determine the concentration of fluorescent antibody to use to obtain maximal intensity of specific fluorescence without
nonspecific staining. This is accomplished by diluting the conjugate
with 0.01 M phosphate-buffered saline at pH 7.5 and staining infected
and uninfected cells.

Antibody added to specimens prepared on small circular cover glasses
can be spread to the edges without running off if the cover glasses
are on a dry surface. In most cases, however, it is necessary to circle
preparations with a scratch made by a diamond marking pencil,
vaseline–ether mixture colored with a fat-soluble dye (Cherry *et al.*,
1960), or with liquid embroidery (Tri-Craft, Inc., 1624 Anaheim Avenue, Harbor City, California) to prevent the conjugate from running.

Staining is done in a moist chamber to prevent the conjugate from
drying. Staining and washing racks for cover glass preparations are

escribed in Section I,L. A chamber is prepared by placing a moist ilter paper in a Petri dish or other closed container. If drying occurs uring staining, pieces of dried fluorescent film may become dislodged rom the edge of the preparation and be distributed over the entire pecimen during subsequent washing and mounting.

The optimal time and temperature for staining should be determined xperimentally. Usually incubation for 20–60 minutes at room tempera- ure or 37°C is satisfactory, although some workers prefer incubation t 4°C for extended periods. After staining, the specimen is washed ith 0.01 M phosphate-buffered saline at pH 7.5 to remove the labeled erum proteins that have not reacted serologically with the specimen. Vashing may be varied from a single dipping of the stained specimen ɔ a wash of one-half hour or longer with several changes of the wash ledium. The thickness of the specimen, the concentration of the stain, nd the volume of the wash medium are factors that determine the me and number of fluid changes required. Ten minutes without any hanges of the wash medium is usually satisfactory for monolayers of ells. Films of fluorescent material sometimes form on the surface of ιe conjugate when extended periods of staining are used. When these lms form, they should be floated off by carefully dipping the specimen ɹ wash medium without previously decanting the stain (Schieble, 965).

Staining with fluorescent antibody can be carried out in several ays, viz., by direct, indirect, or complement staining.

1. *Direct Staining*

1. Add labeled antibody to the preparation to be stained and in- ɪbate to allow the antibody to combine with its homologous antigen. antigen is present, it will be stained with the labeled antibody.
2. Wash to remove labeled proteins that have not combined serologi- ɪlly with the specimen.
3. Mount and examine under a fluorescence microscope. Antigen that ɪs combined with fluorescent antibody will fluoresce.

Direct Staining
Ant ̇gen (A) + Fluorescent antibody (*FAb) → A—*FAb (Stained antigen)

The asterisk in the equation above indicates fluorescence.

A modification of direct staining can be used to determine the ecificity of a staining reaction. *Unlabeled* antibodies incubated with eir homologous antigen will combine with the antigen and will block ɑining by the labeled antibody when it is subsequently added. It should be possible to demonstrate inhibition of staining by unlabeled antibodies if the fluorescent-antibody staining is specific. In practice better inhibition is demonstrable if mixtures of labeled and unlabeled antibody are added together (Goldman, 1957).

2. Indirect Staining

1. Add *unlabeled* antiviral antibody (γ-globulin) to the specimen containing the viral antigen and incubate.

2. Wash to remove uncombined serum proteins.

3. Stain with *labeled* antiglobulin antibody prepared against γ-globulin of the species of animal used for the preparation of antibody in step 1. For example, if the antiviral antibody used in step 1 is prepared in rabbits, a labeled antirabbit γ-globulin antibody is used in step 3. Thus, in the presence of viral antigen the unlabeled antibody reacts with the antigen and is in turn stained by its homologous labeled antibody added subsequently. In the absence of viral antigen the unlabeled antibody does not react with the specimen, and there is no staining when the labeled antiglobulin antibody is added.

4. Wash to remove uncombined labeled proteins, mount, and examine.

Indirect Staining

Antigen (A) + Rabbit antibody (RAb) → A—RAb

A—RAb + Fluorescent antirabbit γ-globulin antibody (*FARγGAb) →

A—RAb—*FARγGAb (Stained antigen)

As before, the asterisk indicates fluorescence.

The indirect method of staining can also be used as a qualitative and/or quantitative test for antibody. If antibody is present when a preparation known to contain antigen is incubated with an unknown serum, it will attach to the antigen. This antibody can be detected by a labeled antiglobulin antibody prepared against globulin of the same species of animal from which the unknown serum was obtained.

3. Complement Staining

Complement is bound by most antigen–antibody reactions, consequently the occurrence of such serologic reactions can be detected by subsequent staining with a fluorescent-anticomplement antibody (Goldwasser and Shepard, 1958).

1. Add heat-inactivated antiviral antibody and guinea pig complement to the microscope slide containing the specimen. Antibody will react with the viral antigen and fix the complement.

2. Wash to remove any unfixed complement and other uncombined serum proteins.

3. Stain with labeled anti-guinea pig complement antibody to deermine if complement was fixed.

Complement Staining

Antigen (A) + Antibody (Ab) + Complement (C) → A—Ab—C
—Ab—C + Fluorescent anticomplement antibody (*FACAb) →
A—Ab—C*FACAb (Stained antigen)

The asterisk indicates fluorescence.

K. SPECIFICITY TESTING

Coons and Kaplan (1950) outlined the tests used to demonstrate he specificity of a fluorescent-antibody conjugate.

1. Inhibition of specific staining by unlabeled antibody (see Section J,1).

2. Reduction of staining by precipitation of antibody in a conjugate ith its homologous antigen.

3. Failure to obtain staining with normal tissues or tissues infected ith unrelated organisms.

4. Lack of staining when infected tissues are stained with conjugates repared from preimmunization bleedings or heterologous antiserums.

L. IMMUNOFLUORESCENT-FOCUS AND IMMUNOFLUORESCENT CELL-COUNTING METHODS

A technique that is gaining in popularity is the quantitation of fectious virus by immunofluorescent focus and immunofluorescent cell ounting.

In the immunofluorescent-focus counting method, cell monolayers fected with virus are incubated in contact with a solid maintenance edium that localizes the spread of infection. After small microscopic ci of infected cells have formed, the cells are freed from the overlay edium, stained with fluorescent antibody, and the localized areas of fected cells are counted with the fluorescence microscope.

Hotchin (1955) infected chick cell monolayers grown in Petri dishes th fowl plague virus. After plaques developed under a methyl-llulose medium, the viscosity of the medium was reduced by adding ld saline to the cultures, and the medium was removed with a pipet. otchin suggested that such monolayers could be stained with fluores-nt antibody. Rapp *et al.* (1959), using a modification of Hotchin's chnique, enumerated immunofluorescent foci of measles virus-infected

cells by fluorescent-antibody staining of monolayers of cells grown o'
cover glasses.

Spendlove and Lennette (1962) further modified the technique b;
incubating cover glass cultures of vaccinia virus-infected cells in con
tact with an agar surface. After viral plaques formed, the agar wa
softened by gentle heat, which permitted the cover glasses to be re
moved without disruption of the cell sheets. The plaques were demon
strable by fluorescent-antibody staining and by hemadsorption. Plaqu
purification of the virus was effected by isolating virus from the aga
beneath cover glass cultures containing single plaques. The agar tech
nique was later used for the assay of the reoviruses (Spendlove et al
1963), while a different agar method was used by Vogt and Rubi
(1963) for assaying avian myeloblastosis virus.

Other investigators have stained smears of infected cells or mono
layers of infected cells incubated under a liquid medium. Proportiona
counts of infected and uninfected cells were made, or single infecte
cells were counted. Using these latter methods, the cultures must be har
vested before infection spreads to other cells or immune serums must b
added to the cultures to prevent spread of infection.

Some of the viruses that have been enumerated in this way ar
influenza virus (Deibel and Hotchin, 1959), Newcastle disease viru
(Wheelock and Tamm, 1961), adenovirus (Philipson, 1961), vaccini
virus (Easterbrook, 1961; this is but one of the several publication
from Fenner's group in Australia in which immunofluorescent ce
counting has been used to assay pox viruses), cytomegalovirus (Good
heart and Jaross, 1963; Rapp et al., 1963), Sendai virus (Hinum
et al., 1963), psittacosis virus (Hahon and Nakamura, 1964; Haho
and Cooke, 1965), adenovirus (Connor and Marti, 1964), polyomaviru
(Sheinin, 1964), reovirus (Spendlove et al., 1964; Spendlove and Scha
fer, 1965; Loh and Soergel, 1965; Loh et al., 1965), SV40 virus (Levin
et al., 1965), respiratory syncytial virus (Schieble et al., 1965), an
vaccinia and variola viruses (Carter, 1965).

The advantages of the immunofluorescent cell-counting method are
(1) a greatly reduced time required for assay, (2) conservation of viru
cells, and media, (3) harvested cultures can be stored and stained ;
any time, (4) noncytocidal viruses, viruses that produce abortive ii
fections, or viruses that do not spread to adjacent cells can be assaye
(5) less difficulty with the cell cultures, since they have to be mai
tained for a relatively short time, and (6) large numbers (over 100C
of infected cells can be counted accurately on a single cover gla
culture.

Some of the limitations of the technique with certain host–viru ystems are: (1) unreliable results owing to spread of infection or synchronous appearance of antigen in infected cells, (2) the effort nvolved in preparing labeled antibody and in counting infected cells, nd (3) the lack of advantage with viruses that form plaques rapidly.

McClain et al. (1967) made a comparative study of the assay of eoviruses by plaque and immunofluorescent cell-counting methods. ubtle differences in virus strains were detectable only when both ethods were used; these differences were of value in genetic studies. he technique can also be used in demonstrating infectious nucleic cid (Schaffer and Spendlove, 1965) and multiplicity reactivation McClain and Spendlove, 1966).

The procedure for immunofluorescent cell counting as developed in his laboratory (Spendlove and Lennette, 1962; Spendlove et al., 1963, 964) is described below.

1. Place from one to five circular 15-mm cover glasses in a 60-mm etri dish and prepare cover glass cultures as described in Section ,H,1.

2. When confluent cell sheets have formed, remove the outgrowth edium by aspiration and wash twice with 4-ml washes with a serum-ess medium.

3. Aspirate as much of the second wash medium as possible and dd 0.02–0.04 ml of the appropriate virus dilution per cover glass. are must be taken in this step to prevent damage to the cell sheets wing to drying. The Clinac "Standard" pipeter (LaPine Scientific ompany, 6001 South Knox Avenue, Chicago, Illinois) provides an ccurate and controllable method for adding the virus inoculum. The rge rubber tube of the pipeter should be replaced with a tube of nall diameter.

4. Incubate the cultures at 37°C in a moist 5% CO_2 atmosphere allow for infection of the cells.

5. Add 4 ml of a maintenance medium containing serum (also im-une serum if it is needed to prevent spread of infection) to each lture and incubate until stainable virus antigen develops.

6. Aspirate the medium from the dishes and beneath the cover asses by pushing them part way up the side of the dish with a long spirating needle.

7. Dry the cover glasses for 10 minutes at 37°C.

8. Fix in cold acetone for 5 minutes at room temperature and then ecant the acetone from the Petri dishes. The cover slips can be ored at −20°C after step 7 or 8. The white styrene metabolic-hibition test trays (Linbro Chemical Company, 681 Dixwell Avenue, ew Haven, Connecticut) described by Melnick and Opton (1956) are

convenient for storing 15-mm circular cover slips. The cover glasse
are placed in the cups of a tray and are held in place by superimposin
the bottom of a second tray over them. The two trays can be tape
together to make an airtight chamber. To remove a cover glass from th
tray, insert a syringe needle upward through the bottom of the cuj
or pick up the cover glass by bringing it in contact with a flat tut
connected to an aspirator.

9. Prepare staining racks (Fig. 2) by cutting metabolic-inhibitio
trays (see step 8) into square sections which contain 16 cups. Inve
the rack, with the open side of the cups down, over a piece of filt
paper in a 150-mm diameter Petri dish. Number the upper (convex
side of each cup consecutively with a pencil. Flood the staining rac
with water then pour off all but enough to moisten the filter pape
[Racks for staining and washing cover glasses have also been describe
by Deinhardt and Dedmon (1965).]

10. Add cover glass cultures (cell side up) to the projecting cuj
of the staining rack. The cover glasses are held in position by th
water that remains after the racks are wet.

11. Add 2 drops of the diluted conjugate to each cover glass cultur
cover the Petri dish, and incubate at 37°C for 20 minutes or longe

12. Prepare a washing rack from the styrene trays described in ste
8 (see Fig. 2). Cut the tray into square sections which contain 1
cups. Number at the side and drill holes ⅛ to ¼ inch in diameter i
the bottom of each cup. Place the washing rack in a large Petri dis
(150 mm in diameter) with the concave side of the cups facing uj
ward. Fill the dish with 0.01 M phosphate-buffered saline at pH 7.5.

13. After staining, pour the labeled antibody off cover glass cultur
and transfer them to cups in the washing rack; wash for 10 minute

14. Gently aspirate the wash medium, place the wash rack on
paper towel, and dry the stained cells at 37° for 10 minutes. The ce
side of the cover glass will dry while the other side will remain mois

15. Place the wash rack over a small perpendicular rod so it projec
through the hole in the bottom of the cup and raises one side of tl
cover glass. Pick up the cover glass with forceps and wipe the buffere
saline from the cellfree side. If the saline is not removed, it will crysta
lize and will fluoresce when the preparation is examined.

16. Mount cell side down on a drop of buffered glycerol. The numb
on the washing cup should correspond with the number on the micr
scope slide.

17. Scan the entire cover glass culture using the lowest magnific
tion that is appropriate and count the number of fluorescing cel
An alternative is to count the cells on a known area of the cover gla

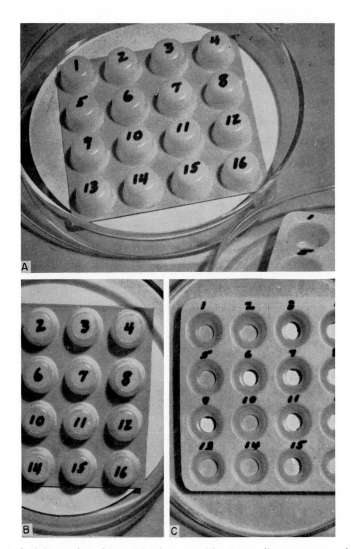

FIG. 2. Staining and washing racks for use with 15-mm diameter cover glass cultures. Cultures to be stained are placed on the numbered projections (A and B) with the cell side up. The cover glasses are held in place by small droplets of water placed on each projection. The filter paper beneath the rack is moistened with water, labeled antibody is added to each culture, and the dish is covered and incubated. After staining the fluorescent antibody is poured off the cultures and they are transferred (cell side up) to a well in the staining rack (C) that is flooded with phosphate-buffered saline. The cultures are removed from the rack by projecting a vertical rod up through the hole in the bottom of each well.

Some workers count a designated number of fields and calculate the fraction of the total area counted; we have counted the cells in one scan from edge to edge through the center of the cover glass. Such a scan takes into consideration any nonrandom distribution of infected cells and does not require one to select fields and to keep track of the number of fields counted. An accurate factor for a microscope can be determined by comparing a count obtained by scanning the entire cover glass with that obtained by one scan through the center of the same cover glass. A statistically significant number of counts must be compared. Sampling errors must also be considered, i.e., how many infected cells must be counted in a single scan to give a representative sample.

II. Staining with Acridine Orange (AO)

Differential staining of nucleic acids by aminoacridines such as AO appears to owe to the manner in which the dye binds to the nucleic acid molecules. When AO is bound to ribonucleic acid (RNA) under conditions that allow for extensive dye binding, the bound dye molecules interact with each other; this results in a shift of the absorption spectrum of the dye from 490 (the wavelength of maximum absorption of unbound dye) to 465 mu. The resulting fluorescence is metachromatic (different from that of the unbound AO) and is emitted in the red part of the spectrum. With differential staining the binding of dye with deoxyribonucleic acid (DNA) is sufficiently light that the bound dye molecules are separated and do not interact. The absorption spectrum of the dye shifts from 490 to 502 mμ, with a resulting green emission (Loeser et al., 1960).

Lerman (1961, 1963, 1964) has proposed, when the concentration of dye molecules to atoms of DNA phosphorus is low, that acridines bind to DNA by being inserted (intercalated) between normally neighboring base pairs in a plane perpendicular to the helix axis. The space for the dye molecule is provided by an extension and local untwisting of the DNA helix. This view has been supported by Isenberg et al. (1964), but Drummond et al. (1965) presented evidence showing that exact and complete intercalation is not a necessary condition of strong dye binding. They proposed other less regular models, in which the positive ring nitrogens of the acridines are close to the DNA phosphates, and acridine rings partially interact with the DNA base rings

AO is currently the most popular of all fluorochromes. It can be used not only as a differential stain for RNA and DNA but also in conjunction with enzyme tests to determine whether a viral nucleic acid single or double stranded. The nucleic acids of viruses have been ꞇudied intracellularly and in smears of purified virus.

Vital staining of cells is another important application of the amino-ꞇridines. Under the appropriate conditions, aminoacridines are con-ꞇntrated in and stain the lysosomes of cells. This has particular ꞇterest, since the cytopathic effect of certain viruses has been related ꞇ their effect on lysosomes and on lysosomal enzymes (Allison and ꞇandelin, 1963; Allison and Burstone, 1964; Allison and Mallucci, ꞇ65; Mallucci and Allison, 1965; Allison and Paton, 1965).

In addition to being a differential stain of nucleic acids and a vital ꞇain of lysosomes, AO and certain other related compounds are muta-ꞇnic and also induce photodynamic inactivability upon viruses grown ꞇ their presence.

Review articles on the use of aminoacridines in virological studies ꞇave been written by Anderson et al. (1959), Mayor and Melnick ꞇ1961/1962), Mayor (1962, 1963), Pollard and Starr (1962), and ꞇallis and Melnick (1965).

Staining of intracellular viral inclusions, purified virus, and vital ꞇaining with AO will be described in this section. The section will ꞇnclude with a description of enzyme digestion tests and histochemi-ꞇal staining, two methods used to confirm results obtained with ꞇuorescent-antibody and AO staining.

A. ACRIDINE ORANGE STAINING OF INTRACELLULAR VIRUS

Since differential staining by AO is dependent upon the degree of ꞇye binding to the nucleic acids, factors that control binding, i.e., dye ꞇncentration, pH, and staining time, must be controlled. Armstrong ꞇ1956) stained sections of paraffin-embedded tissue and found that ꞇe amount of acridine orange R taken up by the sections, stained ꞇith a 1 : 2000 dilution of the dye, increased with rising pH. Above ꞇH 6 all sections fluoresced red and below pH 1.5 there was little dye ꞇptake, and little more than blue autofluorescence of the tissue was ꞇvident. Differential staining occurred between pH 3.6 and 5.2.

Most of the methods described for the preparation of specimens for ꞇuorescent-antibody staining can be used for AO staining (see Section ꞇH). The method of fixation is not critical, although Armstrong ꞇ1957) reported (cited by Anderson et al., 1959) that specimens usu-ꞇlly fluoresce more intensely when fixed briefly in Carnoy's fluid. He ꞇlso reported excellent results with unfixed tissues preserved at −70°C ꞇnd sectioned at −20°C. Fluorescence was reduced if the specimens ꞇere fixed in osmium or picric acid containing fixatives.

Mayor (1964) has cautioned in AO staining that there may be a

deterioration of brilliance, particularly of RNA components, if hy
drating and staining solutions are not freshly prepared or if the stain
ing procedure is unduly prolonged. Another pitfall reported by Pollar
and Starr (1962) is the extraction of AO staining material b
phosphate-buffered saline. They recommended that phosphate-buffere
saline not be used as a carrier of enzymes used in confirmatory test
or for prolonged washing of preparations fixed in acid–alcohol.

Differential staining can be accomplished with the following protoco
which is a composite of the staining techniques used by Armstron
(1956), Mayor (1961), and Pollard and Starr (1962):

1. Fix cultures or tissues to be examined in Carnoy's fluid (1 par
glacial acetic acid, 6 parts absolute ethanol, and 3 parts reagent-grad
chloroform) for 5–10 minutes. The preparations are not dried prio
to fixing.

2. Hydrate by respective dips in 80, 70, and 50% ethanol and dis
tilled water.

3. Place in McIlvaine's buffer at pH 3.8 for 5–10 minutes. McIlvaine'
buffer is prepared from stock solutions of (A) 0.1 M citric acid an
(B) 0.2 M Na_2HPO_4. To prepare a buffer solution of pH 3.8, mi
12.90 ml of solution A with 7.10 ml of solution B.

4. Stain for 5 minutes in 0.01% AO solution. A 10 $\times$ concentratio
of stock AO solution prepared in distilled water is diluted 1 : 10 wit
McIlvaine's buffer at pH 3.8 prior to use.

5. Rinse for 2–3 minutes in fresh McIlvaine's buffer, blot gently
and mount in McIlvaine's buffer at pH 3.8.

Mayor (1964) modified the technique for staining intracellular viru
to make it more sensitive. She was able to detect a labile RNA pro
duced as a result of an adenovirus stimulus and to distinguish it fror
cellular RNA. To render the nucleic acids less prone to nonspecifi
extraction, AO was added to fluid used in each step after fixatior
electrolytes in the staining and hydrating solutions were kept to
minimum, and the total processing time was as brief as possible.

B. ACRIDINE ORANGE STAINING OF PURIFIED VIRUS

Nucleic acid in smears of purified virus can be stained with AC
With the appropriate staining conditions and with the use of relevan
enzyme tests, the technique can be used not only to distinguish be
tween DNA and RNA but can also differentiate between single- an
double-stranded nucleic acids (Mayor, 1962). Other tests used to de
termine the type of viral nucleic acid have been discussed by Wilne
(1965). These tests include (1) inhibition of growth of DNA viruse
by halogenated derivatives of deoxyuridine, (2) selective staining o

)NA cores of deoxyviruses by uranyl acetate prior to examination y electron microscopy, and (3) histochemical staining for DNA and (NA in intracellular inclusions.

Methods other than AO staining for determining single or double trandedness of extracted viral nucleic acids have been described by iomatos and Tamm (1963), Langridge and Gomatos (1963), and Kleinschmidt et al. (1964).

The color of staining in smears of unfixed purified virus stained with ,O is determined by the concentration of AO bound to the nucleic cids. The extent of AO binding is partially dependent upon the per-neability of the virus and the degree of binding of the protein coat f the virus to the nucleic acid. Carnoy's fixative alters the permeability f viruses and facilitates staining to its full potential. Therefore, in-ormation concerning permeability of the virus capsid, the degree of nteraction between the capsid and the nucleic acid core, and which 'iruses are likely to be inactivated photodynamically can be obtained y comparing color reactions developed by fixed and unfixed prepara-ions of purified virus stained with AO (Mayor, 1962).

The following is the procedure described by Mayor and Hill (1961) or the staining of purified virus:

1. Dry a droplet containing approximately 10^{10} virus particles on the enter of a cover glass and fix in Carnoy's fluid for 5 minutes or longer.

2. Hydrate in an alcohol–water series, rinse in distilled water, and place in McIlvaine's buffer at pH 4.0 for 10 minutes.

3. Stain in 0.01% AO in McIlvaine's buffer at pH 4.0 for 5–10 min-tes, rinse in fresh buffer for 2–3 minutes, and mount in buffer.

Mayor and co-workers have stained double-stranded DNA viruses nd single-stranded DNA and RNA viruses by this method. The louble-stranded DNA viruses stained yellow-green and the viruses vith single-stranded DNA or RNA stained red.

Bradley (1965a) has modified the procedure described by Mayor and Iill (1961). In addition to staining single-stranded RNA and double-tranded DNA viruses characteristically, the technique distinguishes between single- and double-stranded DNA viruses without the use of nzymes. The double-stranded RNA of reovirus stains like double-tranded DNA (Bradley, 1965b).

The following is Bradley's procedure:

1. Dry a droplet of virus suspension (10^{10}–10^{12} particles/ml of buffered aline) on a microscope slide. The saline contains 1.27 gm of Na_2HPO_4,).41 gm of KH_2PO_4, and 7.36 gm of NaCl/liter at pH 7.2.

2. Fix in Carnoy's fluid for 5 minutes, rinse in absolute alcohol, nd dry in a stream of warm air.

3. Stain for 5 minutes with AO in the following modified Mc-

Ilvaine's buffer: 6 ml of 0.1 M citric acid, 4 ml of 0.15 M Na$_2$HPO$_4$, an
0.1 ml of 1% AO at pH 3.8.

4. Rinse in the buffer used in step 3 without AO.

5. Transfer to 0.15 M Na$_2$HPO$_4$ for 15 minutes.

6. Shake off excess liquid and examine slides under an ultraviole
lamp (direct viewing is substituted for the fluorescence microscope
with a wavelength of 257 mμ. Note the color of the smears. If th
smears are red, the slides are placed in 0.1 M citric acid and ar
examined in ultraviolet light at intervals of 1, 2, and 3 minutes
the color changes are noted.

Preparations of double-stranded DNA viruses fluoresce green afte
phosphate treatment (step 5). If the smear stains green, there is n
need for treatment with citric acid. Viruses with single-stranded DNΛ
and RNA stain flame red after phosphate treatment. With a subse
quent citric acid exposure, RNA viruses do not fade over the 3-minut
period, whereas the single-stranded DNA viruses fade noticeably an
the staining may change to green.

C. Vital Staining with Aminoacridines

The usefulness of vital staining in the differentiation of DNA an
RNA in cells using AO or other fluorochromes is at present in ques
tion. This owes mainly to the variations in staining that can occu
with cell injury or with variability in the conditions of exposure o
the cells to the dye. In addition to the difficulty of controlling stain
ing conditions, it is not practical to use vital staining to follow th
development of viral nucleic acids in infected cells, since the ligh
used to illuminate the specimens for microscopic examination maγ
kill or injure the host cells.

M. K. Wolf and Aronson (1961) studied a number of differen
tissues grown in perfusion chambers for periods up to 20 days i
the presence of various concentrations of AO. Dye concentrations o
10^{-5} gm/ml permitted no outgrowth from any tissue studied an
promptly killed established cultures. One millionth of a gram o
AO/ml was not highly toxic if the cultures were protected from
photodynamic injury, and resulted in brilliantly fluorescent cells.

An aspect of vital staining currently recognized as having consid
erable importance is the localization of AO in lysosomes of cells
Under the appropriate staining conditions, the lyosomes appear a
brilliantly fluorescent red cytoplasmic particles. They have been re
ferred to as acridine orange particles (AOP) by Robbins and Marcu
(1963).

Robbins and Marcus (1963) carried out *in vitro* studies to gain insight into the mechanism of entrance, accumulation, and ultimate distribution of AO in HeLa cells. The variables, pH, time, dye concentration, and the metabolic state of the cell were found to exert a profound influence on the time course and distribution of staining.

In further studies Robbins *et al.* (1964) found that the brilliantly fluorescent cytoplasmic particles that accumulate in HeLa cells treated with AO represent acid phosphatase-positive multivesicular bodies (lysosomes). There appear to be multiple interactions between the lysosomes and the dye. In one type of interaction not requiring energy the dye diffuses into the cell and probably binds to the phospholipid moiety of the lysosomal membrane. There are two energy-requiring types of interaction. When the concentration of AO is rapidly raised to high levels followed by removal of the dye, there is first a cytoplasmic reddening with a subsequent rapid, energy-requiring accumulation of AO in the lysosomes. When vital staining is accomplished by low concentrations of AO for long periods of time in the presence of the appropriate energy source, there is an induction of phospholipid accumulation (myelin figures) in the lysosomes.

The effects of acridine dyes on viral synthesis has been reviewed by Mayor (1963), and induced photosensitivity by Wallis and Melnick (1965).

Robbins and Marcus (1963) used the conditions listed below as a standard reference system for vital staining of HeLa cells.

1. Prepare a fresh dye solution for each experiment from an AO stock solution (1 gm of AO/2000 ml of distilled water) by diluting the stock solution 1 : 500 with Earle's balanced salt solution or with the appropriate growth medium if the cells are to be held for long periods.

2. Stain vitally for 15 minutes under conditions of physiological pH and temperature. The ratio of stain volume to cell volume should be large (10,000 : 1, or 50 ml/15-mm diameter cover glass culture) so the dye solution will not be depleted by the cells.

With the above staining conditions the juxtanuclear particles (lysosomes) display a brilliant flame-red color, the nucleoli are bright yellow, and the nucleoplasm and cytoplasm are a diffuse green.

D. CONFIRMATION OF FLUORESCENT-ANTIBODY AND ACRIDINE ORANGE STAINING RESULTS

Results obtained with fluorescent-antibody and fluorochrome staining should be complemented and confirmed with other methods. A brief description of enzyme-digestion tests and some histochemical staining methods that can be used in conjunction with fluorescence microscopy are given below. It is suggested that histochemical books be consulted for a more detailed description of additional staining techniques available for studying virus infections.

1. Enzyme-Digestion Tests

Nuclease and/or protease digestion can be used prior to staining with fluorochromes or other histochemical stains, or they can be used with electron microscopy [Bernhard and Tournier (1962) distinguished between viral proteins, DNA, and RNA in thin sections of infected cells embedded in water-soluble plastics]. The latter method offers a means of confirming results at the level of resolution of the electron microscope.

Viral preparations should be exposed to the different enzymes in various sequences. Mayor (1963) tabulated results obtained with AO staining and enzyme digestion and reported that digestion of double- and single-stranded bacteriophage DNA in viruses requires only DNase treatment, while digestion of double-stranded DNA in animal viruses requires treatment by a proteolytic enzyme followed by DNase. Digestion of single-stranded RNA in animal viruses requires only RNase treatment; however, Gomatos and Tamm (1963) found the double-stranded RNA of reovirus to be resistant to RNase. Mayor and Melnick (1961/1962) used a DNase–pepsin–DNase sequence to show that DNA viruses replicating in the nucleus did not stain green with AO as a result of DNA absorbing to the surface of the virus.

In addition to using the different enzymes in various sequences, it it is also desirable to use a control consisting of the enzyme carrier without enzyme; the carrier system alone may extract viral material (Pollard and Starr, 1962). Finally, it may be appropriate to vary the time of enzyme digestion; Bernhard and Tournier (1962) stated that enzyme treatment is more specific with short exposure.

a. Proteolytic Enzymes. Most investigators have used 0.02% pepsin in 0.02 M HCl or in acetate buffer at pH 2.0. Exposure time has ranged from 10 minutes to 2 hours at 37°C.

b. Nucleases. Procedures that are representative for treating viral preparations with nucleases were described by Mayor (1964). She used 0.01% DNase in 0.025 M Veronal buffer containing 0.003 M $MgSO_4$. RNase was used at 0.05% in glass-distilled water at pH 7.0. Some investigators prepare the RNase in McIlvaine's buffer at pH 3.8

or 4.0 (Mayor and Hill, 1961; Pollard and Starr, 1962). The digestion time is 30 minutes at 37°C.

The treatment of preparations of virus with suitable enzymes under the appropriate conditions will result in removal of specific viral material. This digestion can be detected by subsequent staining.

2. Histochemical Stains

The time required for optimal fixation or staining in the procedures described may have to be varied if especially thick or thin specimens are stained.

a. May-Grunwald-Giemsa Stain. This stain is used as a differential stain for nucleoproteins. Deoxyribonucleoproteins stain red–purple and ribonucleoproteins stain blue.

1. Rinse several times with warm balanced salt solution.

2. Fix in absolute methanol for 5–10 minutes.

3. Stain for 5–10 minutes in May-Grunwald stain (National Aniline Division, Allied Chemical Corp., 40 Rector Street, New York). To prepare the May-Grunwald solution, 2.5 gm of dye is dissolved, brought to 1000 ml with absolute methanol, and aged for 1 month.

4. Stain for 10–20 minutes in Giemsa (National Aniline Division, Allied Chemical Corp., 40 Rector Street, New York) diluted 1 : 10 with distilled water. The Giemsa stock is prepared by heating 1.0 gm of stain for 1.5–2 hours at 55°–60°C in 66 ml of glycerol to which 66 ml of absolute methanol is added.

5. Rinse with distilled water and dehydrate by respective rinses in acetone–xylene (1 : 1), acetone–xylene (1 : 2), and xylene.

6. Mount in Canada balsam, DPX, or Euparal.

b. Hematoxylin (Harris') and Eosin Stain. Hematoxylin is a widely used histological stain that can be used alone or with a counterstain. When eosin is used as a counterstain, the nuclei appear blue and the cytoplasm stains pink.

1. Fix the cultures for 10 minutes in Helly's fluid. Helly's fluid is prepared by adding 5 ml of Formalin to 100 ml of Zenker's stock solution just before using. Zenker's stock solution contains 25 gm of potassium dichromate, 50 gm of mercuric chloride, and 1000 ml of distilled water. Ten grams of sodium sulfate is also added by some workers. Heat to dissolve.

2. Wash repeatedly with 80% alcohol until the yellow color disappears, and then wash for several minutes with distilled water.

3. Stain overnight in a dilute solution of Harris' hematoxylin

(2–3 drops/10 ml of distilled water). The hematoxylin is prepared as follows: (a) Dissolve 1 gm of hematoxylin crystals in 10 ml of 95% alcohol. (b) Dissolve 20 gm of ammonium alum in 200 ml of distilled water by heating and mix with the dissolved hematoxylin. (c) Bring rapidly to a boil, remove heat, and add 0.5 gm of mercuric oxide. (d) Reheat the solution until it becomes a dark purple, then cool immediately by immersing in cold water. Two to 4% glacial acetic acid can be added to improve nuclear staining, but this results in a less stable solution. (e) Filter before use.

4. Wash thoroughly in tap water and then in distilled water.

5. Check the staining microscopically. The stain may be removed, if necessary, with acid alcohol (5% concentrated HCl in 70% alcohol). The blue color of the hematoxylin can be restored by dipping the preparation in 0.2–0.3% ammonia water. Repeat step 4 if acid alcohol is used.

6. Counterstain with a 0.5% solution of aqueous eosin to the intensity desired (5 minutes or longer).

7. Dehydrate with two 1-minute washes with 95% alcohol, repeat with absolute alcohol, and conclude with three 2-minute washes with xylol.

8. Mount in Canada balsam.

c. *Macchiavello's Stain.* Macchiavello's stain is commonly used for staining rickettsia and members of the psittacosis–lymphogranuloma group of viruses. The viruses and rickettsia stain bright red, cell nuclei stain deep blue, and the cytoplasm stains light blue.

1. Dry the preparation in air and fix with gentle heat.

2. Stain for 4 minutes. To prepare the stain, dissolve 0.25 gm of basic fuchsin in 100 ml of phosphate buffer ($M/5$, pH 7.4). Filter through coarse filter paper directly onto slide.

3. Rinse with 0.5% citric acid solution and wash thoroughly with tap water.

4. Counterstain for 10 seconds with 1% aqueous methylene blue.

5. Rinse in water and blot dry.

d. *Seller's Stain.* Seller's stain is used to demonstrate Negri bodies in impression smears of brain tissue from rabid animals. The cytoplasmic inclusion bodies of rabies (Negri bodies) stain red, while other cellular structures stain blue or purplish blue.

1. Make an impression smear of tissues to be examined.

2. Immediately immerse in the stain for 5 seconds. Prepare the stain by making 1 gm-% stock solutions of basic fuchsin and methylene blue in absolute methyl alcohol. Mix 1 part of the basic fuchsin solution with 2 parts of the methylene blue solution.

3. Rinse with tap water or $M/150$ phosphate buffer at pH 7.0 and dry.

e. Feulgen Stain. The Feulgen stain is specific for DNA and can be used for staining nuclei and for intracytoplasmic and intranuclear inclusions that contain DNA.

1. Fix for several minutes in Carnoy's fluid (glacial acetic acid, 1 part; absolute alcohol, 6 parts; and reagent-grade chloroform, 3 parts).

2. Rinse in cold 1 N HCl, hydrolyze in 1 N HCl at 60°C for 10 minutes, and wash in cold 1 N HCl.

3. Stain in Feulgen reagent (Coleman's) for 0.5–1 hour. To prepare Coleman's Feulgen reagent, dissolve 1 gm of basic fuchsin in 200 ml of boiling water. Cool and add 2 gm of potassium metabisulfite ($K_2S_2O_5$) and 10 ml of 1 N HCl. Let the solution bleach for 24 hours at room temperature, then add 0.5 gm of activated carbon (Norite). Shake for 1 minute and filter through coarse filter paper.

4. Wash three times for 3 minutes each in freshly prepared potassium metabisulfite solution. Prepare the solution by adding 5 ml of 1 N HCl to a solution of 0.5 gm of potassium metabisulfite in 100 ml of distilled water.

5. Wash in distilled water for 5–10 minutes.

6. Dehydrate in 95% alcohol and in absolute alcohol.

7. Clear in xylol.

8. Mount in Canada balsam, Euparal, or Permount. DNA appears in shades of reddish purple.

E. CONCLUSIONS

It is reasonable to assume that new techniques will be forthcoming and that methods and equipment used in fluorescence microscopy will become more refined. There is, however, one approach to virus methodology that is available at present to the virus investigator for furthering his research. This is the greater application of different techniques to the study of virological problems, and in part accounts for this publication. The techniques of fluorescence microscopy lend themselves beautifully to this coordinative approach; the study of virus–host cell interactions in a single cell can serve as an example.

Techniques are presently available for marking and following a single cell through various procedures (Robbins and Gonatas, 1964); a fixative (acrolein) has been recommended for preparing virus-infected cells for fluorescent-antibody and acridine orange staining and for preserving the cellular fine structure for electron microscopy

(Mayor and Jordan, 1963); and a water-soluble embedding medium has been described for preparing viral specimens for sectioning for electron microscopy (McLean and Singer, 1964). Thus, it should soon be possible to observe a single infected cell successfully in the living state by phase-contrast microscopy and by microspectrophotometry (Leuchtenberger, 1964); then after appropriate fixation by immunofluorescent and acridine orange staining, by autoradiography; and finally, by electron microscopy after embedding, sectioning, and staining with antibodies labeled with electron-dense ferritin molecules.

The above are but a few of the techniques that can be applied to a study of virus–host cell interactions; the example was given to illustrate the varied information that can be acquired through the use of available techniques and those that are in developmental stages. The purpose of this chapter was to describe basic procedures, and thus did not encompass all of the important aspects and techniques of fluorescence microscopy. Consequently, the reader is encouraged to search the literature for additional technological avenues to use in the solution of virological research problems.

ACKNOWLEDGMENTS

The investigations of the author and his colleagues reported in this communication were supported by Public Health Service grant AI-01475 from the National Institute of Allergy and Infectious Diseases to the California State Department of Public Health. Thanks are extended to the library staff of the School of Public Health of the University of California at Berkeley for services provided in the compilation of literature, and to G. K. Turner Associates, Palo Alto, California, for the use of their library facilities.

REFERENCES

Allen, J. C. (1963). *J. Lab. Clin. Med.* **62,** 517.
Allison, A. C., and Burstone, M. S. (1964). *Histochemie* **3,** 462.
Allison, A. C., and Mallucci, L. (1965). *J. Exptl. Med.* **121,** 463.
Allison, A. C., and Paton, G. R. (1965). *Nature* **207,** 1170.
Allison, A. C., and Sandelin, K. (1963). *J. Exptl. Med.* **117,** 879.
Anderson, E. S., Armstrong, J. A., and Niven, J. S. F. (1959). *Symp. Soc. Gen. Microbiol.* **9,** 224.
Armstrong, J. A. (1956). *Exptl. Cell Res.* **11,** 640.
Armstrong, J. A. (1957). *J. Anat.* **91,** 570.
Baumstark, J. S., Laffin, R. J., and Bardawil, W. A. (1964). *Arch. Biochem. Biophys.* **108,** 514.
Bernhard, W., and Tournier, P. (1962). *Cold Spring Harbor Symp. Quant. Biol.* **27,** 67–82.

Beutner, E. H. (1961a). *Bacteriol. Rev.* **25**, 49.
Beutner, E. H. (1961b). *N.Y. State J. Med.* **61**, 444.
Bradley, D. E. (1965a). *Nature* **205**, 1230.
Bradley, D. E. (1965b). Personal communication.
Carter, G. B. (1965). *Virology* **25**, 659.
Cebra, J. J., and Goldstein, G. (1965). *J. Immunol.* **95**, 230.
Chadwick, C. S., McEntegart, M. G., and Nairn, R. C. (1958a). *Lancet* **I**, 412.
Chadwick, C. S., McEntegart, M. G., and Nairn, R. C. (1958b). *Immunology* **1**, 315.
Cheever, F. S. (1964). *Bacteriol. Rev.* **28**, 400.
Cherry, W. B., Goldman, M., and Carski, T. R. (1960). "Fluorescent Antibody Techniques in the Diagnosis of Communicable Diseases." U.S. Govt. Printing Office, Washington, D.C.
Clayton, R. M. (1954). *Nature* **174**, 1059.
Connor, J. D., and Marti, A. (1964). *Proc. Soc. Exptl. Biol. Med.* **117**, 38.
Coons, A. H. (1956). *Intern. Rev. Cytol.* **5**, 1–23.
Coons, A. H. (1958). *Gen. Cytochem. Methods* **1**, 400–421.
Coons, A. H. (1964). *Bacteriol. Rev.* **28**, 397.
Coons, A. H., and Kaplan, M. H. (1950). *J. Exptl. Med.* **91**, 1.
Coons, A. H., Leduc, E. H., and Kaplan, M. H. (1951). *J. Exptl. Med.* **93**, 173.
Curtain, C. C. (1958). *Nature* **182**, 1305.
Curtain, C. C. (1961). *J. Histochem. Cytochem.* **9**, 484.
Dedmon, R. E., Holmes, A. W., and Deinhardt, F. (1965). *J. Bacteriol.* **89**, 734.
Deibel, R., and Hotchin, J. E. (1959). *Virology* **8**, 367.
Deinhardt, F., and Dedmon, R. E. (1965). *Nature* **205**, 1122.
Drummond, D. S., Simpson-Gildemeister, V. F. W., and Peacock, A. R. (1965). *Biopolymers* **3**, 135.
Easterbrook, K. B. (1961). *Virology* **15**, 404.
Felton, L. C., and McMillion, C. R. (1961). Anal. Biochem. **2**, 178.
Fothergill, J. E. (1964a). *In* "Fluorescent Protein Tracing" (R. C. Nairn, ed.), 2nd ed., pp. 4–33. Williams & Wilkins, Baltimore, Maryland.
Fothergill, J. E. (1964b). *In* "Fluorescent Protein Tracing" (R. C. Nairn, ed.), 2nd ed., pp. 35–59. Williams & Wilkins, Baltimore, Maryland.
Fothergill, J. E., and Nairn, R. C. (1961). *Nature* **192**, 1073.
Frommhagen, L. H., and Spendlove, R. S. (1962). *J. Immunol.* **89**, 124.
George, W. H., and Walton, K. W. (1962). *Nature* **194**, 693.
Goldman, M. (1957). *J. Exptl. Med.* **105**, 557.
Goldstein, G., Slizys, I. S., and Chase, M. W. (1961). *J. Exptl. Med.* **114**, 89.
Goldstein, G., Spalding, B. H., and Hunt, W. B., Jr. (1962). *Proc. Soc. Exptl. Biol. Med.* **111**, 416.
Goldwasser, R. A., and Shepard, C. C. (1958). *J. Immunol.* **80**, 122.
Goldwasser, R. A., Kissling, R. E., Carski, T. R., and Hosty, T. S. (1959). *Bull. World Health Organ.* **20**, 579.
Gomatos, P. J., and Tamm, I. (1963). *Proc. Natl. Acad. Sci.* **49**, 707.
Goodheart, C. R., and Jaross, L. B. (1963). *Virology* **19**, 532.
Gornall, A. G., Bardawill, C. J., and David, M. M. (1949). *J. Biol. Chem.* **177**, 751.
Griffin, C. W., Carski, T. R., and Warner, G. S. (1961). *J. Bacteriol.* **82**, 534.
Hahon, N., and Cooke, K. O. (1965). *J. Bacteriol.* **89**, 1465.
Hahon, N., and Nakamura, R. M. (1964). *Virology* **23**, 203.
Hers, J. F. Ph. (1963). *Am. Rev. Respirat. Diseases* **88**, 316.
Hinuma, Y., Miyamoto, T., Ohta, R., and Ishida, N. (1963). *Virology* **20**, 405.

Hiramoto, R. N., and Hamlin, M. (1965). *J. Immunol.* **95,** 214.
Hodgman, C. D., ed. (1949). "Handbook of Chemistry and Physics," 31st ed., p. 2097. Chem. Rubber Publ. Co., Cleveland, Ohio.
Hotchin, J. E. (1955). *Nature* **175,** 352.
Isenberg, I., Leslie, R. B., Baird, S. L., Jr., Rosenbluth, R., and Bersohn, R. (1964). *Proc. Natl. Acad. Sci. U.S.* **52,** 379.
Kaufman, L., and Cherry, W. B. (1961). *J. Immunol.* **87,** 72.
Kleinschmidt, A. K., Dunnebacke, T. H., Spendlove, R. S., Schaffer, F. L., and Whitcomb, R. F. (1964). *J. Mol. Biol.* **10,** 282.
Langridge, R., and Gomatos, P. J. (1963). *Science* **141,** 694.
Lerman, L. S. (1961). *J. Mol. Biol.* **3,** 18.
Lerman, L. S. (1963). *Proc. Natl. Acad. Sci. U.S.* **49,** 94.
Lerman, L. S. (1964). *J. Cellular Comp. Physiol.* **64,** Suppl. *1,* 1.
Leuchtenberger, C. (1964). *Biblioteca Microbiol.* **4,** 18.
Levine, S. I., Goulet, N. R., and Liu, O. C. (1965). *Appl. Microbiol.* **13,** 70.
Levy, H. B., and Sober, H. A. (1960). *Proc. Soc. Exptl. Biol. Med.* **103,** 250.
Liu, C. (1963). *Clin. Pediat. (Philadelphia)* **2,** 490.
Liu, C. (1964). *In* "Diagnostic Procedures for Viral and Rickettsial Diseases" (E. H. Lennette and N. J. Schmidt, eds.), 3rd ed., pp. 177–193. Am. Public Health Assoc. New York.
Loeser, C. N., West, S. S., and Schoenberg, M. D. (1960). *Anat. Record* **138,** 163.
Loh, P. C., and Soergel, M. (1965). *Proc. Natl. Acad. Sci. U.S.* **54,** 857.
Loh, P. C., Hohl, H. R., and Soergel, M. (1965). *J. Bacteriol.* **89,** 1140.
Louis, C. J. (1957). *Stain Technol.* **32,** 279.
McClain, M., and Spendlove, R. S. (1966). *J. Bacteriol.* **92,** 1422.
McClain, M., Spendlove, R. S., and Lennette, E. H. (1967). *J. Immunol.* **98,** 1301.
McDevitt, H. O., Peters, J. H., Pollard, L. W., Harter, J. G., and Coons, A. H. (1963). *J. Immunol.* **90,** 634.
McKinney, R. M., Spillane, J. T., and Pearce, G. W. (1964a). *Anal. Biochem.* **7,** 74.
McKinney, R. M., Spillane, J. T., and Pearce, G. W. (1964b). *Anal. Biochem.* **8,** 525.
McKinney, R. M., Spillane, J. T., and Pearce, G. W. (1964c). *J. Immunol.* **93,** 232.
McLean, J. D., and Singer, S. J. (1964). *J. Cell Biol.* **20,** 518.
Mallucci, L., and Allison, A. C. (1965). *J. Exptl. Med.* **121,** 477.
Marshall, J. D., Eveland, W. C., and Smith, C. W. (1958). *Proc. Soc. Exptl. Biol. Med.* **98,** 898.
Mayersbach, H. (1958). *Acta Histochem.* **5,** 351.
Mayor, H. D. (1961). *Texas Rept. Biol. Med.* **19,** 106.
Mayor, H. D. (1962). *Progr. Med. Virol.* **4,** 70.
Mayor, H. D. (1963). *Intern. Rev. Exptl. Pathol.* **2,** 1.
Mayor, H. D. (1964). *J. Exptl. Med.* **119,** 433.
Mayor, H. D., and Hill, N. O. (1961). *Virology* **14,** 264.
Mayor, H. D., and Jordan, L. E. (1963). *J. Cell Biol.* **18,** 207.
Mayor, H. D., and Melnick, J. L. (1961/1962). *Yale J. Biol. Med.* **34,** 340.
Melnick, J. L., and Opton, E. M. (1956). *Bull. World Health Organ.* **14,** 129.
Mims, C. A. (1964). *Bacteriol. Rev.* **28,** 30.
Nairn, R. C., ed. (1964a). "Fluorescent Protein Tracing," 2nd ed. Williams & Wilkins, Baltimore, Maryland.
Nairn, R. C., ed. (1964b). "Fluorescent Protein Tracing," 2nd ed., pp. 103–137. Williams & Wilkins, Baltimore, Maryland.

Nairn, R. C., Richmond, H. G., and Fothergill, J. E. (1960). *Brit. Med. J.* **II**, 1341.

Ornstein, L., Mautner, W., Davis, B. J., and Tamura, R. (1957). *J. Mt. Sinai Hosp.*, *N.Y.* **24**, 1066.

Paronetto, F. (1963). *Proc. Soc. Exptl. Biol. Med.* **113**, 394.

Peterson, E. A., and Chiazze, E. A. (1962). *Arch. Biochem. Biophys.* **99**, 136.

Philipson, L. (1961). *Virology* **15**, 263.

Pollard, M., and Starr, T. J. (1962). *Progr. Med. Virol.* **4**, 54.

Porath, J., and Flodin, P. (1959). *Nature* **183**, 1657.

Porro, T. J., and Morse, H. T. (1965). *Stain Technol.* **40**, 173.

Porro, T. J., Dadik, S. P., Green, M., and Morse, H. T. (1963). *Stain Technol.* **38**, 37.

Price, G. R., and Schwartz, S. (1956). *In* "Physical Techniques in Biological Research" (G. Oster and A. W. Pollister, eds.), Vol. 3, pp. 91–148. Academic Press, New York.

Price, L. H. (1965). *Stain Technol.* **40**, 209.

Rahman, A. N., and Luttrell, C. N. (1962). *Bull. Johns Hopkins Hosp.* **110**, 66.

Rapp, F., Seligman, S. J., Jaross, L. B., and Gordon, I. (1959). *Proc. Soc. Exptl. Biol. Med.* **101**, 289.

Rapp, F., Rasmussen, L. E., and Benyesh-Melnick, M. (1963). *J. Immunol.* **91**, 709.

Rappaport, B. Z., Walker, J. M., and Booker, B. F. (1964). *J. Immunol.* **93**, 782.

Riggs, J. L., Seiwald, R. J., Burckhalter, J. H., Downs, C. M., and Metcalf, T. G. (1958). *Am. J. Pathol.* **34**, 1081.

Riggs, J. L., Loh, P. C., and Eveland, W. C. (1960). *Proc. Soc. Exptl. Biol. Med.* **105**, 655.

Robbins, E., and Gonatas, N. K. (1964). *J. Cell Biol.* **20**, 356.

Robbins, E., and Marcus, P. I. (1963). *J. Cell Biol.* **18**, 237.

Robbins, E., Marcus, P. I., and Gonatas, N. K. (1964). *J. Cell Biol.* **21**, 49.

Sainte-Marie, G. (1962). *J. Histochem. Cytochem.* **10**, 250.

Schaeffer, M., Orsi, E. V., and Widelock, D. (1964). *Bacteriol. Rev.* **28**, 402.

Schaffer, F. L., and Spendlove, R. S. (1965). Unpublished results.

Scherer, W. F., ed. (1955). "An Introduction to Cell and Tissue Culture," pp. 2–4. Burgess, Minneapolis, Minnesota.

Schieble, J. H. (1965a). Personal communication.

Schieble, J. H., Lennette, E. H., and Kase, A. (1965). *Proc. Soc. Exptl. Biol. Med.* **120**, 203.

Sheinin, R. (1964). *Virology* **22**, 368.

Sinha, R. C., and Reddy, D. V. R. (1964). *Virology* **24**, 626.

Smith, C. W., Metzger, J. F., and Hoggan, M. D. (1962). *Am. J. Clin. Pathol.* **38**, 26.

Smith, M. L., Carski, T. R., and Griffin, C. W. (1962). *J. Bacteriol.* **83**, 1358.

Spendlove, R. S. (1966). *Proc. Soc. Exptl. Biol. Med.* **122**, 580.

Spendlove, R. S., and Lennette, E. H. (1962). *J. Immunol.* **89**, 106.

Spendlove, R. S., and Schaffer, F. L. (1965). *J. Bacteriol.* **89**, 597.

Spendlove, R. S., Lennette, E. H., Knight, C. O., and Chin, J. N. (1963). *J. Immunol.* **90**, 548.

Spendlove, R. S., Lennette, E. H., Chin, J. N., and Knight, C. O. (1964). *Cancer Res.* **24**, 1826.

Steiner, R. F., and Edelhoch, H. (1962). *Chem. Rev.* **62**, 457.

Tobie, J. E. (1958). *J. Histochem. Cytochem.* **6**, 271.

Toussaint, A. J., and Anderson, R. I. (1965). *Appl. Microbiol.* **13**, 552.

Vogt, P. K., and Rubin, H. (1963). *Virology* **19**, 92.

Wallis, C., and Melnick, J. L. (1965). *Photochem. Photobiol.* **4**, 159.

Weber, G. (1952). *Biochem. J.* **51**, 155.

Wheelock, E. F., and Tamm, I. (1961). *J. Exptl. Med.* **113**, 301.

Wilner, B. I. (1965). "A Classification of the Major Groups of Human and Other Animal Viruses," 3rd ed. Burgess, Minneapolis, Minnesota.

Wolf, M. K., and Aronson, S. B. (1961). *J. Histochem. Cytochem.* **9**, 22.

Wolf, P. L., Pearson, B., Rosenblatt, M., Vasquez, J., and Jarkowski, T. (1965). *Am. J. Clin. Pathol.* **43**, 47.

Wood, B. T., Thompson, S. H., and Goldstein, G. (1965). *J. Immunol.* **95**, 225.

Young, M. R. (1961). *Quart. J. Microscop. Sci.* **102**, 419.

11 Electron Microscopy of Isolated Virus Particles and Their Components

Robert W. Horne

I. Some General Remarks on the Application of the Electron Microscope to the Study of Biological Structure at the Macromolecular Level

A. INTRODUCTION

The development of the electron microscope from an instrument demonstrating a resolution slightly better than the light microscope to an essential research tool capable of resolving 4 Å has taken place within the relatively short period of about 30 years. The resolving limit of the electron microscope is dependent not only on the instrumental design and performance but also on the specimen structure to be resolved. These two problems have often been considered as separate issues owing to the difference in the rate of progress between instrumental design and specimen-preparation techniques. For many years the problem of resolving structure approaching atomic dimensions was generally considered to be of academic interest.

With the more recent advances in specimen-preparation techniques, it is clear that the biologist may be able to make greater use of the potential high resolving power of the electron microscope. The interpretation of the image at these high levels, on the other hand, presents a number of new problems. These difficulties, together with image effects in the form of "noise" and contrast effects superimposed on the specimen from substrates and interference patterns, will be discussed later. The important improvements in instrumental design and resolving power have resulted from a number of investigations on lens design, stability of the accelerating voltage, object decontamination, and specimen cooling. In considering the requirements for an "optimum electron-objective" lens, Glaser (1941) calculated and designed a form of single-field condenser objective lens. Although this lens was considered some 20 years ago, it has only recently been possible to overcome some of the more practical difficulties in its construction. Moreover, there were other instrumental problems that had to be eliminated before the single-field objective lens could be employed to full advantage (Ruska, 1962, 1965; Riecke, 1962).

It seems probable that the single-field objective lens will be capable of extremely high performance, and recent results have shown that a linear resolution of 0.33 Å and point-to-point resolution of about 1.7 Å is possible (cf. Komoda and Otsuki, 1964; Dowell, 1963; Ruska, 1965). The question of the relationship between the *total* thickness of the object and the depth of field in a highly corrected lens must be considered in relation to the operation of the instrument. It follows from this that focusing will become more critical, and it is essential to have adequate illumination at the high magnifications necessary for high-resolution work. These requirements are also of some practical importance, since visualizing structural features at the molecular level will require a better understanding of interaction of the electron beam with the specimen. Recognition of the structural alterations owing to electron irradiation may be difficult to detect and interpret, particularly in the case of small particles.

The development of the double-condenser illuminating system has ensured that adequate illumination is available at the final screen at high instrumental magnifications. Double-condenser illumination has the disadvantage of increasing the carbonaceous contamination rate of the specimen and other surfaces during electron irradiation. Specimen-contamination rates may range from 1.0 Å/second to 4 Å/second or higher, depending on the cross-sectional area of the illuminating beam in the plane of the specimen. Vacuum conditions, grease, and vacuum seals, together with general column cleanliness, may also contribute considerably to the contamination problem in the electron microscope.

One of the most satisfactory devices designed for reducing the contamination rate is a cooling ring or cold surface located near the specimen (cf. Heide, 1965). These devices are capable of reducing the contamination rate to values ranging from about 0.1 Å/second to 0.4 Å/second, assuming that the other contributing factors mentioned above are also reduced to a minimum. The more confused the background becomes, the greater the difficulty encountered in the interpretation of

high-resolution electron micrographs. Much of the background "structure" comes from layers of carbonaceous material deposited on the specimen, which has a profound effect on the detail in biological material
capable of being resolved. This is illustrated in the electron micrographs shown in Fig. 1. The contamination rate observed in these micrographs was calculated to be about 1.2 Å/second. Serious contamination
is already evident in the first micrograph, which was recorded as rapidly
as possible.

It is essential that if detail at the molecular level is to be resolved in
biological specimens, some form of efficient cooling device for decontamination must be used. Moreover, the operator must have access to
the necessary liquid coolants.

B. Definition of High Resolution

It has been pointed out by Cosslett (1955) that there appears to be
a direct relationship between the resolution available from a given object and its thickness, and for practical electron microscopy of biological objects the available resolution will be approximately one-tenth of
the total object thickness. This owes to the blurring of the image by
chromatic confusion of the electrons as the specimen thickness increases. Distances approaching atomic dimensions from specimens possessing regular lattice arrays are defined as "linear" resolution and can
be obtained from specimens examined under certain inclined illuminating conditions where the specimen is relatively thick. The majority of
biological particles have to be measured or detected from preparations
with a more or less irregular structural pattern, and the measured
values are defined as *point-to-point* resolution. For high-resolution
problems where structural features approach dimensions below 30 Å,
the thickness of the object must be kept to a minimum. This requirement for extremely thin specimens is not always easy to achieve for
electron microscopy.

Probably the most serious effect associated with recording electron
micrographs showing a resolution below 30 Å, is associated with changes
in contrast with very small changes in the focusing values of the objective lens. These contrast effects may result from structure in the
specimen support films being confused with structural features in the
particles, or a combination of both (cf. Thon, 1964). It would appear
that very small structural detail must not only be recorded on two separate plates but also observed in images where a through focal series is
taken by changing the objective focal setting by about 0.6 μ.

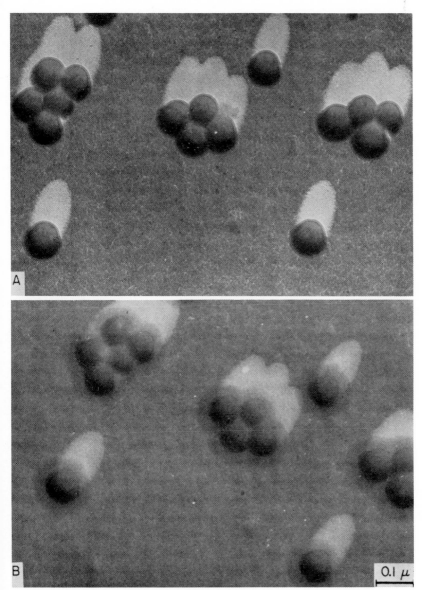

FIG. 1. (A) The electron micrograph shows latex spheres after irradiation in the electron microscope using double-condenser illumination. The diameter of the illuminating spot was approximately 5 μ and the specimen was irradiated for 1 minute. (B) The same area irradiated under identical conditions as (A) for 5 minutes. Severe contamination by carbon deposits can be seen on the particles and supporting film together with the effect on the detail resolvable.

II. Specimen-Support Films

A. INTRODUCTION

The preparation of most biological material for examination in the electron microscope involves a considerable amount of time and skill. A great deal of preparative effort can be wasted if the specimen-supporting films fail after being placed in the microscope and become irradiated with the electron beam. Most of the trouble encountered arises from excessive thickness of the supporting films and consequently from drift attributable to thermal gradients produced by the beam. In some instances they are found to disrupt completely or are not stable mechanically. The choice of supporting film or substrate will depend on the type of specimen it has to carry. For the reasons mentioned in Section I, very small viruses must be supported by thin films, otherwise the film thickness approaches that of the specimen and will often result in an amount of granulation being recorded in addition to the details from the specimen. The choice is very often a compromise between film thickness, stability, and the amount of material deposited on the support.

There are a number of materials and techniques used in the preparation of supporting films, but the final choice will be limited by the above considerations as well as by transparency to the electron beam. The methods can be divided into two main procedures, described below.

B. PLASTIC FILMS

It is general practice to use either Formvar [poly(vinyl Formol)] or collodion (nitrocellulose) dissolved in a suitable volatile solvent for plastic films. Films of collodion or Formvar can be cast on a distilled water surface or spread onto a cleaned glass surface (see Table I).

TABLE I
PLASTIC FILMS AND SOLVENTS

Plastic	Solvent	Concentration
Formvar	Ethylene dichloride	0.2–0.5%
	Chloroform	
	Dioxane	
Collodion	Ethyl or amyl acetate	0.5–1.0%
	Acetone	
Poly(vinyl alcohol)	Water	0.5–1.0%
Cellulose acetate	Acetone	0.2–0.5%

Freshly cleaved mica cut to the size of a standard microscope slide presents an ideal surface, since it is free from the many surface defects associated with glass. Uniform thickness of plastic films tends to reduce the thermal gradients produced during irradiation in the electron beam, which ultimately affect the final image quality. Films with constant thickness are difficult to reproduce by the spreading techniques. Two of the standard methods for coating specimen grids with plastic films are illustrated in Figs. 2A and 2B. In Fig. 2A, the plastic film is floated

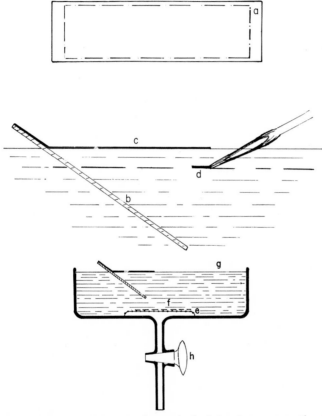

FIG. 2. (A) The diagram illustrates the method of forming a supporting film on a water surface. A slide coated with the required film is scratched near the edges, as indicated by the dotted line (a), and immersed in the water. Slow insertion of the slide (b) will release the film (c). A grid (d) held between a pair of forceps is raised to make contact with the film. (B) An alternative method for coating a large number of grids is shown in the diagram. A fine metal gauze (e) is arranged at the bottom of a circular dish to support the grids (f). The film is released or formed at the water surface (g) and lowered with the water level controlled by the tap (h). When dry, the gauze is removed together with the coated grids.

onto the surface from the mica or glass and lowered onto the grids, with
the water level controlled by the draining tap, as shown in the more detailed diagram in Fig. 2B. An alternative procedure is to allow a drop
of the collodion or Formvar film solution to spread on the water surface
and drain the water container as shown. Some attention should be paid
to the attachment of the film to the grids. A frequent cause of drifting
in the electron beam results from poor thermal and mechanical contact
with the copper supports, as shown in Fig. 3A. Grids can be slightly
bent to form a more convex surface to ensure good contact with plastic
films, but overbending or distortion should be avoided (Fig. 3B). Plastic
films covering specimen grids are generally not suitable for the study of
isolated particles such as viruses and large proteins unless they have
been stabilized by a further coating of some conducting material. This
can be achieved either by shadowing techniques or coating the films
with a thin carbon layer.

Fig. 3. (A) Grids presenting a concave surface may result in the film making contact only at the periphery of the support. Stability of the support films can be improved by ensuring that the maximum contact with the grid bars takes place as
shown in (B).

C. Evaporated Films

Evaporated films generally take the form of a thin carbon layer and
can be produced using the technique originally described by Bradley
(1954). The apparatus, which is placed in the high vacuum chamber
of an evaporating plant, is shown in Fig. 4. The approximate positions
within the vacuum chamber of the carbon-arcing device, slides, and
porcelain-thickness indicator are illustrated in Fig. 5. By passing a
suitable current through the carbon rods, an arc is formed that evapo-
rates the carbon onto the required surfaces. It has been found convenient to shape the carbon rods by turning them in a small lathe or similar device, as shown in Fig. 6. This allows the region of small diameter
to be evaporated and produces a more constant thickness in batches of
films.

Separation of the evaporated carbon films from the glass or mica surface is carried out in the same manner as illustrated in Fig. 2A. Grids
can be coated by holding them with forceps and raising the grid slowly
to make contact with the carbon layer at the water interface. Grids

previously coated with the plastic films can be placed directly in the evaporator and coated in the same manner as shown in Fig. 5. Carbon films alone are suitable for spraying techniques, but tend to break or fragment if drops of suspension are placed directly on the surface from

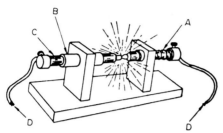

Fig. 4. The diagram shows the basic arrangement for mounting two carbon rods for carbon evaporation. Two carbon rods (A and C) are held in alignment by the insulating supports (B) and in contact by the weak coil spring over the rod A. Arcing takes place when a suitable current is passed through the carbon rods via the leads D. This device is placed in the evaporator chamber shown in Fig. 5.

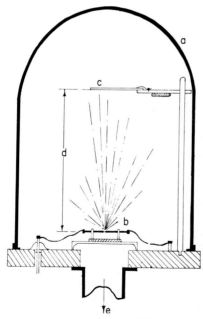

Fig. 5. Carbon or metals can be evaporated in the apparatus illustrated. The vacuum chamber (a) contains the evaporating device (b) and slide or specimen (c). High vacuum is produced by the high-vacuum pumps connected at (e) to give a chamber pressure of about 10^{-5} Torr. The distance (d) separating the evaporating source and slide (c) is about 15–19 cm.

pipets. Plastic films stabilized with carbon are recommended where i
is necessary to mount specimens from small pipets or platinum loops
Some difficulties may be encountered in separating very thin carbo
films from glass or mica slides after they have been placed in a wate
trough. The method of ion bombardment of the glass slides before coat
ing with carbon has been described by Towe (1965). Cleaned slides ar
placed in the evaporating chamber and pumped in the usual manne
by the mechanical pump. A glow discharge from a suitable high-voltag
source is applied within the chamber to bombard thoroughly the glas
surfaces. The chamber is evacuated to high vacuum followed by evap
oration of the carbon.

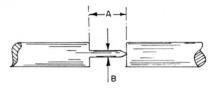

Fig. 6. For the evaporation of carbon it is convenient to shape the rods as show
in the diagram. The dimensions of A and B will determine the approximate amour
of carbon evaporated.

Carbon-coated slides can be placed in Petri dishes fitted with mois
filter papers, which tend to assist the separation of the films from th
slides. Final separation of the carbon layer is performed by immersin
the slide in the trough, as described in Section II,B. Ion bombardmen
introduces a negative charge at the glass surface, which is favorab
for the attraction of water molecules and consequently aids the separa
tion of the carbon film.

Although carbon-supporting films have the important advantages c
being relatively thin and are stable in the electron beam, a seriou
limitation is encountered in the structure resulting from contrast effec
superimposed on the structure of the specimen. This is particularl
noticeable in instruments capable of very high resolution. The surfac
detail of virus particles or their isolated components are often obscure
by the background structure from the carbon. This is of some impo
tance, as the majority of viral components are of relatively low molec
ular weight and difficult to resolve if their size approaches the thicknes
of the substrate.

D. HOLEY FILMS

The extreme thinness of the object required for very high resolutio
may be overcome by spreading the specimen over holes. Plastic film

possessing approximately circular holes have been used by Huxley and Zubay (1960) and Harris (1962). The presence of suitable holes in the supporting film has the additional advantage of indicating the level of focusing and astigmatic error. Holey films are not always easy to produce unless the procedures are standardized. Films with holes ranging from 0.05 to 25 μ can be produced by the addition of a small quantity of glycerol to a 0.25% solution of Formvar using the procedure described by Harris (1962). The mixtures of glycerol and plastic shown in Table II are spread thinly on mica or glass slides and allowed to dry

TABLE II
PREPARATION OF HOLEY FILMS

Formvar (parts)	Glycerol (parts)	Maximum hole diameter (μ)
8	1	25
16	1	14
32	1	7
120	1	4

at room temperature. Accelerating the drying period by the application of heat will produce pseudoholes, and this form of artificial drying should be avoided. Dried films are floated free from the glass or mica surface and mounted on grids, as described earlier, and finally coated with a fine layer of evaporated carbon.

There are a number of other methods for preparing specimen-support films, including evaporated silica or silicon monoxide films, and the reader is referred to the more detailed methods described by Bradley (1965a).

III. Mounting of Isolated Virus Particles and Components

A. DIRECT MOUNTING

Virus particles in aqueous solution can be mounted directly onto filmed grids from finely drawn glass pipets or platinum loops. The major portion of the deposited droplet is drained slowly from the specimen support using a pointed piece of filter paper or pipet, leaving a thin liquid layer at the surface. After allowing a suitable period for drying, the mounted specimen can be transferred to an evaporator for shadow casting. One of the disadvantages with mounting droplets is associated with an uneven distribution of virus particles or their components over the specimen surface. Liquid suspensions containing very high concentrations of virus will tend to form large aggregates during the final drying period. On the other hand, suspensions with small amounts of virus will produce a poor distribution of particles for photographing in the electron microscope.

A more serious problem encountered with the slow drying procedure from droplets is concerned with the collapse or possible disruption of intact virus particles owing to the large surface-tension forces during drying. The original liquid suspension may contain a high proportion of intact and infective virus, but on examination in the electron microscope many of the particles may be difficult to identify or count. Another difficulty is associated with suitable suspending media for electron microscopy. A number of viruses are not stable when resuspended in distilled water, and they may require suitable buffering conditions. Many buffers in use tend to produce small crystallites on drying, which also add to the problem of interpretation of air-dried specimens. Backus and Williams (1949, 1950) have discussed in more detail the problem of virus supsensions containing nonvolatile components. Certain virus preparations may be dialyzed against a 2% solution of ammonium acetate or ammonium carbonate. It was also pointed out that the pH range of ammonium acetate and ammonium carbonate will vary during drying. The former tends to drop to about pH 4.0, and the latter was found to reach values of about pH 10.

B. Spray Guns and Spraying Techniques for Mounting Virus Particles

Small droplets can be sprayed onto specimen-support films by the use of relatively simple spray gun devices. Spraying methods have several advantages over the large-drop mounting procedure. Small droplets of about 5–20 μ in diameter will dry more rapidly, and disruptive effects may be reduced. The volume of virus suspension required for spraying is relatively small, but will allow a large number of prepared grids to be made available for electron microscopy. Another obvious advantage is the application of spraying to particle counting, a subject to be discussed later.

A variety of spray guns have been described as suitable for electron microscopy and have been reviewed in more detail elsewhere (cf. Horne, 1965a). The most widely used spray gun for virus work is illustrated in Fig. 7. Small volumes of liquid of about 0.1–0.2 ml are sufficient to be inserted into the chamber. A small modification in the form of an outlet tube has to be added to the gun as supplied to allow it to be operated in the horizontal position shown in the diagram. The Vaponefrin gun will spray small droplets with a size range of about 5–20 μ in diameter. It should be mentioned that owing to the electrostatic charge effects between the surface of the liquid droplets and the specimen supports, a high proportion of the droplets will be deflected, and it may be necessary to operate the hand bulb about 40 times to ensure that sufficient droplets are distributed on the grids. Spreading of the droplets on the specimen-support surface will depend on the number of virus particles in the droplet or suspension as well as on surface tension and charge of both particles and substrate surface. The diameters of the droplets tend to vary over the range of sizes mentioned above, and particles over 1 μ across are difficult to spray.

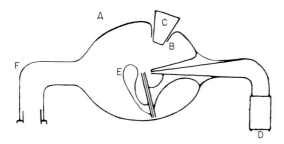

Fig. 7. The diagram illustrates the cross section of the Vaponefrin glass spraying device. Liquid suspensions are inserted into the chamber A through the aperture B. The aperture is sealed by the stopper C, and air pressure is supplied by a hand bulb attached to the air inlet D. Droplets strike the diffuser bulb at E and are sprayed onto prepared grids through the right-angle extension F.

There are a number of occasions when it is necessary to spray infectious or toxic material for examination in the electron microscope. A simple apparatus for use with the Vaponefrin spray gun has been described by Horne and Nagington (1959) and is shown in Fig. 8. The entire apparatus acts as a closed system and is easily decontaminated.

C. SPRAYING AND FREEZE-DRYING VIRUS PARTICLES

For improving the three-dimensional structure of virus particles Wyckoff (1946) and Williams (1953) have described methods for freeze-drying. The procedure used by Wyckoff made use of a precooled copper block containing filmed copper grids. Droplets of the virus suspension were placed on the cooled grids and rapidly transferred to a vacuum chamber or coating unit for pumping. The specimens were then shadowed after drying and examined in the electron microscope. Owing

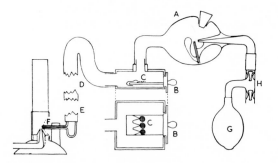

Fig. 8. A simple and effective device for spraying infectious material is shown in the diagram. Droplets are produced from the spray gun A and are deposited onto prepared grids C attached to the sliding support B, and enclosed in a sealed plastic box. The hand bulb G supplies the air pressure via the nonreturn valve H. Any excess vapor from the chamber is passed into two decontaminating flasks inserted at D and E. The final outlet is inserted through a Bunsen flame shown at F. (From Horne and Nagington, 1959.)

to the poor transfer of heat and consequent slow cooling, only a limited amount of preservation can be expected using this method, as it is essential that proper sublimation conditions be established and controlled.

The apparatus described by Williams (1953) is shown in Fig. 9 and

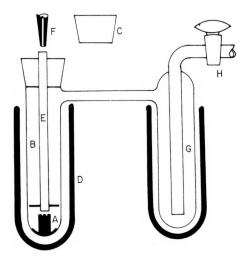

Fig. 9. Freeze-drying apparatus (see text). A, copper block containing filmed grids held in position by vacuum grease; B, sublimation chamber; C, glass stopper; D sublimation vacuum flask; E, spray tube; F, spray gun outlet; G, cold trap; H vacuum line and tap. (From Williams, 1953.)

s used in conjunction with a Vaponefrin spray gun of the type shown
in Fig. 7. Filmed grids are placed on the surface of a copper block and
lowered into the sublimation chamber cooled to about $-70°C$ by the
surrounding CO_2–alcohol coolant. The spray tube connected to the gun
is inserted, and droplets containing sufficient virus are sprayed down
the cold chamber and are frozen prior to being deposited on the grids.
After removal of the spray-tube assembly, the sublimation tube must
be sealed and connected to an efficient vacuum system and pumped
for a period of about 15 minutes. The temperature of the sublimation
chamber is then raised to about $-30°C$ to allow sublimation to occur
and pumped for a further 30 minutes. During the pumping period the
second chamber acts as a suitable cold trap and is filled with liquid
nitrogen or other coolant. A final vacuum pressure of about 10^{-4} Torr
is adequate, but sublimation is possible if the system is connected to a
good mechanical pump and sufficient time is allowed for drying to be
completed.

After suitable pumping the sublimation chamber is removed from
the coolant and allowed to reach room temperature with the vacuum
apparatus connected. The pumping system is then stopped and air is
admitted slowly into the freeze-drier through the tap or air inlet. The
specimens can be shadowed ready for examination in the electron microscope. For many biological structures in the form of viruses and particles
this method is capable of producing very good results. The disadvantage
lies in not being able to prepare a large number of virus samples quickly
and to make accurate estimates of the droplet volumes.

V. Shadow-Casting Techniques

A. INTRODUCTION

Biological structures in the form of viruses and their components are
relatively transparent to the electron illuminating beam, and it may
be difficult to either detect isolated particles or to estimate their size
and shape. One of the earliest and most successful methods for enhancing the contrast in isolated particles for electron microscopy was the
technique of shadow casting (Williams and Wyckoff, 1944, 1946; Williams and Backus, 1949). The advantages of the shadow-casting procedure are 2-fold: first, contrast in the specimen is considerably improved, and second, it introduces a three-dimensional appearance to
the specimen. The latter allows some estimate to be made of the
approximate height of the object recorded on the electron micrographs.

B. Methods for Evaporating Metals

The basic arrangement for evaporating a metal of high atomic number onto the specimen is illustrated in Fig. 5 (the carbon source in Fig. 5 is replaced by the device for evaporating metals). It is necessary to arrange for the electrode holders to accommodate either wire or metal strips. The most widely used wire heaters are formed from tungsten wire in the shapes shown in Fig. 10A. For certain metals to

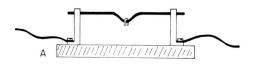

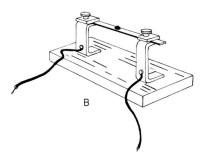

Fig. 10. (A) The drawing shows the basic apparatus used for evaporating metal available in wire form. A small length of metal is placed on a V-shaped tungsten filament and heated by passing current through the leads. (B) An alternative device for evaporating metal in powder form. A tantulum or molybdenum strip is clamped between two supports mounted on insulating material. The strip is heated by passing current through the two leads. Both of these devices form part of, or are placed in an evaporating plant illustrated in Fig. 5.

be evaporated, it is convenient to use metal strips or evaporating boats made from thin tantalum or molybdenum sheet in the form illustrated in Fig. 10B. There is a wide range of shadow-casting materials, including chromium, platinum, gold–palladium alloy (60 : 40), uranium, platinum–iridium, and others. Several of these metals are more suitable for high-resolution work than others owing to the low granulation effects they produce in the specimen. Metals such as platinum or uranium, with low granulation levels, are much more difficult to evaporate. Chromium, on the other hand, is easy to use as a shadowing material

but is only useful for relatively low-magnification work. For a more
detailed account of the shadowing process the reader is referred to the
article by Preuss (1965).

C. SHADOWING ANGLES

In selecting a suitable shadowing angle the size of the virus particles
must be taken into consideration. The diagram in Fig. 11 illustrates
the relationship between the angle of the evaporating source and the
length of shadow and height of the particle. Obviously specimens of

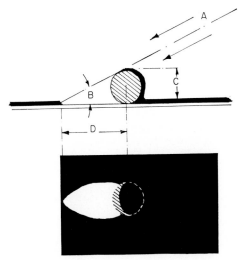

FIG. 11. The diagram illustrates the formation of a shadow produced from a
spherical object mounted on the substrate. Metal is evaporated from the direction
A at an angle B. The approximate height C of the object can be calculated from
the length of shadow D and angle B. Some allowance for the metal thickness deposited onto the specimen must be taken into consideration when estimating the
particle size.

small size or low molecular weight would be more clearly detected
when shadowed at low angles. Shadowing can also be useful in attempts
to determine the shape of certain particles. This was clearly demonstrated in the study of tipula iridescent virus by Williams and Smith
(1958). The virus particles were shadowed in two known directions,
and the direction angles and shadowing angles carefully noted. After
careful analysis of the shadows formed in the electron micrographs,
models were constructed and their shadows photographed from visible
light. The shape and shadows produced from the models confirmed the
icosahedral shape of the tipula virus (Fig. 12).

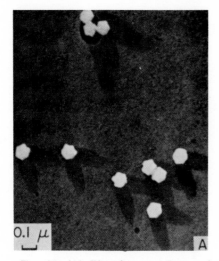 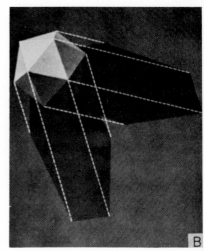

Fig. 12. (A) The electron micrograph shows a preparation of tipula iridescent virus shadowed in two directions. The shape of the particle and shadows cast are well defined. (B) A model of an icosahedron illuminated in a light source producing the same features of shadows as seen in (A). (By kind permission of R. C. Williams and K. M. Smith.)

D. Limitations of Shadowing for High-Resolution Studies

With the rapid development of instruments of very high resolution, it is clear that shadowing can be useful only to within certain limits of resolution and magnification. The electron micrograph shown in Fig. 13 of tobacco mosaic virus was shadowed with uranium, and the specimen was shadowed in an experimental evaporator. The evaporator was specially designed for electron microscopy and fitted with trapped Hg pumps and mechanical pumps (Cosslett and Horne, 1955). It can be seen that the shadows formed are remarkably sharp, but the granulation produced from the metal deposit has obscured detail at the molecular level. Attempts to reduce possible scattering from the vacuum chamber by inserting apertures between the metal source and specimen have met with only limited success. The fundamental problem of migration of the evaporated metal to form granules or crystallites on the specimen remains. Moreover, the structural changes in the specimen caused by the evaporated metals at extremely high temperatures remain unknown. Nevertheless, for many problems shadowing techniques can contribute much to our knowledge concerning the gross morphology of virus particles.

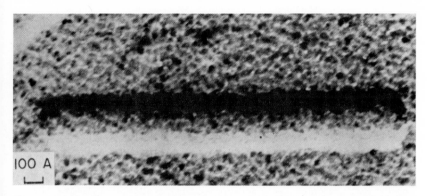

FIG. 13. The electron micrograph shows a fragment of tobacco mosaic virus shadowed at a low angle. At this magnification the shadow contour remains sharp, but the granulation on the surface of the virus rod and supporting film obscures much of the fine detail.

V. Replica Techniques

The basic replica techniques used in the study of metal surfaces have been successfully applied to virus crystals and to individual virus particles (cf. Price and Wyckoff, 1946; Matthews *et al.*, 1957). Suspensions containing virus particles are thinly spread and dried down onto glass slides or rectangular cover slips and shadowed using the methods described earlier. A thin layer of evaporated carbon is deposited onto the shadowed specimen, and the slide is slowly immersed in a concentrated solvent capable of removing or digesting the viral material. This also allows the carbon replica to be released from the slide and transferred to a series of water baths to remove solvents. The washed replicas are picked up directly with electron microscope specimen grids.

There is a large variety of techniques for obtaining replicas from crystalline structures and biological materials, and the reader is referred to the methods discussed by Bradley (1965a). The interpretation of electron micrographs of replicas presents a number of special problems. Artifacts in the form of small regular "components" may result from the buildup of carbon on the specimen if low angles of evaporation are used. Drying artifacts will be replicated by the carbon, which will impose limits on the amount of detail replicated from the original object (Fig. 14). Replicas from viruses for high-resolution work produced from very thin carbon films are extremely difficult to handle mechanically and mount on grids.

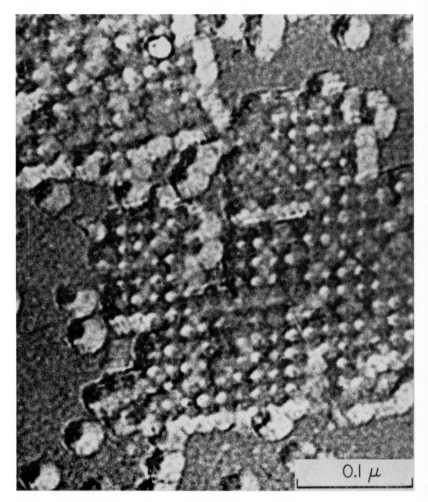

Fig. 14. A region from an electron micrograph of a carbon replica of turnip yellow mosaic virus.

VI. Positive Staining of Virus Particles and Their Components

A. Introduction

The density and preservation of a wide range of virus particles can be improved for examination in the electron microscope by the use of fixation and positive staining procedures. The combined fixation and electron-dense properties of osmium tetroxide are well known, and by simply placing a small droplet of virus suspension onto a filmed grid followed by exposure to osmium vapor, contrast of the particles can be considerably enhanced (cf. Valentine, 1960, 1962). Other fixatives such as formaldehyde and glutaraldehyde followed by staining with phosphotungstic acid, uranyl acetate, or lead hydroxide can also be applied to improve preservation and contrast in isolated virus particles. Fixation times and the uptake of heavy metal stains will vary to some extent, depending on the chemical procedures used and the type of protein present in the specimen.

B. POSITIVE STAINING OF VIRUS PARTICLES

The part of the virus particle containing the nucleic acid or core region can be stained with uranyl acetate and lead hydroxide (Huxley and Zubay, 1960). Some care should be taken in the preparation of staining solutions in order to avoid the presence of small electron-dense precipitates appearing on or around the virus particles to be examined. Staining solutions should be freshly prepared in glass-distilled water, centrifuged, and finally filtered before use. Small droplets of virus suspension are placed on the surface of filmed grids and allowed to dry. A small dish containing the staining solution (1% uranyl acetate) is prepared, which will allow the grids to be floated with the specimen surface in contact with the staining solution. As already mentioned, the length of time needed for staining to become effective will vary with the type of specimen, but periods of about 30–60 minutes may be necessary. From the experiments described by Huxley and Zubay (1961) it was found that certain virus cores revealed considerable density after being initially stained with uranyl acetate for 6 hours followed by lead hydroxide for 1.5 hours.

C. POSITIVE STAINING OF NUCLEIC ACID

The staining of isolated strands of nucleic acid from virus material is more difficult, and the effects of heavy metal stains have been discussed by Stoeckenius (1961). One of the problems frequently encountered in the study of DNA is concerned with depositing the material onto specimen-support films. Spraying techniques that produce pools or aggregates of DNA with radially projecting strands have been described by Hall (1956). Some reduction in the size of the aggregates can be achieved by subjecting the solution to treatment with ultra-sound prior to spraying.

The experiments described by Beer (1961), Beer and Zobel (1961) and Thomas and Berns (1961) have shown that their preparative procedures gave the best indication of spreading of the DNA by streaking the films across the grid surface. The direction of the streaking was noted, and the excess DNA drained from the grid in the same direction Long strands were observed without undue aggregation taking place on the specimen-support surface. It should be mentioned that the DNA in these experiments was obtained from T4 bacteriophage and suspended in 0.1 M phosphate buffer. The suspensions were dialyzed against a number of volatile and nonvolatile buffers for periods of several hours before being mounted for electron microscopy. Kleinschmidt and Zahn (1959) have also given details of methods for spreading solutions of DNA for examination in the electron microscope. Their method was to mix the DNA solution with protein in approximate ratios of 1 : 10 to 1 : 100 and spread the mixtures on the water surface of a Langmuir trough. The effect was to produce a protein monolayer, together with the DNA. The monolayer was compressed by hand to an approximate pressure of 0.6–1.0 dyne/cm, and the layer was picked up on specimen-support films and examined in the electron microscope.

There are a number of heavy metal stains capable of increasing the contrast in strands of DNA, including salts of uranium, lanthanum, lead, thorium, thallium, and silver in aqueous solutions. Stoeckenius (1961) has pointed out that most of these stains are somewhat erratic in their staining properties, since many preparations failed to improve the contrast in DNA strands. The same grids when shadowed clearly indicated the presence of nucleic acid.

The precise mechanism of positive staining is not fully understood and requires further study to enable some of the techniques in present use to be more reproducible. In a detailed study on the electron densitometry of stained virus particles, Hall (1955) investigated the relative amounts of different stains absorbed over a wide pH range by bushy stunt virus. These quantitative studies have indicated how the size and density of a given virus particle may vary depending on the type of stain or fixative used. Hall has also pointed out that analysis by visual inspection is often very misleading, as the appearance to the eye is dependent on a variety of factors, including photography, exposure, specimen thickness, and the amount of stain taken up. It was suggested that in the case of bushy stunt virus, efficient staining conditions took place at low pH values, which were likely to be disruptive.

The author has found that many virus particles examined in the electron microscope following positive staining often appear totally dense. Consequently, any small detail within the particle or surface structure is often obscured by the scattering of electrons from the densely stained area. Moreover, not all viruses will react with positive stains even after prolonged treatment.

VII. The Application of Negative Staining Techniques to the Study of Virus Structure

A. INTRODUCTION

Methods for surrounding or embedding the specimen in a suitable stain have been known in light microscopy for over 75 years. Such techniques were found particularly useful in attempts to resolve the surface detail and fine appendages of bacteria and other microorganisms by outlining them with India ink and other opaque materials. The effects of surrounding small particles were observed by Hall (1955) when describing several anomalous images in the electron microscope following a series of quantitative studies on stained virus particles. Hall remarked that although the effect was opposite to that required for electron stains, the visibility of particles of low scattering power could be enhanced by surrounding them rather than impregnating them with dense material. Similar observations were reported by Huxley (1957) on the structure of tobacco mosaic virus (TMV) rods and fragments. The electron-dense staining procedure was similar to that described by Hall (1955), and the central region in TMV was revealed together with their external shape. There have been several reports of "reversed" images in the electron microscope. For instance, Farrant (1954) when studying specimens containing ferritin molecules also observed similar anomalous contrast effects.

The extensive studies on the structure of T-even bacteriophages and their components by Brenner et al. (1959) using a wide variety of chemical and physical methods clearly required a technique suitable for electron microscopy that would enable a large number of samples to be examined rapidly. Most of the standard preparative procedures when applied to their phage studies, which included freeze-drying, shadowing, positive staining, and thin sections, imposed limitations in one form or another. For these reasons the negative staining method described by Horne and Brenner (1960) and Brenner and Horne (1959) was intended as a routine procedure for the rapid examination of virus particles at very high resolution. This same method was subsequently applied to a wide variety of biological objects other than viruses, and has been reviewed in detail elsewhere (Horne, 1965a,b).

B. Comparison of Image Contrast between Positive and Negative Staining

The enhancement of contrast in small particles by positive staining involves reacting a suitable electron stain with the material to be examined. Contrast observed in the final image will depend on the number of electrons scattered from the stained particles in depth and the amount of stain taken up. In the diagram shown in Fig. 15A, electrons are being scattered from the particle, with relatively few electrons being scattered over wide angles from the surrounding area or supporting film. Contrast in the final image can be further increased by inserting physical apertures in the objective lens (25–30 μ in diameter), which prevent the widely scattered electrons from contributing to the image.

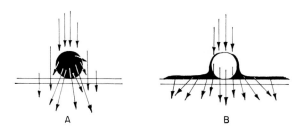

Fig. 15. (A) The spherical object shows electrons being scattered from the dense region corresponding to positive staining. (B) In the case of negative staining the scattering occurs from the electron-dense areas surrounding the specimen, resulting in a reversal of the contrast seen in the electron microscope.

For electron optical reasons there is a lower limit for the diameter of the objective contrast aperture, which is imposed by diffraction effects. Moreover, apertures with a diameter of 25 μ are difficult to clean and are more likely to limit the resolution by introducing astigmatism in the image due to carbonaceous deposits building up on the surface from the illuminating beam.

In the case of negative staining, the contrast seen on the final image is reversed when compared with the positive staining method. The number of widely scattered electrons is considerably increased, as illustrated in Fig. 15B. Virus particles are embedded in a "glass" of amorphous electron-dense material, and the specimen appears as a relatively electron-transparent particle surrounded by a dense region. From experiments on the effect of inserting various sizes of objective aperture, the author has observed that there is little advantage to be gained in employing objective apertures with diameters below 50 μ.

The gain in contrast is negligible when smaller diameter apertures are used. Astigmatic errors can be considerably reduced when using larger apertures of 50–70 μ in diameter with a consequent gain in resolving power.

At this point we might consider the anomalous contrast effects observed by Meyerhoff and Müller (1965) in preparations containing polystyrene latex particles lying free and others embedded in phosphotungstate acting as a negative stain. They reported the anomalous result of the marked increase in the brightness of the embedded particles. The difference between the densities of the free-lying particles and those measured in the presence of negative stain was calculated to be about 20%. Removal of the negative stain by washing reduced the brightness of the particles to the level of those unstained. Similar observations were made on some inorganic crystals.

Meyerhoff and Müller have suggested that these anomalous contrast effects could result from the regions containing the negative stain charging up to sufficient electrostatic values to cause the stain to act as a microlens. They also indicated that the success of the negative staining procedure might result from microlens effects occurring within the beam at local sites. Whether or not this form of anomalous contrast is attributable to charging effects resulting in the formation of microlenses remains to be seen. Further studies by Ferrier and Murray (1966) at the Cavendish Laboratory in Cambridge, England, using low-angle electron-diffraction techniques applied to negative staining may produce more general information about the mechanism of contrast associated with this technique. Normally, supporting films of high electrical and thermal conductivity are essential to ensure that these anomalous effects are kept to a minimum.

C. CONDITIONS FOR NEGATIVE STAINING

An essential requirement for negative staining is that the reaction of the stain with the specimen be kept to a minimum. The effect of a given negative stain on the viability of viruses or microorganisms in suspension should be observed. A negative stain found suitable for one type of virus or specimen may be quite unsuitable for another, and optimum conditions for preservation in liquid suspension, drying, contrast, and mounting should be established. During a series of investigations on the application of negative staining to biological structure, the author has observed that the structural features presented in a given object frequently depend on the stain used and the staining conditions employed. Penetration of different electron-dense materials at different pH values also influences the amount of information made available from the specimen at the molecular level.

In an earlier publication Valentine and Horne (1962) assessed the properties of a number of electron-dense materials of high solubility that were considered to be suitable for use as negative stains. More recently a number of additional materials of high molecular weight have been applied with success when mixed with certain specimens. Table III lists the negative stains that are in general use, most of which have been found to produce reasonable contrast and preservation. Certain sensitive specimens show evidence of disruption at the

TABLE III
NEGATIVE STAINS

Type of stain[a]	Concentration	pH Range
Potassium phosphotungstate	1–2%	6.5–8.0
Sodium tungstate	1–2%	6.5–8.0
Ammonium molybdate	2–3%	6.0–8.0
Tungstoborate	1–2%	6.0–7.0
Lithium tungstate	1–3%	6.5–8.0
Lanthanum acetate	1–2%	5.0–7.0
Uranyl acetate	0.5–1%	4.5–5.2
Uranyl acetate–EDTA	0.5–1%	4.5–7.0
Uranyl formate	0.5–1%	4.5–5.2

[a] There are a number of heavy metal stains other than those listed above, but the granulation effects observed on drying limit their application to high-resolution electron microscopy.

molecular level in the presence of some negative stains. Electrostatic charge effects, for instance, produced by the potassium phosphotungstate polyanion adsorbing to the surface of cation groups may result in sufficient charge to cause local disruption of membranes.

If negative staining is to be successful when applied to high-resolution studies of virus particles, it is essential for both the electron-dense stain and the specimen material to spread as a more or less uniform layer over the grid surface. The spreading properties of the mixtures will depend on a number of variables. The concentration and volume of a negative stain in relation to the concentration, size, shape, and molecular weight of the particles will affect the spreading properties of a given preparation. Suspensions containing a relatively large amount of negative stain and low concentrations of particulate material will often result in the formation of large electron-dense globular pools, as shown in Fig. 16A. Virus particles or their components will

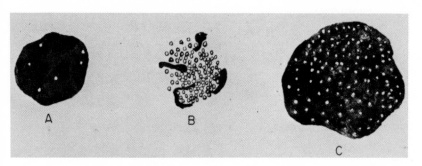

FIG. 16. (A) Large dense areas of negative stain with few particles visible as a result of poor spreading of the specimen on the film. (B) Poor spreading may also result when the particle concentration or volume is far in excess of the amount of negative stain. (C) An even distribution of particles and density of negative stain should be visible from preparations deposited by spraying or from droplets.

appear deeply embedded in the negative stain or completely obscured. Droplets containing too much protein or particles in proportion to the amount of negative stain tend to dry in the form of large aggregates or are poorly distributed and badly preserved (Fig. 16B). Under ideal spreading conditions the droplets should appear as shown in Fig. 16C, with good particle separation and free from effects caused by thick layers of electron-dense material.

Apart from the poor definition as well as the possible collapse of viruses mentioned above, errors in estimating their size, shape, and volume may result from poor spreading conditions. Although it is not always possible, it is preferable to make mixtures with high concentrations of virus particles either for spraying or droplet preparation. The concentration of particles in the virus suspension can be reduced or adjusted to the volume and concentration of the negative stain selected. Good spreading of the mixture of negative stain and virus is largely a matter of trial and error, but phage or other particles of about 1000 Å across in suspensions containing about 10^9–10^{12} particles/ml can be mixed with an equal volume of negative stain for spraying directly onto prepared grids. With lower concentrations of virus it is preferable to deposit mixtures by pipet or platinum loop methods. Most of the difficulties encountered with spreading and negative stains have been associated with very small components or low molecular weight material. In high concentrations these often remain aggregated in solution or following drying down. Dilution may not be advantageous, owing to mere separation of the existing aggregated particles. Bovine serum albumen, on the other hand, when used in concentrations of about 0.005–0.05% can be mixed with some preparations to assist with the spreading of droplets.

The plastic or carbon substrates themselves may seriously limit the amount of spreading during final preparation. It is recommended that films be freshly made when they are to be used for negative staining techniques. Carbon films that have been exposed to the atmosphere for more than a day or so appear to change their surface charge considerably, a factor that will seriously affect spreading.

Virus suspensions must also be free from material or buffers possessing components that will form small crystallites during drying on the grids. Buffering conditions must be taken into consideration when suspensions are prepared for negative staining. Volatile buffers, including 2% ammonium acetate or 2% ammonium carbonate, have been used with a number of virus suspensions. Suitable virus preparations should be dialyzed against either these buffers or glass-distilled water before negative stains are added. Many viruses and viral components are prepared from density gradients containing sucrose, which presents special problems for negative staining. Low concentrations of sucrose or similar media can be tolerated in the preparation if suitable precautions are taken (Horne and Whittaker, 1962; Whittaker, 1963). Under the appropriate conditions of particle size, negative stain, and sucrose concentration, good preservation together with detail from subcellular fractions were observed in the electron microscope. A final concentration of about 0.08–0.1 M sucrose after mixing with the negative stain was found to be optimum. Interference from residual amounts of sucrose was seen to be limited to the centers of droplets, and areas on or near the droplet edges were more suitable for photography.

D. Interpretation of the Image from Negatively Stained Preparations

The precise way in which the specimen is embedded in a given negative stain is not fully understood, and until a number of points concerning preservation, penetration, and contrast, as well as reactions of various negative stains with the specimen, are clarified, it is not possible at this stage to make any hard or fast rules regarding the interpretation of the image. There are pertinent questions relating to whether one or both sides of a virus particle are presented at a given time in the electron micrographs. The appearance of the particle may depend on a variety of conditions associated with spreading and penetration of a given type of negative stain. During their studies on the structure of orf virus, Nagington et al. (1964) applied a wide variety of negative stains to virus preparations together with stereo techniques in attempts to observe their different penetrating properties. Some of the structural features revealed in the presence of potassium phosphotungstate indicated that both the upper and lower surfaces of orf virus were being presented simultaneously (Fig. 17A). The same material treated with ammonium molybdate produced images in which only one side of the particle was visible (Fig. 17B).

The considerable changes in the appearance of structural features of biological structure following negative staining have been carefully studied by Horne *et al.* (1967). These authors have selected the well-characterized collagen protein and observed the mode of aggregation to form fibrils in the electron microscope (Grant *et al.*, 1965). Different structural features and components can be enhanced by different negative stains adjusted to a range of pH values. It is becoming increasingly clear from these and other studies that it is essential to apply a variety of negative stains to a given specimen to ensure that all of the morphological information can be obtained from the electron micrographs. The appearance of viruses and macromolecules in negatively stained preparations may depend on the proportion of the polypeptide chain present in the α-helical form. In a personal communication, Dr. A. J. Rowe has suggested that many compact molecules are not penetrated by negative stains, and only an outline of the particle is revealed. Some proteins, on the other hand, may become deeply penetrated by electron-dense material, which may enhance more of the internal detail within the molecule.

E. The Application of Stereo Methods to Negatively Stained Objects

Stereoscopic methods have proved to be of value in assisting with the interpretation of electron micrographs. The normal method used for obtaining stereo pairs of electron micrographs is to allow the specimen to be tilted between the first and second electron micrographs. For most practical purposes the tilting devices fitted to conventional microscopes are arranged to tilt the specimen through an angle of about 8°. For many of the problems in which stereo pairs have been shown to be of use relatively low instrumental magnifications have been employed. But in the case of high-magnification stereo tilting, where the specimen is frequently thin, certain problems can arise. Very small changes in stage movement during actual operation of the stereo drive will often result in the movement of the selected particles out of the field of view on the final screen. There is a relationship between the

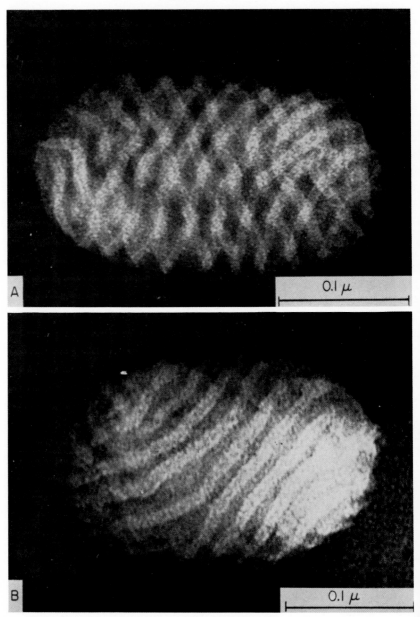

Fig. 17. (A) The particle of orf virus was prepared for electron microscopy by negative staining using potassium phosphotungstate. Both the upper and lower surfaces are presented in the electron micrograph. (B) The same virus preparation as shown in (A), but prepared in the presence of ammonium molybdate. Only one side of the particle is visible and demonstrates that the crisscross pattern in (A) results from the superimposition of both the upper and lower surfaces.

height of the object and the angle through which it must be tilted. Consequently, it is not always possible to judge from visual inspection of the final screen the correct tilt angles to be employed. Experiments to determine the optimum parallactic displacement can be carried out by tilting the specimen from side to side, but severe contamination of the object by carbonaceous deposits during such long exposure to the beam must be considered during this process.

Owing to the rotational component in the magnetic electron lens, a certain amount of distortion will be introduced into the stereo image compared with light optical systems. This distortion will tend to increase with the depth of the specimen and to some extent with the strength of the magnetic field. The evaluation of stereo electron micrographs and the determination of the third dimension of objects visualized in the electron microscope have been discussed in detail by Helmcke (1954, 1955, 1965).

Interpretation of the surface lattices of certain icosahedral viruses is often difficult unless positions of the relevant rotational symmetry axes can be accurately determined. The current papilloma–polyoma "controversy" is an example illustrating some of the problems in constructing three-dimensional models from electron micrographs. Capsids arranged in an icosahedral skew lattice can exist in certain viruses with a left-handed pattern or in a right-handed pattern in other viruses. These patterns have been discussed by Horne and Wildy (1961), Caspar and Klug (1962, 1963), and by Finch and Holmes in this volume. Stereo methods have proved to be of extreme value in the attempts to determine the absolute hand of papilloma viruses (Finch and Klug, 1965). For these experiments large tilt angles were necessary, with the cartridge employed being capable of tilting over angles of 20°–45° (Valdrè, 1962). From the stereo electron micrographs it was concluded that when only one side of the papilloma virus particle was presented in the image it was the side located nearest the substrate. The results also indicated a certain amount of flattening of the papilloma virus particles within the negative stain. It is clear that wide-angle stereo techniques applied to electron microscopy may well form an essential procedure when attempting to interpret certain structural features recorded in electron micrographs of negatively stained preparations.

F. NEGATIVE STAINING OF SUBCELLULAR COMPONENTS FROM VIRUS-INFECTED CELLS

The advances in methods for the separation of a large number of subcellular components and cell organelles have enabled detailed morphological studies of these structures to be made possible. Particulate fractions from tissue homogenates can be examined in the electron microscope following preparation by either positive or negative staining procedures (cf. Gray and Whittaker, 1960; Horne and Whittaker, 1962; Whittaker, 1963). There are a number of problems encountered in studying the structure of subcellular components by conventional histological methods. The main problem is that the large number of fractions requiring morphological identification and control during one experiment presents a difficult and time-consuming task. These factors are of particular practical importance when studies are planned in the form of growth-cycle experiments, where cell homogenates have to be fractioned at known time intervals following virus infection.

Modification of the original procedures described by Gray and Whittaker (1960), Horne and Whittaker (1962), and Whittaker (1963) may be necessary for different tissues or cell cultures. Many subcellular components are likely to be disrupted in the presence of some negative stains owing to hypotonic damage. It follows from this that some form of fixation may be necessary before the subcellular components can be mixed with negative stains. Both formaldehyde and osmium have been used with some success as fixatives prior to negative staining. Osmium in concentrations of about 0.1–0.5% in 0.32 M sucrose for a few minutes will act as a suitable fixative without undue loss of contrast owing to positive staining. The partially fixed suspension when mixed with a negative stain is then deposited by loop or pipet onto the filmed grids and allowed to dry.

A simple method enabling fragments and subcellular components to be examined from bulk tissue has been described by Parsons (1962, 1963). A fine needle was inserted into the selected tissue area, which removed a number of cells on extraction. The needle was then carefully lowered onto the surface of a solution of 2% potassium phosphotungstate adjusted to pH 6.0–7.0, which was placed in a hollow microscope slide. This process was observed under the low-power microscope to follow the spreading of the cells. Careful removal of the needle allowed the detached cells to spread slowly at the liquid surface, and these cells were picked up on carbon-coated plastic filmed grids. The grids were lowered film downward on the selected areas. The excess liquid was removed with a filter paper after an interval of 1 or 2 minutes. After allowing for a suitable drying period, the specimens were examined directly in the electron microscope.

An alternative procedure for studying cells and cell fragments that enables frozen sections to be negatively stained has been used successfully by Almeida and Howatson (1963). The technique was originally applied to the study of subcellular particles by Fernandez-Moran

(1962a), but can be used to observe cell-associated virus during growth-cycle experiments.

Infected cells were sampled at suitable intervals during the growth cycle after virus infection. About 10^6–10^7 cells were sedimented at low speeds for a period of about 5 minutes to form a pellet. Nutrient Medicon was used to resuspend the pellet in a volume of about 0.5 ml previously diluted with glass-distilled water. After transferring the suspension to a Parafilm mold corresponding to the size of a No. 00 gelatin capsule, the material was then rapidly frozen at —20°C. Frozen sections from the Parafilm mold were cut on a freezing microtome at —20°C. It was essential for the sections to be cut as thin as possible, and a certain amount of skill and practice were required at a microtome setting of 4 μ. Thin sections were collected on a depression slide and thawed at room temperature. Thawed cell fragments were mixed with a suitable negative stain (KPT) and droplets of the mixture were placed on filmed grids. Spreading conditions have to be established largely by trial and error, since thick specimens frequently result and should be avoided. This technique has been applied to observations on cells containing both nuclear and cytoplasmic viruses. The structural features of adenovirus, herpes, polyoma, SV40, vaccinia, and others have been resolved in detail. In spite of the presence of some cell debris, capsomeres and other features were clearly recorded.

In a series of experiments on the development and structure of poliovirus, Horne and Nagington (1959) examined fragments of cells infected with virus. At regular intervals following inoculation HeLa cells were harvested during the growth cycle for up to 7 hours and centrifuged at 1000 rpm for 3–4 minutes. The supernatant was discarded and the pellets were immediately frozen to —20°C in an alcohol bath. For the preparation of specimens for electron microscopy, frozen pellets were thawed at 37°C and suspended in 4% aqueous ammonium acetate to give an approximate concentration of 5×10^7 cells/ml. For spraying purposes it was necessary to use the apparatus shown in Fig. 8, to avoid contamination of the atmosphere. It was emphasized that poliovirus was not inactivated when mixed with a solution of 3% KPT at pH 6.2 used as a negative stain. It was observed that if higher pH values were used in the negative staining process, the spraying mixture of virus and stain became highly viscous, possibly owing to hypotonic disruption of cell material. Special precautions were used in transferring sprayed grids to and from the electron microscope specimen chamber.

These experiments clearly demonstrated that partially assembled or complete virus particles could be observed at various intervals during the growth cycle, but identification of the various cytoplasmic bodies could not be established by the use of this technique.

G. BACTERIAL VIRUSES, BACTERIA, AND BACTERIAL COMPONENTS

The basic problems posed by morphological studies on bacteria and bacterial viruses can be considered as follows: (1) thin sections of bacteria infected with virus (see Chapter 12 in this volume); (2) high-resolution studies on isolated phages and their components; and (3) the interaction between phages and bacterial hosts together with structural alterations in both observed at the macromolecular level. It was shown by Brenner et al. (1959) that a wealth of information could be seen in negatively stained preparations of T-even phages. Furthermore, the negative staining technique enabled electron microscopy and the complex methods employed for separating phage components to be brought much closer together.

Potassium phosphotungstate was used as a negative stain in the original experiments on intact and "triggered" phages, producing high contrast and good preservation (Fig. 18). Suspensions of T-even phages were found to retain their infectivity after being mixed with an equal volume of 2% KPT adjusted to pH 7.0. These viability experiments suggested that there was little interaction between the negative stain and phage protein in aqueous suspension. Structural changes caused by drying down artifacts or induced intentionally by chemical treatment were easily detected. Moreover, it was possible to carry out rapid monitoring of the purity and separation stages of the phage components during ultracentrifugation and chemical analysis. It is more than sufficient to mention that these phage studies in parallel with negative staining and electron microscopy indicated the importance of relating morphological features to data derived from other physicochemical procedures.

In recent years negative staining methods have been applied to a wide range of bacterial viruses with a view to establishing their morphological characteristics (cf. Bradley and Kay, 1960; Horne and Wildy, 1963; Eiserling and Romig, 1962; Daems et al., 1961; Fernandez-Moran, 1962b; Tromans and Horne, 1961; Anderson, 1961; Brinley-Morgan et al., 1960; Dawson et al., 1962; Bradley, 1965b; and others). The interaction between bacterial viruses and their hosts can be observed to a limited extent directly in the electron microscope. Droplets of washed bacteria can be placed on a filmed grid, followed by the addition of a further drop of phage (Thornley and Horne, 1962). After allowing a suitable interval for adsorption to take place, the excess liquid is drained from the grid and a further droplet containing a suitable negative stain is added and mixed on the film. The draining of excess negative stain is repeated as before and the preparation is left to dry. Bacteria with phages attached to their surfaces can be seen and photographed at high magnifications. The ratio of phage particles to bacteria should be determined by experiment to avoid the presence of an excess of unadsorbed phage in the background.

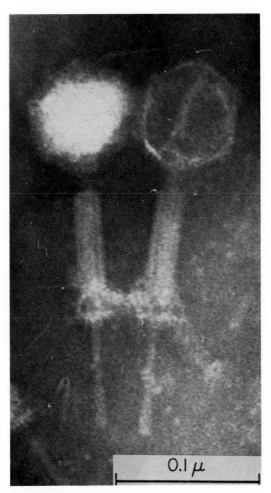

FIG. 18. The electron micrograph shows two phage particles prepared by the negative staining procedure. Structural features of the tail components and head are well defined, but contraction of the tail sheath appears to have occurred following mixing with the negative stain. The particle on the left shows the head filled with nucleic acid, whereas the particle on the right has released its nucleic acid, which has been replaced by the electron-dense material.

Samples obtained from bacterial cell walls or wall fragments with ad
sorbed phages are also informative when prepared under suitable condi
tions. The methods for isolating and purifying bacterial cell wall
have been reviewed in detail by Salton (1964). Cell walls or envelop
fragments can be mixed with negative stains as described above an
examined in the electron microscope. The electron micrograph show
in Fig. 19 shows particles of T-even phages adsorbed and "triggered
on the surface of a cell envelope fragment. Both the contraction an
penetration of the tail components can be seen in detail.

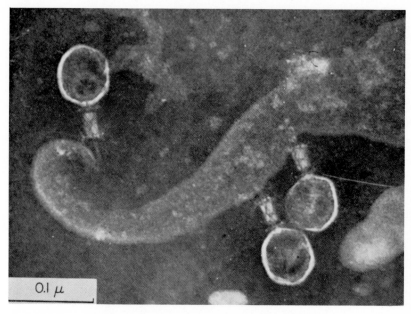

Fig. 19. Phage particles are seen attached to the surface of a fragment of cel
envelope material. The method of preparation is described in the text.

Experiments on visualization of the injection mechanism of phag
with the aid of the electron microscope have been less successful. This
owes largely to the techniques available and is also associated with the
poor results observed in preparations of negatively stained strands o
DNA. The specific adsorption of phage to the flagella of motile *Salmonella typhi* described by Meynell (1961a,b) suggested a possible system
to observe directly the transfer of nucleic acid from phage to host. A
number of attempts were made to establish suitable conditions fo
negative staining (Horne and Meynell, unpublished data), but the problem of identification of the nucleic acid within the phage tail an

agellum presented special difficulties. Negative staining of the attach-
nent of the phage particles to flagella of the motile organisms was
arried out as described earlier for intact bacteria. The adsorption on
almonella phage is shown in the electron micrograph in Fig. 20. Posi-
ive staining of the phage nucleic acid revealed its presence in the head
egions and partially extending through the phage tail. Unfortunately,
onsiderable disruption of the flagellin protein occurred at the low pH

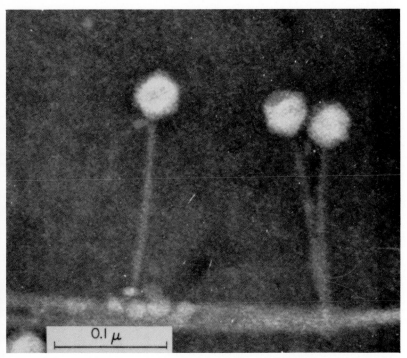

FIG. 20. The electron micrograph was obtained from a preparation of *Salmonella*
yphi phage, which is associated with motile cells. Phages are clearly seen attached to
portion of the bacterial flagellum. (Negatively stained preparation.)

alues used for positive staining with uranyl acetate. Further work on
he combination of negative staining and fixation with agents such as
lutaraldehyde followed by positive staining may well enable studies of
his type to produce valuable information.

H. ANIMAL AND PLANT VIRUSES

The ability of the original negative staining method to reveal struc-
ure in electron micrographs of T-even phages at the macromolecular

level encouraged the extension of the technique to the study of a wide range of animal and plant viruses. The methods for the preparation of animal and plant viruses are essentially similar to those used for the phage experiments. For details of the results obtained relating to the different types of virus particles and their morphological characteristics the reader is referred to the review publications of Horne and Wildy (1961, 1963), Valentine (1962), Horne (1962), Valentine and Horne (1962), Wildy and Horne (1963), and Caspar and Klug (1963)

The methods in current use for the examination of animal and plant viruses with the aid of negative staining methods can be considered under four main headings:

1. Intact and purified preparations of virus particles
2. Development of virus particles in cell fragments
3. Studies on the interaction of virus with host-cell cytoplasmic material
4. Direct observations on the interaction of antibody molecules with virus particles and their components.

Some of the techniques applied to experiments designed to examine cell fragments were discussed in Section VII,D.

In practice it is not difficult to mount suspensions containing isolated plant or animal viruses when mixed with negative stains. For good results it is essential that the suspensions contain sufficient numbers of particles. This is not always possible, and it presents a major difficulty in the study of the morphology of some new viruses that are difficult to grow in tissue culture. Spraying methods are only successful if the suspensions contain 10^7 or more particles/ml. With lower concentrations droplet mounts must be made according to the methods described earlier.

A number of experiments with the aid of the electron microscope have indicated that it is possible to observe the interaction of virus particles with host-cell material. From their studies on the agglutination of allantoic membranes by influenza virus, Hoyle et al. (1962) were able to show that disruption of the virus occurred rapidly. Chorio-allantoic membranes were removed from 14-day-old eggs and suspended in saline, followed by an incubation period for 2 hours at 37°C. The suspensions were then centrifuged at low speed for 10 minutes and finally at 25,000 g for 1 hour. Final pellets were resuspended in 1% ammonium acetate, and samples were checked for purity in the electron microscope. Mixing virus and cytoplasmic material together resulted in a rapid agglutination of virus and cell material. Agglutination was observed to disappear 2–3 minutes after mixing. These effects were studied by spraying the mixed components over a period of several minutes

n the presence of a negative stain (2% KPT at pH 6.8). Electron mi-
rographs indicated that there was mutual disruption of the viral and cell
components.

The initial association between vaccinia and adenovirus type 7 was
described by Dales (1962). Whole mounts were made from infected
tissue culture cells swollen under controlled conditions and subjected
to a short fixation in 2% osmium tetroxide solution prior to mixing with
potassium phosphotungstate. Examination of these preparations at
about 2 hours after inoculation with high virus multiplicities revealed
virus particles in close association with the surfaces of the host cells or
enveloped within the membranes.

These two examples of the initial association between virus and host-
cell material illustrate the type of experiment that can be carried out
by the application of negative staining methods to electron microscopy. Similar experiments by the use of thin sections would be difficult
and time consuming, but it must be emphasized that both techniques
are capable of contributing valuable information to this type of study.

A recent procedure for obtaining viral material from crude extracts
of plant material has been described by Hitchborn and Hills (1967).
The experiments consisted of two methods for examining extracts of
plants infected with turnip yellow mosaic virus, broad bean mottle virus, and potato X virus. Sap material was expressed from macerated
infected leaves and centrifuged at low speed directly or following heat
treatment at 55°C for 15 minutes or after the material had been frozen
for 2 hours at −10°C and thawed. Supernatant material was found to
be too dense for electron microscope preparations, and dilution by
about 10 times was necessary. An equal volume of the diluted sap was
added to a drop of 2% potassium phosphotungstate at pH 6.5 previously
placed on a filmed grid. The drops were then mixed by removing them
with a fine pipet and finally depositing a small droplet of the liquid onto
the film surface. Excess material was drained with the aid of a filter
paper, and the grid was immediately examined in the electron
microscope.

The second method was a modification of the "dip" technique previously described by Brandes (1957, 1964). A small piece of plant epider-
mis was peeled from the under surface. The torn surface was allowed
to make contact with a small droplet of stain placed on a filmed grid by
drawing the grid over the selected area. Excess stain was drained as
before, and specimens were transferred directly to the microscope.

These simple methods enabled large numbers of virus particles to be
made visible in the electron micrographs (Fig. 21). The methods are
not only simple but they eliminate to some extent the possibility of

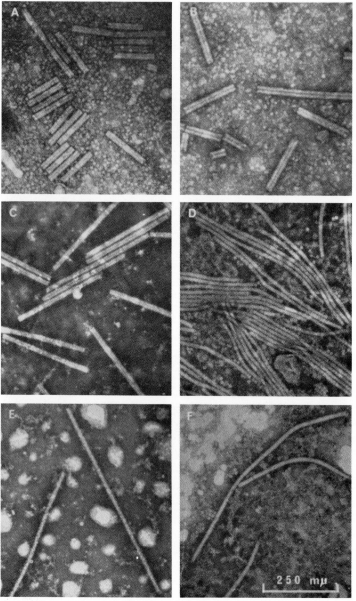

FIG. 21. Electron micrograph of negatively stained crude extracts from plants infected with (A) barley stripe mosaic virus; (B) tobacco rattle virus; (C) tobacco mosaic virus; (D) potato virus X; (E) potato virus M; and (F) tobacco severe etch virus. (By kind permission of Hitchborn and Hills, 1967.)

filamentous particles becoming disrupted during centrifugation at high speeds. This is of importance when investigating size and length distributions in viruses.

I. INTERACTION OF ANTIBODY WITH VIRUS ANTIGENS OBSERVED IN THE ELECTRON MICROSCOPE WITH THE AID OF NEGATIVE STAINING

The electron microscope can play an important role in allowing direct observations to be made on the interaction of antibody molecules with virus particles or viral antigens. Some of the more recent results have shown that considerable detail can be resolved in electron micrographs of suitably prepared specimens containing antibody and viruses in the presence of negative stains (cf. Anderson, 1962; Hummler et al., 1962; Almeida et al., 1963; Lafferty and Oertelis, 1963; Watson and Wildy, 1963; Feinstein and Rowe, 1965; Valentine and Pereira, 1965).

Owing to the fact that the molecular weights of antibody molecules and viral antigens are relatively low compared with the intact virus, very high-resolution electron microscopy is essential for this type of investigation (Feinstein and Rowe, 1965). Some of the methods employed in the preparation of virus and antisera are described in detail in the publications mentioned above. There are no special techniques required for mounting specimens in the presence of negative stains, but different types of negative stains may be required for certain virus particles. Hummler et al. (1962) prepared their specimens by preincubating virus and antibody in agglutination tubes and then placing small drops of the mixed components on carbon-coated grids by means of a small platinum loop. The droplet was immediately washed with glass-distilled water, and a further drop of KPT (2%) containing 0.2% sucrose was added to act as a negative stain. Any excess fluid was removed slowly by applying a pointed piece of filter paper to the edge of the drop. Specimens were then transferred immediately to the electron microscope. Agglutination of virus particles by rabbit serum could be observed directly in the electron microscope.

Similar negative staining procedures were used by Almeida et al. (1963) in their examination of antigen–antibody complexes of verruca and polyoma viruses. In order to estimate the concentration of virus particles, mixtures were made with known concentrations of 880 Å diameter Dow latex spheres, and determinations were made by the method of Pinteric and Taylor (1962). The quantity of virus was kept constant by the addition of saline buffer. Mixtures of antigen–antibody complexes were kept for 1 hour at 37°C and stored for several hours at

2°C. They were then centrifuged at 2000 rpm at 2°C and finally washed twice in phosphate saline equal in volume to the original antigen–antibody mixture. A small volume of distilled water (0.1 ml) was used to suspend the washed pellets. Potassium phosphotungstate at a concentration of 3% adjusted to pH 6.0 with potassium hydroxide was used as a negative stain. The mixture was placed on carbon–Formvar-coated grids in the form of small drops. Excess fluid was drained as described earlier, and the specimens were examined in the electron microscope.

In a detailed series of studies of virus–antibody complexes Lafferty and Oertelis (1963) obtained high-resolution electron micrographs of antibody molecules attached to the surface of influenza virus (Fig. 22). Pellets from virus–antibody complexes after centrifugation at 100,-

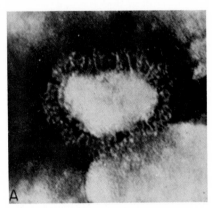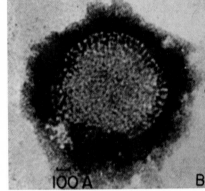

FIG. 22. (A) The electron micrograph shows a particle of influenza virus with antibody molecules associated with the surface projections following the interaction of antibody with virus material. (B) Normal untreated influenza virus showing well-defined surface projections. (By kind permission of Lafferty and Oertelis, 1963.)

000 g for 30 minutes were resuspended in 0.15 M sodium chloride. The centrifugation was repeated and the pellets resuspended in distilled water followed by a further stage of centrifugation. Suspensions for electron microscopy were resuspended in a volume equal to half the volume used in the original mixture containing virus–antibody complexes. Mixtures of virus and antibody were placed in an equal volume of 1% sodium phosphotungstate and stored overnight at room temperature. Droplets of negatively stained material were placed on grids as described earlier.

At low concentrations of antibody, two-site attachments of the molecules were seen in the electron micrographs. Two-site attachment was indicated by the "bridging" of two of the surface spikes on influenza virus by one antibody molecule. Particles showing saturation of the viral surface revealed antibody attached through both active sites of the molecule (Fig. 22A and B).

Experiments to determine whether or not the envelopes of herpes simplex virus possess a common antigen with the capsid have been described by Watson and Wildy (1963). It was possible to demonstrate that the envelope consists almost entirely of host-cell material and that the capsid has different antigenic components.

The application of the electron microscope to the study of virus architecture at the molecular level has been most elegantly demonstrated by Valentine and Pereira (1965) in their study of the antigens and structure of adenovirus. Combined experiments resulting from the use of electron microscopy and immunology enabled the three antigens associated with adenovirus type 5 to be identified. Fractions containing purified antigen A were deposited from a small platinum loop onto grids coated with nitrocellulose films stabilized with evaporated carbon. The grids containing the droplets were then placed face downward to make contact with the surface of an aqueous solution containing 4% sodium silicotungstate (Wilcox et al., 1963). Examination of the grids in the electron microscope revealed particles of 80 Å and approximately spherical in shape. The molecular weight of these spherical particles was calculated to be about 210,000.

The antigen B when prepared for electron microscopy by the use of the same method appeared as a structure possessing three components in the form of a round head identical to antigen A, a rodlike tail of 200 Å long and 20 Å wide, with the third component of 40 Å in diameter attached to its base (Figs. 23–25). The molecular weight of the intact antigen B was estimated to be about 280,000. Antigen C appeared as the rodlike component of up to 200 × 20 Å, with the spherical structure at one end of 40 Å in diameter. Antigen B was observed to be less stable than the other antigens. Storage for long periods or digestion with trypsin resulted in the particles dissociating into a form identical to antigen C (Fig. 24). The experiments have confirmed the need to establish optimum conditions for the mounting and negative staining of small, sensitive viral components. This is further emphasized by the identification and location of the antigens on the intact virions. Under suitable staining conditions a number of the virus particles contained in the droplets were seen to possess projections from the capsid at points of 5-fold symmetry. These projections were identified as antigen B, and it was determined that antigen A forms the major part of the capsid being distributed on the faces and at the edges (Fig. 25).

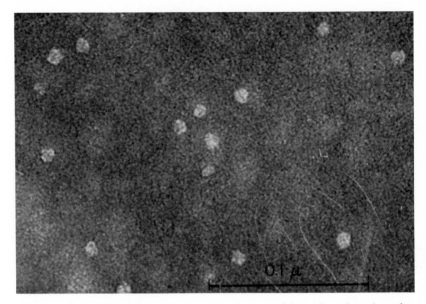

Fig. 23. Electron micrograph of a preparation containing adenovirus A antigen. (By kind permission of Valentine and Pereira, 1965.)

VIII. Particle Counting

It is possible with the aid of the electron microscope to design experiments that will enable virus particles to be counted within certain limits of accuracy. Williams and Backus (1949) and Kellenberger and Arber (1957) have described methods in which latex spheres in known concentration are mixed with virus suspensions in known proportions and deposited onto specimen grids. Small droplets from a spray gun containing the mixed suspensions were shadowed and examined in the electron microscope. At suitable magnifications the complete droplet areas were photographed and the ratio of latex to virus particles estimated to give a virus particle count (Williams and Backus, 1949). An alternative technique employing filtration procedures has been used by Kellenberger and Arber (1957). Mixtures of latex spheres and virus were passed through suitable collodion filters that were finally transferred to grids. The grids were examined in the electron microscope to determine the ratios of latex to virus within a given area.

One of the difficulties frequently associated with particle counts is concerned with estimating the approximate volumes of the droplets. Very small uniform droplets deposited from a carefully designed micropipet system were obtained by Sugar (1957). The pressure necessary to

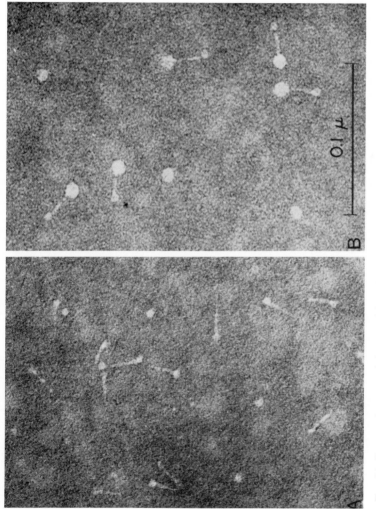

FIG. 24. Preparation containing particles of antigen B together with antigen C. (By kind permission of Valentine and Pereira, 1965.)

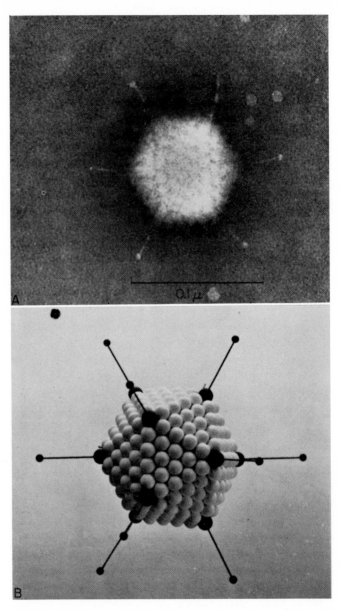

Fig. 25. (A) A high-resolution electron micrograph showing the typical features of shape and symmetry associated with adenovirus particles. Rodlike structures can be seen extending from the apexes of the icosahedral capsid and are associated with the B antigen. (B) A model constructed to show the symmetry of the adenovirus capsid and the positions of the three antigens. The white spheres represent the distribution of the A antigen on the faces and edges of the triangular facets of the capsid. The large black spheres illustrate the position of the B antigen on the axes of 5-fold rotational symmetry. The rodlike structures represent the C antigen extending from the capsid surface. (By kind permission of Valentine and Pereira, 1965.)

force liquid through extremely fine bore pipets was controlled from hydraulic heads. Optimum results giving droplet patterns of 10 μ in diameter were obtained when the pipet system was placed in a moist chamber controlled at a suitable temperature. A more convenient device for the production of droplet samples has been designed and used by Harris (1964). The apparatus is a modification of a system described by Wolf (1961), in which it was demonstrated that small droplets could be produced from a vibrating needle. There are several advantages to be gained from the device described by Harris (1964): (1) only a very small volume of virus suspension is required for operation (0.005 cm^3); (2) droplets of uniform size measuring about 2–10 μ in diameter can be produced by changing the dimensions of the vibrating needle; (3) small droplets can be photographed at high magnification, thus enabling more accurate particle counts to be made. For practical details concerning the vibrating needle apparatus the reader is referred to the publication of Harris (1964).

In a series of studies on particle counts by direct sedimentation experiments, Sharp (1949, 1960, 1965), Sharp and Beard (1952), and Sharp and Overman (1958) have described methods for quantitative analysis of virus particles present in crude extracts and purified suspensions. Virus particles were sedimented onto collodion films or collodion films prepared in the presence of gelatin to improve attachment of certain particles to the film. A small magnet embedded in a plastic holder was placed in the centrifuge tubes to retain the stainless-steel specimen-support grids. The sedimentation speeds and time were dependent to some extent on the size of the virus particles. Particles were counted per unit area (mean) directly from the electron micrographs.

In many of the methods in which the specimen must be air dried and then shadowed, particles tend to collapse or form aggregates. Moreover, it is not always possible to distinguish the particles consisting of intact viruses containing nucleic acid from "empty" capsids. In addition, there is the presence of cell debris that frequently falls within the size range of many virions and may be included in the particle counts.

The identification, preservation, and distribution of virus particles can be more positively determined when particle counts are made in the presence of negative stains (Watson, 1962; Watson et al., 1963). These authors have shown that particle counting applied to viruses can be put on a more quantitative basis because a number of the difficulties mentioned above were considerably reduced in the presence of negative stains. The experiments have shown that the methods used by Watson and his colleagues are particularly useful in the determination of particle-infectivity ratios and in relating the morphological features of virions with infectivity.

It is not possible within the scope of this article to describe all of the various methods in present use for particle counting, nor is it possible to discuss the merits for analysis associated with the techniques. The advantages and disadvantages of the more important approaches to counting viruses have been described in detail by contributors to "Quantitative Electron Microscopy" (see Bahr and Zeitler, 1965).

IX. Calibration of the Electron Microscope

A. Introduction

For many of the applications of electron microscopy to biological problems the magnification accuracy is sufficient when the calibration is within a tolerance of about 10%. In those studies where it is necessary to relate the physical dimensions of particulate material to molecular weights determined by other methods, a more accurate determination of the statistical variation of magnification of a given electron microscope becomes essential. Ideally, the tolerance should be within about 1%, but in practice many of the standard production instruments fall far short of this value. Variations in magnification can be attributed to gradual changes in the accelerating voltage, changes in lens focal length owing to variations in coil current or thermal drift, hysteresis, and position of the specimen in the objective plane (cf. Reisner, 1965).

B. External Reference

In a careful investigation of the methods required to determine the magnification in the electron microscope, Elbers and Pieters (1964) have described an accurate procedure to give a tolerance of better than 1%. They followed the original method of Hall (1953), which enabled them to calculate the sources of error and their contributing amounts. According to Elbers and Pieters (1964), the most serious source of error originated from variations in the position of specimen along the objective lens axis. With the aid of replicas obtained from diffraction gratings containing 28,800 lines to the inch, a calibration or correction curve was plotted to give percentage variations of magnification of the objective lens system as a function of the object plane position. Any changes in the position of the specimen could be estimated from the objective lens potentiometer settings either above or below the calibrated focal plane. For the reasons mentioned earlier, it was also necessary to arrange for an external compensator device that was capable of monitoring the lens current and high tension. The insertion of a sensitive milliammeter in the objective lens supply circuit was not accurate enough for the very small variations encountered, and thus a circuit with a precision potentiometer and galvanometer was required. Details concerning the technical requirements for constructing a suitable compensator for the Siemens Elmiskop I have been described by Elbers and Pieters (1964).

C. INTERNAL REFERENCE

The application of accurately ruled cross gratings for determination of magnification and image distortion have recently been described by Bahr and Zeitler (1965). In their experiments a form of all-metal replica of two optical gratings ruled at 2160 lines/mm was used as a reference material. These particular cross-ruled gratings were described as the most accurate produced to date. Moreover, this type of grating was capable of allowing more accurate estimates of the projector lens distortion across the final image to be made over a wide range of magnifications (i.e., $\times$ 5000–40,000). Variations in magnification across the final image result from distortion in the projector lens systems of certain microscopes and can reach values as high as 2–3%. Projector distortion should be taken into consideration when wide-range magnification calibration is attempted, and it may vary from one type of instrument to another.

For many experiments it is sufficient to mix a standard internal reference material with the virus suspension to be examined. Small quantities of Dow latex spheres of about 880 Å in diameter can be mixed with the specimen or alternatively sprayed onto the grids after the virus suspension has dried. The number of spheres should be sufficiently distributed to allow only a few to be photographed within a given field. Statistical variations in the sizes of latex spheres as well as instrumental factors must be taken into consideration when measurments are made. Calibration of the electron microscope at high magnification requires special mention, since the reference material must be sufficiently small and more accurate. Microdensitometer recordings of shadowed specimens photographed at magnifications above $\times$ 40,000 show that it is difficult to indicate the precise beginning or ending of the shadowed zones. Platinum phthalocyanine crystals have been carefully characterized by x-ray diffraction and electron microscopy (Menter, 1956). These small crystals were used by Markham et al. (1964) as an internal magnification standard during their studies on the structure of plant viruses. In certain orientations of the crystals the spacings of the lattice planes have been resolved, showing a distance of 12 Å. There are two problems that may be encountered when using platinum phthalocyanine crystals for magnification calibration. One is associated with the possibility that lattice spacings will change during irradiation with the electron beam. High-intensity illuminating beams should be avoided; they make focusing and lattice orientation difficult. The second problem is insuring that sufficiently thin crystals are contained within the area to be photographed.

Ferritin molecules have been well characterized by the methods of x-ray diffraction, chemical analysis, and electron microscopy. The protein shell of the molecule has an estimated mean diameter of 105 Å in the dehydrated form. Measurements of the distances between the iron micelles have shown them to be about 50–70 Å. These small molecules are not difficult to detect in the electron microscope and can be mixed with certain specimens to act as an internal magnification standard.

D. Photographic Errors

It is common practice to make measurements from photographic prints of electron micrographs. This requires accurate calibration of the photographic enlarger, as small variations are likely to be introduced by wear of mechanical parts of the instrument. Stretching or shrinking of photographic papers during the processing is also a contributing factor, according to the experiments carried out by Markham *et al.* (1964).

X. *Conclusion*

In recent years remarkable progress has been made in the electron microscopy of viruses. Rapid development in instrumental design coupled with new preparative techniques have demonstrated that it is possible to observe structural features of viruses at the macromolecular level. Virions appear to belong to a remarkable family of geometrical shapes, some with extraordinary architectural complexity. Much of this information has resulted from the work on isolated particles involving careful analysis of the electron micrographs in relation to data derived from x-ray diffraction and biochemical studies. But how the virion transfers its nucleic acid to the host cell and what constitutes the remarkable series of events that follows initial infection are questions that require much more investigation. The assembly of capsids, nucleocapsids from structure units, and capsomeres within infected cells poses morphological problems of considerable importance.

From recent experiments relating to the details visible in biological objects observed in the electron microscope at the molecular level, it is clear that contamination of the specimen by deposits of carbon coupled with image-phase contrast effects are imposing a serious limitation (Horne et al., 1967). If the morphological details relating structure to function at the molecular level are to be determined with the aid of the electron microscope, some improvements in specimen decontamination and support films will have to be forthcoming.

REFERENCES

Almeida, J. D., and Howatson, A. F. (1963). J. Cell Biol. 16, 616.
Almeida, J. D., Cinader, B., and Howatson, A. F. (1963). J. Extl. Med. 118, 327.
Anderson, T. F. (1961). Proc. 2nd Reg. Conf. (Eur.) Electron Microscopy, Delft, 1960 p. 1008. Almquist & Wiksell, Uppsala.
Anderson, T. F. (1962). Symp. Intern. Soc. Cell Biol. 1, 251.
Backus, R. C., and Williams, R. C. (1949). J. Am. Chem. Soc. 71, 4052.
Backus, R. C., and Williams, R. C. (1950). J. Appl. Phys. 21, 11.
Bahr, G. F., and Zeitler, E. H., eds. (1965). "Quantitative Electron Microscopy." Williams & Wilkins, Baltimore, Maryland.
Beer, M. (1961). J. Mol. Biol. 3, 263.
Beer, M., and Zobel, C. R. (1961). J. Mol. Biol. 3, 717.
Bradley, D. E. (1954). Brit. J. Appl. Phys. 5, 65.
Bradley, D. E. (1965a). In "Techniques for Electron Microscopy" (D. Kay, ed.), 2nd ed., p. 58. Blackwell, Oxford.
Bradley, D. E. (1965b). J. Roy. Microscop. Soc. [3] 84, 257.
Bradley, D. E., and Kay, D. (1960). J. Gen. Microbiol. 23, 553.
Brandes, J. (1957). Mitt. Biol. Boundesanstalt Land- Forstwirtsch., Berlin-Dahlem 9, 151.
Brandes, J. (1964). Mitt. Biol. Bundesanstalt Land- Forstwirtsch., Berlin-Dahlem 110, 130.
Brenner, S., and Horne, R. W. (1959). Biochim. Biophys. Acta 34, 103.
Brenner, S., Streisinger, G., Horne, R. W., Campe, S. P., Barnett, L., Benzier, S., and Rees, M. W. (1959). J. Mol. Biol. 1, 281.
Brinley-Morgan, W. J., Kay, D., and Bradley, D. E. (1960). Nature 188, 74.
Caspar, D. L. D., and Klug, A. (1962). Cold Spring Harbor Symp. Quant. Biol. 27, 1.
Caspar, D. L. D., and Klug, A. (1963). In "Viruses, Nucleicacids, and Cancer," p. 27. Williams & Wilkins, Baltimore, Maryland.
Cosslett, V. E. (1955). In "Physical Techniques in Biological Research" (G. Oster and A. W. Tollister, eds.), Vol. 1, p. 461. Academic Press, New York.
Cosslett, V. E., and Horne, R. W. (1955). Vacuum 5, 109.
Daems, W. T., Van De Pol, J. H., and Cohen, J. A. (1961). J. Mol. Biol. 3, 225.
Dales, S. (1962). J. Cell Biol. 13, 303.
Dawson, I. M., Smillie, E., and Norris, J. R. (1962). J. Gen. Microbiol. 28, 517.
Dowell, W. C. T. (1963). Optik 20, 535.

Eiserling, F. A., and Romig, W. R. (1962). *J. Ultrastruct. Res.* **6**, 540.
Elbers, P. F., and Pieters, J. (1964). *J. Ultrastruct. Res.* **11**, 25.
Farrant, J. L. (1954). *Biochim. Biophys. Acta* **13**, 569.
Feinstein, A., and Rowe, A. J. (1965). *Nature* **205**, 147.
Fernandez-Moran, H. A. (1962a). *Res. Nervous Mental Disease Proc.* **40**, 235.
Fernandez-Moran, H. A. (1962b). *Symp. Intern. Soc. Cell Biol.* **1**, 414.
Ferrier, R., and Murray, R. (1966). *J. Roy. Microscop. Soc.* **85**, 323.
Finch, J. T., and Klug, A. (1965). *J. Mol. Biol.* **13**, 1.
Glaser, W. (1941). *Z. Physik* **117**, 285.
Grant, R. A., Horne, R. W., and Cox, R. W. (1965). *Nature* **207**, 822.
Gray, E. G., and Whittaker, V. P. (1960). *J. Physiol. (London)* **153**, 35.
Hall, C. E. (1955). *J. Biophys. Biochem. Cytol.* **1**, 1.
Hall, C. E. (1956). *J. Biophys. Biochem. Cytol.* **2**, 625.
Hall, C. E. (1953). "Introduction to Electron Microscopy." McGraw-Hill, New York.
Harris, W. J. (1962). *Nature* **196**, 499.
Harris, W. J. (1964). *J. Sci. Instr.* **41**, 636.
Heide, H. G. (1965). *In* "Quantitative Electron Microscopy" (G. F. Bahr and E. H.
    Zeitler, eds.), p. 402. Williams & Wilkins, Baltimore, Maryland.
Helmcke, J. G. (1954). *Optik* **11**, 201.
Helmcke, J. G. (1955). *Optik* **12**, 253.
Helmcke, J. G. (1965). *In* "Quantitative Electron Microscopy" (G. F. Bahr and
    E. H. Zeitler, eds.), p. 201. Williams & Wilkins, Baltimore, Maryland.
Hitchborn, J. H., and Hills, G. J. (1965). *Virology* **27**, 528.
Horne, R. W. (1962). *Ann. N.Y. Acad. Sci.* **101**, 475.
Horne, R. W. (1965a). *In* "Techniques for Electron Microscopy" (D. Kay, ed.),
    2nd ed., p. 328. Blackwell, Oxford.
Horne, R. W. (1965b). *In* "Quantitative Electron Microscopy" (G. F. Bahr and
    E. H. Zeitler, eds.), p. 316. Williams & Wilkins, Baltimore, Maryland.
Horne, R. W., and Brenner, S. (1960). *Proc. 4th Intern. Conf. Electron Microscopy,*
    Berlin, 1958 Vol. 2, p. 625. Springer, Berlin.
Horne, R. W., and Meynell, E. Unpublished observations.
Horne, R. W., and Nagington, J. (1959). *J. Mol. Biol.* **1**, 333.
Horne, R. W., and Whittaker, V. P. (1962). *Z. Zellforsch. Mikroscop. Anat.* **58**, 1.
Horne, R. W., and Wildy, P. (1961). *Virology* **15**, 348.
Horne, R. W., and Wildy, P. (1963). *Advan. Virus Res.* **10**, 101.
Horne, R. W., Cox, R. W., and Grant, R. A. (1967). *J. Roy. Microscop. Soc.* **87**,
    123.
Hoyle, L., Horne, R. W., and Waterson, A. P. (1962). *Virology* **17**, 533.
Hummler, K., Anderson, T. F., and Brown, R. A. (1962). *Virology* **16**, 87.
Huxley, H. E. (1957). *Proc. Reg. Conf. (Eur.) Electron Microscopy, Stockholm,*
    1956 p. 260. Academic Press, New York.
Huxley, H. E., and Zubay, G. (1960). *J. Mol. Biol.* **2**, 10.
Huxley, H. E., and Zubay, G. (1961). *J. Biophys. Biochem. Cytol.* **11**, 273.
Kellenberger, E., and Arber, W. (1957). *Virology* **3**, 245.
Kleinschmidt, A. K., and Zahn, R. K. (1959). *Z. Naturforsch.* **14b**, 770.
Komoda, T., and Otsuki, M. (1964). *Japan. J. Appl. Phys.* **3**, 666.
Lafferty, K. J., and Oertelis, S. J. (1963). *Virology* **21**, 91.
Markham, R., Hitchborn, J. H., Hills, G. J., and Frey, S. (1964). *Virology* **22**, 342.
Matthews, R. E. F., Horne, R. W., and Green, E. M. (1957). *Proc. Reg. Conf.*
    (Eur.) Electron Microscopy, Stockholm, 1956 p. 261, Academic Press, New York.

Menter, J. W. (1956). *Proc. Roy. Soc.* **A236,** 119.
Meyerhoff, K. H., and Müller, G. (1965). *In* "Quantitative Electron Microscopy" (G. F. Bahr and E. H. Zeitler, eds.), p. 342. Williams & Wilkins, Baltimore, Maryland.
Meynell, E. (1961a). *Nature* **190,** 564.
Meynell, E. (1961b). *J. Gen. Microbiol.* **25,** 253.
Nagington, J., Newton, A. A., and Horne, R. W. (1964). *Virology* **23,** 461.
Parsons, D. F. (1962). *Proc. 5th Intern. Conf. Electron Microscopy, Philadelphia, 1962* Vol. II, Art. X1. Academic Press, New York.
Parsons, D. F. (1963). *J. Cell Biol.* **16,** 620.
Pinteric, L., and Taylor, J. (1962). *Virology* **18,** 359.
Preuss, L. E. (1965). *In* "Quantitative Electron Microscopy" (G. F. Bahr and E. H. Zeitler, eds.), p. 181. Williams & Wilkins, Baltimore, Maryland.
Price, W. C., and Wyckoff. R. W. G. (1946). *Nature* **157,** 764.
Reisner, J. R. (1965). *In* "Quantitative Electron Microscopy" (G. F. Bahr and E. H. Zeitler, eds.), p. 137. Williams & Wilkins, Baltimore, Maryland.
Riecke, W. D. (1962). *Optik* **19,** 81.
Ruska, E. (1962). *Proc. 5th Intern. Conf. Electron Microscopy, Philadelphia, 1962* Vol. I, Art. A1. Academic Press, New York.
Ruska, E. (1965). *J. Roy. Microscop. Soc.* [3] **84,** 77.
Salton, M. R. J. (1964). "The Bacterial Cell Wall." Elsevier, Amsterdam.
Sharp, D. G. (1949). *Proc. Soc. Exptl. Biol. Med.* **70,** 54.
Sharp, D. G. (1960). *Proc. 4th Intern. Conf. Electron Microscopy, Berlin, 1958* Vol. II, p. 542. Springer, Berlin.
Sharp D. G. (1965). *In* "Quantitative Electron Microscopy" (G. F. Bahr and E. H. Zeitler, eds.), p. 93. Williams & Wilkins, Baltimore, Maryland.
Sharp, D. G., and Beard, J. W. (1952). *Proc. Soc. Exptl. Biol. Med.* **81,** 75.
Sharp, D. G., and Overman, J. R. (1958). *Proc. Soc. Exptl. Biol. Med.* **99,** 409.
Stoeckenius, W. (1961). *J. Biophys. Biochem. Cytol.* **11,** 297.
Sugar, I. (1957). *Proc. Reg. Conf. (Eur.) Electron Microscopy, Stockholm, 1956* p. 127. Academic Press, New York.
Thomas, C. A., and Berns, K. I. (1961). *J. Mol. Biol.* **3,** 717.
Thon, F. (1964). *Proc. 3rd Reg. Conf. (Eur.) Electron Microscopy, Prague, 1964* Vol. A, p. 127. Czech. Acad. Sci., Prague.
Thornley, M., and Horne, R. W. (1962). *J. Gen. Microbiol.* **28,** 51.
Towe, K. M. (1965). *Rev. Sci. Instr.* **36,** 1247.
Tromans, W. J., and Horne, R. W. (1961). *Virology* **15,** 1.
Valdrè, U. (1962). *J. Sci. Instr.* **39,** 278.
Valentine, R. C. (1960). *Proc. 4th Intern. Conf. Electron Microscopy, Berlin, 1958* Vol. 2, p. 577. Springer, Berlin.
Valentine, R. C. (1962). *Advan. Virus Res.* **8,** 287.
Valentine, R. C., and Horne, R. W. (1962). *Symp. Intern. Soc. Cell Biol.* **1,** 263.
Valentine, R. C., and Pereira, H. G. (1965). *J. Mol. Biol.* **13,** 13.
Watson, D. H. (1962). *Biochim. Biophys. Acta* **61,** 321.
Watson, D. H., and Wildy, P. (1963). *Virology* **21,** 100.
Watson, D. H., Russell, W. C., and Wildy, P. (1963). *Virology* **19,** 250.
Whittaker, V. P. (1963). *Biochem. Soc. Symp. (Cambridge, Engl.)* **23,** 109.
Wilcox, W. C., Ginsberg, H. S., and Anderson, T. F. (1963). *J. Exptl. Med.* **118,** 307.
Wildy, P., and Horne, R. W. (1963). *Progr. Med. Virol.* **5,** 1.
Williams, R. C. (1953). *Exptl. Cell Res.* **4,** 188.

Williams, R. C., and Backus, R. C. (1949). *J. Appl. Phys.* **20**, 98.
Williams, R. C., and Smith, K. M. (1958). *Biochim. Biophys. Acta* **28**, 464.
Williams, R. C., and Wyckoff, R. W. G. (1944). *J. Appl. Phys.* **15**, 712.
Williams, R. C., and Wyckoff, R. W. G. (1946). *J. Appl. Phys.* **17**, 23.
Wolf, W. R. (1961). *Rev. Sci. Instr.* **32**, 1124.
Wyckoff, R. W. G. (1946). *Science* **104**, 36.

12 *The Application of Thin Sectioning*

C. Morgan and H. M. Rose

I. Introduction

The advantage provided by thin sectioning of fixed and embedded tissue is the opportunity to observe the morphologic responses of the host cell and to study viral differentiation at sequential stages of infection. The disadvantage is difficulty in acquiring sufficient data. The challenge is to correlate structure with function. Obviously, one must integrate, in so far as it is possible, the information gained by the examination of thin sections with results achieved by the use of other techniques, such as chemical analysis, negative staining, and x-ray diffraction.

There are several excellent books on the preparation of cells and tissues for electron microscopy. These are worth citing, because in general methods best suited for the preservation of cellular fine structure are also the most useful for study of viral structure. Perhaps the most complete, concise, and up-to-date is "Histological Techniques for Electron Microscopy" by Pease (1964). This book also contains a list of sources for chemicals and equipment. An excellent, detailed description of thin sectioning with brief but clear accounts of fixation, embedding, and ancillary techniques is provided by the second edition of "Thin Sectioning," published by Ivan Sorvall, Inc., Norwalk, Connecticut. (One should not be put off by its pardonable emphasis on the Sorvall microtome.) A very short (76 pages) but useful manual is "Electron Microscopy" by Mercer and Birbeck (1961). Kay's "Techniques for Electron Microscopy" (1961), besides chapters on preparation of biological specimens, has an excellent, simple description of the electron microscope by Agar. Siegel's "Modern Development in Electron Microscopy" (1964) is notable for a chapter on ultramicrotomy by a master of the art, Keith Porter. A recent Symposium (Quantitative Electron Microscopy) has been published as a supplement to *Laboratory Investigation*, Volume 14, pp. 733–1340, June, 1965. While many of the papers are highly technical and few have to do with thin sectioning *per se,* the symposium provides an excellent review of current problems related to microscopy and to various types of specimen preparation.

With such information readily available, it would seem unnecessary for this chapter to deal in detail with the numerous methods and variations on methods that have been reported. Rather an attempt will be made to select those techniques that have proved to be reliable and of general use in the study of intracellular virus. One is encouraged in this undertaking by the impression that after a decade of rapid and often revolutionary changes a stage has been reached at which only minor modifications in methodology are currently appearing.

II. History

The first electron microscope to be manufactured for commercial use was that of Siemens in 1939. Production, however, was interrupted by the war. Two years later RCA developed a microscope (Zworykin *et al.,* 1941) that was produced commercially in 1944 as the EMU 2 series. For a decade this instrument set the standard for electron microscopy.

The first biological preparation to be examined was a fragment of a plant root in 1934 (Marton, 1934), while the first virus observed was tobacco mosaic virus in 1939 (Kausche *et al.,* 1939). Despite advances in resolution, improvements in viral purification, and the remarkable increase in definition provided by shadow casting (Williams and Wyckoff, 1946), it became evident that if information were to be obtained regarding the way in which viruses develop and how they effect cells some method must be devised that would permit visualization of viruses within their host cells. Porter *et al.* (1945) reported an ingenious technique whereby tissue culture cells were grown on Formvar. The Formvar with attached cells was subsequently transferred to specimen grids. After fixation it was possible to see through the thin, peripheral portions of the cell, and in this way intracellular virus (the mammary tumor agent) was first observed (Porter and Thompson, 1948).

For some time attempts had been made to section cells.* As far back as 1939, von Ardenne had reported a method of cutting wedge-shaped sections such that the margin, just before the steel knife ceased to cut, was penetrable to the electron beam. O'Brien and McKinley

---

* The reader is referred to Gettner and Ornstein (1955) for a complete review of this subject.

(1943) and Fullam and Gessler (1946) attempted to adapt centrifuges into high speed microtomes. An important practical advance was provided by Pease and Baker (1948), who inserted a wedge into the conventional Spencer microtome thus reducing the increment of advance. Another significant step was the adoption of a thermoplastic substance (methacrylate) as an embedding medium (Newman et al., 1949). Using a modified Spencer microtome equipped with steel knives to cut sections of methacrylate-embedded tissue, it was possible to demonstrate tobacco mosaic virus (Black et al., 1950) and fowlpox virus (Morgan and Wyckoff, 1950) within the cytoplasm of infected cells. Owing in part to the fact that there was no bypass mechanism, the sections were so thick that, before viewing the specimen, the methacrylate had to be dissolved with consequent distortion of cellular architecture. (It is a tribute to the stability of these viruses that under such circumstances they were not only recognizable but reasonably well preserved.)

At this point, with the attention of so many scientists directed toward the necessity of obtaining suitably thin sections, advances came rapidly. The bypass principle, wherein the specimen returned to the cutting position without passing the knife edge, was pioneered by Claude (1948) and adopted with various modifications by Gettner and Ornstein (1953), Porter and Blum (1953), Sjöstrand (1953), and others. With the construction of the trough or boat (Claude, 1948), the use of knives made from fractured glass (Latta and Hartmann, 1950), and the development of a simple and practical microtome (Porter and Blum, 1953) that was soon produced commercially, thin sectioning became generally practicable.

Before the technique could provide much significant information, however, one further problem—that of fixation—remained to be solved. Traditional fixatives for light microscopy, such as Formalin, failed not only to stain significant details of structure, but also failed to stabilize certain cellular and viral components to the impact of the electron beam (Morgan et al., 1956a). It remained for Palade (1952) in a classic paper to investigate the use of osmium tetroxide (OsO_4) as a preservative of fine structure. Although originally introduced by Schultze in 1864, Strangeways and Canti (1927) were the first to observe in detail, by means of dark field microscopy, the lifelike appearance of cells fixed by this reagent, while Porter et al. (1945) were the first to employ it on whole-cell mounts for electron microscopy. It was Palade (1952), however, using the technique of thin sectioning, who systematically explored the effects of buffers on the preservation of fine structure afforded by osmium tetroxide. He concluded that "1 per cent OsO_4 buffered at pH 7.3–7.5 with acetate–veronal buffer is recommended as an appropriate fixation for electron microscopy."[*] Not only was it appropriate, but is has remained the basic fixative, against which all others must be judged, to the present time.

By use of the foregoing techniques, Gaylord and Melnick (1953) initially described internal viral structure in thin sections. Subsequently, reports appeared that, in a preliminary way at least, showed stages in the development of viruses (Morgan *et al.*, 1954a,b, 1956b).

III. Fixation

It is quite impossible to list precise rules of fixation. An instance of the variable way in which fixatives can act is provided by study of the nuclear material in bacteria. After fixation in osmium tetroxide alone this material consists of fine, parallel filaments (Kellenberger *et al.*, 1958), whereas if glutaraldehyde, followed by osmium tetroxide, is used it exhibits coarse, dense, branched filaments (Morgan *et al.*, 1966). One might be inclined to say that the former fixative is better, but the latter is admirable for mammalian cell nuclei and can be shown to preserve bacteriophage membranes within bacteria far better than does osmium tetroxide (Margaretten *et al.*, 1966).

Even when the choice of a fixative has been made, the precise manner of buffering and the duration of the process of fixation are difficult to evaluate. In most laboratories, including the authors', certain procedures are used simply because they work. This is not to say that other methods may not be better, but it does say that a time comes during the long, tedious, and perplexing problem of evaluation when the investigator almost arbitrarily standardizes his techniques in order to obtain sufficient information for the problem under investigation.

Certain general statements can be made about methods of fixation, but in the last analysis each investigator must determine which of them is most suitable for the particular virus and cell system under investigation.

A. FORMALIN

Formalin is used chiefly for the preparation of viruses for enzyme digestion studies (Bernhard and Tournier, 1962), for histochemical staining (de Thé *et al.*, 1963), or for the application of labeled anti-

---

[*] For a more recent study of the effects of different types of buffers on osmium tetroxide fixation the reader is referred to Wood and Luft (1965).

bodies (Morgan *et al.*, 1962). Under these cirumstances, when it is necessary to maintain chemical or antigenic activity, optimal fixation must be sacrificed. As mentioned previously, the chief deficiencies of Formalin are lack of staining and failure to stabilize viral structure under the impact of the electron beam. It should be emphasized, however, that if the conditions of the experiment permit postfixation in osmium tetroxide before dehydration and embedding, remarkably good preservation can be achieved.

The authors generally use 4% formaldehyde (10% Formalin) in Sorenson's phosphate buffer (pH 7.2) with 0.33 M sucrose. To this is added 10^{-2} M $MgCl_2$.

Sorenson's Phosphate Buffer

Solution A: 6.9 gm   of NaH_2PO_4 + 500 ml   of H_2O
Solution B: 7.09 gm   of Na_2HPO_4 + 500 ml   of H_2O
Mix 20 ml of solution A with 80 ml of solution B.

The duration of fixation is 30–60 minutes. If necessary, shorter fixation of tissue culture cells in monolayers can be employed.

B. ACROLEIN

Mayor and Jordan (1963) have investigated the use of this reagent in preserving the antigenicity of SV40, reovirus, poliovirus, and adenovirus. On the basis of their fluorescence microscopy results, they reported that acrolein is superior both to Formalin and glutaraldehyde. However, Dales *et al.* (1965) in a study of reovirus found quite the reverse, namely, that acrolein was inferior and "left only a very faint reactivity."

C. POTASSIUM PERMANGANATE

With improvements in embedding and staining of sections, this fixative is seldom used at present. As in the case of Formalin, it has been employed for histochemical studies (Epstein, 1962a,b; Epstein and Holt, 1958). The method described by Luft (1956) is generally followed. The striking contrast of cytoplasmic membranes, which he noted, probably results from "unmasking" and staining of the phospholipoproteins (Bradbury and Meek, 1960). In studies of herpes simplex virus fixed in potassium permanganate, Epstein (1962b) reported that the outer limiting membrane was a triple-layered structure. The significance of this is not entirely clear.

Postfixation in osmium tetroxide greatly improves preservation. It is also possible to fix the sections in OsO_4 fumes before examination.*

Luft's (1956) Permanganate Fixative

Buffer

Sodium veronal	14.7 gm
Sodium acetate	9.7 gm
Water	500 ml

To this is added an equal volume of 1.2% potassium permanganate and the pH is adjusted to 7.4.

The suggested duration of fixation is 20–30 minutes.

D. Chrome-Osmium

Dalton (1955) in a brief abstract described a fixative composed of $K_2Cr_2O_7$ with KOH, OsO_4, and NaCl. Use of this reagent seems to show adequate preservation of virus and host cell (Dalton et al., 1961, 1964; Shalla, 1964), although the specific advantage it offers is somewhat obscure. Since the authors have had no personal experience with this fixative, they are not qualified to discuss it.

E. Osmium Tetroxide

This is a basic fixative in electron microscopy. Bahr (1954) in an extraordinarily thorough study examined the reaction of OsO_4 with 280 compounds ranging from histidine and glycogen to peanut oil and penicillin. Reasoning that OsO_4 stains tissue by virtue of a reduction reaction that results in the deposition of osmium, he mixed the substances to be tested with 0.01 M OsO_4 in a test tube and recorded the degree of blackening. He found a strong reaction with sulfhydryl groups and double bonds such that unsaturated lipids and proteins were stained, whereas saturated hydrocarbons and carbohydrates were not. A striking observation was the "inertness" of nucleic acids. Bahr himself commented that "the results are derived from reactions under relatively well-known in vitro conditions and cannot be transferred directly to a cellular system." Whether or not this is the explanation, it is difficult to imagine that the densely stained core of viral particles so frequently

---

* The use of OsO_4 fumes has not received the attention it deserves. Sections on carbon-coated Formvar grids are merely placed in a closed container with OsO_4 crystals. The contamination, which may result from immersion of the sections in a solution, is thus avoided.

encountered is not in considerable part at least composed of nucleic acid. The digestion of the core of reovirus with ribonuclease and of adenovirus with deoxyribonuclease (Bernhard and Tournier, 1962), as well as the removal of the core of herpes simplex virus with deoxyribonuclease (Epstein, 1962b), would tend to support this assumption. Moreover, studies (Rosenkranz et al., 1966) on vaccinia virus reveal that an effect of hydroxyurea, which blocks DNA synthesis, is to prevent the formation of the dense eccentrically located material, originally called the necleoid, of the immature form of the virus (Morgan et al., 1954b). It should be evident from the foregoing remarks that the effect of OsO_4 on nucleic acids and nucleoproteins needs further investigation. Stoeckinius and Mahr (1965) by quantitative determination of the reaction of OsO_4 with a variety of fatty acids and phospholipids reported that in most cases 1 gram-atom of osmium is bound per mole of $C=C$ double bond of the starting material. Similar studies have also been carried out on the reaction of OsO_4 and $KMnO_4$ with amino acids, peptides, and proteins (Hake, 1965).

A number of different buffers have been proposed. The one suggested by Millonig (1961) is currently used in the authors' laboratory and has been found to give consistently satisfactory results.

Solution A:	2.26%	$NaH_2PO_4 \cdot H_2O$
Solution B:	2.52%	NaOH
Solution C:	5.4%	Glucose
Solution D:	41.5 ml	Solution A
	8.5 ml	Solution B

Fix in 45 ml of solution D, to which is added 5 ml of solution C and 0.5 gm of OsO_4 crystals. The pH should be 7.2. Store in a lightproof bottle.

The length of fixation approximates 30 minutes. Prolonged fixation results in extraction of cellular components and consequent distortion of fine structure.

F. GLUTARALDEHYDE

In a careful, comparative study of several aldehyde fixatives, Sabatini et al. (1963, 1964) suggested that glutaraldehyde was particularly effective. Useful as a fixative for histochemical studies (Epstein and Holt, 1963; de Thé, 1964; Dales and Kajioka, 1964; Dawson et al., 1965), it is more widely employed as an adjunct to OsO_4. The latter alone, with proper handling and a bit of luck, is difficult to surpass, but glutaraldehyde followed by OsO_4 is consistently so good that this combination must be rated as the best general method of fixation currently available. An increasing number of papers attest to the value of this double fixation in revealing new or hitherto poorly visualized components of cell structure. The method has not been tried on a sufficient variety of viruses to assess its efficacy with certainty, but initial studies of vaccinia virus (Dale and Kajioka, 1964; Kajioka et al., 1964), reovirus (Dales et al., 1965), tobacco mosaic virus (Kolehmainen et al., 1965), adenovirus (Morgan, 1967), parainfluenza virus (Howe et al., 1967), and bacteriophage (Margaretten et al., 1967) indicate that it has great promise. A practical advantage of using glutaraldehyde is that the fixed tissue, after thorough washing, can be left overnight, or even longer, without appreciable extraction or distortion of fine structure. OsO_4 is then applied just before dehydration and embedding. No other fixative allows this latitude of procedure.

There is one cardinal rule to remember, namely, that thorough washing is necessary before fixation in OsO_4. Excess residues of glutaraldehyde apparently prevent binding of osmium. Shortcuts in this part of the procedure have caused more than one investigator to set glutaraldehyde aside as a second-rate fixative.

The standard procedure in our laboratory is as follows: The glutaraldehyde as purchased comes at a concentration of 25%. This is diluted to 3% in distilled water. One part of this solution is added to 2 parts of Sorenson's buffer (see Section III,A) making a final concentration of 1% at pH 7.2–7.5.

The period of fixation for mammalian cells is generally 1 hour.

For fixing bacteria, 200 mg of $MgCl_2$ is added per 100 ml and the pH is adjusted to 6.1 with HCl. The period of fixation is 3 hours.

If osmium tetroxide (Section III,E) is to be used for postfixation, the cells are washed and then can be fixed either immediately or after storage in the refrigerator.

There are a number of reports on the advantage of carrying out the entire fixation procedure at 4°C. With respect to viral structure and the general preservation of cell detail, the authors are not convinced that much is to be gained by this modification.

IV. Embedding

The number of plastics currently available makes the problem of evaluating them rather difficult. The writers have largely employed epoxy resin (Epon 812) for the past few years. Tests of other plastics strongly recommended by eager proponents have resulted in less satisfactory preservation. Preservation, of course, is hard to define and frequently comes down to a general impression, for whatever that may be worth.

At this point it cannot be emphasized too strongly that each embedding medium is slightly different and requires facility in handling. To evaluate properly a variety of embedding plastics it is necessary to use them with care and attention for several weeks or even months. This the writers have not done.

Inspection of published micrographs suggests that Epon 812 (Finck, 1960) is the peer of any of the plastics now employed. Its two most serious drawbacks are shared to a greater or lesser extent by all current embedding media. First, different lots of the plastic seem to vary slightly in quality. Second, difficulty in cutting makes the use of diamond knives essential if there is need for the steady production of large numbers of sections, and, unfortunately, good diamond knives are not easy to obtain.

A. METHACRYLATE

This embedding plastic, so long the standby of electron microscopists, is now largely of historical interest. Polymerization "explosions" combined with sublimation and flow under the electron beam render it virtually useless. It should not be forgotten, however, that methacrylates are soluble and therefore, when necessary, they can be more easily removed from sections than most plastics currently in use. Also, specific water-soluble methacrylates have found application in histochemical studies (see Section IV,D).

B. EPOXY RESIN

The following method is based upon the procedure of Luft (1961).

Mixture A:	Epon 812 (Shell Co.)	62 ml
	Dodecenyl succinic anhydride	100 ml
Mixture B:	Epon 812	100 ml
	Nadic methyl anhydride	89 ml
A/B:	3/7 4/6 5/5 6/4	
	Harder Softer	

The proportions depend upon the age of the Epon. It is generally best to make up the A and B mixtures 2–3 weeks in advance and let them "cure" at room temperature. They may then be stored at 4°C. Proportions of $4/6$ or $5/5$ are most often employed, but as the Epon ages $6/4$ may be necessary to prevent the block from becoming too brittle.

The accelerator DMP [2,4,6-tri(dimethylaminomethyl)phenol], 0.15 ml per 10 ml of the final mixture, is added and mixing is accomplished in a disposable syringe by slow mechanical rotation for 30–45 minutes. Thorough mixing is absolutely essential for consistent results. The capsules containing the tissue are filled and left overnight in a 40°C oven. They are then transferred to a 60°C oven for at least 48 hours before sectioning is attempted.

The procedure of fixation, dehydration, and embedding currently employed by the authors will now be described. If whole tissue is to be examined, it is important that very small blocks be employed (no more than 1 mm on a side) because osmium tetroxide penetrates slowly. Tissue cultures can be fixed on the glass, then scraped off and spun into pellets for dehydration. With certain types of cells the pellets tend to disintegrate during dehydration, in which case it is advisable to fix the cells after they have been pelleted.

The dehydration steps are arbitrary. For the sake of consistency the following schedule is followed in the authors' laboratory:

1. 1% Glutaraldehyde	1 hour
2. Wash 10 times in Sorenson's buffer* at 7 minute intervals (store overnight at 4°C or proceed directly to step 3)	
3. 1% Osmium tetroxide	30 minutes
4. Wash 3 times in buffer	
5. 30% Ethyl alcohol	10 minutes
6. 70% Ethyl alcohol	10 minutes
7. 80% Ethyl alcohol	10 minutes
8. 95% Ethyl alcohol	10 minutes
9. Absolute ethyl alcohol (with molecular sieve)	10 minutes
10. Absolute ethyl alcohol (with molecular sieve)	10 minutes
11. Propylene oxide (with molecular sieve)	10 minutes
12. Propylene oxide (with molecular sieve)	10 minutes
13. Propylene oxide and Epon (1 : 1 ratio)	1–3 hours
14. Tissue or pellet trimmed for embedding	
15. Embed in Epon	
16. 40°C Oven overnight	
17. 60°C Oven 48–72 hours	

* The exact nature of the buffer (so long as it is isotonic and at a neutral pH) probably does not matter.

The duration of curing at 60°C has a direct bearing on the sectionin qualities of the plastic.

It has been suggested that steps 13–16 be prolonged. In the authors experience this neither improves preservation appreciably nor facili tates sectioning.

C. OTHER WIDELY USED EMBEDDING MEDIA

The most common of these are Araldite, first reported by Maalø and Birch-Anderson (1956), improved by Glauert and Glauert (1958) and modified by Luft (1961); Vestopal, pioneered by Ryter an Kellenberger (1958); Maraglas, suggested by Freeman and Spurloc (1962) and Spurlock et al. (1963).

D. WATER-SOLUBLE PLASTICS

Polyepoxide, Durcupan (Ciba), permits trypsin and pepsin to ac on thin sections, but appears to prevent the use of nucleases (Ledu and Bernhard, 1961). Rosenberg et al. (1960) introduced glyco methacrylate (2-hydroxyethyl methacrylate), which allowed digestior by ribonuclease and deoxyribonuclease (Leduc and Bernhard, 1962) The major difficulty in the use of this embedding plastic (GMA) is the extreme variability of preservation. Moreover, even when preserva tion is adequate the action of the enzymes is often erratic (see furthe discussion in Section IX,C,2).

The procedure recommended by Bernhard and his colleagues is a follows:

Solution A:	Glycol methacrylate (GMA)	97%
	Ammonium persulfate	0.5%
Solution B:	Methyl methacrylate	15%
	Butyl methacrylate	85%
	Benzoyl peroxide, add 2% by weight	

The methacrylate is added to facilitate sectioning. All steps are t be carried out at 4°C.

1. Fixation for 15 minutes in Formalin or acrolein
2. 70% GMA, 15 minutes
3. 80% GMA, 15 minutes
4. 97% GMA, 30 minutes
5. 1 Volume of 70% solution A + 30% solution B ⎫
   1 Volume of GMA 97% ⎬ 30 minutes
   ⎭
6. Prepolymerize mixture of 70% solution A and 30% solution I in 60°C water bath

7. Place tissue in this prepolymerized mixture after cooling

8. Polymerize 48 hours with UV light in 4°C cold room

A modification of the foregoing is the use of 2-hydroxypropyl methacrylate (HPMA). Leduc and Holt (1965) in a beautifully illustrated paper report that this plastic provides consistent preservation of fine structure while permitting the use of nucleases. Sydney Breese (1967) has also had considerable success with it. Our attempts to embed tissue culture cells in HPMA (from Rohm and Haas Co., Philadelphia) gave very unsatisfactory results, and we can only conclude that different lots of the plastic must vary with respect either to infiltration or polymerization. It should also be added that, for reasons not immediately apparent, tissue culture cells seem to behave in a less satisfactory manner than do blocks of tissue (see also Section X,F).

V. Sectioning

Sectioning is often called an art; as with any art, it requires manual dexterity, practice, patience, and the will to succeed. Some persons have the gift to section extraordinarily well, others adequately, and some not at all. For technical details, the reader is referred once again to Porter's chapter in "Modern Developments in Electron Microscopy" (Siegel, 1964).

A. Microtomes

The two microtomes most widely used in the United States are the Sorvall and the LKB. Each has its advocates. The writers have had no personal experience with other instruments, such as the Leitz, Reichert, and Cambridge ultramicrotomes. Reports from their respective users suggest that they are perfectly satisfactory. As a general rule, that microtome works best which the operator knows best and with which he has had the most experience.

B. Knives

Glass knives can be used but diamond knives, originally described by Fernandez-Moran (1953, 1956), are much superior and are nearly essential for sectioning Epon 812. Unfortunately, however, good diamond knives are difficult to obtain. Current methods of sharpening them are secret and erratic, and it is largely a question of luck whether one receives a knife capable of cutting without scratching or causing "com pression."* Regarding the latter, which is by all odds the most annoy ing and consistent defect encountered, the cutting angle of the kni with respect to the block is critical and differs for each knife. Onl by trial and error can the proper angle be determined. Another fact to bear in mind is that different lots of Epon, and even different en beddings in the same lot, vary with respect to their propensity to "com press." Lastly, some types of tissue are more prone to compression tha others.

It is difficult to imagine a greater contribution to the preparatio of tissue for electron microscopy than the development of a techniqu whereby diamond knives could be produced with consistently good cu ting properties.

VI. Specimen Grids and Supporting Film

A. GRIDS

A wide variety of grids are available, but for general use 200 mesh copper grids of the Athene type (made by photoengraving–etch ing) are satisfactory. For serial sections, the Sjöstrand type (parall slits of two different widths) are useful. If Formvar is not employe 400-mesh grids are preferable to provide sufficient support.

B. FORMVAR

A clean glass slide is dipped into a solution of ethylene chloride o chloroform containing 0.25% Formvar. After removal and drying, th edges of the slide are scraped and the Formvar is floated onto th surface of distilled water by passing the glass slide at an angle into th water. There are two important points. First, the glass slides shoul be wiped with a dry cloth or lens tissue. If they are cleaned with de tergent or with caustic chemicals the Formvar is very difficult to re move. Second, if the solvent is not anhydrous or the humidity of th laboratory air is high, holes will appear in the Formvar as it dries The grids are placed on a copper screen that is submerged and brough up under the Formvar. A light coating of evaporated carbon is applie to increase stability.

For high resolution, it is frequently useful to place the sections di rectly on uncoated grids and examine them either with or withou a carbon coating.

* Whether or not the closely spaced thick and thin bands actually result from com pression or from high frequency vibration has never been satisfactorily determined.

C. Carbon Evaporation

A number of satisfactory evaporators are availible. (The authors currently employ a simple instrument sold by Mikros, Inc.) Carbon electrodes, one of which is pointed and abuts against the other, are heated in a glass container evacuated by a diffusion pump. The extent of carbon deposition is observed by placing a white piece of porcelain, part of which is covered by a drop of oil, near the specimen grids. Only with practice can one judge the amount of carbon necessary to stabilize the specimen without decreasing contrast or producing a granular background in high resolution micrographs. (A granular appearance may also result if the vacuum is insufficient.)

II. Staining

Staining is essential for the study of viruses and cells embedded in the newer plastics. There are a variety of stains and of techniques for using them. A useful summary of their action has been published by Peer (1965). As a general rule, the authors use uranyl acetate and lead citrate.

A. Uranyl Acetate

This stain was introduced by Watson (1958) and has been studied by Marinozzi and Gautier (1962) as well as others.

The procedure employed by the authors is: To a mixture of equal parts of distilled water and ethyl alcohol, add uranyl acetate to a concentration of 1%. Filter through a Millipore membrane (0.45-μ pore size). Immerse the sections on the grids for 1–3 hours and wash thoroughly with distilled water. The staining solution can be kept for at least 1 month at room temperature if it is shielded from light.

B. Lead Citrate

The major difficulty encountered with this stain is precipitation. None of the methods so far described entirely circumvents this problem, although it occurs infrequently if one follows the technique described below, as outlined by Reynolds (1963):

Add 1.33 gm of Pb$(NO_3)_2$ and 1.76 gm of $Na_3C_6H_5O_7 \cdot 2H_2O$ to 30 ml of distilled water. Shake intermittently for 30 minutes. Then add 8 ml of N NaOH and dilute to 50 ml with distilled water. This stock solution (pH 12) can be stored at room temperature in a tightly stoppered flask for several months.

Staining Procedure

Allow the precipitate to settle and carefully pipet off 0.05 or 0.1 ml of the clear supernatant fluid. Add this to 9.95 ml of 0.01 N NaOH and filter through a Millipore membrane (0.01-μ pore size). Use the stain promptly. Place pellets of NaOH in a Petri dish (to remove CO_2) and close the dish. After a few minutes put a drop of the stain on a piece of Parafilm paper in the Petri dish. Stain the section for 5 minutes by floating the grid, section side down, on the drop of stain. Wash the grids thoroughly in 0.02 N NaOH followed by distilled water.

C. Phosphotungstic Acid

Although not widely used for the examination of viruses in thin sections, the degree of detail that can be obtained, especially of surface membranes—as illustrated by Berkaloff and Colobert (1963) in their study of influenza virus and by Berkaloff (1963) in micrographs of Sendai virus—warrants further exploration of this stain. According to these authors, Araldite sections, mounted on grids without a Formvar substrate, were stained 1.5–3 minutes in 2% phosphotungstic acid dissolved in absolute ethyl alcohol, to which a few drops of acetone were added. The sections were washed in absolute alcohol.

D. Silver Nitrate

Interesting results have been reported by Marinozzi (1963). To the writers' knowledge, this stain has not yet been applied to studies of viral structure.

VIII. The Electron Microscope

Owing to certain aspects of microscopy that are peculiar to the examination of thin sections, a few comments may be in order. Microscopes are passing through a period of such rapid change that the evaluation now of specific instruments would be of little value six months hence. There are, however, certain basic factors that should be considered when choosing an instrument. Unfortunately, until very recently the designers have spent the major part of their effort chasing that elusive factor, resolution, and have paid little attention to other features, which often are of greater importance to the biologist.

A. RESOLUTION

There is no question that occasionally a specimen turns up that can nd should be examined at very high resolution, i.e., 4–5 Å. Obviously, hen, a microscope should be capable of such performance. But equally nd usually more important is the consistency with which a micro- cope can maintain adequate resolution of 8–10 Å, because this is the evel of performance that is required 99% of the time. Since it may take ours or even days of scanning to find particularly rare forms of a irus or of lesions in a cell, it is essential that when they are found a uitable picture can be obtained.

B. SERVICE

As a corollary to the above, the competence and availability of serv- ce engineers is a key factor.

C. OPERATION

Excessive complexity of instrumentation results in loss of perform- nce time, and this can be a serious drawback to biological work in vhich hundreds of pictures are generally required to amass significant ata.

D. CONTRAST

Because the contrast of sections is low—a factor augmented by igh accelerating voltages—the degree of contrast of the image will be lirectly proportional to the information that can be gained from in- pection of the fluorescent screen and to the percentage of in-focus nicrographs that are obtained.

E. MAGNIFICATION

Scanning is usually done at low magnification (2000–6000 $\times$), where- is high resolution micrographs are generally taken at 50,000–100,000 $\times$. Therefore, the lens system should be designed to permit this range of magnification while maintaining compensation and alignment.

F. CONTAMINATION

Contamination of sections is very rapid at the intense beam con- centration necessary to obtain sufficient illumination for work at high magnification. The contaminant is a structureless deposit that, by diminishing contrast, makes focusing difficult and obscures fine details of structure. It builds up at a rate that is directly proportional to beam intensity and inversely proportional to the degree of vacuum. Anticontamination devices cooled with liquid nitrogen effectively augment the vacuum if placed in the vicinity of the specimen. They will doubtless become obligatory for high resolution microscopy, and careful testing by actual use is necessary to evaluate their performance.

G. Image Intensification

The apparatus consists of two devices: a receptor that intensifies the illumination to a greater or lesser extent and a television screen that renders the image visible to the viewer. The enormous magnification provided by the television screen allows accurate focusing at low magnification. With the use of fine-grain film, negatives can be obtained that, when optically enlarged, reveal considerable detail over relatively large fields; this is an extremely important consideration if lesions involving gross segments of the cell are under study. The image intensifier also facilitates compensating the instrument for astigmatism. Lastly, contrast is augmented by the television screen, a very useful attribute if extremely thin sections are viewed at high resolution. One of the most publicized aspects, the very low electron-beam intensity necessary to activate the receptor, would seem at first glance to provide little advantage in view of the efficient anticontamination devices that are available. The chief drawback to the whole device at present is the poor resolution of the image on the television screen and this, it appears, is a difficult technical problem to overcome.

IX. *Ancillary Techniques*

The study of infected cells prepared for electron microscopy with the traditional techniques described above has provided, and continues to provide, useful and interesting information regarding the manner in which viruses differentiate and the ways in which host cells react. There still remains, however, a considerable gulf between knowledge gained by chemical analysis and the interpretation of events at the morphologic level. It has been difficult to correlate data acquired by the chemist with data obtained by the electron microscopist because the former summarizes a series of events in a large population of cells over a period of time, whereas the latter records events taking place in relatively few cells at one instant in time. Moreover, the occurrence of a foreign substance that is easily recognized by the chemist can be inferred by the microscopist only if this material aggregates in some characteristic form, causes some peculiar alteration in the host cell or can be labeled in a specific manner. In studying viruses it must be borne in mind that the differentiation of the particles themselves is a late or terminal event in the course of infection; but it is the events that precede the appearance of morphologically recognizable virus that are chiefly of interest. In an effort to overcome some of the foregoing problems and thus to extend the information provided by study of thin sections, a variety of techniques have been and are being developed.

A. CORRELATIVE LIGHT AND ELECTRON MICROSCOPY

Advantage can be taken of many histochemical reactions and staining methods available to the light microscopist if the same cells can be identified in contiguous thick and thin sections (Bloch et al., 1957; Godman et al., 1960). The simplest method is first to cut the thin section then the thick section. After suitable staining* of the latter, a photographic negative of the section is made at low power in the light microscope. With this negative as a guide, the same cells can be readily located on the fluorescent screen of the electron microscope. The major drawback is, of course, that the structures to be studied must be large enough, or aggregated in sufficiently large masses, to be clearly recognizable in the light microscope. Moreover, certain methods of preparing cells for histochemical study are poorly suited to the preservation of fine structure.

B. AUTORADIOGRAPHY

This important contribution is discussed in detail elsewhere in this volume. Suffice it to note here that the degree of localization of radioactive compounds at the ultrastructural level continues to be limited mainly by the concentration necessary to produce significant exposure of silver on the sections and by the size of the silver grains currently available.

---

* A useful, though not specific, stain for Epon-embedded tissue is described by Trump et al. (1961). Toluidine blue permits remarkably clear visualization of the tissue in the light microscope. A method of removing Epon by immersing sections in a solution of ethyl alcohol saturated with NaOH has been reported to allow a variety of staining procedures for light microscopy (Lane and Europa, 1965).

C. Histochemistry

1. *Enzyme Staining*

Although this would appear to be a promising field of study, little work has been done on viruses. Adenosinetriphosphatase, which is present in many cell membranes, has been identified at the surface of herpes simplex virus (Epstein and Holt, 1963), the viruses of avian myeloblastosis (Novikoff *et al.*, 1962; de Thé *et al.*, 1963, 1964) and avian leukemia (de Thé, 1966), as well as fowl plague and Newcastle disease viruses (Dawson *et al.*, 1965). The principle of this stain is to incubate the cells after Formalin or glutaraldehyde fixation in a solution containing glycerophosphate and lead nitrate (Wachstein and Meisel, 1957). The adenosinetriphosphatase splits off the terminal phosphate that, combining with lead, forms a precipitate readily visible in the electron microscope. The fixed cells may be treated directly after washing or may be frozen and treated after sectioning in a cryostat. The tissue is then postfixed in OsO_4, dehydrated, and embedded in Epon.

The problem of applying histochemical reactions to the study of viral structure is that the number of enzyme systems directly associated with viruses and amenable to staining is limited—so limited in fact, that to date only adenosinetriphosphatase has been identified. This enzyme coats the surface of cells and presumably adheres to some viruses during the process of release at the cell surface. The enzyme is not synthesized as a result of infection and appears to play no role in viral penetration, development, or release.

An interesting study by Dales and Kajioka (1964) employed a stain for acid phosphatase. Tissue culture cells were fixed for 5 minutes in 1% glutaraldehyde, washed in cacodylate buffer, incubated in a Gomori medium, washed in acetic acid, fixed in OsO_4, dehydrated, and embedded in Epon. Deposition of lead revealed the presence of acid phosphatase in vacuoles containing phagocytosed vaccinia virus. The authors concluded that the breakdown of virus as a preliminary step in the initiation of infection "probably results from hydrolysis by lysosomal enzymes, the presence of which is indicated by tests for acid phosphatase."

2. *Enzyme Digestion*

Thomas and Williams (1961) succeeded in digesting the cores of purified, ethanol-fixed, methacrylate-embedded Tipula iridescent virus by treating sections with trypsin and DNase. Pepsin removed the peripheral coat. To our knowledge this interesting work has not been extended to studies of intracellular methacrylate-embedded viruses. Epstein (1958, 1962b) and Epstein and Holt (1960) reported that the cores of extracellular Rous virus, adenovirus, and herpes simplex virus were susceptible to the action of nuclease after fixation in $KMnO_4$.

It remained for Bernhard and his colleagues to demonstrate the action of nucleases on viruses within their host cells. Dercupan (Ciba) (Leduc and Bernhard, 1961), was originally found to permit the use of pepsin and trypsin, but not nuclease (Bernhard et al., 1961). Subsequently, it was observed (Bernhard and Tournier, 1962) that Formalin fixation followed by embedding in glycolmethacrylate (see Section IV, D) polymerized at 4°C with ultraviolet light did allow digestion of the cores of reovirus with RNase and of adenovirus with DNase. Studies by Marinozzi (1963) on enzymatic digestion of nuclear components in normal cells suggest that significant information should be gained by the application of these techniques to virus-infected cells.

The major difficulty, as has already been mentioned, is the problem of preserving fine structure in the water-soluble plastic. The preservation illustrated by Bernhard et al. (1961) seems to be the exception rather than the rule. Despite careful prepolymerization of the glycolmethacrylate, extensive distortion and extraction are apt to occur. In addition, some viral cores appear to become dislodged or dissolved out merely by the action of the water on which the sections are floated from the knife. This further complicates interpretation. Finally, section thickness is a critical factor, for DNase does not appear to act on polyomavirus cores, presumably, as suggested by Bernhard and Tournier (1962), because the diameter of this virus is so small relative to the section thickness that penetration of the enzyme is impeded. In support of their conclusion is the fact that digestion of adenovirus and reovirus cores does not occur in the thicker parts of the sections. Despite these drawbacks, Bernhard and his colleagues have introduced an important method whereby the knowledge of viral structure and development revealed by thin sectioning can be much advanced. Further exploration of this and allied techniques deserves attention.

D. LABELED ANTIBODIES

With the publication by Singer (1959) of a method whereby antibodies could be conjugated with ferritin, a technique became available which permitted specific immunochemical identification of viruses and of viral proteins by electron microscopy. Since recent reviews of methods of conjugation and applications of the conjugate are available (Morgan et al., 1962; Rifkind et al., 1964), the subject will be mentioned here only briefly. To date, eight viruses have been tagged. These (in chronological order of publication) are T2 bacteriophage Lee, (1960), influenza (Rifkind et al., 1960), tobacco mosaic (Singer and Schick, 1961), vaccinia (Morgan et al., 1961), equine abortion (Metzger and Smith, 1962), parainfluenza (Reczko and Bögel, 1962), rabies (Atanasiu et al., 1963), and reovirus (Dales et al., 1965).

Viruses on the surface of infected tissue-culture cells are tagged by flooding the cells while still attached to a cover slip with the solution of ferritin-conjugated antibody for 5–15 minutes. After thorough washing in buffered, isotonic saline at 4°C the cells are scraped from the glass and centrifuged gently into a pellet that is fixed, dehydrated, and embedded in the usual manner.

In order to tag intracellular virus and viral proteins, it is necessary to render the cell permeable to the relatively large antibody–ferritin conjugate. Perhaps the most reliable method is to freeze and thaw the cells. After fixation for brief periods (5–15 minutes) in 4% Formalin,* which assists in preserving fine structure without inactivating antigens, the cells are frozen by immersion of Leighton tubes containing cover slips with attached cells in a CO_2–alcohol bath. After thawing, the cover slips are flooded with the ferritin conjugate, washed, and fixed in the manner described above. The method can be applied equally well to cells in suspension, in which case the cells are frozen as a pellet and resuspended in the conjugate after thawing. Washing is carried out by repeated centrifugation and suspension in buffer. By means of the foregoing methods it has been possible to label the intracellular viral antigens of influenza and vaccinia viruses before their assembly into viral particles (Morgan et al., 1961, 1962).

Dales and co-workers (1965) have used dilute solutions of digitonin to disrupt cells in suspension. This technique requires great care in order to obtain sufficient disruption without extensive extraction, and it is therefore advisable to follow the reaction by observation of the cells in a darkfield or phase microscope (Dales, 1967). At the proper moment, the cells are centrifuged into a pellet and fixed briefly in Formalin or glutaraldehyde. After thorough washing, the pellet is immersed in a solution of the ferritin–antibody conjugate, washed repeatedly, and then fixed in glutaraldehyde followed by OsO_4. In this manner it has been possible to label intracellular reovirus (Dales et al., 1965).

Although the above techniques are satisfactory for most tissue cul-

---

* Unfortunately, prefixation in glutaraldehyde preserves fine structure so well that freezing does not render the cells sufficiently permeable.

ture cells, they do not permit sufficient penetration of the conjugate into blocks of tissue or closely packed pellets. For the latter it is necessary to freeze the tissue and cut sections 10–50 μ thick in a cryostat (Morgan *et al.*, 1961). The aggregate of sections is then thawed and immersed in a solution of ferritin-conjugated antibody. After washing by repeated cycles of suspension and centrifugation in saline, the sections are fixed and embedded for thin sectioning. Another method, pioneered by Andres *et al.* (1962), is to mince the tissue with a razor blade. This can be done either with or without Formalin fixation. The very small fragments are then placed in the solution of conjugate, washed, fixed, and embedded. Penetration of ferritin under such circumstances is somewhat variable, but a significant percentage of the cells are sufficiently close to the surface of the fragments to permit adequate entry of the conjugated antibody.

It is evident that until such time as the ferritin-conjugated antibody can be applied directly to thin sections the technique has limitations. Freezing, for example, does not permit the conjugate to penetrate mature virus, and hence internal viral components cannot be labeled. Unpublished studies by the authors have shown that the use of water-soluble embedding media, such as glycol methacrylate, avoids the attachment of ferritin to the plastic, which occurs when standard embedding media are employed, but does not prevent nonspecific adherence of ferritin to a variety of cellular proteins, most notably components of the nuclear chromatin.* It is essential that further exploration of this aspect of the problem be carried out.

E. FREEZE DRYING AND FREEZE SUBSTITUTION

Sjöstrand and Elfvin (1964) report interesting details of cellular fine structure after freezing, desiccating, and embedding. The tissue was frozen in liquid nitrogen, dried under vacuum, gradually brought to room temperature, fixed in osmium fumes, and embedding in Vestopal. This technique has not, as yet, been applied to viruses.

Another method, which has been investigated more extensively, is freeze substitution. Bullivant (1965) in a recent review of the subject shows impressive pictures of unfixed tissue embedded in methacrylate. Although there are various methods, Bullivant adds increasing concen-

---

* Singer and McLean (1963) have suggested that embedding tissue in a mixture of anionic, cationic, and bifunctional crosslinking methacrylates permits the application of ferritin conjugates to sections.

trations of glycerol to the cells, freezes them in propane cooled by liquid nitrogen and transfers the tissue at $-75°C$ to anhydrous methanol. After about 2 weeks, methacrylate is substituted and polymerization is carried out at $-25°C$ by means of ultraviolet light. Unfortunately, the state of preservation is variable and considerable experimentation remains to be done in order to achieve consistent results. A detailed report introducing several modifications and refinements has been published by Rebhun (1965).

F. DEHYDRATION OF UNFIXED TISSUE WITH INERT AGENTS

As Pease (1966a) has stated, this "technique should be regarded as a physical method of tissue preservation, rather than a chemical one." Unfixed slices of tissue are rapidly dehydrated (in 2–3 minutes) with agitation in ethylene glycol and embedded in 2-hydroxypropyl methacrylate (HPMA), which has been partially prepolymerized by heating at 80°C after addition of 1% benzoyl peroxide. After cooling, 5% of a crosslinking agent, divinylbenzene, is added with stirring. The embedded tissue is finally polymerized at 60°C. In a second paper, Pease (1966b) discusses the problems of sectioning this material. He suggests using ethylene glycol in the boat to avoid the extraction of water-soluble components. Anhydrous staining is performed by employing a solution of 2% phosphotungstic acid in ethylene glycol.

Pease's micrographs, illustrating sections of kidney, liver, and muscle, are exceedingly impressive. Our attempts to embed tissue culture cells, however, have met with repeated failures. Distortion and extraction are so severe that fine structure is virtually unrecognizable. (Certain viruses, such as vaccinia, can be identified but appear to have undergone some extraction.) Pease refers to this problem in his first paper by remarking that "invariably we have found the superficial cell layers of our tissue slabs have been destroyed" and adds, "thus, for the present, it seems unlikely that isolated cells can be successfully dehydrated exactly in the manner described, although more refined protective procedures perhaps can be developed." We have attempted to embed centrifuged pellets of tissue culture cells and also blocks of agar-embedded cells, all to no avail. Moreover, the problems of sectioning are, to say the least, trying. The block has a propensity to "wet" and if the fluid in the boat is lowered sufficiently to avoid this, the sections are difficult to float off the knife onto the fluid. It is evident that until such time as the technique can be applied to tissue cultures it will have limited usefulness for the study of viral structure and development.

G. Unembedded Tissue

Bernhard and his colleagues (Bernhard and Nancy, 1964; Bernhard, 1965; Tranzer, 1965) have accomplished a technical *tour de force* in sectioning tissue devoid of any embedding plastic. The principle is to fix the tissue briefly in glutaraldehyde, Formalin, or acrolein and then immerse it in dilute gelatin. (Unfixed tissue has also been used.) The specimen is frozen and cut on a Porter-Blum type microtome in a cryostat at −35°C. The trick, of course, is to transfer the frozen sections directly from the knife to the specimen grid. This has been accomplished by mounting the specimen grid attached to an electrode (charged with 5000–10,000 volts) directly above the specimen in such a manner that the section is attracted by electrostatic forces and flies off the knife to the grid (Koller and Bernhard, 1964; Koller, 1965). Sections of intracellular adenovirus have been stained with phosphotungstic acid and show arrays of capsomeres on many of the viral particles (Tranzer, 1965). Needless to say, the technique is tedious and difficult, but the published micrographs are of great interest and hold promise for the further use of negative stains and for the application of ferritin-conjugated antibodies directly to sections.

X. Conclusion

The preceding remarks describe briefly the ways in which thin sectioning can be applied to studies of viruses and host cells in the electron microscope. The bibliography, far from being exhaustive, cites but a few key references, tending to point out wherever possible those papers that actually discuss the use of a particular method for the examination of viral structure and development.

It cannot be emphasized too strongly that those who intend to embark on studies requiring such a multiplicity of techniques should take the time to work for 6–12 months in a laboratory actively engaged in this type of research. By reading, one may acquire some conception of the problems, but one is unlikely to discover their solution.

XI. Illustrations

The micrographs are grouped at the conclusion of this section in order to facilitate comparison of the different methods used in preparing the specimens. For additional information on the effects of various fixatives on vaccinia and adenovirus, the reader is referred to a brief but beautifully illustrated study by Peters and Büttner (1965).

The authors thank Dr. de Thé for his micrograph showing the localization of adenosinetriphosphatase on the surface of avian myeloblastosis virus and Drs. Tournier and Bernhard for their prints illustrating the action of ribonuclease on reovirus.

FIG. 1. A choriollantoic membrane infected with vaccinia virus, fixed for 4 hours in neutral Formalin and embedded in methacrylate. The micrograph was obtained by exposing the plate for 50 seconds in an RCA EMU 2E with the condenser current set at maximum intensity. Instrumental magnification was 2000 ×. Viral particles are clearly defined.

FIG. 2. The same area micrographed under the same conditions, but after brief exposure of the field to normal electron-beam intensity. Incineration of virus and cytoplasmic components is evident. Magnification was 18,000 ×.

FIG. 3. Mature vaccinia virus after 4 hours of fixation in OsO_4. Embedded in methacrylate. Viral cores are adequately preserved, but the peripheral membranes are poorly defined, and the prolonged fixation has resulted in severe extraction of the cytoplasm. The knife has caused considerable compression of the virus.

FIG. 4. Vaccinia virus fixed in $KMnO_4$ for 20 minutes, washed, and postfixed in OsO_4 for 20 minutes. Methacrylate embedded. Details of the core are lacking but the peripheral components of the virus are well preserved. The variation in appearance owes to the differing orientation of the virus in the section and to the level at which the particles have been cut. Magnification was 40,000 ×.

FIG. 5. Site of synthesis of vaccinia virus in the cytoplasm of a HeLa cell. OsO_4 for 20 minutes. Methacrylate embedded. These early forms of the virus with developing peripheral membranes and dense, eccentric cores are well defined. Cytoplasmic membranes are also evident (in the upper portion), but ribosomes are poorly preserved. Magnification was 45,000 ×.

FIG. 6. An area similar to that illustrated in the preceding figure. The technique outlined in Section IV,B was followed, i.e., glutaraldehyde for 1 hour, followed by OsO_4 for 30 minutes, and Epon embedding. The section was stained with uranyl acetate and lead citrate (Sections VII,A and B). The extraordinary preservation of aggregated viral proteins, virus in process of formation, ribosomes, cytoplasmic filaments, and nuclear matrix speaks for itself. The nuclear membrane has been transected obliquely and is therefore not well defined in this field. Magnification was 45,000 ×.

FIG. 7. An intranuclear crystal of adenovirus. OsO_4 for 20 minutes. Methacrylate embedded. The internal structure can be made out, but the particles appear spherical with diffuse peripheral coats.

FIG. 8. A similar crystal after fixation in $KMnO_4$. Methacrylate embedded. The sections were stained with osmium fumes followed by lead citrate. Contrast is greatly enhanced. (Note the reduplicated nuclear membranes at the periphery of the micrograph.) The internal structure of the virus is not well defined, but the margins are sharply demarcated and the hexagonal contour of the virus is evident. Magnification was 50,000 ×.

FIG. 9. An intranuclear crystal of adenovirus. Glutaraldehyde and OsO_4 fixation. Epon embedded. Section stained with uranyl acetate and lead citrate. The two characteristic viral forms, one dense, the other with a well-demarcated core of low density, are evident. This was a relatively thick section micrographed at 100 kV accelerating voltage in an RCA 3G. Toward the center and at the lower right, the particles overlap within the section. Magnification was 50,000 ×.

FIG. 10. Another crystal treated in the same manner as in the preceding instance, but here the section is thinner and the magnification is sufficient to reveal details of viral structure. In the upper half of the field the virus is central to the plane of section. Below, the section passes between rows of viral particles. Magnification was 110,000 ×.

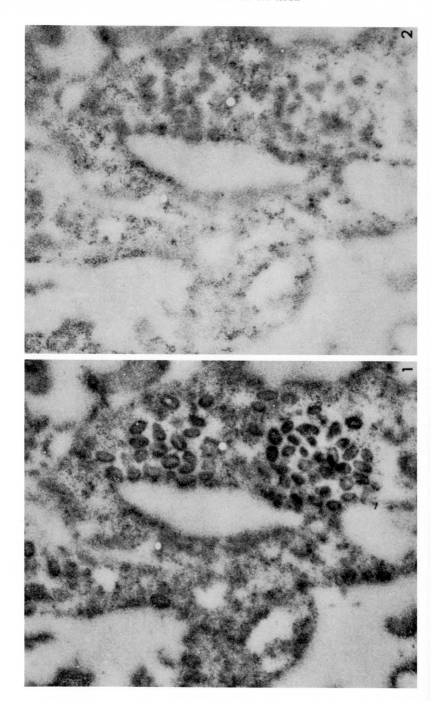

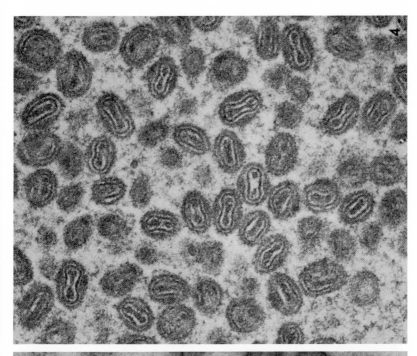

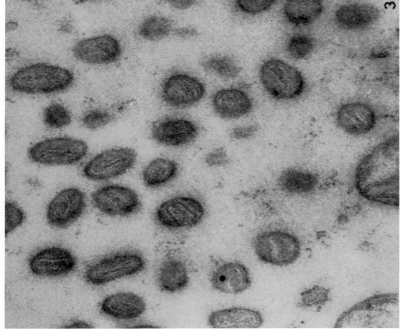

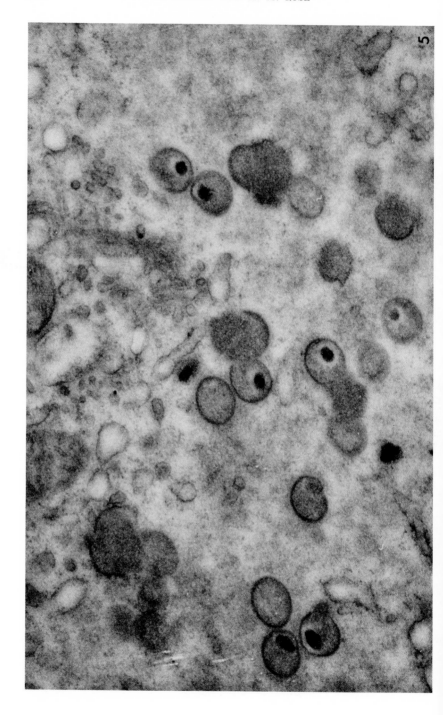

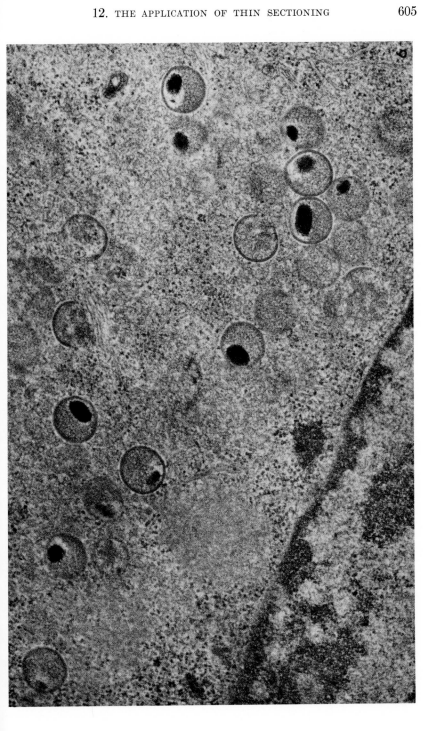

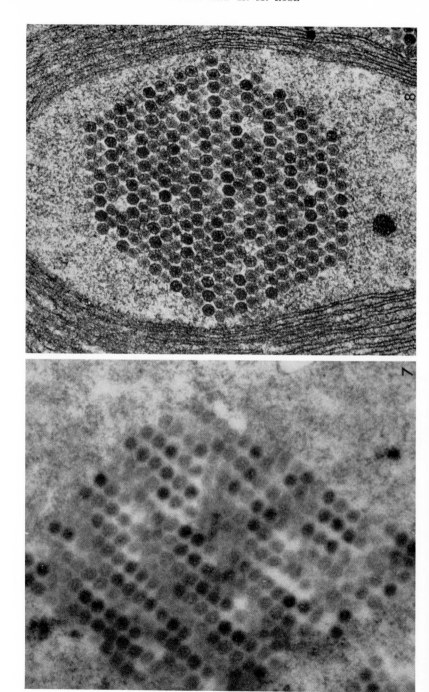

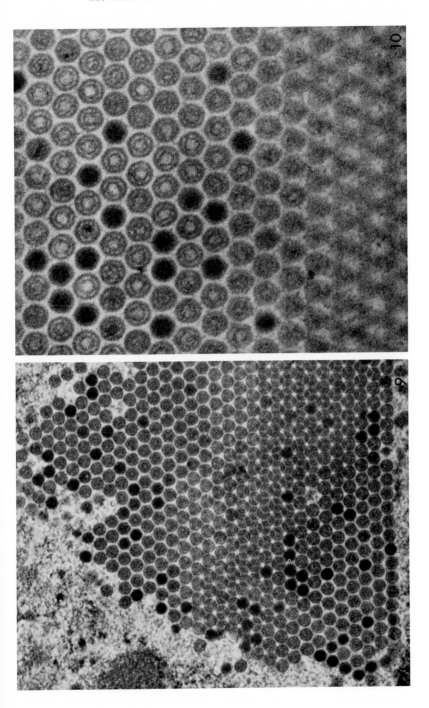

FIG. 11. Influenza virus at the surface of a chorioallantoic cell. OsO₄ fixed for 20 minutes. Methacrylate embedded. The internal membrane is sharply defined, but the core and peripheral coat are indistinct.

FIG. 12. Influenza virus treated as above but viewed in a considerably thicker section. The cores are seen slightly better and the diffuse peripheral coat is more evident. Magnification was **100,000** ×.

FIG. 13. Short, filamentous forms of influenza virus. Glutaraldehyde and OsO₄ fixation. Epon embedded. Uranyl acetate and lead citrate stained. Comparison with the filaments at the upper right of Fig. 12 shows the improvement in preservation of internal components. The peripheral spikes can be made out on several particles.

FIG. 14. Spherical and filamentous forms of influenza virus treated in the same manner. One particle (see arrow) central to the plane of section shows remarkable structural detail, including well-defined surface projections. Magnification was **140,000** ×.

FIG. 15. Avian myeloblastosis virus stained for adenosinetriphosphatase. Lead deposits coat the viral particles. Magnification was **70,000** ×.

FIG. 16. The intranuclear, soluble antigen of influenza virus labeled with specific ferritin-conjugated antibody after freezing the cell. Postfixed in OsO₄. Methacrylate embedded. The adjacent nuclear matrix is virtually devoid of ferritin. Magnification was **100,000** ×.

FIG. 17. Vaccinia virus labeled with ferritin-conjugated antibody. The cell was frozen in 0.88 M sucrose, immersed in the conjugate for 1 hour, washed, fixed in OsO₄, and embedded in Epon. Despite freezing the viral structure is well preserved. The nucleus at the lower right contains some scattered, nonspecific ferritin granules. It is impossible to tell whether the distortion of the mitochondrion at the upper right has resulted from freezing or reflects the advanced stage of infection. The section was not stained and hence exhibits low contrast. Magnification was **60,000** ×.

FIG. 18. Reovirus fixed in acrolein and formalin and embedded in glycol methacrylate. The section was treated with DNase. A few viral cores have been extracted by water, but the majority are intact.

FIG. 19. A similar preparation treated with RNase. Particles central to the plane of section show digestion of their dense core. Magnification was **60,000** ×.

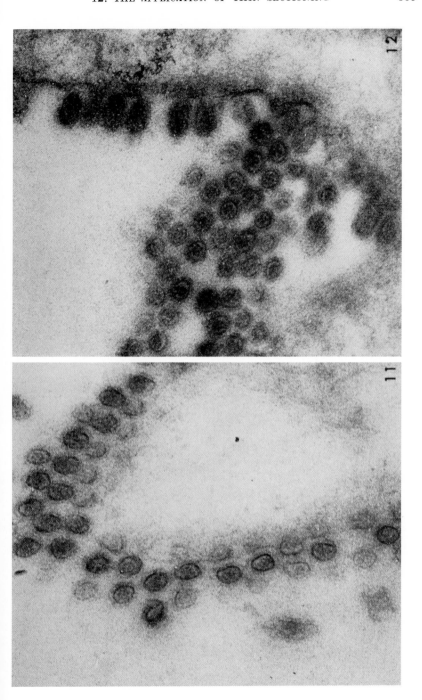

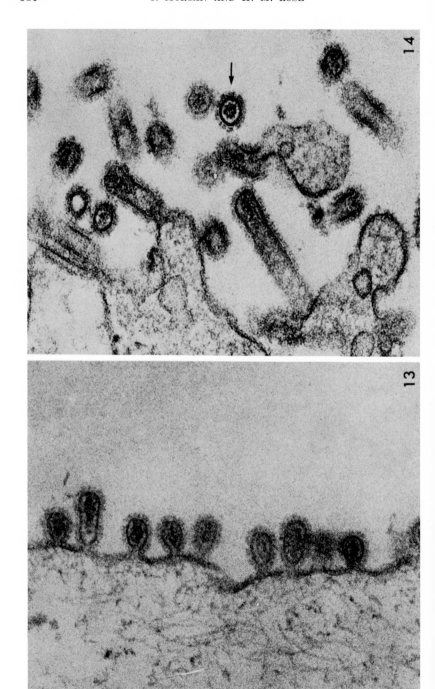

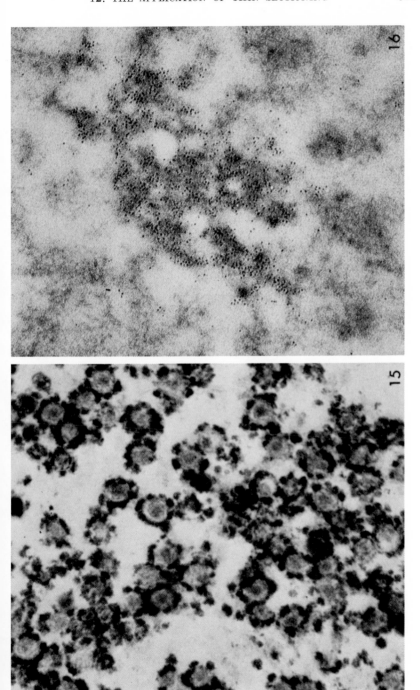

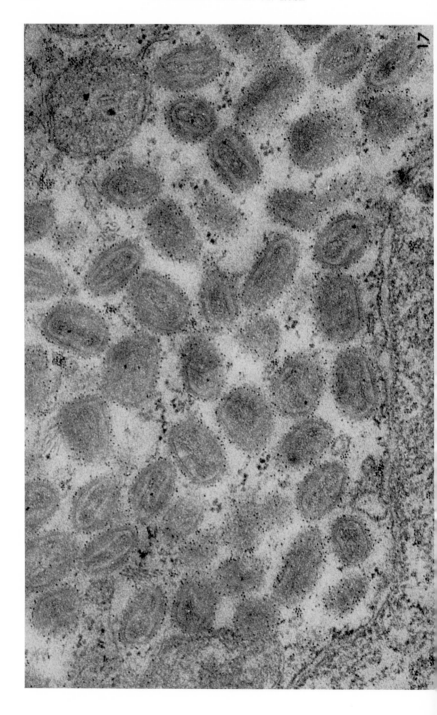

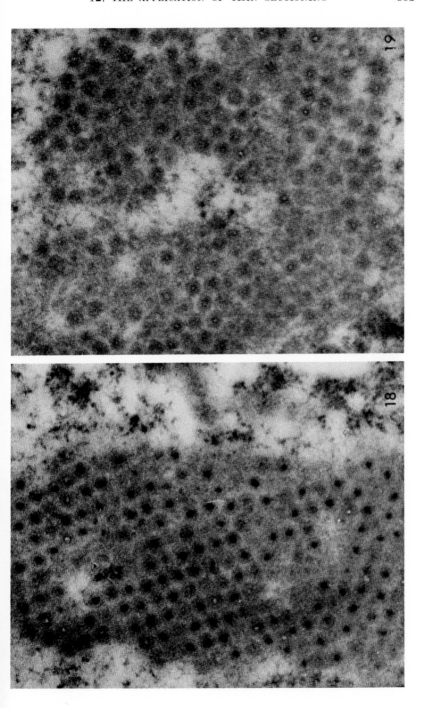

References

Andres, G. A., Morgan, C., Hsu, K. C., Rifkind, R. A., and Seegal, B. C. (1962). *Nature* **194**, 590.

Atanasiu, P., Orth, G., Sisman, J., and Barreau, C. (1963). *Compt. Rend.* **257**, 2204.

Bahr, G. F. (1954). *Exptl. Cell Res.* **7**, 457.

Beer, M. (1965). *Lab. Invest.* **14**, 1020.

Berkaloff, A. (1963). *J. Microscopie* **2**, 633.

Berkaloff, A., and Colobert, L. (1963). *J. Microscopie* **2**, 57.

Bernhard, W. (1965). *Ann. Biol.* **4**, 5.

Bernhard, W., and Nancy, M. T. (1964). *J. Microscopie* **3**, 579.

Bernhard, W., and Tournier, P. (1962). *Cold Spring Harbor Symp. Quant. Biol.* **27**, 67.

Bernhard, W., Granboulan, N., Barski, G., and Tournier, P. (1961). *Compt. Rend.* **252**, 202.

Black, I. M., Morgan, C., and Wyckoff, R. W. G. (1950). *Proc. Soc. Exptl. Biol. Med.* **73**, 119.

Bloch, D. P., Morgan, C., Godman, G. C., Howe, C., and Rose, H. M. (1957). *J. Biophys. Biochem. Cytol.* **3**, 1.

Bradbury, S., and Meek, G. A. (1960). *Quart. J. Microscop. Sci.* **101**, 241.

Breese, S. (1967). Personal communication.

Bullivant, S. (1965). *Lab. Invest.* **14**, 1178.

Claude, A. (1948). *Harvey Lectures* **43**, 121.

Dales, S. (1967). Personal communication.

Dales, S., and Kajioka, R. (1964). *Virology* **24**, 278.

Dales, S., Gomatos, P. J., and Hsu, K. C. (1965). *Virology* **25**, 193.

Dalton, A. J. (1955). *Anat. Record* **121**, 281.

Dalton, A. J., Potter, M., and Merwin, R. M. (1961). *J. Natl. Cancer Inst.* **26**, 1221.

Dalton, A. J., Haguenau, F., and Moloney, J. B. (1964). *J. Natl. Cancer. Inst.* **33**, 255.

Dawson, C. R., Epstein, M. A., and Hummeler, K. (1965). *J. Bacteriol.* **89**, 1526.

de Thé, G., Heine, U., Sommer, J. R., Arvy, L., Beard, D., and Beard, J. W. (1963). *J. Natl. Cancer Inst.* **30**, 415.

de Thé, G., Becker, C., and Beard, J. W. (1964). *J. Natl. Cancer Inst.* **32**, 201.

de Thé, G. (1966). *Int. J. Cancer* **1**, 119.

Epstein, M. A. (1958). *Nature* **181**, 1808.

Epstein, M. A. (1962a). *Nature* **194**, 116.

Epstein, M. A. (1962b). *J. Exptl. Med.* **115**, 1.

Epstein, M. A., and Holt, S. J. (1958). *Brit. J. Cancer* **12**, 363.

Epstein, M. A., and Holt, S. J. (1960). *Nature* **187**, 1050.

Epstein, M. A., and Holt, S. J. (1963). *J. Cell Biol.* **19**, 337.

Fernandez-Moran, H. (1953). *Exptl. Cell Res.* **5**, 225.

Fernandez-Moran, H. (1956). *J. Biophys. Biochem. Cytol.* **2**, Suppl., 29.

Finck, H. (1960). *J. Biophys. Biochem. Cytol.* **7**, 27.

Freeman, J. A., and Spurlock, B. O. (1962). *J. Cell Biol.* **13**, 437.

Fullam, E. F., and Gessler, A. E. (1946). *Rev. Sci. Instr.* **17**, 23.

Gaylord, W. H., and Melnick, J. L., (1953). *J. Exptl. Med.* **98**, 157.

Gettner, M. E., and Ornstein, L. (1953). *J. Appl. Phys.* **24**, 113.

Gettner, M. E., and Ornstein, L. (1955). *Phys. Tech. Biol. Res.* **3**, 627.

Glauert, A. M., and Glauert, R. H. (1958). *J. Biophys. Biochem. Cytol.* **4**, 191.

Godman, G. C., Morgan, C., Breitenfeld, P. M., and Rose, H. M. (1960). *J. Exptl. Med.* **112**, 383.

Hake, T. (1965). *Lab. Invest.* **14**, 1208.

Howe, C., Morgan, C., de Vaux St. Cyr, C., Hsu, K. C., and Rose, H. M. (1967). *J. Virol.* **1**, 215.

Kajioka, R., Siminovitch, L., and Dales, S. (1964). *Virology* **24**, 295.

Kausche, G. A., Pfankuch, E., and Ruska, H. (1939). *Naturwissenschaften* **27**, 292.

Kay, D. (1961). "Techniques for Electron Microscopy." Thomas, Springfield, Illinois.

Kellenberger, E., Ryter, A., and Séchaud, J. (1958). *J. Biophys. Biochem. Cytol.* **4**, 671.

Kolehmainen, L., Zech, H., and von Wettstein, D. (1965). *J. Cell Biol.* **25**, 77.

Koller, T. (1965). *J. Cell Biol.* **27**, 441.

Koller, T., and Bernhard, W. (1964). *J. Microscopie* **3**, 1958.

Lane, B. P., and Europa, D. L. (1965). *J. Histochem. Cytochem.* **13**, 579.

Latta, H., and Hartmann, J. F. (1950) *Proc. Soc. Exptl. Biol. Med.* **74**, 436.

Leduc, E. H., and Bernhard, W. (1961). *J. Biophys. Biochem. Cytol.* **10**, 437.

Leduc, E. H., and Bernhard, W. (1962). *In* "The Interpretation of Ultrastructure," (Harris, R. J. C., ed.) pp. 21–45. Academic Press, New York.

Leduc, E. H., and Holt, S. J. (1965). *J. Cell Biol.* **26**, 137.

Lee, S. (1960). *Exptl. Cell Res.* **21**, 249.

Luft, J. H. (1956). *J. Biophys. Biochem. Cytol.* **2**, 799.

Luft, J. H. (1961). *J. Biophys. Biochem. Cytol.* **9**, 409.

Maaløe, O., and Birch-Andersen, A. (1956). *Symp. Soc. Gen. Microbiol.* **6**, 261.

Margaretten, W., Morgan, C., Rosenkranz, H. S., and Rose, H. M. (1966). *J. Bacteriol.* **91**, 823.

Marinozzi, V. (1963). *J. Roy. Microscop. Soc.* [3] **81**, 141.

Marinozzi, V., and Gautier, A. (1962). *J. Ultrastruct. Res.* **7**, 436.

Marton, L. (1934). *Bull. Acad. Roy. Med. Belg.* [Sect. 1] **20**, 439.

Mayor, H. D., and Jordan, L. E. (1963). *J. Cell Biol.* **18**, 207.

Mercer, E. H., and Birbeck, M. S. C. (1961). "Electron Microscopy." Thomas, Springfield, Illinois.

Metzger, J. F., and Smith, C. W. (1962). *Lab. Invest.* **11**, 902.

Millonig, G. (1961). *J. Appl. Phys.* **32**, 1637.

Morgan, C. (1967). Unpublished studies.

Morgan, C., and Wyckoff, R. W. G. (1950). *J. Immunol.* **65**, 285.

Morgan, C., Ellison, S. A., Rose, H. M., and Moore, D. H. (1954a). *J. Exptl. Med.* **100**, 195.

Morgan, C., Ellison, S. A., Rose, H. M., and Moore, D. H. (1954b). *J. Exptl. Med.* **100**, 301.

Morgan, C., Moore, D. H., and Rose, H. M. (1956a). *J. Biophys. Biochem. Cytol.* **2**, Suppl., 21.

Morgan, C., Rose, H. M., and Moore, D. H. (1956b). *J. Exptl. Med.* **104**, 171.

Morgan, C., Rifkind, R. A., Hsu, K. C., Holden, M., Seegal, B. C., and Rose, H. M. (1961). *Virology* **14**, 292.

Morgan, C., Rifkind, R. A., and Rose, H. M. (1962). *Cold Spring Harbor Symp. Quant. Biol.* **27**, 57.

Morgan, C., Rosenkranz, H. S., Chan, B., and Rose, H. M. (1966). *J. Bacteriol.* **91**, 891.

Newman, S. B., Borysko, E., and Swerdlow, M. (1949). *J. Res. Natl. Bur. Std.* **43**, 183.

Novikoff, A. B., de Thé, G., Beard, D., and Beard, J. W. (1962). *J. Cell Biol.* **15**, 451.

O'Brien, H. C., and McKinley, G. M. (1943). *Science* **98**, 455.

Palade, G. E. (1952). *J. Exptl. Med.* **95**, 285.

Pease, D. C. (1964). "Histological Techniques for Electron Microscopy," 2nd ed. Academic Press, New York.

Pease, D. C. (1966a). *J. Ultrastruct. Res.* **14**, 356.

Pease, D. C. (1966b). *J. Ultrastruct. Res.* **15**, 555.

Pease, D. C., and Baker, R. F. (1948). *Proc. Soc. Exptl. Biol. Med.* **67**, 470.

Peters, D. H. A., and Büttner, D. (1965). *Lab. Invest.* **14**, 1234.

Porter, K. R., and Blum, J. (1953). *Anat. Record* **117**, 683.

Porter, K. R., and Thompson, H. P. (1948). *J. Exptl. Med.* **88**, 15.

Porter, K. R., Claude, A., and Fullam, E. F. (1945). *J. Exptl. Med.* **81**, 233.

Rebhun, L. I. (1965). *Federation Proc.* **24**, Suppl. 15, S–217.

Reczko, E., and Bögel, K. (1962). *Arch. Ges. Virusforsch.* **12**, 404.

Reynolds, E. S. (1963). *J. Cell Biol.* **17**, 208.

Rifkind, R. A., Hsu, K. C., Morgan, C., Seegal, B. C., Knox, A. W., and Rose, H. M. (1960). *Nature* **187**, 1094.

Rifkind, R. A., Hsu, K. C., and Morgan, C. (1964). *J. Histochem. Cytochem.* **12**, 131.

Rosenberg, M , Bartl, P., and Lěsko, J. (1960). *J. Ultrastruct. Res.* **4**, 298.

Rosenkranz, H. S., Rose, H. M., Morgan, C., and Hsu, K. C. (1966). *Virology* **28**, 510.

Ryter, A., and Kellenberger, E. (1958). *J. Ultrastruct. Res.* **2**, 200.

Sabatini, D. D., Bensch, K., and Barrnett, R. J. (1963). *J. Cell Biol.* **17**, 19.

Sabatini, D. D., Miller, F., and Barrnett, R. J. (1964). *J. Histochem, Cytochem.* **12**, 57.

Schultze, M. (1864). *Verhandl. Naturhist. Ver. Preuss. Rheinlande* **21**, 61.

Shalla, T. A. (1964). *J. Cell Biol.* **21**, 253.

Siegel, B. M., ed. (1964). "Modern Developments in Electron Microscopy." Academic Press, New York.

Singer, S. J. (1959). *Nature* **183**, 1523.

Singer, S. J., and McLean, J. D. (1963). *Lab. Invest.* **12**, 1002.

Singer, S. J., and Schick, A. F. (1961). *J. Biophys. Biochem. Cytol.* **9**, 519.

Sjöstrand, F. S. (1953). *Experientia* **9**, 114.

Sjöstrand, F. S., and Elfvin, L. G. (1964). *J. Ultrastruct. Res.* **10**, 263.

Spurlock, B. O., Kattine, V. C., and Freeman, J. A. (1963). *J. Cell Biol.* **17**, 203.

Stoeckinius, W., and Mahr, S. C. (1965). *Lab. Invest.* **14**, 1196.

Strangeways, T. S. P., and Canti, R. G. (1927). *Quart. J. Microscop. Sci.* **71**, 1.

Thomas, R. S., and Williams, R. C. (1961). *J. Biophys. Biochem. Cytol.* **11**, 15.

Tranzer, J. P. (1965). *J. Microscopie* **4**, 319.

Trump, B. F., Smuekler, E. A., and Benditt, E. P. (1961). *J. Ultrastruct. Res.* **5**, 343.

von Ardenne, M. (1939). *Z. Wiss. Mikroskop.* **56**, 8.

Wachstein, M., and Meisel, E. (1957). *Am. J. Clin. Pathol.* **27**, 13.

Watson, M. L. (1958). *J. Biophys. Biochem. Cytol.* **4**, 475.

Williams, R. C., and Wyckoff, R. W. G. (1946). *J. Appl. Phys.* **17**, 23.

Wood, R. L., and Luft, J. H. (1965). *J. Ultrastruct. Res.* **12**, 22.

Zworykin, V. K., Hillier, J., and Vance, A. W. (1941). *Trans. AIEE* **60**, 157.

13 Autoradiographic Methods for Electron Microscopy

Nicole Granboulan

After the first results published by Liquier-Milward (1956), a resolution superior to that achieved by light autoradiography was demonstrated for electron autoradiography by Van Tubergen (1961) with H-labeled bacteria. Since then the technique has been considerably improved by Caro and Van Tubergen by the use of thin sections of samples labeled with tritium combined with a layer of small grain emulsion (Caro, 1961, 1962; Caro and Van Tubergen, 1962). The resolving power was shown to be in the order of 0.1 μ (Caro, 1962). The method was further improved by the use of emulsions with smaller grains (P. Granboulan, 1963; Bachmann and Salpeter, 1964; P. Granboulan and Audran, 1964).

Electron autoradiography has become an important method in biology and has already led to several very valuable investigations. At the present time there are only a few works in the field of virology that are concerned with its use with animal, vegetal, or bacterial viruses, but it seems evident that the technique will be more and

617

more employed in such work. It offers several different and interestin
approaches for the localization of synthetic processes in a virus-in
fected cell during the replication of the virus, for the comparison c
metabolism in virus-infected and noninfected cells, and, at least i
some cases, for following the fate of the viral genome in the host cel

This section considers the different methods of electron autoradiog
raphy. We shall not present here the data concerning the problem o
resolving power, theoretical or experimental, since they may be foun
elsewhere (Caro, 1962; P. Granboulan, 1965; Bachmann and Salpete
1965).

I. Specimen Label

A. Choice of the Isotope

Until now only β-emitters were employed. The use of α-emitter
appears possible but not physiologically practical.

The isotope of choice is tritium. It is the most easily adapted isotop
because of its low average energy and consequently its high specifi
ionization: ^{3}H emits a β-particle of 18 keV maximum energy an
therefore gives excellent resolution and sensitivity.

It is known that a loss of resolution together with an increase i
background and a decrease in efficiency occur as the energy of th
emitted β-particles increases. Other isotopes have been tried:

1. ^{125}I. This seems to be promising because of its short half-life an
low-energy electrons. It has regularly given good results since its firs
use in electron autoradiography (Kayes et al., 1962).

2. ^{35}S. (Godman and Lane, 1964.)

3. ^{14}C. (Caro, 1964.)

4. ^{32}P. (Caro, 1964, 1965.) It was recently demonstrated that thi
isotope can give a resolution of about 0.3 μ compared with 0.1
for the ^{3}H. Therefore, the use of emitters of β-particles having a
energy between those of ^{32}P and ^{3}H is possible with a sensitivity an
a resolution depending on the energy spectrum of the emitted β
particles (Caro, 1965).

B. Labeling of the Specimen

1. Choice of the Precursor

Many precursors labeled with ^{3}H are now available. For a study o
the RNA metabolism it is preferable to use uridine-^{3}H and not cyti
dine-^{3}H. This last precursor enters the DNA metabolism, and the en

ymatic digestion of the DNA is much more difficult and unreliable
n electron microscopy than in light microscopy. In all respects, the
ighest specific activity should be chosen. Precursors must be kept
rozen. It has been demonstrated with thymidine-^{3}H that autode-
truction by radiolysis occurs if the precursor is stored for a long time
Apelgot and Ekert, 1964).

2. Labeling

It is almost impossible to state the doses required to label virus-
nfected cells in culture. The dose depends on the specific activity of
he precursor, the time of incubation, and the cellular material used.
"he incubation time and the dose given will in turn play a part in
letermining the exposure time. Two examples can be given: (1) with
nammalian cells in culture and in exponential growth phase, a dose
•f 100 μc/ml of uridine-^{3}H (specific activity, 1.22 curies per millimole)
or a pulse of 5 minutes gives a mean number of 2.9 grains on the
ucleolus and 5.1 grains on the nucleus for 4 weeks of exposure.
2) With bacterial cells (*Escherichia coli*) a dose of 100 μc/ml of
ridine-^{3}H (specific activity 22.2 curies per millimole) for a pulse of
0 seconds gives a mean number of 2.4 grains per labeled bacterium
or 41 days of exposure.

As far as labeling is concerned, the rationale could be expressed as
ollows: it is possible to obtain about 10 ultrathin sections in 1 μ; 1 μ
s within the range of tritium-emitted particles. This figure corresponds
lso to the minimum thickness of the sections at the optical level. There-
ore, a good relative value can be given with a specific activity of the
issues 10-fold higher than for optical purposes. In any cases, the experi-
nent has to be done for a given dose and exposure time. The results
fter about 1 week of exposure will serve as a guide for further assays.

1. The Emulsions

The nuclear emulsions used for autoradiography are composed of
rystals of silver halide and of gelatin. There are two types of emul-
ions: the first type has crystals with a diameter of 700 Å or greater.
"his type is adapted for cytological purposes because the thickness
f ultrathin sections is in itself a limit for the resolution. These emul-
ions are rich in silver bromide, poor in gelatin, and very easy to handle.
"he second type has crystals with a diameter of less than 700 Å, i.e.,
00–500 Å. These emulsions are poor in silver bromide, rich in gelatin,
nd difficult to handle.

A. Emulsions for Cytological Purposes

The ideal emulsion must be rich in silver bromide, with grains o
regular size and small enough to give a good resolution. It must b
easy to handle and give perfectly reproducible results.

The first emulsions of this type have been abandoned because of th
large size of their crystals: Ilford G5, 0.32 μ; Ilford K5, 0.18 μ (Carc
1962). The two best emulsions are the Ilford L4 introduced by Car
(1962) and the Gevaert NUC 307 introduced by P. Granboula:
(1963).

1. *Ilford L4*

The diameter of the crystals is 0.14 μ and their size is very regula
The principal qualities of the emulsion are its good autoradiographi
resolution (about 0.1 μ; Caro, 1962), low background, high sensitivit
insensitivity to yellow-green light, and good reproducibility of mono
granular layering; in addition, it is easy to store, offers the possibilit
of use for optical autoradiography, and gives very low fading of th
latent image.

2. *Gevaert NUC 307*

The principal advantages are its smaller size and the regularity o
its crystals (700 Å) (P. Granboulan, 1963), factors that give a bette
autoradiographic resolution. The sensitivity of the emulsion was foun
to be similar to that of Ilford L4 (Young and Kopriwa, 1964). It als
gives good reproducibility of monogranular layering (P. Granboular
1965). The level of the background is a little higher than with L4 pe
surface unit under the practical conditions of use. This emulsion is mor
sensitive to yellow-green light and more susceptible to bacterial con
tamination and to deterioration during storage.

B. Emulsions with Very Small Grains

Two emulsions of this type are available, the Kodak NTE intro
duced by Bachmann and Salpeter (1964) and the Lippmann-typ
Kodak-Pathé (France) introduced by P. Granboulan and Audra:
(1964). These emulsions are characterized by the small size of thei
crystals, i.e., diameters of 300–500 Å, by the variability of this diamete
which gives a very large curve of granulometric distribution, and by .
low percentage of silver to gelatin (about 50% for the Lippmann type)

he sensitivity seems to be good, at least for the Kodak NTE (Sal-
eter and Bachmann, 1964). These emulsions, however, are unsuitable
or direct application to specimens because of their high gelatin con-
ent, and the crystals must be concentrated by centrifugation. There-
ore, they are difficult to handle and the reproducibility of the method
 imperfect, although they gave some good results in cytology (Sal-
eter and Bachmann, 1964; P. Granboulan and Audran, 1964). The
ery small size of their crystals, however makes them more interesting
or the study of isolated and nonembedded viruses or macromolecules,
nce in this case the resolution is not limited by the thickness of
trathin sections.

I. Description of the Technique

A. PREPARATION OF THE SPECIMENS

All the methods of fixation, dehydration, and embedding employed
ith electron microscopy can be used. A fading of the latent image
an be produced through chemical interaction between the specimen
nd the emulsion in the case of a fixation with osmium tetroxide. This
ffect can be avoided by putting a carbon layer on the specimen before
yering the emulsion (Bachmann and Salpeter, 1964). Quantitative
udies carried out by Caro (1966) with L4 emulsion and methacrylate-
mbedded bacteria have shown no evidence of chemical interaction
etween the sections and the emulsion. This seems also true for glycol
ethacrylate or 2-hydroxypropyl methacrylate. There is some evidence,
owever, that the emulsion can be desensitized to some extent when
ections of epoxy resins are used. This effect can also be avoided by
utting a carbon layer between the sections and the emulsion (Sal-
eter and Bachmann, 1964). The carbon layer must be used when the
ections are stained with heavy metals (lead or uranyl acetate).

It is easy and useful to combine ultrastructural cytochemistry and
lectron autoradiography. The sections of cells fixed with only an
ldehyde (Formalin, acrolein, or glutaraldehyde) and embedded in a
ydrosoluble plastic (glycol methacrylate, Leduc and Bernhard, 1962;
 2-hydroxypropyl methacrylate, Leduc and Holt, 1965) can be floated
n enzymatic solutions before they are stained and the emulsion layered
N. Granboulan and Granboulan, 1964, 1965).

The ultrathin sections must be flat, smooth, and of a regular thick-
ess (gold). Whatever method is used for the layering, the grids must
e electrolytically prepared because of the necessity of a flat surface

and because the meshes must be of a regular size in order to coun
the background.

When the grids are used for the layering of the emulsion, they ar
covered by a Formvar or collodion membrane and a carbon layer.

Electron autoradiography can also be used on shadow-cast viruse
or macromolecules. In this case, however, because of the interactio
between metals and emulsion, a carbon layer must be put between th
specimen and the emulsion (Caro, 1966).

B. LAYERING OF THE EMULSION AND THE PHOTOGRAPHIC PROCESS

All the manipulations must be made in the dark under safeligh
illumination (Kodak Wratten series 2). After delivery the emulsion
are kept in a cold room at 4°C for a time that varies according t
the type of emulsion; the Ilford L4 can be kept for 2–4 months
the Gevaert NUC 307 for only 2–3 weeks. The dilution of the emulsio
prepared for one experiment is used only once.

1. *Technique with Ilford L4 and Gevaert NUC 307*

a. Layering the Emulsion. These two emulsions come in gel form
They can be used after melting in a water bath.

The ideal layering is monogranular, with crystal closely packed an
uniformly distributed onto the specimen (Fig. 1). Such a method o
layering raised difficult problems in the early. days of electron auto
radiography.

The method, which consists of placing a drop of melted emulsio
on the grids and removing the excess with a filter paper, is simpl
(Liquier-Milward, 1956; Harford and Hamlin, 1961; Przybylski, 1961)
but the layer is often too thick and the distribution of the crystal
uneven because of their displacement during drying. A technique giv
ing more reproducible results consists of dipping the grids fixed o
glass slides into the emulsion (Revel and Hay, 1961; Hay and Reve
1963; Young and Kopriwa, 1964).

An elegant solution was offered by Caro and Van Tubergen (1962
with the technique of the loop after the emulsion has gelled.

 (*i*) *The technique of the loop.* The grids are attached in group
of four on microscope slides by a small portion of their edge to
small piece of double-coated masking tape (Scotch 400). Ten milli
grams of Ilford L4 is melted in 20 ml of distilled water in a beake
at 45°C for 15 minutes. The mixture is thoroughly stirred and th
beaker is placed in an ice bath for 2 or 3 minutes and after that a

)om temperature for 30 minutes. The emulsion is now very viscous.
. thin wire loop of 4-cm diameter is dipped into the emulsion and
lowly withdrawn. The film formed in the loop gels very quickly;
hen it is gelled, it is touched at the surface of the grids and it falls
n them. An expandable loop has also been used (Ehret *et al.*, 1964).

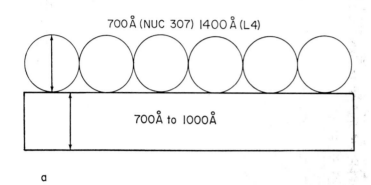

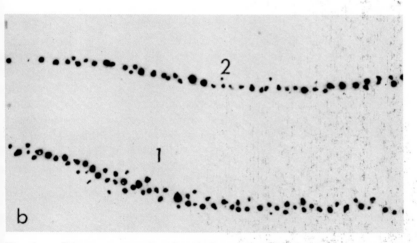

Fig. 1. a, Schema representing the ideal monogranular layering, with crystals
losely and uniformly packed on the specimen. b, Section of a layer of Gevaert
JUC 307 Formalin-fixed and embedded in glycol methacrylate. 1: Tangential
ection; 2: perpendicular section showing the monogranular layering. There exist
me "holes" without crystals, which were pulled off during the sectioning process.
< 30,000. (Courtesy of P. Granboulan, 1965.)

While this technique may work well with L4, it does not with
VUC 307. Other methods were proposed using centrifugation. Koehler
t al. (1963) place a drop of melted emulsion onto the grid and then
pply strong centrifugal field parallel to the surface of the grid. In

the technique proposed by Dohlman *et al.* (1964), the grids are placed
at the bottom of a centrifuge tube in a swinging-bucket rotor and
the tube is filled with diluted emulsion. The grains are sedimented
onto the specimen.

In any event, for quantitative studies—which can be crucial in virol
ogy—the use of grids as a substratum on which to layer the emulsion
does not appear ideal because of the irregularities of their surface.

(*ii*) *Layering on glass slides without grids.* The ideal surface for
layering is large and flat. An even surface is an important factor in
obtaining homogeneous layering, and a large surface is required in
order to keep the edge effects to a minimum and also for good repro
ducibility and easy control. Therefore, the ideal method is the elegant
dipping technique of Kopriwa and Leblond (1962), which is used in
light autoradiography. Such a method, which resulted from further
development of previous investigations, is now ruled out for electron
autoradiography (P. Granboulan, 1965). Some authors have used membranes without grids for coating, but the emulsion is not applied
by dipping (Pelc *et al.*, 1961; Roberts and Chow, 1962). Salpeter and
Bachmann (1964) also used glass slides, but they layered the emulsion
by dropping a small quantity of emulsion and not by dipping. The
dipping procedure is an extremely important aspect of the membrane
technique and is its main advantage. It permits good reproducibility of
monogranular layering, with closely packed and uniformly distributed
grains, easy handling for routine technique even in a nonspecialized
laboratory, offers the possibility of treating together a large number of
slides for layering and photographic process (a condition required for
a quantitative study), yields more constant and lower background
values than with other methods, and may be used with Ilford L4 as
well as with Gevaert NUC 307.

(*iii*) *Preparation of the specimens on the glass slides.* Marks (crosses)
are traced with a diamond on one side of the slide at 2 cm from the
lower edge. The slides are cleaned and then dipped into a solution
of collodion (Parlodion 1.0 gm in 100 ml of amyl acetate) and allowed
to dry at room temperature sheltered from dirt. The sections are
picked up in the hole of a plastic ring having a diameter of a grid
(Marinozzi, 1964). They are laid onto the marks but on the opposite
side of the glass slide. Care must be taken to avoid tearing the
collodion when the plastic ring containing the sections is put on it
(Fig. 2). The water is adsorbed with a filter paper; the sections adhere
to the membrane and the plastic ring can then be removed (Fig. 3)

To prevent the membrane from floating off during dipping and the

Fig. 2. Errors to avoid when the sections contained in the hole of the plastic ring are put on the collodion membrane covering the glass slides. 1: Tearing of the collodion; 2: dirt; 3: threading of the filter paper; 4: sections. The white unfocused area at the bottom of the figure corresponds to the diamond mark. The sections are well put on it. Phase-contrast microscope with dark field. (Courtesy of P. Granboulan.)

subsequent process, it is recommended that one border the bottom of the slides by dipping the lower few millimeters into concentrated collodion. In the subsequent handling the slides are never dipped deeper than the upper limit of the collodion membrane.

(iv) *Layering of the emulsion.* In a dark room the emulsion is melted (45°C for Ilford L4 and 37°C for Gevaert NUC 307) and then diluted in distilled water (1 : 6 for Ilford L4 and 1 : 4 for Gevaert NUC 307). The beaker containing the diluted emulsion must be deep enough to allow a large part of the slide (about 4 cm) to be covered at once, and large enough to allow good mechanical agitation. The diluted emulsion is kept in the water bath about for 1 hour with moderate agitation in order to get a homogeneous suspension.

The slides are coated by dipping, with slow and vertical withdrawal from the emulsion. The slides are then all placed at the same angle of inclination (30°) in order to gel and dry the emulsion (Fig. 3). The temperature and the moisture of the dark room must be controlled (Kopriwa and Leblond, 1962). The slides are then put in storage boxes for the exposure time.

With this method there exists a gradient in the thickness of the emulsion from the top to the bottom of the layer. For conditions described above, the monogranular layer is found in the region of 2 cm from the lower edge of the slide. A control of the layering is always necessary, particularly for a quantitative study (see Section IV).

b. *Exposure Time.* During exposure time the conditions of storage can affect the sensitivity of the crystals, the regression of the latent image, and the background. To avoid regression of the latent image owing to an oxidation of the silver, it has been recommended that the slides be stored in an inert gas (Albouy and Faraggi, 1959; Ray and Stevens, 1953; Herz, 1959). For practicality, the slides (or grids) are kept in slide boxes (made of Bakelite) and stored in a large airtight, lightproof box in the presence of a dehydrant (Drierite or phosphorus pentoxide) at 4°C.

Since the exposure time depends on the dose of the label, the incubation of the label, and the metabolism of the cell, it is difficult to predict. The exposure time is usually determined by developing test slides at regular intervals.

c. *Photographic Process.* There are two classical developers, "chemical" and "physical."

A "chemical" developer characteristically gives silver grains a filamentous shape. The development must be strong enough to easily see this characteristic shape with the electron microscope at the usual magnification (Fig. 4). The advantage of this normal development is its reproducibility.

(*i*) *Normal technique*. The development is carried out in D19 (Kodak) at 18°C for 5 minutes. The glass slides, contained in an open box are plunged into the developer (Fig. 3), which is evenly agitated.

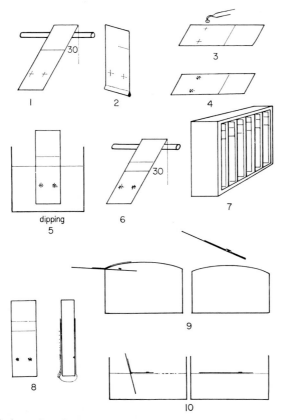

Fig. 3. Technique for electron autoradiography on glass slides as described in Section III,B: 1, drying of the collodion membrane; 2, rim of concentrated solution of collodion on the bottom of the glass slides; 3, deposit of ultrathin sections on the marks by means of a plastic ring; 4, the glass slide is ready for the coating of the emulsion; 5, dipping; 6, gel formation on all the glass slides at the same angle, 30°; 7, open box containing the glass slides for development, fixing, and rinsing; 8, three successive layers on the glass slide—developed emulsion, sections, collodion; 9 and 10, floating the membrane with sections on distilled water. A grid is slipped under each group of sections (9). The glass slide is then lifted and the grid carries the three layers (10). Alternative method: the membrane is entirely floated off; Grids are deposited on sections and the membrane is picked up with filter paper. In this case the sections are between the grids and the collodion. (Courtesy of P. Granboulan, 1965.)

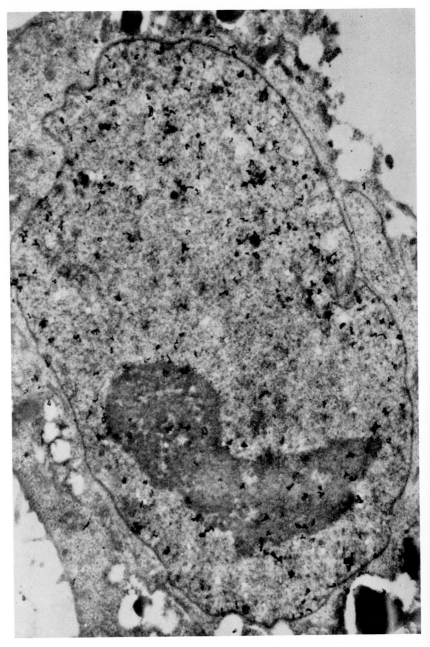

FIG. 4. Monkey kidney cell 24 hours after infection with SV40 virus and labeled with thymidine-^{3}H. Coating was with NUC 307 with the dipping technique. Exposure time: 9 days; gelatin not removed. × 75,000.

After rinsing they are plunged into an acid fixative (buffered hyposulfite without hardener) for 10 minutes, also evenly agitated. The slides are then rinsed in running water and dried at room temperature or in an oven at 37°C. The membrane is floated on distilled water, and either a grid is slipped under the sections or several grids are laid with caution over the membrane, which is then picked up as usual (Fig. 3).

The method described above does not require the removal of the gelatin after development and fixing.

(ii) *Obtaining finer grains.* It may be useful to obtain finer grains in order to obtain a better visualization of the structures present under the developed silver grains. The size of the developed grains can be reduced by using developers other than the following, but the results are less reproducible:

Microdol X (Eastman Kodak): 4 minutes at 18°C
Developer with sodium metaborate

The formula is as follows:

Metol (*p*-methylaminophenol sulfate)	2	gm
Sodium sulfite (crystalline)	100	gm
Sodium metaborate ($NaBO_2 \cdot 4H_2O$)	2	gm
Potassium bromide	0.5	gm
Distilled water	1	liter

The latter developer results in an important loss of sensitivity.

A "physical" developer (Lumière *et al.*, 1911) dissolves the silver bromide, leaving only the latent image upon which silver ions present in the solution are then attached. It gives a better resolution of the latent image, but the results are less reproducible than with a "chemical" developer like D19 (Formula: 0.1 M sodium sulfite dissolved in distilled water at 50°C to which 0.01 M *p*-phenylenediamine is added). This solution is filtered before use. With this developer for 1 minute at 20°C the grains obtained are very small and either spherical or comma-shaped (Caro and Van Tubergen, 1962).

In spite of the fact that better resolution is possible we are not sure that underdevelopment is desirable.

d. Determination of the Background. In all cases the level of background must be determined by counting the number of reduced silver grains in several meshes of the grids, far from the sections. With the NUC 307 it is generally in the order of 0.3 grains/100 μ^2, and less with L4.

2. Technique for Emulsions with Very Small Grains

As mentioned earlier, these emulsions are characterized by a low percentage of silver to gelatin and variability in crystal size. The emulsions are used in two different ways, described in the following sections.

a. *Method Developed for Kodak NTE* (Bachmann and Salpeter, 1964, 1965; Salpeter and Bachmann, 1964). The emulsion is diluted (1 gm/10 ml of water), melted at 60°–70°C, and centrifuged at about 11,000 rpm in a preheated centrifuge for 10 minutes. The bottom of the centrifuge tube is chilled briefly and the supernatant discarded. The remaining concentrated emulsion is reheated and diluted with 1–4 ml of water per gram of the original emulsion.

For the coating, a few drops of the rediluted centrifuged emulsion kept at 60°C are placed with a medicine dropper onto the slide bearing the specimens and held horizontally. The emulsion is then drained and air-dried in a vertical position.

The development is carried out in the Dektol (diluted 1 : 2) for 1 minute at 24°C. To obtain smaller grains, the gold latensification method can be used (James, 1948). In this case the developer is the following: 0.045% Metol, 0.3% ascorbic acid, 0.5% borax, 0.1% potassium bromide (at 24°C).

This method, which seems to be rather easy, has the disadvantage that it does not use the finest grains, which are discarded with the supernatant, but instead crystals with irregular thickness that are present in the pellet.

b. *Technique Developed for the Lippmann-Type Emulsion* (P. Granboulan and Audran, 1964; P. Granboulan, 1965). The technique to be used for this emulsion has not entirely been worked out, but the principle is as follows: The diluted emulsion is centrifuged, producing a pellet that is discarded; a different type of emulsion results, the supernatant, which contains the finest grains. This emulsion is very diluted and therefore to concentrate the crystals the layering is carried out by centrifugation on large concave cylindrical lenses (about 20 cm^2) with a radius of curvature corresponding to the radius of centrifugation. The lenses are covered by a collodion membrane, which bears the specimens. After precipitation the layer which is plurigranular is gelled, poured off with care, and allowed to dry. The next steps are performed according to the technique already described for glass slides layered with NUC 307 or L4. The results obtained on ultrathin sections of SV40 virus labeled with thymidine-^{3}H are shown in Fig. 5.

The advantage of this method, which is a little more complicated

FIG. 5. Portion of a nuclear inclusion of SV40 virus in a monkey kidney cell 4 days after infection and labeling with thymidine-³H. Lippmann-type emulsion from Kodak-Pathé (France). Exposure time: 3 weeks. Development: D-19; very small developed grains. × 50,000. (Courtesy of P. Granboulan, 1965.)

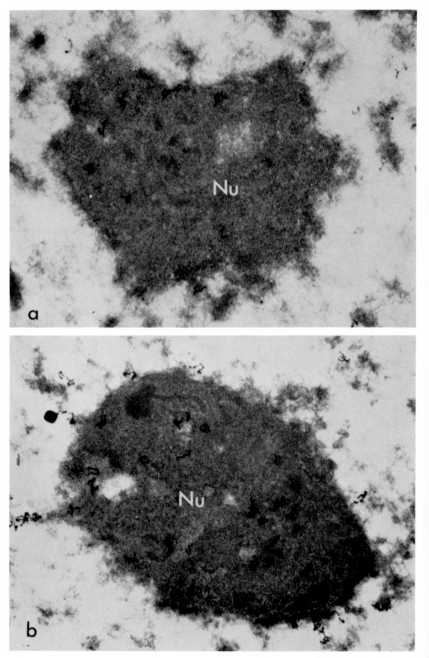

FIG. 6. Nucleoli of monkey kidney cell in culture labeled with thymidine-³H
(4 μc/ml) after 10 hours. Formalin–acrolein fixation, embedding in glycol methacrylate, staining with uranyl acetate. Layering of the NUC 307 emulsion was by the

than that of Bachmann and Salpeter for Kodak NTE, is the use of the finest grains present in the supernatant, which have a rather homogeneous diameter (300–350 Å, including the gelatin shell).

IV. Quantitative Aspects of Electron Autoradiography

The localization of a synthetic process in a virus-infected cell has been made very simple with electron autoradiography, even in small organelles like the nucleolus (Fig. 6) (N. Granboulan and Tournier, 1965). When a synthetic process has been localized in a special cellular site, however, it is essential to obtain quantitative data comparing virus-infected and noninfected cells. A number of conditions are required for these quantitative studies:

1. The layering must always be strictly equal. At the present time this is possible only with L4 or NUC 307. The method of layering on glass slides described above for these emulsions gives very homogeneous and reproducible results from one slide to another provided that the following factors are constant for all slides: dilution of the emulsion, depth of dipping, position of the sections on the slide, temperature and moisture of gelling, conditions of drying, and photographic processing conditions (only a normal development must be used). It is also essential that the sections be put on glass slides cautiously in order to avoid tearing or dirtying the collodion, since these defects provoke an accumulation of emulsion at these sites, and, therefore, an unequal layering (Fig. 2).

The monogranular layering must be controlled. The best method consists of floating the membrane with the emulsion in the region of the sections, fixing it in Formalin, and embedding it in glycol methacrylate or 2-hydroxypropyl methacrylate (P. Granboulan, 1965). Cross sections can be examined in order to be sure of a monogranular layering (Fig. 1b).

2. The most serious problems arise from the presence of sections from biological material. It is difficult to obtain sections of identical thickness, and within the same section there can be differences in thickness of cytological structures, depending upon their hardness and density. Some improvements need to be made in cutting techniques. In order to avoid problems in cutting, the activity can be referred

---

dipping technique. Exposure time: 9 days. a, Noninfected cell. Some reduced silver grains can be seen on the nucleolus (Nu) on the bands of intranucleolar chromatin × 40,000. b, SV40-infected cell after 10 hours. The numerous reduced silver grains on the nucleolus (Nu) reveal a stronger DNA synthesis than in the control × 40,000.

to a standard source located in the section, preferably in the cell itself (Caro, 1961; Budd and Pelc, 1964; Moses, 1964; Van Heyningen, 1964; Nadler *et al.*, 1964; Ross, 1965; N. Granboulan and Tournier, 1965).

The thickness of the sections can be measured with a Reichert-Nomarski interferometer, which Bachmann and Salpeter (1965) also use to determine the thickness of the emulsion layer.

For practical purposes sections of control cells are put on the same slide as sections of the virus-infected cell specimens. A large number of sections must be counted to reduce the errors owing to differences in thickness.

In spite of these difficulties, with the MT2 Porter-Blum or LKB ultramicrotome, and with special attention to the regularity of the

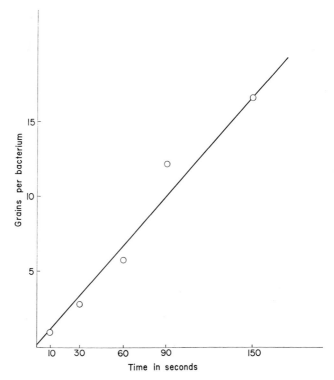

FIG. 7. Rate of incorporation of uridine (5-³H) into *E. coli* RNA measured by number of reduced silver grains per bacterium. Concentration of cells: 2.1×10^8 to 1.1×10^9/ml. Concentration of uridine-³H: 100 μc/ml (specific activity: 24.4 curies/mmole except for the 10-second pulse, where the specific activity was 22.2 curies/mmole). Exposure time: 18 days.

sections, it was possible to obtain good results during quantitative studies on bacteria. The following relationships were found:

1. A linear relationship between the length of exposure time and the mean number of silver grains per bacterium.

2. A linear relationship between the length of incubation in ³H-labeled precursor and the mean number of silver grains per bacterium (Fig. 7) (Franklin and Granboulan, 1965).

3. A regularity of the mean number of silver grains per bacterium in sections of bacteria labeled for the same length of time (30 seconds) with uridine-³H (Fig. 8) (N. Granboulan and Franklin, 1966).

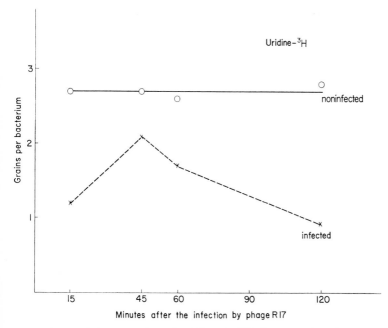

FIG. 8. Rate of incorporation of uridine (5-³H) into uninfected *E. coli* RNA (———) and R17-infected *E. coli* RNA (- - -) at different times of the replication measured by the number of reduced silver grains per bacterium. Multiplicity of infection: 10–20 pfu/cell. Concentration of uridine-³H: 100 μc/ml for a pulse of 30 seconds (specific activity: 24.4 curies/mmole). Exposure time: 18 days. Regularity of the results for uninfected bacteria. Early inhibition of the RNA synthesis in R17-infected bacteria.

V. Advantages and Limitations of This Method

The principal advantage of this method is that it combines ultrastructural and functional data. With autoradiographic resolution it is possible to localize synthetic processes in different cellular sites, even when they are very small. The method developed for quantitative studies allows the comparison of the metabolism in a special cellular site in virus-infected and noninfected cells. Finally, electron auto-radiography permits the study of the fate of labeled viral nucleic acid in the host cell. The application of electron autoradiography to these different areas of virological research is shown by several workers.

The study of synthetic processes in a special cellular site was carried out during the replication of animal viruses (adenovirus 4: Harford and Hamlin, 1965; SV40 virus: N. Granboulan and Tournier, 1965; adenovirus 12: Martinez-Palomo and N. Granboulan, 1967), vegetal virus (tobacco mosaic virus: Hibino and Matsui, 1964), and bacterial virus (RNA bacteriophage R17: N. Granboulan and Franklin, 1966).

The method allowing the comparison of metabolism in virus-infected and noninfected cells was first tried on the eclipse phase of the SV40 virus (N. Granboulan and Tournier, 1965). It has been shown to work well and to be very useful during studies on the replication of the RNA bacteriophage R17 (N. Granboulan and Franklin, 1966). This method can now be widely used in virology, particularly when the metabolism of a small special cellular site must be examined. It is evident that this method cannot show slight differences in metabolism, but it is the only technique that gives at the same time a very precise localization in the cell.

Electron autoradiography was also applied to the problem of the fate of the viral nucleic acid in the host cell. With rather big animal viruses this method has given good results (DNA of the vaccinia virus: Dales, 1963; RNA of the reovirus: Dales, 1965). This field can be rather limited when the molecular weight of the viral nucleic acid is low. However, results were also obtained with polyomavirus during its lytic cycle (de Harven et al., 1965).

The two principal limitations of electron autoradiography are the following: (1) autoradiographic resolution is far poorer than the re-solving power of the electron microscope; and (2) it is a rather slow and, in some cases, delicate technique.

Improvements are still necessary and possible, but even in its present state electron autoradiography is certainly a very useful method in the field of virology.

REFERENCES

Albouy, G., and Faraggi, H. (1959). *J. Phys. Radium* **10,** 105.
Apelgot, S., and Ekert, B. (1964). *J. Chim. Phys.* **61,** 985.
Bachmann, L., and Salpeter, M. M. (1964). *Naturwissenschaften* **10,** 237.
Bachmann, L., and Salpeter, M. M. (1965). *Lab. Invest.* **14,** 303.
Budd, G. C., and Pelc, S. R. (1964). *Stain Technol.* **39,** 294.

Caro, L. G. (1961). *J. Biophys. Biochem. Cytol.* **10**, 37.
Caro, L. G. (1962). *J. Cell Biol.* **15**, 189.
Caro, L. G. (1964). *J. Roy. Microscop. Soc.* [3] **83**, 127.
Caro, L. G. (1965). *Science* **149**, 60.
Caro, L. G. (1966). *Progr. Biophys. Mol. Biol.* **16**, 171.
Caro, L. G., and Van Tubergen, R. P. (1962). *J. Cell Biol.* **15**, 173.
Dales, S. (1963). *J. Cell Biol.* **18**, 51.
Dales, S. (1965). *Virology* **25**, 193.
de Harven, E., Borenfreund, E., and Bendich, A. (1965). *Federation Proc.* **24**, Part I, No. 2, 309.
Dohlman, G. F., Maunsbach, A. B., Hammarstrom, L., and Appelgren, L. E. (1964). *J. Ultrastruct. Res.* **10**, 293.
Ehret, C., Savage, N., and Alblinger, J. (1964). *Z. Zellforsch. Mikroskop. Anat.* **64**, 129.
Franklin, R. M., and Granboulan, N. (1965). *J. Mol. Biol.* **14**, 623.
Godman, G. C., and Lane, N. (1964). *J. Cell Biol.* **21**, 353.
Granboulan, N., and Franklin, R. M. (1966). *J. Bacteriol.* **91**, 849.
Granboulan, N., and Granboulan P. (1964). *Exptl. Cell Res.* **34**, 71.
Granboulan, N., and Granboulan, P. (1965). *Exptl. Cell Res.* **38**, 604.
Granboulan, N., and Tournier, P. (1965). *Ann. Inst. Pasteur* **109**, 837.
Granboulan, P. (1963). *J. Roy. Microscop. Soc.* **81**, 165.
Granboulan, P. (1965). *Symp. Intern. Soc. Cell Biol.* **4**, 43.
Granboulan, P., and Audran, R. (1964). *Compt. Rend.* **259**, 3201.
Harford, C. G., and Hamlin, A. (1961). *Lab. Invest.* **10**, 627.
Harford, C. G., and Hamlin, A. (1965). *J. Bacteriol.* **89**, 1540.
Hay, E. D., and Revel, J. P. (1963). *Develop. Biol.* **7**, 152.
Herz, R. H. (1959). *Lab. Invest.* **8**, 71.
Hibino, H., and Matsui, C. (1964). *Virology* **24**, 102.
James, T. H. (1948). *J. Colloid Sci.* **3**, 447.
Kayes, J., Maunsbach, A. B., and Ullberg, S. (1962). *J. Ultrastruct. Res.* **7**, 339.
Koehler, J. K., Muehlethaler, K., and Frey-Wissling, A. (1963). *J. Cell Biol.* **16**, 73.
Kopriwa, B. M., and Leblond, C. P. (1962). *J. Histochem. Cytochem.* **10**, 269.
Leduc, E. H., and Bernhard, W. (1962). *Symp. Intern. Soc. Cell Biol.* **1**, 21.
Leduc, E. H., and Holt, S. J. (1965). *J. Cell Biol.* **26**, 137.
Liquier-Milward, J. (1956). *Nature* **177**, 619.
Lumière, A., Lumière, L., and Seyewetz, A. (1911). *Compt. Rend.* **153**, 102.
Marinozzi, V. (1964). *J. Ultrastruct. Res.* **10**, 433.
Martinez-Palomo, A., and Granboulan, N. (1967). *Virology* (in press).
Moses, M. J. (1964). *J. Histochem. Cytochem.* **12**, 115.
Nadler, N. J., Young, B. A., Leblond, C. P., and Mitmaker, B. (1964). *Endocrinology* **74**, 333.
Pelc, S. R., Coombes, J. D., and Budd, G. C. (1961). *Exptl. Cell Res.* **24**, 192.
Przybylski, R. J. (1961). *Exptl. Cell Res.* **24**, 181.
Ray, R. C., and Stevens, W. W. (1953). *Brit. J. Radiol.* **26**, 362.
Revel, J. P., and Hay, E. D. (1961). *Exptl. Cell Res.* **25**, 474.
Roberts, J. M., and Chow, P. C. (1962). *4th Intern. Conf. Nuclear Phot., Munich, 1962.*
Ross, R. (1965). *Symp. Intern. Soc. Cell Biol.* **4**, 273.
Salpeter, M. M., and Bachmann, L. (1964). *J. Cell Biol.* **22**, 469.
Van Heyningen, H. E. (1964). *Anat. Record* **148**, 485.
Van Tubergen, R. P. (1961). *J. Biophys. Biochem. Cytol.* **9**, 219.
Young, B. A., and Kopriwa, B. M. (1964). *J. Histochem. Cytochem.* **12**, 438.

AUTHOR INDEX

SUBJECT INDEX

A

Acetic anhydride, as protein acetylating agent, 24

Acetone extraction of antigens, 139

Acetyl imidazole, as protein acetylating agent, 24

Acetylation of protein amino groups, 24

Acid–citrate–dextrose reagent, for hemagglutination tests, 172

Acid phosphatase, stain for, 594

Acridine orange staining of viruses, 506–516
confirmation tests, 511–515
of intracellular virus, 507–508
of purified virus, 508–510

Acrolein, as fixative for electron microscopy, 498, 580

Acylated N-terminal groups, analysis in virus proteins, 8–9

Adenosinetriphosphatase in viruses, staining of, 594

Adenoviruses, acridine orange staining of, 508
electron microscopy of, 373, 374, 601, 606–607
antigen-antibody complexes, 563–564, 565, 566
thin sectioning, 580, 583, 600
unembedded tissue, 599
enzyme-digestion studies on, 595
isolation, 118
oncogenic, transformation assay of, 334
plague assays of, 295
serotypes of, 117
structure studies on, 373, 374
transformation assay of, 314
fluorescent-antibody studies on, 502
immunological identification, 116, 119, 120–121, 130
agglutination test, 192
antigens for, 132, 136

complement-fixation test, 175
hemagglutination test, 168
immunodiffusion, 186
neutralization test, 144, 145, 152, 156

Adenovirus 4, electron autoradiography of, 636

Adenovirus type 7, electron microscopy of, 559

Adenovirus type 12, transformation assay of, 334

African horse sickness virus, plaque assay of, 300

African swine fever virus, immunological identification, 123

Agar, for plaque-assay media, 262

Agarose, in gel filtration, 44

Agglutination tests, for animal viruses, 191–193
for plant viruses, 213–216

Alastrim virus, immunological identification, 127
plaque assay of, 294

Amido black, as virus–protein stain, 36

Amino acid analysis of virus proteins, 2–5
applications, 5
automatic, 2–3
DNP-derivatives, 4, 10
ninhydrin reaction, 3

Amino acid concentrate, for Eagle's medium, 258

Amino acid-sequence analysis of virus proteins, 58–69
by chemical cleavage, 61–62
by enzymatic cleavage, 59–61
peptide separation, 62–68
by specific cleavage, 58–62

Amino acids, for plaque assays, 254

Amino groups, ninhydrin reaction for, 3–4
of proteins, reversible masking of, 23

Aminoacridines, as nucleic acid stains, 506–516

Aminophosphatides, detection of, 86

Ammonium sulfate, serum fractionation using, 484–486

Anaphylaxis test, for plant viruses, 22

Anemone lipid, chromatographic analysis, 83

Animal viruses, classification of, 113–115
  identification of, 118–120
    by immunology, 119–120
  immunological techniques for, 113–198
  isolation, 118
  number of, 117–118
  plaque assay of, see Plaque assay

Antibiotics, for plaque assays, 255–256

Antibody, FITC labeling of, 489–491
  for fluorescent-antibody techniques, 483–484
  labeling, for electron microscopy, 595–596
  of plant viruses, estimation, 231–233
  labeled, 237–239

Antifungal agents, for plaque-assay media, 256

Antigen–antibody complex, detection of, 114

Antigens, viral, preparation, 135–140

Antioxidants, for virus lipids, 80

Araldite, as embedding medium, 586

Arboviruses, immunological identification, 116, 120, 128–129, 130
  antigen preparation, 133–135, 137–138
  complement-fixation test, 175
  electroadsorption, 193
  hemagglutination test, 175
  immunodiffusion, 185
  neutralization test, 141–142, 144, 145, 148, 152, 153, 155, 156
  isolation of, 118
  lipids of, analysis, 78, 93–94
  plaque assays of, 292–298
  serotypes of, 117

Arcton 63, in antigen preparation, 140

Ascites tumor cells, for plaque assays, 267, 277–278

Ascitic fluid, as immune reagent, 129–130, 133–135

Autoradiographic methods in electron microscopy, see Electron autoradiography

Avian BAI virus, lipids of, analysis, 90

Avian leucosis viruses, immunological identification, 123
  plaque assay of, 300
  transformation assays of, 322

Avian leukemia virus, ATPase in, staining, 594

Avian myeloblastosis virus, ATPase in, staining, 594
  electron microscopy of, 608, 611
  fluorescent-antibody studies on, 502
  lipids of, analysis, 94, 95
  transformation assay of, 322–323

Avian pox viruses, plaque assays of, 295

Avian tumor viruses, lipids of, analysis, 78, 94

B

B virus, immunological identification, 121

Bacteria, fixation for electron microscopy, 583
  labeling for electron autoradiography, 619, 634
  RNA phage-infected, RNA polymerase studies on, 100–103

Bacteriophage(s), electron microscopy of, 547, 554–557
  thin sectioning for, 579–583
  fluorescence microscopy, confirmation of, 512
  RNA, see RNA bacteriophage
  structure studies on, 359

Bacteriophage fd, structure studies, 355
  orientated samples for, 454

Bacteriophage MS₂, RNA of, 70–71

Bacteriophage R17, electron autoradiography of, 635

Bacteriophage T₂, ferritin-antibody labeling of, 596

Barley stripe mosaic virus, electron microscopy of, 560
  hemagglutination test on, 226–227

Bence-Jones protein, disulfide derivatives of, 18

Bentonite, for plaque assay, 284

Bentonite flocculation test, for plant viruses, 216

Collodion, as specimen film, 526

Colorado tick fever virus, plaque assay of, 299

Colorimetric analysis of lipids, 86, 89, 92

Column chromatography, for serum fractionation, 484, 486–487

of virus lipids, 81–83

Complement, staining of, in fluorescent-antibody techniques, 500–501

Complement-fixation (CF) test, 114–115, 174–181

complement, 178

diluent, 177

erythrocytes, 178

hemolysin, 178–179

for plant viruses, 224–227

serum for, 177–178

techniques for, 177–181

Contagious pustular dermatitis virus, plaque assay of, 294

Cowpox virus, immunological identification, 127

plaque assay of, 294

Coxsackie viruses, immunological identification, 125, 126

antigen preparation, 131, 134, 137, 139–140

complement-fixation test, 175

fluorescent-antibody test, 185

hemagglutination test, 164

neutralization test, 144

plaque assay of, 299–300

structure studies on, crystals for, 422

by x-ray diffraction, 422

Crimean hemorrhagic fever, neutralization test on, 158

Crystal diffraction, 393–402

structure solution, 402–403

Crystals, symmetry in, 395–400

virus, for x-ray diffraction, 421–424

Cyanogen bromide, in protein structural analysis, 61

Cysteine, analysis, 4

Cystine, in disulfide cleavage, 18

Cytomegaloviruses, fluorescent-antibody studies on, 502

immunological identification, 121

D

DANS, see 1-Dimethylaminonaphthalene-5-sulfonic acid

Dansyl chloride-amino acids, 4

in end-group analysis, 7–8, 10

DEAE-cellulose chromatography, for labeled protein removal, 493

in lipid analysis, 83

for RNA polymerase studies, 105

for serum fractionation, 484, 486

DEAE-dextran, in plaque assays, 291

DEAE-Sephadex chromatography, for labeled protein removal, 493

for serum fractionation, 484, 486

Debye formula, in x-ray diffraction, 415–416

Dehydration of unfixed tissue, 598

Demosterol, gas–liquid chromatography of, 88

Denaturants, in protein functional-group analysis, 15

Dengue viruses, agglutination test, 192

neutralization test, 147, 158

plaque assay of, 298–299

Dextran, in gel filtration, 44–51

Dextrose–gelatin–Veronal reagent for hemagglutination tests, 172

4,4′-Diamidinodiphenylamine dihydrochloride, in plaque-assay media, 256

2′,7′-Dichlorofluorescein reagent, for lipids, 86

Digitonin, in ferritin-antibody studies, 596

1-Dimethylaminonaphthalene-5-sulfonic acid, antibody labeling by, 491–492

as protein label, absorption and emission, 480

1-Dimethylaminonaphthalene-5-sulfonyl chloride, in amino acid analysis, see Dansyl chloride-amino acids

Dinitrophenyl (DNP)-amino acids, analysis, 4

of N-terminal groups, 5–8

Dinitrophenylation, of protein amino groups, 24

Diphtheria virus, fluorescent-antibody studies on, 496

Disulfide bonds, cleavage in virus proteins, 16

by oxidation, 16

by reduction, 18

by thiosulfonation, 17–18

fluorescent-antibody studies on, 502, 503
immunological identification, 116, 117, 119, 127–128
antigen preparation, 132, 136, 137
complement-fixation test, 175
hemagglutination test, 164, 168
neutralization test, 144
isolation of, 118
plaque assays of, 293, 300
RNA, electron autoradiography of, 636
serotypes of, 117
Respiratory syncytial virus, fluorescent-antibody studies on, 502
immunological identification, 123
antigens for, 136
fluorescent-antibody test, 185
plaque assay of, 297
Rhabdoviruses, plaque assays of, 297–298
Rhinopneumonitis virus, *see* Equine abortion virus
Rhinoviruses, immunological identification, 124, 125, 126, 130
type-specific antisera, 131–132
neutralization test on, 144, 145, 158
plaque assay of, 279, 300
Ribonuclease, RNA bacteriophage sensitivity to, 343
trifluoroacetylated, 23
Ribosomes, zonal electrophoresis, 42–43
Rickettsia, Macchiavello's stain for, 514
Rift Valley fever viruses, plaque assay of, 299
Rinderpest virus, immunological identification, 123
plaque assay of, 297
Ring test, for plant viruses, 213
RNA, aminoacridines as stains for, 506
infectious, plaque assay of, 283–286
plant virus, determination, 230–231
in TYMV, x-ray diffraction studies, 432–433
viral, electron autoradiography of, 636
RNA bacteriophages, antiserum preparation, 347
assay of, 339
characteristics of, 338
host specificity, 343

isolation techniques, 341
nucleic acid identification, 347–349
from purified phage, 348
screening procedure, 348
phage-stock preparation, 340
purification, 340–341, 342
resistance to inhibitors of DNA synthesis, 344
ribonuclease sensitivity, 343
selection methods, 337–350
general techniques, 339–341
media and solutions, 339
serological behavior, 346–347
size of, 346
sources of, 339
RNA bacteriophage R17, electron autoradiography of, 636
RNA virus RNA polymerase, 99–111
assay of, 103–105
isolation, 106–110
properties, 109–111
purification of, 105–106
Qβ-type, 106–110
RNA viruses, identification of, 119, 122, 124–126
transformation assay of, 314
Rod-shaped viruses, structure studies, 354–355
Rous sarcoma virus, enzyme-digestion studies on, 595
immunological identification, 123
lipids of, analysis, 79, 91, 94, 95
plaque assay of, 247, 272–274, 287, 290, 300
strains of, 319
transformation assay of, 314, 315, 316, 317, 318–322
in chick cell culture, 320
on chorioallantoic membrane, 322
focus formation, 318–320
in mammalian cells, 321–322
strains' effect on, 319
Rubella virus, immunological identification, 128
fluorescent-antibody test, 185
neutralization test, 145, 158
plaque assay of, 292, 301
Rubidomycin, in RNA bacteriophage isolation, 344

S